MAN AND THE LAND

MAN AND THE LAND
A CULTURAL GEOGRAPHY

George F. Carter

JOHNS HOPKINS UNIVERSITY

HOLT, RINEHART AND WINSTON New York • Chicago • San Francisco • Toronto • London

Cartography: Dyno Lowenstein

PREFACE

There are, as it seems, two ways in which a person may be competent in respect to any study or investigation, whether it be a noble one or a humble one. He may have either what can rightly be called a scientific knowledge of the subject; or he may have what is roughly described as an educated person's competence, and therefore be able to judge correctly which parts of an exposition are satisfactory and which are not. That, in fact, is the sort of person we take the man of general education to be; his "education" consists in the ability to do this.

—ARISTOTLE.*

Too often texts become attempts to supply the vast factual background of a subject rather than to develop the reader's ability to deal with a particular class of data. One could teach factual descriptive geography forever, but with this method the student is likely to know only the specifics he has learned. When, however, principles and processes are isolated and shown at work in real situations, they serve as the key to understanding the dynamic nature of the existing scene.

The difficulty is that the role of principles and processes tends to be obscured by the numerous interactions between man and the land, for the varied races of man with differing cultural-historical backgrounds distributed over a diversified physical earth create a most complex problem. The method used here is to reduce this complexity so that the various factors may be seen clearly at work. This makes it necessary to study one factor at a time, observing what happens when it varies while the other factors are held constant. Since man, land, and culture are the principal factors in human geography, they are studied as constants and as variables.

Race is genetic. Our bodily differences can be shown to be the result of

* *Parts of Animals,* trans. by A. L. Peck. Cambridge, Mass.: Harvard University Press, 1937. Bk. I, p. 53.

standard biological processes, and this is done early in the book. The presentation shows the value of systematic treatment with an emphasis on process. Once this approach has been developed and its validity shown in explaining bodily differences, the same method of examination is extended to an analysis of mental differences among the races. This examination demonstrates the improbability of the existence among the races of mental differences of like degree to the physiological differences. The analysis goes far toward removing mental differences among the races as a causative factor in the differentiation of the earth as occupied by man, and it introduces methods of anaysis of complex situations that are used throughout the book.

Similarly, causative factors in the differentiation of the earth are isolated by imagining a uniform earth peopled by a uniform race. It is then seen that without differences in race or physical environment man may still be expected to develop differing ways of life and, reacting on the physical environment, change the formerly uniform physical environment to a varied one. The three fundamental factors—race, physical environment, and cultural forces—have now been introduced, and we proceed to the complex world of human geography.

With the factor of race approximately eliminated in the opening section of the book and the physical environment reduced in importance though not eliminated, the problem becomes one of reducing the factor of environment still further so that the role of the cultural-historical processes can be seen more clearly.

This is done by comparing regions of similar climatic type around the world. Thus the five areas of winter concentration of rainfall, the so-called Mediterranean climate, are compared and contrasted. Since the climates are similar and all aspects of the physical environment, such as vegetation and soils, are likewise similar to some degree, the major variations must be due to the other factors. With the factor of race previously virtually eliminated, the cultural-historical processes emerge with clarity. This approach by means of analyzing processes is prevented from becoming abstract theorizing because investigation proceeds by means of actual case studies.

With such an approach it is not necessary to treat equally all countries, all parts of the world, or all of time. Accordingly, the extent of treatment of areas, climatic types, and nations varies throughout the text. Interest is less in nations and regions than in observing processes at work. For this purpose one area is best for exemplifying sequent occupance, another the effects of isolation, another the problem of have and have-not nations in terms of basic resources.

The book aims primarily to develop a way of thinking about man's relation to the land, and it is principle and process oriented. Although the main objective is to develop an understanding of how the present situation came about, sufficient earth description is included to give an overall view of the actual earth and the men on it. The book is based on the conviction that an understanding of relatively few underlying principles and processes will enable the student to find meaning in the wide diversity of the earth about him.

The view taken here is in keeping with the oldest view of a liberal education, that attributed to Aristotle. It is hoped that the student will gain from the book the ability to judge correctly in the weighting of race, physical environment, and cultural-historical factors in the development of the humanly occupied earth as we now see it, and thus be better able to judge the probable direction and rate of change in differing areas with differing peoples and differing cultures.

GEORGE F. CARTER

Baltimore, Maryland
January, 1964

CONTENTS

MAPS

MAN AND THE LAND

Introduction

Mount McKinley. Man lives in a varied world of immense extremes and follows differing ways of life. How much of this differentiation is due to land and how much to man? This is the problem of the cultural geographer. *Ansel Adams—Magnum.*

GEOGRAPHERS have always been interested in where different kinds of men live, what their lands are like, and how they make their living on those lands. No geographer has ever been able to touch these problems without trying to explain *why* men are different and live differently in the various lands.

PHYSICAL ENVIRONMENTAL DETERMINISM

Explanations have been varied, but one theme has run through all human geography: that the physical setting of the land determines what man does. Sometimes this is baldly expressed as climatic determinism, such as "the climate makes the man" or "the tropical humid climates are deadening." Sometimes a racist note is added: "The white man cannot thrive in the tropics." Sometimes the point of view is broadened, and the shape of the land, the kind of soil, the position of the land in relation to the sea, and other physical factors of the environment are called upon to explain why men of a particular region are as they are, have their particular kind of politics, and even have the particular religion they believe in. This, in its various forms, is the kind of geographical thought that is called the Physical Environmental Determinist School. Although this designation is often shortened to "environmental determinism," it should be kept clearly in mind that the physical environment only is referred to.

This way of thinking is found very early in the recorded history of man. The writings of Herodotus are filled with it. The Greeks believed their own land to be the perfect environment, and the lands to the south to be progressively too hot for maximum human achievement. They also thought the lands to the north had winters that were too long and hard for their inhabitants to accomplish much. This crude physical environmental determinism runs through the study of geography ever since like a scarlet thread.

Environmental determinism is an idea that never dies. In every generation it is buried by critics only to be resurrected once again. The process thus far has been endless. Nineteenth-century geographers often pled the case of the deterministic point of view. Even such brilliant and broad students as Friedrich Ratzel were dominated by it. From Ratzel it was carried to America by his disciple Ellen Semple. However, the case for the dominance of the physical environment has most forcibly been presented in the United States by Ellsworth Huntington. His many books have so greatly affected the thinking of a whole generation of geographers that most students accept his views even though they may never have heard his name or have read a thing he wrote. The pervading influence of Huntington's deterministic viewpoint has resulted from his numerous books, which are highly readable, sound very plausible, and are often the principal source books for many high school teachers, who do much to mold the thinking of the great majority of people.

It may seem somewhat unfair to attack a man who can no longer defend himself and who did a great deal of good geographical work—and who, according to his many friends, had a warm personality and was a most stimulating thinker. Nevertheless, it is necessary to expose the extremes of his environmental thinking in order to present students with a clear picture of the issue. For this purpose, two quotations from one of Huntington's earliest works, *Civilization and Climate,* written in 1915, will be briefly discussed below. His views and methodology never fundamentally changed from what they were in this early period.

The major generalization made by physical environmental determinists is found in the first quotation: "Today a certain peculiar type of climate prevails wherever civilization is high. In the past the same type seems to have prevailed wherever a great civilization arose. Therefore, such a climate seems to be a necessary condition of great progress." The physical environment has to be right, or man can achieve little. Great achievements require an optimum climate. At present the great achievements are occurring in mid latitudes; this, then, must be the optimum climate. Since great achievements occurred in the past in places that are not now of this climatic type, such places must in the past have had a different climate—the optimum one.

Both the original statement and my paraphrase of it consist of a tissue of half truths and complete errors. There is no one peculiar type of climate that characterizes the present centers of civilization. These centers share only one feature: a mid-latitude location—and that holds true only if such countries as India and Brazil are excluded from consideration. In particular, the climate of England and of New England, which Huntington considered comparable, are in fact not very much alike. Next, there is a vast amount of evidence that indicates that there has been no major climate change in the past 10,000 years. Therefore, the climates of Egypt, Mesopotamia, India, and Central America—all centers of great ancient civilizations—were in the time of their greatness just what they are now. The conclusion quoted, therefore, must be false. Indeed, historically, great civilizations have flourished in all the climates of the world except the polar ones.

The key concept behind environmental thinking is found in the second quotation from Huntington: "We know that the denizens of the torrid zone are slow, and we almost universally agree that this is connected with the damp, steady heat." It is certainly true that most mid-latitude people believe this. It is also true, however, that under conditions of heat and humidity slowness of movement is an efficient reaction. It is not necessary to rush around to keep the body temperature up; to do so will only overheat the body. Hence, when physical work is done under warm humid conditions, slow movement merely takes advantage of physiological climatology: it does not mean that less work is done, only that it is the most efficient way to work under such conditions. Of course, it was not physical work that particularly interested physical environmental determinists; they were even more concerned with mental effort. What they did was to carry over their unfavorable opinion of the slow-but-steady physical work patterns of such climes to a similar assessment of the thought processes in the tropics: these too were assumed to be "slow and backward." It is most difficult to see how this generalization can be justified in view of the achievements of the Egyptian-Mesopotamian-Indian peoples. Indeed the environmental determinists could not maintain their position in the face of this evidence. They therefore changed the climates to suit their theories. Not only was such a procedure suspect as to methodology, but the research of the past fifty years has also confirmed what many other scholars had believed before this new theory was propounded by the environmental determinists: that the great thinking of the early civilizations were carried out under conditions of high heat and high humidity of just the sort that dominates these now culturally stagnant areas. The turn-of-the-century geographers' fascination with physical environmental determinism proved again to be a blind alley—even a seriously misleading school of thought.

It is bad enough that from time to time geographers have fallen into these easy deterministic views, but the pity of it is that others have followed their lead. Although geographers have now turned their backs on such fruitless determinism, espousing a much better balanced view of the role of the physical environment in human affairs, allied fields of knowledge are all too often still following along in the deterministic paths marked out fifty years ago. When history, economics, and political science, even on the college level, refer to geographic factors, all too often they take a strongly physical environmental determinist view. In lower-level schools, one seldom meets anything but determinism. The notion is appealing because there obviously is some relationship between human activity and the land on which these actions occur.

THE CENTRAL PROBLEM

Here then we meet the central problem in human geography. What *is* the nature of the relationship between man and his environment? Is man the creature of the environment? Does the physical environment shape his actions, determine his fate, and foretell his future? Is the history of Asia to be viewed as a series of climatically determined human pulsations? This was Huntington's theme. Are the tropics doomed by the enervating effect of heat and humidity to a perpetually low cultural status? Is the white man doomed to failure in the tropics—will he always be unable to adjust physiologically to the heat and humidity? Is New England possessed of the most stimulating climate possible? There are still those who would say yes to some or perhaps all of these questions. A cultural-historical approach suggests that the answer in each case must be No.

On the other hand, is it possible to claim that man is utterly independent of the environment? Surely this is not true. But then, just what is the true relationship between the two? How is it possible to judge? One approach is to ask whether it is an accident of history or physically environmentally determined that the underdeveloped countries of the world are in the equatorial regions today. Is there something about heat and humidity that inevitably stifles man's ambitions, limits his mental achievements, and hampers his physical efforts? Or, are the tropical races of man simply "inferior," perhaps due to the millenia long impact of hot and humid climates? We will probe such questions in the chapters that follow and will attempt to demonstrate that the physical environment is but a stage on which the play is acted—and that man is both the playwright and the actor. The physical environment is at all times inert, impassive, noncompelling —unable to exert an influence, to assert itself, to compel, urge, coax, encourage or discourage man. The environment simply exists. This is a strong statement, perhaps an overstatement, but it may serve as a corrective to the opposite, vastly greater overstatement of the role of the physical environment as the all-determining factor in human geography.

THE CULTURAL-HISTORICAL COMPARATIVE METHOD

In the social sciences we cannot freely experiment with societies and economies and the people who compose them—at least not in those societies that believe in the fundamental value of the individual. This is, in one sense, a handicap. If we could experiment in the manner of the physical and biological sciences, we would be able to hold all geographical variables contant except one: imagine being able to put first one race and then another into the identical physical, historical, and cultural conditions to measure their reactions. Or, what might we learn if we could hold race constant while we changed the environment—first holding climate constant while we varied types of soils, then soils while we varied the climate, and so forth.

In fact, we can come remarkably close to such experimentation in the real world by using the entire surface of the world during all of the time we can in any way record, for there is hardly a combination of man and land that has not been experienced. This cultural-historical method will be used here. Our interest will center not on individual man, but on mankind. We will be concerned less with political history than with the history of culture. Man's relation to his environment changes continuously as his knowledge (culture) grows and his outlook changes. Emphasis here will be on culture and the processes that underlie cultural growth and change, for these are the mainsprings that govern the man-land relationship. Culture, the totality of man's learned behavior—and this is responsible for most of behavior, for very little of it in man is instinctive—is like a filter. It prevents the total environment from acting on man directly. Man sees his physical environment, so to speak, through tinted glasses—and the various tints, by filtering out different colors in the landscape, give the men of different cultures totally different views of the world. The result is that men may react quite differently even under identical environmental situations.

This phenomenon of culture operates even in those areas where the impact of the environment is a strong, direct one. Men raised in warm, humid climates, react to the heat and humidity in a physiological sense just as much as men that have more recently moved in to such areas, even though the newcomer seems more unhappy with his environment. His reaction does not necessarily prove anything about either man or the environment. Newcomers are usually unhappy with a different environment: the hill man misses the hills of home when he is in the plains; the forest man misses his trees when in the desert; the desert man, used to the vast open spaces with unencumbered views, feels shut in when in a humid, tree-filled region.

We cannot, with the ordinary man, simply acknowledge his physiological reactions and jump to conclusions about his environment. Man's physiology is in part affected by his psychology, and his psychology is in large part determined by his culture. True, we cannot ignore man's physiology, but it must be kept in perspective—just as the physical environment must be. The cultural, social, and spiritual aspects of man are the determining factors in human geography—or so we will insist here.

CLIMATIC-REGIONAL COMPARISON

It is necessary for any work to follow some plan. This is particularly true for this book, for within its set outline, a certain amount of wandering in subject matter and geographical location is going to occur. The time-honored plan of a climatic division of geography—Dry Lands, Wet Tropics, Grasslands, and so forth—has been chosen. Such a division may lead the student to expect the arid lands, being alike in climate, vegetation, land forms and soils, to prove similar in ways of human occupance. Geography has in fact very often been taught in just this way! Here, however, just the opposite will be found to

be the case: it will be demonstrated that physically similar geographical regions have *not* always caused similar human reactions.

It is often possible to hold a number of variables constant, for some climatically similar regions are also physically very much alike. Norway, the Panhandle of Alaska with adjacent British Columbia, the southern coast of Chile, the west coast of the South Island, New Zealand, are all marine west coast climates. The similar climate is responsible for similar vegetation and similar soils. In addition, all are on a coast, all are mountainous, and all were only recently freed from heavy glaciation that left very similar land forms. This climatically-based category gives us a uniform physical environment, but four different locations. It also presents us with at least three different races of man. The cultures in these regions in the past were utterly different. Was this due to race, to location, or to something else? In the past few hundred years, the political, economic, and at times the racial picture of these regions has been subject to enormous changes. What have such changes wrought in each case? In answering these questions, the roles of race, environment, and culture begin to emerge; the differing social and political changes that occur in similar and unvarying physical environments indicate that such happenings cannot be due to the uniform physical environment.

In this book racial differences are going to be largely ignored. There may be racial differences in the mental realm just as there are differences in the physical realm, such as skin color, but we do not know just what such mental differences are, and just what their role might be. This state of knowledge suggests that compared with such factors as cultural forces, mental differences among the races of mankind must be relatively minor, as indeed are their physical differences—hair forms, skin color, or body proportions.

To attempt to deal with man on the earth through a vast expanse of time is an enormous task. Man alone is a large topic. The physical earth is sufficiently complex that there are dozens of specialized subjects dealing with its physical aspects alone. But this itself is part of our difficulty today. We have subdivided knowledge to such an extent that very few people any longer even try to see the inter-relationships among these numerous subjects. We are living in a period of great, and productive, specialization. But we are also in extreme danger of being unable to see the forest for our fascination with individual trees.

Reality is like the forest. It is a unity. There is really no geology, biology, chemistry, and history: they are part of one great whole—reality. We have simply divided things up for greater ease in studying the matter. This is both legitimate and desirable, so long as we understand what we are doing. Too often, we lose track of the larger framework; the tendency grows for each to think that "his tree" is the most important factor in the whole picture—and that the whole of the universe is to be understood in its terms.

We will try here to put some of these things back together. We cannot take all of knowledge through all of the time and put it in one small book. But no matter how imperfectly and incompletely we accomplish the job, there is something to be gained in trying to put the many different specialized studies of man and geography back together to see how they work.

1-The Origin of Man

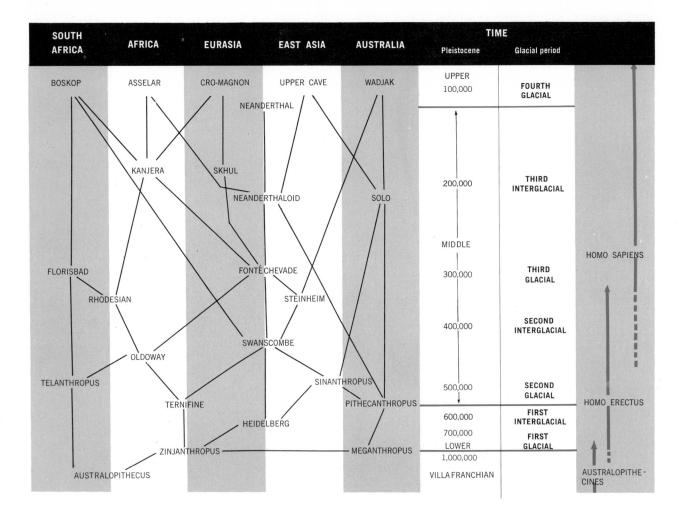

SINCE ONE of the principal themes of the climatic determinists is that the climate, especially the heat and humidity of the tropics, is deadening to man's mental work—and to some extent to his physical accomplishments too—we will examine this problem first. We can well begin with the origin of man, for this immediately raises some counterquestions.

ADAPTATION, PHYSIOLOGY, CLIMATIC IMPACTS

If we look at man as the early theorizers on evolution did, we can make some interesting comparisons. We certainly are remote from an origin in the water. Our best swimmers are sad competitors for a fish. We are not of an arctic origin, for we are among the most naked of all animals. We lack the desert adaptation of the camel or of some of the desert animals that never need to drink. Quite clearly we must have had our origin in some relatively warm and moist land area. We surely are not adapted to any other area. We now live in all areas, but we do this in spite of our physical natures, not because of them. We have had to invent fire, clothing, and housing in order to live outside the subtropics. Just looking at our physical selves, we would conclude that we must have originated in the tropics or subtropics, and in the humid parts of them at that.

Figure 1-1 (*opposite*) The Phylogenetic Trellis. The diagram shows the varied fossil finds of men arranged vertically with the earliest forms at the bottom, and with geographical distribution suggested by placing African forms to the left and Australian forms to the right. The lines are intended to suggest something of the nature of probable intermixture.

Time is given in general terms as Upper, Middle, and Lower Pleistocene for the glacial part of the Pleistocene and Villafranchian for the preglacial part of the Pleistocene. The time of the Villafranchian–Lower Pleistocene boundary may be about one million years.

The many names for individual finds can be reduced to three stages: *Homo sapiens, Homo erectus,* and *australopithecines.* These stages are not sharply defined and on the borderlines there is room for anthropological disagreement on the placement of individual fossil men. Nevertheless, the over-all picture and the placement of the great majority of the finds is clear.

OLD WORLD ORIGIN OF MAN

If we leave this speculative approach and take up what we know of man from such fields as paleontology and archeology, we find this idea fully confirmed. Man quite clearly arose in the Old World (Eurasia and Africa, as opposed to the New World, North and South America). There is no subhuman ancestry in the New World out of which man could have evolved. In the tropical and subtropical parts of the Old World there are numerous fossils as well as living members of the monkey and ape tribe that are potential ancestors of the human forms. Prehuman forms are found ranging from Southeast Asia through India and Arabia and extending into Africa. In this broad belt of the Old World, numerous kinds of tailless primate forms were developing in various directions during the sixty million or so years before man appeared. It was somewhere in this zone that man arose.

That man's physical being is related to this animal world is easily demonstrated. Our A, B, and O blood types are also found in the chimpanzees and gorillas. The Rh factor is found in the Rhesus monkey. In body structure and musculature we are clearly related to the monkey and anthropoid group. Sometimes the details point one way, sometimes another.

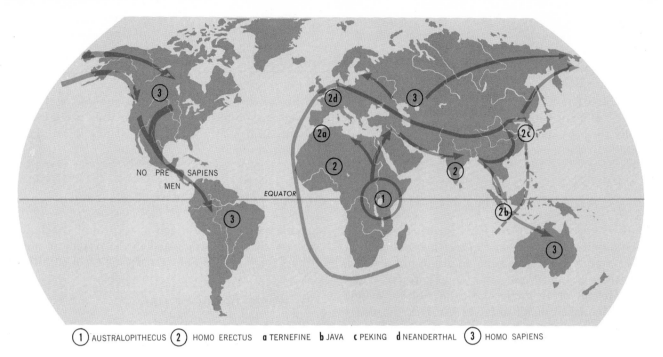

1 AUSTRALOPITHECUS 2 HOMO ERECTUS a TERNEFINE b JAVA c PEKING d NEANDERTHAL 3 HOMO SAPIENS

Map 1-1 The Spread of Mankind over the World

Using a three-stage separation of mankind, the spread of man over the globe must have presented a pattern somewhat like the highly generalized one of this map. The first manlike beings were probably in Africa. From there they seem to have spread out about the beginning of the Middle Pleistocene, perhaps one million years ago. This early dispersion carried men across North Africa, into Southeast Asia, and northward into China, where man appears to have been living at Peking about 400,000 years ago. Extension into Indonesia was also possible during glacial periods when the lowered sea level permitted man to walk at least as far as Celebes. It is similarly possible that man at this time could reach the Philippines and Japan, but it is more likely that it was not till the appearance of sapiens men that these lands were reached. The New World and Australia were seemingly late in being reached. For the New World this may be explained by the rigors of the very cold climate that had to be endured at the Bering Strait gateway from the Old World to America. There were less serious barriers to man's reaching Australia, and early dates for man there would seem likely. The entry to America may have been plural: by shore-dwelling shellfish gatherers quite early, and by skilled arctic hunters somewhat later. This possibility is suggested by the two arrows. Note that the location of sapiens men in peripheral locations does not mean that they evolved there, but that only when sapiens men had appeared did mankind spread into these areas.

Our relationship to the chimpanzees and gorilla may have been overstressed, for we have some anatomical details that are more monkeylike than anthropoid. This mixture of traits suggests an early divergence by man's ancestral line from some common stock and a very long separate course of development.

Evolution in relation to religion is often a stumbling block for students. Life quite certainly has evolved. The geological record begins with no evidence of life, then shows traces of simple life, and finally more and more complex life. Man is unquestionably the most complex form of life in terms of the development of his central nervous system. He is also one of the latest forms of life to appear. So far, all is scientific.

Man differs from all other animals in possessing speech, culture (the vast complex of learned behavior), and an ability to think abstractly that sets him far apart in these areas from all the other animals. In all else, blood, bone, and even the details of individual muscle attachments, he shows clearly the animal origin of his body. All of this can be true, and to the best of our knowledge is true, and yet it does not, or should not conflict with religious beliefs. It leaves man as a part of a physical universe for whose origin we have no natural explanation. It says nothing whatsoever about man's spiritual qualities. While science can indeed point to a physical origin of man's body, it has absolutely nothing to say about soul, spirit, or God. Rather it should be said: it cannot speak scientifically on these matters. Science deals with the material of the earth and its phenomena. It can go no further.*

We find then, in the Old World, in the broad belt of warm and often humid lands extending from southern Asia into Africa, a long series of animal precursors of man and then the predecessors of modern man. The picture shifts about as further knowledge is gained. It was not long ago that we pointed to Java as having the earliest form of man. Now we point to Africa.

African Origin

In Africa in the Upper Pliocene, that is, about 2,000,000 years ago, there existed at least two forms of erect-walking animals roughly intermediate in physical make-up between the small-brained anthropoids—such as the modern gorilla and chimpanzee—and the larger brained early men. We have a large amount of fossil material to work from: from South Africa, perhaps 300 specimens representing about 100 individuals; from East Africa and the Far East, about a dozen specimens. These creatures are known as *australopithecines*.

They are easily distinguished from the monkeys and the anthropoids by their teeth. The incisor teeth form an even topped row. The canine tooth is of the same height as the incisors—that is, it does not project like a tusk. The back teeth are molars—grinders. This is exactly the way that our teeth are arranged. The monkeys and the gorilla and chimpanzee have tusklike canines, and their back teeth are much less specialized for grinding.

There are two forms of the *australopithecines*. One is a large bulky-bodied form with immense molar teeth. Individuals probably stood about five feet high and weighed a few hundred pounds. This is *Paranthropus*. His molars are unique in the hominoids and indicate a great specialization for vegetable foods. He seems to have lived in moist tropical areas and to have eaten coarse vegetable materials that required much crushing and grinding. Although his total tooth pattern is human, the degree of specialization for vegetable foods is beyond anything else known in the human line.

His near relative, was *Australopithecus*. This was an erect-walking creature. He had a long head, a low forehead, and the high point of his skull was well above the brow ridge level. The skull lacked heavy structures such as immense ridges and crests for massive muscular attachments. In this it is more like our own relatively smooth skull. The teeth are much like those of early men. The absence of specialized cutting teeth indicates that this creature was not a carnivore. The absence of specialized grinding teeth indicates that he was not an herbivore. The presence of both kinds of teeth suggest that he was an omnivore—an unspecialized hunter and food gatherer. This is precisely what the earliest men were like in their food-use pattern.

---

* When the origin of man is discussed here, it is his physical origin that is being discussed. As a scientist I can say little about his spiritual birth. As an individual I can affirm that I believe in God and a spiritual part to man. As a scientist I can point out the approximate time and place where man begins to behave in a manner quite different from all the other animals. But that is all that I can do, and all that any scientist can legitimately do. Regrettably, some scientists and some religious people go far beyond the limits of their field, often to the detriment of the subject discussed.

Australopithecus was a small creature, perhaps about four feet in height and weighing some forty or fifty pounds. His cranial capacity was about 500 cubic centimeters, the same as for *Paranthropus* and the gorilla, but the latter were much larger animals. Hence Australopithecus had much more brain for his size than they had. In posture, tooth, skull, and food habits, *Australopithecus* is an apt candidate for the role of the human precursor.

MAN THE TOOLMAKER

The truly distinctive thing about man is his pattern of learned behavior, and the earliest traces that we have of this typical behavior are the tools that man learned to make and taught his offspring to make. This activity, then, becomes the critical test of transition from "monkey to man." *Australopithecus* had a pint-sized brain as compared with early man's quart-sized brains. What could he do?

The question is hotly disputed, but opinion seems to be swinging toward the acceptance of at least some tool making for some of these creatures, especially for *Australopithecus*. Both the evidence of bone and stone suggest that this creature is on the human ancestral line.

The use of tools probably played a large part in man's development. If *Australopithecus* did begin using tools, his food-gathering ability probably multiplied by some figure such as five or ten. Imagine digging roots with your bare hands; then doing it with a sharpened stick, or a piece of bone with a splintered (hence pointed and sharp) end, or with a stone broken so as to have an edge to it. In case of attack, imagine the contrast between hitting with your bare fist and hitting with a sharp-edged rock in your fist. The tool user gains enormous advantages. This would be reflected in increase in his numbers, in ability to displace other animals from desirable feeding grounds, and in the ability to extend the range of the species over wide areas. It seems likely that progressive *Australopithecus* forms began to spread out of South Africa toward the end of the early Pleistocene era, and that tool using played an important part in allowing them to do so.

ORIGIN OF RACIAL DIFFERENCES

These early men were relatively few in numbers. They were spread over the tropics and subtropics of the Old World. They were isolated by the seas and mountains, at times by the glaciers and at other times by the deserts. Contact, hence intermarriage and gene flow, and hence the sharing of variations, must have been extremely rare. Under these conditions in any sexually reproducing population, the separated groups will slowly become different.

There are numerous factors that cause this differentiation. Sexual reproduction assures constant variation by the division of the chromosomes and the assembling of half a set of hereditary characters drawn from the mothers' line of descent and the other half from the fathers' line. At the same time, random changes occur in the genetic material. The results are variation. Children are never exactly like their parents, nor exactly like their siblings (except in the case of identical twins). Selection, in terms of the physical environment, works upon this variation.

Change will occur, however, even without such selection. Studies of small groups of people that are effactually separated from other groups of people show that the two sets of people gradually become different even if living side by side. Studies of this kind have been made on religiously isolated groups. There are in the eastern United States religious groups that maintain themselves as intermarrying, separate cultural units. We know the ancestry of such groups. They are northwest European in origin and largely German. We can compare them with their Old World ancestry, with the other German people that came to America, and with the other European groups that live around them in America. Since all of these people live in the same physical environment, they are subject to the same selection by physical environment. Nonetheless, they vary significantly. Tests of minor traits with known patterns of heredity—such as ability to taste certain chemicals, appearance of hair on the first or second joints of the fingers, and the like—show that these small religiously isolated groups of people have diverged from their parent groups. There is no physical environmental reasons for this divergence. It is the result of a phenomena called *genetic drift.*

If out of any group one set of individuals are chosen at random, there is a high probability that they will not include all the traits of the whole group, but in fact that they may contain a few traits that are rare in the whole group. For instance, from a group of 100 people that included ten red-headed people, a random selection of ten people might contain two or three red heads or no red heads. If two or three red heads were selected, the percentage of red-headed people in the small group would then be two or three times as high as in the original group. If the small group then wandered off into an area where they formed a separate breeding group, they would form a population with an unexpectedly high amount of red-haired people in comparison with the group from which they were derived. Or, assuming the heredity of red hair to be genetically simple, omission of all red heads would lead to a nonred-haired population. There is no variation, no selection by physical environment involved. This is genetic drift.

Early in man's history conditions were ideal for the operation of genetic drift. Populations were small. Little groups wandered off into widely separated areas and thereafter had very little contact with other groups for very long periods of time. At the same time conditions were ideal for the impact of the physical environment, and hence for selection. The less cultural equipment man has, the more directly the physical environment acts on him. Cold will eliminate those with little resistance faster among unclothed people than among people that wear clothing. Among modern men, the person with a low metabolism can simply put on another sweater or push up the thermostat. For very early men, such things were not possible. The earliest man probably lacked fire, wore no clothing, and had little if any housing; individuals in cold areas that could not withstand cold were simply eliminated. Only the cold-resistant survived to produce children, who on the whole would tend to inherit their parents' cold resistance. Similarly, individuals that had little resistance to extremes of heat, sun exposure, or a particular disease would not survive.

When man's precursors spread out of Africa, they probably did so in tiny bands. Their movement was also probably aided by the glacial periods. The shifts in climatic patterns that put Scandinavia under ice a mile thick, brought greatly increased rainfalls to the Sahara, probably making much of it a grassy scrub-forest landscape. Such an environment would have then been suitable for root, seed, and small-game gathering creatures that were on the way to becoming man. Little bands of perhaps ten or twenty individuals probably spread into the Sahara region. Some might then have crossed from Africa via the Sinai peninsula into Arabia. This formidable desert area would have been much more livable during a glacial period. Once in Arabia, the way lay open for the incipient men to spread eastward to India and Southeast Asia, and westward to Gibraltar.

Three Stages of Advancement

The origin of man can be greatly simplified if it is considered as having consisted of a three-stage advance. The first stage is the African situation that we have been considering. Out of these creatures with a 500-cubic-centimeter cranial capacity developed a more progressive form that used tools. This tool-using creature then spread widely and eventually gave rise to the next stage, *Homo erectus.* The major physical change was an increase in brain size from about 500 cubic centimeters to about 1000 cubic centimeters. The final stage reached is the *Homo sapiens,* modern man with cranial capacities varying from an average of about 1100 to 1400 between races of men, and from less than 1000 to over 1800 cubic centimeters of the cranial capacity in specific individuals.

All living men are *Homo sapiens,* as are all the Upper and some Middle Pleistocene men. Most Middle Pleistocene men are considered as *Homo erectus.* It cannot be stressed too strongly that the boundaries from one type to the other are gradational, that there is little agreement among the experts as to placement of borderline cases, and that almost anything that we can say today is subject to change tomorrow if we gain some new knowledge (see Figure 1–1, page 8).

Once man had spread over the warm and humid land and subhumid parts of the Afro-Eurasian land mass he was effectually separated into small groups. It was easy for men to move, for there was no opposition from their own kind. Should they try to move back into areas from which they had come, however, they would find there the descendants of the people they had left behind now firmly in possession of the desirable camping, gathering, and hunting areas and resistant to the intrusion of competitors. Thus the original spread would be easy, but would be primarily a one-way process: into the unoccupied lands. Once there were no more unoccupied lands, movement would slow down greatly. With vast areas of the world occupied, the differing groups of men would be increasingly separated from effective contact with one another. The isolation of the men of Africa from those of Asia would be virtually absolute, and such isolation would guarantee both cultural and biological divergence.

The simple fact of distance would be multiplied by such physical barriers as mountains, rivers, and seas and their effect would be heightened at times by the disappearance of the glaciers. Melting glaciers would cause rising sea levels and, for example, isolate the men on each island group in Indonesia— at least until men invented water craft capable of crossing the open water. Even then, it is not realistic to think of large groups of men crossing such water gaps. But, unless sizable numbers of people make such crossings, there is little gene flow, hence little exchange of the differing characteristics that would be accumulating in each such isolated group. In this way, differences would increase through time.

Similar barriers to the easy exchange of genes would be erected in the desert areas. While glacial periods might make the deserts easily traversible, even attractive, to early man, the interglacial periods would re-establish the deserts in all their harshness. Before the innovation of irrigation and pastoralism, few people would live in deserts, and fewer still would cross them. The Sahara, the Arabian and the Thar deserts would themselves then act as barriers —until a return to glacial conditions made them once more potential zones of travel and of the meeting and mixing of the kinds of men that had been becoming increasingly differentiated during interglacial times. Such time periods may be thought of as alternating, each lasting roughly 100,000 years. First 100,000 years of isolation; then 100,000 years of some mixing on the edges of the formerly more completely isolated groups. It is therefore under the conditions of the vast periods of isolation that the variations in mankind probably arose, the variations that became the basis for different races.

FORESHADOWING OF MODERN RACES

By the time of the second interglacial period, perhaps 400,000 years ago, man was living near Peking, China. He lived in caves, used fire, and made crude stone tools in a variety of forms. Peking may be thought of as climatically somewhat like Pittsburgh, Pennsylvania; hence men at Peking clearly survived a hard winter, and he did so by using techniques that no other animal uses. Physiological climatology suggests that these men could have survived in that region without any clothing, but it also seems quite possible that man was already beginning to use the skins of some of the animals that he was killing for food as a cover to ward off the cold.

Peking man had a cranial capacity within the lower range of modern men. Whether he is labeled *Homo erectus* or *Homo sapiens* is a matter of scholarly judgment. Franz Weindenreich thought that he could find a number of Mongoloid traits in Peking man, and that he probably played a part in the origin of the modern Asiatic races. In terms of the

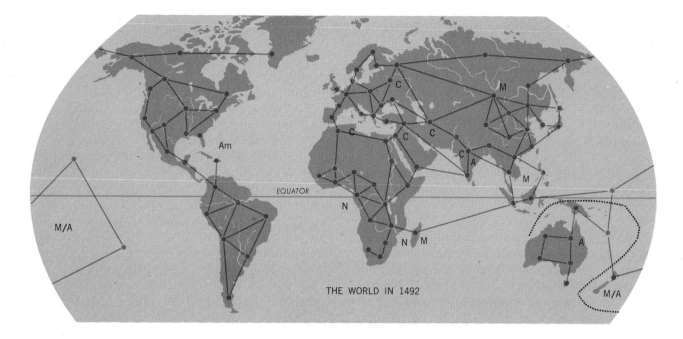

Map 1-2 Gene Flow and the Races of Man

The dots indicate centers of population, and the lines suggest something of the flow of genes through interbreeding of populations. The letters refer to the major races: C for the Caucasoids, N for the Negroids, M for the Mongoloids, and A for the Australoids. The American Indians are designated Am, for Amerind. The letters M/A suggest Australoid and Mongoloid mixture. The boundary between the Oceanic Australoids and the Polynesians is marked by a curved line. There were centers of easy gene flow in the Old World: in Africa south of the Sahara, in Europe and the Near East, in Asia, and in Australia. Major racial groups center in these areas. The zones of limited gene flow mark the marginal racial areas and are zones of transition in race type. That the Americas failed to develop separate racial types—for example, a marked division between North and South America in race type —suggests that the process is a very slow one and that the time available in America was too short.

anthropological picture presented here, this would seem reasonable. While the Java man is certainly an earlier variant of the early human group (*Homo erectus*), the Peking man is a more advanced geographical variant of this same Asiatic group. Mixed with other types of men that reached Asia by various routes in later times, Peking man therefore is probably part of the basic stratum of the present Asiatic races of mankind.

In Europe at this same time there were other kinds of men spreading beyond the tropical homeland of man. In the Middle Pleistocene, *Homo erectus* is probably represented in Germany by the jaw found near Heidelberg in the Mauer Sands. Other early examples of *Homo erectus* have been found in North Africa (*Atlanthropus*). There are suggestions of even more advanced types of men at Swanscombe, England, at this time. The Swanscombe cranium lacks the face section, but the rest of the skull is not readily distinguishable from a *Homo sapiens* of modern European type.

At this Middle Pleistocene period, then, there were men in Asia and Europe who approached the lower limits of modern men in cranial capacity, were definitely tool makers, and seem to foreshadow the races that came eventually to dominate their regions. In terms of the role of isolation in variation, these results are exactly what one would expect if a progressive *Australopithecus* form approaching the *Homo erectus* stage of development spread over the tropics and subtropics of the Old World.

In each more or less isolated part of the world, according to this picture, variations would arise. Each major section of the Old World would therefore have developed its own geographical variation from the basic human stock. Some of the differences would, expectedly, be adaptive; some would be accidental; but differences there would be. Accordingly, one would expect centers of difference in East Asia, India, Western Europe, and Africa south of the Sahara, with a zone of intermingling in the Middle East. Apparently, however, there was enough gene flow to prevent separate species from coming into being during the long periods of isolation. Since later human history has been marked by the increasing mobility of mankind, the differentiation created by extreme isolation now can be expected slowly to dissolve.

RACE AND PHYSICAL ENVIRONMENT

For our purposes, we must consider the role of physical geography in all of this development and, in particular, look at the problem of race differences from the point of view both of physical make-up and of possible mental differences.

Skin Color and Climate

That the races of man are physically adapted to differing environments is strikingly clear. In the Old World, correlation between skin color in man and the solar intensities of his environment exists, and if allowances are made for relatively recent migrations of people, the correlation increases.

Some movements are historically known. The Lapps are yellow-brown-skinned people from Asia who have moved westward into an area of low sun intensity. The Sahara west of Egypt was occupied by very dark-skinned people until later Roman times, when the introduction of the camel to the brunette peoples along the Mediterranean edge of North Africa enabled them to spread over the Sahara.

Even the presence of brunette Europeans in Egypt is suspect. They split a Negroid Nubia from a Negroid Sahara. Current research suggests that agriculture was introduced into Egypt from Mesopotamia. Quite possibly, a new race entered the Nile at this time, about 5000 B.C.

The spread of Indo-European-speaking, light-skinned people into India just prior to 1500 B.C. is well known. This movement displaced the skin-color line.

If the original skin-color distribution was closely adjusted to climate, then the present distributions suggest thrusts by light-skinned peoples into Arabia and thence into Egypt. Similarly, the break in dark-skin distributions in Southeast Asia suggests an expansion of the yellow-brown-skinned people into that area. The survival of dark-skinned peoples in isolated areas in the Philippines, Malaya, and on islands in the Indian Ocean seems to support the theory of an early continuous distribution of dark-skinned peoples in the Asiatic equatorial region. While a detailed study would modify the sweeping generalizations made both on Map 1–3 and in this discussion, the main conclusion would probably remain the same: that skin color is climatically adaptive, and variations very old.

The most striking thing about these correlations is that while they are very good in the Old World, they are very poor in the New World. This suggests that man either has not been present in the New World long enough to be marked by the environment in the way that he has been in the Old World, or that by the time he reached the New World he

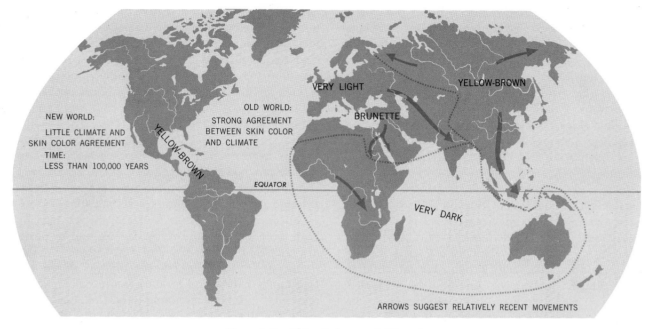

Map 1-3 Skin Color and Climate

In the Old World there is a clear correlation between climate and the locations of the major divisions of skin color. The light-skinned peoples are in the northwest where the greatest amount of cloudiness throughout the year is found. The very dark skins are in the equatorial regions where the greatest intensity of sunshine is experienced. The yellow-brown skins are in the areas seasonally exposed to moderate intensity followed by low intensity of solar radiation. It was primarily the yellow-brown-skinned peoples that peopled America, and despite the passage of a few tens of thousands of years and a range of climate as great as that in the Old World, no comparable intensity of skin color difference has developed. The pattern of skin-color intensity and insolation intensity is not perfect in the Old World, probably due to recent movements of mankind. Dark-skinned peoples held all the Sahara west of the Nile Valley prior to introduction of the camel in late Roman times. The very-dark-skinned Bantu Negroes spread out of the high sun-intensity area of the Sudan in recent times to occupy much of Africa. The lighter skinned Europeans moved into northwest India about 1500 B.C., displacing the skin-color line somewhat. The yellow-brown peoples have expanded into Southeast Asia and Indonesia, breaking into the former distribution of the dark-skinned peoples—remnants of whom are found in the Philippines, Malaya, and the Indian Ocean. At some time in the remote past the distribution of skin color may have been much more closely correlated with the climatic zones than it is now. Very-dark-skinned people probably originally occupied all of the equatorial zone of high sun intensity in the Old World.

was already so well-equipped culturally that the environment had relatively little impact on his physical being. We will return to this question after discussing the variation of mankind in the Old World.

In the Old World, variations in skin color occur within the major racial groups. It is quite clear that light-skinned people originally were located in northwestern Europe, an area of extremely low sun intensity. Around the sunnier Mediterranean, people were brown-skinned. In the fiercely sunny North African, Arabian, and Ethiopian areas, men otherwise European in racial characteristics are dark-skinned.

The advantages of pigmented skin are obvious to anyone who has ever been sunburned. A severe sunburn can be fatal. The inability of a fair-skinned person to stand exposure to high sun intensities greatly limits his efficiency in open tropical lands such as the low-latitude deserts and the savannas. In such areas, dark skins have a survival advantage and light skins are selected against. This action must have been immensely more effective in early times when men wore less clothing and had minimum housing.

In fact, anyone who has suffered greatly from sunburn might wonder what possible function might be served by light skins. A clue to such a function was gained when it was noticed in London that rickets were more prevalent among dark-skinned slum children than among light-skinned children living under equally poor conditions of food, shelter, and clothing. Rickets is a vitamin-deficiency disease, the required vitamin being manufactured when the fats in the skin are irradiated by sunlight. In London, therefore, the coloring matter of the dark-skinned slum children screened out much of the penetrating solar energy. The light-skinned children, although also on a substandard diet, absorbed a maximum amount of the very weak sunlight of the London winter, enough irradiation to manufacture the needed vitamins.

Primitive man frequently experienced periods of famine when he ran short of energy-supplying foods and thus of vitamin supplies. The critical period in Western Europe was probably during the winter low-sun period, when those individuals with a lighter skin would have had a survival factor in their favor. It seems significant, at least, that the earliest penetration by man into a cloudy, mid-latitude climatic zone was into Northwest Europe and that region is also the center of fair-skinned mankind. The only other apparent answer could be found in genetic drift, but that seems inapplicable in a case where the trait in question has obvious survival value.

Man was not able to reach the other cloudy mid-latitude (long-winter) climates until much later. The American regions representative of this climate were not reached by man until the Upper Pleistocene, and the Australian-Tasmanian occupation of similar climates may date to about the same time. Whatever the time interval, however, it was apparently not enough for this selection factor to achieve any result.

Heat, Cold, and Body Form

Heat and cold place major stresses on our bodies. We are heat-producing machines. We burn food to operate our body processes and to maintain an even body temperature. Departure from the normal 98.6° Fahrenheit body temperature is accompanied by discomfort when the change is of a degree or two, by acute distress when it is of five degrees, and by possibly fatal results in the case of ten degrees.

Our ability to produce heat is limited. If we lose heat faster than we can produce it, our body temperature will fall. For men living in cold climates, especially for ill-equipped men, it would obviously be advantageous to have the ability to minimize heat loss.

There are various ways to do this: presence of fur for insulation; circulation changes to minimize surface temperatures while keeping the deep body areas warm; body-shape adaptation to minimize heat loss. Man has not developed fur, although he has in later time developed the cultural trait of using animal furs for insulation. Physiological changes have been detected in some culturally ill-equipped people living in mid-latitude climates. The natives of Australia could restrict blood flow to their arms and legs, let their limb temperatures drop, and thus sleep unhoused and unclothed in temperatures down to freezing. The people of Tierra del Fuego had a basal metabolism (rate of heat production) one and one half times as great as ours. These are people who were virtually unclad and unhoused.

The coldest climates early penetrated by man, and the coldest winter area inhabited by man, are found in the continental interior of Eurasia. The body build of the Mongoloid people, the race that originated in this area, has distinctive adaptations for cold. They are short-limbed, thick-bodied people. This body form minimizes the area from which heat can be lost.

In a warm climate the problem is to dissipate the heat produced simply by existing, as well as the heat produced by working. Unless this can be done there will be a rise in body temperature. Heat is dissipated by perspiring, by evaporation from the lungs, and by radiation from the skin. The more surface area from which heat can be radiated and from which perspiration can be evaporated, the better the cooling system will work. The ability of the body to lose heat to its surroundings is aided by a sizable difference between the temperature of the body and that of the surrounding environment, by dry air into which perspiration can be evaporated readily, and by moving air, which removes the air saturated by evaporated perspiration and brings more absorbent or cooler air once again into contact with the body. In the warm, moist tropics the air may be near body temperature and already nearly saturated with moisture. Heat loss is then difficult. In the dry tropics air temperature may go above body temperatures, but the dry air then makes evaporative cooling very efficient. To achieve heat loss is still a problem, however. Not unexpectedly, tropical races often tend to be tall and slender, for this body form gives them the maximum surface area to aid heat loss.

Other Physiological Adaptations

Bodily adaptation to climate probably goes much further than we yet understand. The Mongoloid facial type is a flat one, with a fatty layer under the skin, a form that affords a minimum of exposure of facial parts and thus defends against freezing. Mongoloids are also relatively beardless: Under conditions of extreme cold, a beard catches moisture from the breath and soon becomes an ice mask. Europeans have beards: they live in less cold environments, where ice is unlikely to accumulate in the beard, and the beard can serve as insulation.

But there is a limitation to this kind of explanation. For example, tropical people are also largely beardless. This line of reasoning also leads to such questions as: Was man originally beardless? Did the European race develop body hair through genetic drift, perhaps in the warm Near East, and thence spread it into Northwest Europe? Or did the trait develop adaptively and later racial movements then carry it back into subtropical regions?

Body hair is more than a nuisance. By harboring disease-bearing parasites, it can be a positive detriment. Since there seems to be good reason not to be hairy, must there not have been a positive function served by hairiness? Protection against cold seems the likeliest function. Yet, hairiness would seem to be an old trait, since American Indian groups living for tens of thousands of years in climates similar to the Europeans are no hairier than those living in the tropics.

If the long head of hair of the Mongols and the Europeans is useful against cold, is the short hair of the Negro useful against heat? It would seem so: Thick masses of hair around the neck and shoulders would be most unwelcome in heat and humidity. Women with long hair often adopt a short hairdo for the summer, or pin their hair up. The Negro can be said to have a permanent summer coiffure.

This list of adaptive traits can be extended. Noses with longer nasal passages are useful for warming and humidifying the bitterly cold dry air of the continental interiors. This is another good example of the problems and pitfalls in such explanation. The classic long Semitic nose does not seem to fit into this idea. However, the large, often hooked Semitic nose did not originate in the eastern Mediterranean; it was brought into that region by the Armenoids coming from some part of Southwest Asia, an area of great winter cold. This trait could be a case of the migration of men in relatively recent times (the past few tens of thousands of years?) resulting in the scrambling of adaptive traits (fixed in the preceding few hundreds of thousands of years?) At the same time, it is also noteworthy that the Mongols living in very cold climates do not have large noses. Does the risk of freezing a projecting

The Races of Man Indonesian Girl, Java. An example of the mixed race resulting from the Mongoloid spread into the Indo-Malay area. *Embassy of Indonesia.*

American Indian. Crow woman with her daughter. *Museum of the American Indian, Heye Foundation.*

nose more than offset the gain of warming the inspired air? Or is this simply a nonadaptive difference?

The development of physical differences that fitted man for different environments and simply the drifting apart due to the isolation of population groups are the obvious reasons why men became different in different geographical areas of the Old World. These geographically separated and physically different groups of men are the races of mankind. The evidence presented here suggests that these races are of very ancient origin. The contrary view, however, is more often held, and the origin of races is placed subsequent to the spread of Upper Paleolithic men during the last glaciation. The evidence from America seems crucial here.

MAN AND RACE IN PRE-COLUMBIAN AMERICA

The time of the first peopling of America is a hotly disputed question. The time has moved steadily back from 5000 to 10,000 to 40,000 years and now to seri-

ous consideration of a last interglacial time about 100,000 years ago. The first entrants were already *Homo sapiens.* This establishes a minimum age for *sapiens* men of 50,000 years, and a possible age in excess of 100,000 years.

The first Americans were long-headed, relatively small people, with moderately strong developed brow ridges. Attempts to describe them in terms of other races often leads to calling them Australoid, or Melanesoid, meaning that they suggest men of those types. They most certainly were not typical Mongoloids (round headed, smooth browed). The appropriate kinds of men are just beginning to be reported in China. At Tzu-yang, Szechwan province, and at Liu-chiang, Kwangsai province, men of primitive *Homo sapiens* type not yet fully Mongoloid have been found in the Upper Pleistocene deposits. Perhaps the short, swarthy, bearded, non-Mongoloid Ainu of Japan are another example of the kind of men derived from some early Asiatic types of man. Other Asiatic people entered America later, some of

Mediterranean Type. A fisherman from the eastern Mediterranean. *Embassy of the United Arab Republic.*

Bushman of the Kalahari. This is so distinctive a type of man that he is sometimes set apart as a Capoid race. Notice the extreme form of curly hair. *Information Service of South Africa.*

Australian Natives. The broad nose, curly hair, and dark brown skin approaches the Negro race type. There are sufficient differences, however, to set this type of man apart as a race. *Australian News and Information Bureau.*

Negro Boy, Southwest Africa. The dark brown skin, protusion of the lower face, everted lips, and low-bridged nose are all marks of the classic Negro type. *Smithsonian Institution.*

the North American tribes closely resembling the Paleo-Siberian people. Typical Mongoloid people entered America later still.

The first entrants are of greatest interest. Whether they were here for 50,000 or 100,000 years, the time was insufficient to accomplish much if any racial differentiation to fit these men to the array of climates in the New World. In the Old World such climates, plus, time, plus isolation (partly geographical and partly cultural), produced the major races of the world.

The first men to enter the New World were excessively primitive in culture. They surely had little housing and clothing to shield them from environmental impacts. Yet there are negligible skin-color, hair-form, or small body-form differences among the American Indians from one climatic type to the other. The inhabitants of Tierra del Fuego form a minor exception and will be discussed later.

The degree of isolation of one group from another in America is neatly illusrated by the diversity of languages in Indian America. There are few large areas dominated by one linguistic stock. Instead there is enormous complexity, with innumerable tiny groups speaking totally unrelated languages. This complexity suggests isolation for long expanses of time. Consider, for instance, that after 5000 years the Indo-European languages are, at least to a linguist, very obviously closely related. Movement in America was apparently relatively rare, and isolation was the rule, a situation favorable to the development of racial diversity. The absence of racial diversity must then mean that there was too little time for it to occur. If the age for man in America is of the order of magnitude of 50,000 to 100,000 years, then, reasoning backward, the age of the major races of mankind must indeed be quite great.

The general conclusion is that variation and selection have always operated on man and that isolation, genetic drift, variation, and selection have created the races of mankind. The races must be very old, for Europeans by Middle Pleistocene time seem to be foreshadowed in the Swanscombe and Fontéchevade fossils, and Mongols in the *Sinanthro-*

pus. By Upper Pleistocene time, when *Homo sapiens* entered America, there was not sufficient time—despite identical climatic variation in the Old World and the New World acting on people of similar cultural level—to create similar degrees of difference in the New World as in the Old World. Depending on what time estimates are used for the origin of *sapiens* man, and the time of the first peopling of America, there was five to ten times longer a period for variation to occur in the Old World than existed in the New World. The degree of racial variation in the two areas can then be said to be proportional to this time difference.

ENVIRONMENT AND ACCOMPLISHMENT: MAN IN THE TROPICS

To return to the environmental-determinist theme again, no matter whether man originated in Asia or Africa it seems clear that he is—as our cursory glance at his physical being would lead us to guess—a product of the warm and humid lands. If man originated in the tropics, why should that climate be the one for which he is most poorly fitted? If man evolved in a warm and humid climate, should not that climate be the one to which he is best suited, just as monkeys thrive in their tropical and subtropical homes and perish when they get too far out of them?

According to our previous reasoning, man should be more adapted to heat and humidity and to the relatively unchanging seasons of the tropics and subtropics than to any other type of climate. If his beginning is placed about 1,500,000 years ago in Africa, more than 1,000,000 years passed before we find him moving into the truly cold climates and remaining there—and it was only a minority of mankind that moved in the cold climate at that. The bulk of mankind quite sensibly stayed in the warm, comfortable humid climates. Our view of this whole process is distorted by the fact that at the moment we have some rather large groups of mankind in the higher mid-latitudes, but in terms of man's history this is a quite recent phenomenon. Man's history is one of warmth and moistness. Since it was not in the "cold and stimulating climates" that man arose, but in the warm and humid ones, this is where he should be physiologically at home.

In fact, contrary to what is often claimed, there have been great civilizations both in warm and humid and hot and dry climates. We can well argue that more great ideas originated and more basic inventions were conceived in those regions than have yet come out of the "cool and stimulating climates"! The latter phrase itself is the result of a highly selective and momentary view of history. It reflects a view of the world as it is now and, even more, as it was in the hundred years from 1850 to 1950, when the North Atlantic nations were probably at their peak of world dominance.

Physiology, Climatology, Psychology

If we try to measure the physiological impact of the climate on man, we find both interesting data and difficult problems. It becomes surprisingly hard to determine just what we are measuring. For instance, it was once proposed to find out what the immediate effects of the physical environment were on groups of people at work. Two groups of people were selected: a group of girls and a group of men, both doing a wiring-assembly job. For both groups systematic changes were made in the working conditions. Temperature, humidity, and air movement were varied. The two groups were subjected to all kinds of heat and cold. Until extreme ranges—beyond anything that one would experience under natural conditions—were reached, the working groups simply ignored the changes.

For the women, a record was kept of their hours of sleep, their social engagements, their family affairs, and the like. It was thought that this might be important to their work output. Instead, it was found that the most important factor in the work situation was how the individual girl felt about the girl who worked nearest to her. The next most important factor was how the group was working as a whole. Introducing a new girl into the group was much more disturbing to their accomplishment than any-

thing except the most outrageously extreme changes in the heat and the humidity. By and large, the girls felt that they were participating in a very special study and felt secure in their jobs; as a result they were content and willing and eager to work. This may be thought of as the role of culture. Perhaps we ought to change the old saw about "it isn't the heat, it's the humidity," to "it isn't the heat, it's the attitude."

The men were quite different. They did not work up to their capacity at all: neither in terms of their intelligence nor in terms of their dexterity. They did not even work to maximize their economic gain; they acted as a faintly hostile group whose main function was to maintain group integrity, even if it cost them money individually. But again, there was little or no relation in all of this to the physical environment. The men maintained the same attitude whether their work environment was steamy as a tropical forest or as cold as the subarctic. Under severe environmental stress, therefore, the factors that determined achievement or lack of it were psychological-cultural, and physiological reactions appeared most strongly in terms of the differing psychology of male and female.

Physiological climatologists state that under warm, moist conditions of a moderately severe kind there can be expected some reduction of circulation efficiency, some discomfort due to sweating, sticky clothes, and a resultant reduction of patience and alertness and judgment. But, they add, with a high degree of motivation a fairly high standard of performance can be maintained by selected individuals under conditions verging on those which will produce physical collapse. In other words, right up to the point of collapse, man can do anything if he really wants to do it. This is certainly what the experimental work with the girls' group showed. Physiological literature on the subject contains descriptions of the true physiological failure of the body under extreme cases of heat and humidity, but it also indicates that under the conditions likely to be found in the shade of the tropics the capacity of the healthy, trained, and acclimatized worker is not likely to be much affected. Perhaps noteworthy is the fact that children one-year old appear to stand the stress of heat much more readily than do adults. It is not clear just why this is so, but even the physiologists—who might interpret reactions as evidence of physiological strain more readily than psychologists might—agree that this equanimity may be a reflection of the child's power to ignore minor strains such as climatic discomfort.

It therefore becomes quite difficult to see just how climatic strains, and in particular heat and humidity effects, could have the enervating effect claimed by those who see in the "deadly effect of the tropics" the reason for the absence of civilization there. And, if it is so difficult to make a convincing picture of physiological impact of the heat and humidity of the tropics, how much more difficult it is to make a similar argument of any convincing proportions for high altitudes, high latitudes, hills, or dales. Man must make an adjustment for most environments, and for some, such as very high altitudes, that adjustment must begin early in life. However, once the adjustment is made, man seems able to do equally well in any environment; and so far as our present data goes, most races do about equally well in all environments.

RACE AND MENTALITY

The notion that the various races of mankind are mentally different in large degree is not borne out by consideration of the function of the brain and the manner in which selection would operate. The brain is a complex machine—analogous to the computing machines now being constructed. It operates our automatic functions such as breathing and heart operation, and there is little room for selection to work here. The brain also controls our conscious muscular activities, but throwing a spear, shooting an arrow, driving a car, or operating a typewriter are the same operations in all climates. Nor can one readily pick out any work requiring significantly different mental development in other physical environments such as mountains versus plains, or forests versus grasslands. If this is true, there would seem to be no reason for differential selection on a physical environmental basis.

Functionally, the brain is a problem-solving machine. Man is forever faced with problems. In the past: Can I make the tree before the tiger gets there? Now: Can I make the curb before the light changes? Men must grow up, find a mate, and supply and shelter a family. The multiple forms of marriage and family structure that have existed over the ages do not change the fundamentals; they only change the form in which they are presented to the individual. Men must continually make social decisions that determine their success or failure, their survival or death. There is a constant selection against the stupid, and it acts equally strongly in all physical environments. A stupid mistake in the arctic may bring death by freezing, in the desert by thirst, in the wet tropics by poisonous snakes. The brighter man in the arctic gets more seals or caribou, in the desert finds hidden water and scarce game, and in the jungle avoids the tiger and traps the elephant. Selection for better minds, yes; but by climatic or any other physical environmental pattern, no.

Such processes operate through time. It might be argued that man to a considerable extent makes his own environment, and that some men have been living in significantly different man-made environments so long that they could now be distinctively different mentally; that there are differing, genetically adapted mental types selected for hunting, for farming, for city dwelling. There certainly are great differences in the amount of time that various groups of people have been exposed to these differing ways of life. There are a few people left on earth that are living in the Lower Paleolithic unspecialized hunting and gathering stage, and perhaps an equal number living in the Upper Paleolithic specialized hunting stage. A great many people in the world are still living on a Neolithic level: simple villagers making their living from primitive agriculture. Only a small fraction of the total of mankind lives an urban life, and for most of them it is a phenomenon of the last few centuries. Unless the selective process operates very rapidly, few people indeed can be expected to show biological adaptations to urban life.

The history of the past 5000 years is filled with examples of people who jumped in very brief spans from one level to the other of this sequence, with no measurable genetic mental changes. Apparently they had the inherent ability to live a fully civilized life even though they had until a few centuries ago lagged in a Paleolithic way of life.

While there is considerable argument about just when man becomes man, almost everyone would agree that by 500,000 years ago men very much like modern men were on the scene. Their way of life was that of unspecialized hunters and gatherers, somewhat like the people of Australia or the Great Basin in the United States until a century ago. A few people became specialized hunters about 30,000 years ago, fewer people became farmers 10,000 years ago, and still fewer people became urban people about 500 years ago. It is difficult to say just what the effect of all of this is on human minds.

One might say that on a 500,000-year time scale mentally we should be: 90 percent hunters and gatherers, 9 percent hunters, .9 percent farmers, and .1 percent urbanites. This proportion assumes mental adaptation in proportion to the time that we have lived that kind of a life, implies long periods to establish mental types suited to ways of life, and suggests long retention of the basic patterns. Although such assumptions are probably true, however, no one has demonstrated a genetically fixed mental type for gatherers, hunter, farmers, or urbanites. The fact that so many races of men have adapted so quickly and so successfully to the requirements of modern urban commercial life, even though they started from entirely differing ways of life, suggests that the fundamental requirements for each way of life are much the same. Life's most basic problems are social and interpersonal, and not basically different for the men of Paleolithic, Neolithic, or urban way of life. If, then, some races have had representatives in the urban way of life longer than others, there is little evidence that they have gained a genetically based—that is racial—advantage.

If such advantages were rapidly gained, and fixed genetically, we should find marked differences within races. The world's leaders should be the people of the Near East, for they became village-dwelling farmers nearly 10,000 years ago, and urban dwellers by at least 5000 years ago. In contrast, the people of northwest Europe did not become farmers until about 5000 years ago, and only a minority became civilized (literally, living in cities) about 100 years ago, and only within this century has city dwelling really become a numerically dominant way of life for them.

Twist and turn this as we will, then, the argument from the nature of the mind as determined by its problem-solving function, brings us back again and again to expect considerable uniformity in the minds of men and provides us with no clear basis for expecting mental differences of considerable degree in minds developed under varying physical or even economic environments. This is not to say that there are no such differences, but to suggest that both in terms of function and of time, these differences are seemingly minor, if they exist at all.

Tests of Racial Differences in Abilities

Tests of race variation in general intelligence and in special abilities fail thus far to support any clear-cut racial distinctions. Each race seems to have a normal distribution curve of ability: a few people of very high ability; some of good ability; a mass of average ability; some of poor ability; and a few people of very limited ability. In terms of the similarity of man both physically and socially, as we have seen, this is about what we might expect.

Intelligence tests have shown racial differences. In America, Negroes on the average test lower than whites; however, southern Negroes test lower than northern Negroes, and educated northern Negroes test higher than semiliterate southern whites. This could be misinterpreted as the result of the stimulating climate of the temperate north versus the deadening climate of the tropical south. It is very probable that educated southern Negroes could be found who would test higher than a white group from the slums of Chicago or New York, or one of the decadent rural areas of New England. The meaningfulness of intelligence tests has been greatly improved, but they still cannot avoid the effects of varying opportunity, motivation, and the deep psychological impacts of varied social positions in society.

RACE AND ACHIEVEMENT

We can try another approach. If we look at the races of the world in terms of the locations of centers of great cultural achievement, we find the following picture (see Maps 1–1 and 2–1). The enormous cultural achievements centered in Mesopotamia, Palestine, Egypt, Greece, and Rome are the work of the Mediterranean race, the basic stratum of the so-called European race. The achievements of India must be credited to a related race: early achievements to the Dravidian people, and later achievements to the mixed Dravidian–Indo-European after 1500 B.C. The Chinese accomplishment is of course the achievement of the Mongoloid people, stimulated to some extent by ideas streaming eastward from the Near East. Accomplishments in Southeast Asia (Burma, Siam, Indonesia) are the results of ideas coming in from both India and China, and being utilized by the slender, brown-skinned races of that area. In America, culture first reached the level of civilization in the Middle-American area (southern Mexico to northern Chile). This accomplishment was the work of the American Indians, people of Asiatic origin, and may have resulted from the stimulus of ideas reaching them within the last few thousand years via the Pacific. This review leaves conspicuously out of the picture such regions as Australia and Tasmania; Melanesia; Africa south of the Sahara; the subarctic areas of both the Old and New Worlds; and most of the subtropics of the New World as well.

Much evidence now points to the Near East as *the* center of the origin of civilization. Egypt early received impulses from this center. Later the stream of ideas flowed westward up the Mediterranean, and northwestward into Europe. North Africa, like South Africa, made abortive starts toward civilization. Carthage is an example of an area where the cultural loss was neither racially nor climatically caused. Ideas also flowed northeastward to China and eastward to India. Trade surely was a major factor in this cultural flow, for we have evidence of sea trade going from Mesopotamia to the Indus Valley of India via of the Bahrain Islands in the Persian Gulf as early as 2000 B.C. From India and China, developments in Southeast Asia and Indonesia were stimulated. With due allowance for deserts, mountains, and distances (and even greater allowances for the accidents of history), the effect is somewhat as though a rock were thrown into a somewhat irregularly shaped puddle: the ripples agitate the nearby waters greatly, the distant waters only later and slightly, and the sheltered distant coves hardly at all (see Map 11–1). It is a peculiarity of man on earth that the Old World race farthest from this center of activity is the Negro race. Melanesia, Australia, and Tasmania are remote lands; Africa south of the Sahara is also. This explanation is not the only one possible, but it will be left here for the moment and the details dealt with in later chapters.

Distance alone is an insufficient answer to differences in development, as is illustrated by the happenings in America. A massive flow of ideas was carried by peoples across the immense Pacific to set off the civilizational growth in Indian America.* Note that this flow of people and ideas bypassed Melanesia. Was this because Melanesia is a great Negro area or because there was nothing in Melanesia to attract these people? For example, after 1500 the Spanish explored the Pacific and established an outpost at Manila. They ignored black Melanesia, but they also ignored brown Polynesia. They were not discriminating against race but making an economic choice. Neither Polynesia nor Melanesia were economically developed. Neither were they well located for trade with China and Southeast Asia, and it was these areas of spice, silk, porcelain, and other desirable goods that were the goals. Race had little if anything to do with the decision.

* This topic will be dealt with in some detail in Chapter 2.

When Asiatics contacted America and their ideas took root in Middle America and began to grow, the spread of culture was again roughly symmetrical. Since the racial base of pre-Columbian America can be taken as uniform and that within this one race every cultural stage from lower Paleolithic to the Bronze Age has been found, we see that cultural growth closely parallels proximity and opportunity to receive ideas. This reasoning is an example of what can be deduced by using time and space to test ideas—as if in a laboratory experiment. We can conclude that racial arguments based on past performance therefore are inconclusive.

Finally, the European view of cultural history can be viewed from a number of vantage points. If one were to take a learned Egyptian's view of the world in 2000 B.C., it might be as follows: The perfect climate for mental achievement is the hot, desert climate. Here a brown-skinned, dark-eyed, slender, superior race has developed to the peak of human achievement. Look at the Egyptian-Mesopotamian-Palestinian achievements. Note too that farther south it is too hot; men are burned black and accomplish little. And farther north, on the other side of the Mediterranean, men have to endure cold winters, are lighter-skinned, and accomplish little.

Yet 1500 years later it was the Greeks, men "on the other side of the Mediterranean," who would be the most accomplished scientists, architects, and dramatists of the world. Their view was that *they* had the optimum climate. Egypt was too hot, and equatorial Africa more impossible. The lands to the north of them were even worse. Winters were horribly long and cold, and summers short. The bleached-out people of that land not only had never accomplished anything (good evidence therefore of their racial inferiority), but they obviously were never going to accomplish anything because of their miserable climate.

Two thousand years later, the racist theory held that these northern freakish blonds (in fact, the only partially albino variation in all of mankind) constituted *the* superior race, and the physical environmental determinists claimed that these cold northern lands were mentally the most stimulating in the world.

It should be clear now that neither race nor physical environment (especially climate) can be *the* answer. It seems doubtful that even in combination they yield a satisfactory answer; we must look much more deeply into the problem. The final answer does seem to be the presence of achievement when the opportunity is also available. The Negro race now has that opportunity, though it has had it only briefly. Men in New Guinea and Africa south of the Sahara are somewhat in the position of the northwest Europeans who, brought suddenly and forcibly into contact with the advanced cultures of the Mediterranean by the 500-year-long Roman conquest of their region, were jolted out of their primitive, tribal, agricultural way of life, and emerged, 1000 years after Rome collapsed, as the world's dominant people. Had men from Mars viewed the barbaric state of Europe after the fall of Rome, would they have been justified in deciding that the blondish race was mentally inferior because after 500 years of opportunity they were still barbarians? The difficulty with too many views of modern problems is the lack of such perspective.

Today the emergent people seem to expect instant civilization, yet cannot in the nature of things accomplish this miracle. Their critics too easily attribute their failure to their tropical habitat, or to their race, depending on the circumstances of the emergent people and the bias of the critic. No people are likely to accomplish in a decade, or even a century, what other peoples have required millenia to accomplish. Even given modern rapid communications, improved standards of living, the free education available to so many today—and unheard of in the past—it seems unrealistic to expect a mass of mankind of whatever race suddenly to blossom. Individuals may make rapid changes, but masses of men change slowly—and this theme will be illustrated here again and again for differing races in differing physical and social environments. It should provide a saner base for viewing expectable achievement for all people of whatever race anywhere.

HYPOTHETICAL MAN ON AN UNREAL EARTH

One way to deal with complex problems is to simplify them. Much of the confusion over the relationship between men and climates and locations is that there are so many combinations of man and land. Our earth is almost infinitely complex. In a sense, no two parts of it are alike. Climate, soils, geology, vegetation, and drainage combine in a myriad of forms. Man seems equally complex. He is divided into numerous races, possessed of highly varied cultures, and distributed over this physical earth like a mixed up jigsaw puzzle. The easiest way to simplify this problem so that we begin to see the nature of it is to imagine an unreal earth and to populate it with a theoretical people.

A UNIFORM EARTH

Instead of the complex physical earth of reality, we can imagine an earth that is a simple plain. Let this earth have no oceans dividing the continents. Let the climate be uniform: no tropics; no polar climates; instead, a mild subtropical climate everywhere. Let the vegetation be a parklike landscape with more grass than trees. Soils will be uniform too. We will assume a uniformly random distribution of animals: many small animals and some big game. We can also assume similar geology everywhere, but it need not be all one great limestone plain. It can be somewhat like the present crust with basalts, limestones, coal measures, and granites, but with these differing materials so distributed that any area 100-miles square has approximately the same array of minerals. Our physical earth is then uniform from pole to pole; there is no advantage to any location in respect to oceans, climates, preferred soils, or other resources. There would be no basis whatever for a difference among men caused by the physical environment, for the physical environment would exert the same influences on all men.

The population of this earth will be made up of one kind of man, uniformly distributed over the earth.

There will be no question of whether one group will be different in innate capacity from any other group. There will be individual variation, of course, but the percentage distribution of morons, geniuses, and just average people will be the same everywhere. All these people will speak the same language, and they will all have the same way of life: the simplest of human economies. They will be hunters and gatherers with no specialization either toward hunting or gathering. This stage is probably where man did begin in his cultural climb, so it makes an ideal starting point for discussion.

We now have a most unreal world, but a most interesting one from the point of view of considering the origin of different ways of life on the earth. There are no physical-environmental causes that could lead to differences; we have simply eliminated them. We have done the same for any possible racial differences: What will happen? Will things remain unchanged? If change occurs, will it be the same everywhere? Why should change occur at all?

If we were to find that change does occur, then we would have learned something interesting. It would suggest that neither differences in physical environment nor in race nor in way of life are necessary for change. This would not mean that race and environment would have nothing to do with cultural change, but it would certainly change our perspective on the causative factors of change.

INVENTION AS THE CAUSE OF CHANGE

Suppose that in this uniform world a group of people are gathered around a fire for their evening meal. A stew of meat and roots and wild seeds is cooking in a vessel on the fire. This assumes that these people possess pottery—an unusual thing among hunters and gatherers, but it does occur among such people as the Diegueño of southern California. Everyone in the family is dipping into the kettle to fish out some food. The food is hot, and the efficiency of their eating is being hindered by the scorching of their fingers. One of the young men of the family in desperation takes a stick and spears a choice piece of meat, removing it from the kettle without scorching himself.

This is an invention: a special way of doing something has been created. The family would undoubtedly be astonished. They now have important decisions to make. It is easy to see that a natural reaction would be anger. The young man is getting away with the best food and not even burning his fingers. His father might deal him a clout on the side of the head, and that would be the end of that invention. Or the family might look on in amazement and not copy him at all, shrugging it off as just another of the eldest son's idiosyncrasies. Or, finally, they might all seize sticks and learn to spear pieces of meat without burning themselves. In this last case, cultural change has occurred; this family is now different in one trait from all the other families in the world. Note that neither race nor physical-environmental differences have played any part in this process.

The process of invention is difficult to understand fully and deserves much more discussion than can be given it here. Do inventions occur because of "need"? This one was certainly "needed" because without it there was always the possibility of burning one's fingers. But generations had come and gone without anyone else feeling this need. The need was always there, but apparently here was the first person to realize it. Once the invention was made, of course, the "need" became apparent. This, in fact, seems to be the usual rule, and it greatly diminishes the force of old saying that "necessity is the mother of invention." The great problem is why one individual suddenly breaks through the accepted pattern to create something utterly different.

Sometimes we can get glimpses of the process. In this case, there were prior conditions that set the stage for the invention. Clearly, if these people had not cooked their food, the need to avoid handling hot foods would not have arisen. Probably these people had some tools that they used in their hunting and gathering. If we study primitive people living on this cultural level, we find that they often used pointed sticks or twigs: to pry lizards out of cracks in rocks or to hold spiny fruits such as cactus apples. If we assume that in our example such things were in use for these purposes, then we see them as antecedents, as the prior conditions that set the stage for the invention.

Ultimately, we are looking at the problem of how the human mind works—how problems are solved. The process of invention occurs when certain individuals are able to hold more ideas in view at one time and to see them in more new combinations than most other people can. These are the creative people in all societies; so far as we know, they occur at random in all races. It is also possible that they do not occur at random but that—like certain kinds of aptitudes such as musical and artistic ability that are more easily recognized—they occur in certain family lines with greater frequencies than others. However, such considerations need not bother us here, for we have assumed a uniform race situation, with family lines of varied ability uniformly distributed over the earth.

Frequency of Invention

Under these circumstances, the question arises, whether or not this invention might be made more than once, by separate individuals independently. Surely no one can say that it could not happen; there are numerous cases of simultaneous inventions—the telephone, the use of anesthetics, the application of calculus, and other innovations come readily to mind. All these inventions come late in time when the men making them were all part of a group working on common problems from a common background, and either directly or indirectly were in touch with one another's work. When we can put our finger firmly on the history of one of these inventions, in this case an innovation in thought such as Darwin's theory of evolution, we find in fact that it was "in the air" and even more or less clearly stated by a number of men for about a century. Thinking along these lines can be found even as early as the Greeks. In this light the simultaneous "invention" of evolution by Darwin and Wallace seems much less mysterious.

When we take some specific idea such as the alphabet, we find that all of the alphabetic writing in the world can be traced back to a single point of origin. The same is true of the wheel, the true arch, and a great number of other inventions or innovations. The list of inventions for which there is much evidence of separate origin tends to shrink as our detailed knowledge grows. The requirements for the creation of a new idea, getting it accepted locally, and spreading it afar are apparently sufficiently rigorous that it holds down to minimum levels the independent appearance of things.

Diffusion

It is not enough that the invention must occur, even though this itself is difficult. Once made, the invention must be taken up by the immediately surrounding group; if the invention is really to live, it must spread to others—there must be diffusion.

This step, of course, is easy to put into our hypothesis of the uniform earth. Suppose that the young man who has made this invention has been praised rather than beaten, and that the whole family is now using these clever little skewers to snatch things from the stew pot. Let us also suppose that this young man visits a neighboring family group in the next valley, where there is a daughter about his age. If this is a clever young man, he is likely to arrive at this neighbor's camp with some game, perhaps a pair of rabbits, and get himself invited to stay to dinner. Finally comes the critical moment: the food is ready, but hot.

Should the young man use his meat spearer now or wait until he is safely married into the family? If he uses it now, should he eat the piece of meat himself, hand it to the girl, or offer it to her father? This is obviously touchy business. Maybe the mother is the real head of the family; or maybe they will think him an apple-polishing sissy for not having the courage to go ahead and eat it himself. Or, they may, no matter what he does, think his act a foreign

affectation and run him out of camp. Although this account has almost reached the comic-strip level of discussion, it makes simple and clear the type of situation that is easily documented in the history of invention. These processes of invention, acceptance, and diffusion are real, and they have acted through time to limit severely the appearance of new ideas.

We can suppose that the diplomacy of the young man is up to the occasion this time, and that soon another family joins the magic group that eats with the aid of wooden skewers rather than with their unaided fingers. This is a momentous thing: suddenly the world is divided into those who do this and those who do not. Without race or environment entering the picture, the world has become differentiated culturally into those who do and those who do not eat with their fingers.

In the natural course of things this idea would be bound to spread somewhat. One might assume that it would spread uniformly in all directions over this uniform earth. This need not be true. Poor personal relations between one group of families and another could cause the rejection of the idea by a block of people in some area. The people beyond these curmudgeons might have welcomed the idea if it had ever reached them; but it cannot. Thus the spread of the idea might very well become most uneven and the differentiation of the world in terms of this idea anything but a simple concentric pattern of spread from the original center.

CHANGE AND ITS CONSEQUENCES

We can assume that changes would go on at some very slow rate all over the earth. We can document the fact that for mankind the rate of change through most of history has been one of incredible slowness, and that for all branches of mankind out of touch with the explosive growth of ideas in one or two centers, there has been virtually no advance. Certain changes did occur on this natural earth of ours, however. Some men became experts at hunting and specialized in that. Others became increasingly interested in plants. These differences we can assume would arise on our uniform earth also.

Specialized Hunters

Hunting is a man's game. It suits his personality. It features great physical coordination, cunning and planning, and a big payoff. It is a gambler's game. After watching the game for days and planning when to hide at the point that the buffalo is bound to pass on his way to the water, everything turns on split-second action. There is a half ton of meat in the pot—or nothing. The gathering of roots and seeds and berries suits a woman's nature. She is handicapped by childbearing and child caring; she cannot go the long distances and do the strenuous things that the man can. Woman is patient: she is content to do the repetitive things over and over again; she likes to play it safe. She may not make a killing at seed gathering, but there will surely be a little gruel for everyone. Women concentrated on the plant foods.

Some men are better athletes than others, and hunting is an athlete's game. In a family where the father is a great success with the bow and arrow, there will be more game brought to camp. The sons will be trained by their father and will also bring in plenty of game. Mother and the sisters will be kept busy dressing hides and drying meat. There will be less and less time for them to get out and gather seeds and roots and berries. It does not matter of course, for there is plenty of nutritious meat in camp. Pursuit of game normally concentrates on the biggest game; one arrow can kill one rabbit or one deer. Big game is limited in number. If one comes to pay more and more attention to it, it becomes necessary to move more frequently to find areas where there are abundant supplies of the desired animal. It is easy to see how a family that specialized in hunting would become highly mobile, would have more sedentary women, and would perhaps drift toward male dominance since the men were the important breadwinners.

The changes started in this one family will have a chance to spread. They may not, of course: the sons may not like hunting; or the neighbors may frown upon undue emphasis on it. In this case the idea is rejected, and the start at cultural differentiation dies. However, let us suppose that the idea catches on. The daughters-in-law and sons-in-law bring close ties with other families in the region. They tell of this way of life with its abundance of rich meat and warm skins. It sounds good and presently the people for a considerable area around are paying more attention to hunting and less attention to other pursuits. Another culture area has now arisen: specialized hunters have appeared. They could, of course, appear more than once, in more than one part of the earth. There could, of course, be several kinds of hunting. One group might take to hunting elephants and be content with making a kill every two weeks. Another might specialize on deer and aim to make a kill twice a week.

The consequences of these differences would be slight at first, but they would be cumulative. In the end they would lead to very great differences in all aspects of life. Emphasis on hunting would probably lead to improvement of hunting tools. Presently there might even be the invention of totally new hunting equipment; new ways of doing things would certainly be invented. These new activities and the thoughts associated with them would require appropriate words to express them. Vocabulary differences would then arise. Languages differ for less cause than this. Compare English and American. These two languages are drifting apart despite the shortness of time that we have been separated, and the closeness of the ties that we have maintained. On the primitive level, there would be no contact between the peoples on one side of this uniform world we are discussing and the other. Although there would be no barriers other than distance and people, these would be quite enough.

We can also consider the effects that hunting might have on man physically. Hunting places a premium on certain qualities. The more successful hunter will often have more of these qualities than do others. In times of famine, he and his family will be better off, more of them will survive and have children, and thus more of the good hunter's favorable traits will be passed onto his offspring. The traits desirable in a hunter are not necessarily the same as those that make a good farmer or fisherman. However, this kind of speculation is a difficult area. We know less definitely of what makes a good hunter or farmer, and most of what we know suggests that cultural tradition is often more important than biological inheritance. However, the possibility remains that ways of life might conceivably lead to differing physical make-up.

A still further change would presently make itself apparent. An emphasis on hunting and a lessening of interest in plants would slowly but inexorably shift the whole aspect of the landscape. It makes a difference to plants whether or not they are harvested by man, but more of this later. Animals also respond to hunting, for hunting tends to strike a balance and to keep the level of game fixed. Hunting tends to influence not only the animals hunted but also all the animals even remotely concerned with the primary game animal. And through them, a whole range of other animals are affected, as well as the plant world on which they feed.

For example, if much large game is regularly killed, there may be plenty of offal around and scavengers such as the jackals, wolves, buzzards, and all similar animals will increase in numbers. This in turn may have extensive repercussions. The existence of more wolves, for example, may mean that more dens are dug that will eventually supply homes for still other animals. More wolves may mean keeping the number of rabbits down, and this trend will allow more grass to grow, which in turn may favor the livelihood of still another animal. The chains of cause and effect that exist in nature are astonishingly intricate and far reaching; a change in any link in one of these chains may be felt in distant and seemingly unrelated ways and places. The effect of so simple a thing as shifting major attention toward hunting most certainly would then have both social, cultural, and physical environmental effects, and probably would react on physical man also.

Fire

There is another thing that hunters over much of the world have learned to do that has a tremendous impact on their physical environment. They have learned that fire can be used to drive game in desired directions. Sometimes the purpose is to drive game past the hunters, at other times to drive it into traps or to stampede it over cliffs. Fire is highly effective: animals will flee before it. Man can judge wind and distance and, knowing the habits of the animals, can drive the game where and when he wants it. Of all the deadly tricks that the hunter has mastered, this may be the most far reaching in its effects, for fire can almost totally remake the land.

Fire is the enemy of perennial vegetation such as trees; frequent fire is very likely to create a grassland. When the land is characterized by open forests, with grass growing through them and with a pronounced dry season, frequent fire is certain to limit tree growth and give the grasses a competitive advantage. To thrive, grass needs sunlight; therefore trees can shade grass out. In rainy lands, grass predominates in the open places where rocks outcrop, the frequently disturbed stream banks, and similar spots where perennial vegetation cannot maintain a foothold. Toward more arid regions, trees experience increasing difficulty maintaining sufficient density of growth to maintain a dense ground shade. The roots of the trees must be able to spread out in order to absorb sufficient water. Grasses will then appear between the trees. During the wet season, there is water enough for all. The grasses hurry through their life cycle and get through the following dry season by dropping their seeds in the ground to await the next favorable growing season. The tree survives by a deeper root system, and often by such protective devices as shedding its leaves.

But fire comes with the dry season. The grass is consumed, but it does not matter. Only the dry straw is there to burn; the grass has done its work. Although some of the seeds may be burnt, many of them are lodged in the ground and a future generation of grass is assured. The tree, however, is vulnerable, especially when it is young. The seedling's stem may be heated through and killed. If the tree is a little larger, its thin bark may be roasted and the living tissue beneath the bark killed. Large trees, of course, often have bark thick enough to withstand considerable fire, but if the fires come with such frequency that the young trees cannot survive, when the old trees succumb one by one, only the grasses will remain. They will flourish on the increased sunlight and the decreased competition of the trees for the precious water. With the trees will go the animals dependent on trees: the tree squirrels, the arboreal birds, and all the rest. With the increase in grasses a different group of animals will increase, among them the large grazing animals man is interested in.

Although these effects are most visible on the edge of the dry lands of our real earth—as opposed to the hypothetical earth that we have been discussing—they are equally true for all of the earth. Even in tropical rain forests man creates grasslands by his persistent setting of fires. We will take this up later.

When vegetation alters, the soil is also changed. Grass has deep fibrous roots; when it dies annually, these roots die. Their decay adds organic matter through a thick layer of the earth. This is the opposite of the action of trees: they tend to live for a long time; their roots are more permanent. By dropping leaves, as well as fruit and branches, trees add organic matter to the surface of the earth, rather than to a thick layer. Grassland soils are therefore blacker, more humus-rich, and in total very different from the soils formed under forests.

Our uniform physical earth is therefore developing variety in its soils and vegetation and its associated animal life through the divergence in kinds of activities that are quite expectable in man. Far from a picture of the physical environment forming man, the idea before us is that man, in this case specialized hunters, can shape his physical environment.

Gatherers Become Farmers

In other areas of our uniform earth the way of life might change little, or a different type of change might occur: the women might shoulder more and more of the burden of supplying the food. We know that among some primitive people the women claimed the rights to gathering in certain areas. Here they knew virtually every kind of plant and its uses: they knew which grass bore seeds; where it grew best; and when the time was ripe to harvest it. They also knew the plants that had edible tubers—Australian women knew that if they cut off the vine from the tuber and stuck the vine back in the disturbed ground from which they had just dug the tuber, the vine would grow and in a year or two another tuber would appear there. Such knowledge verges on the beginning of agriculture. This "invention," or recognition of cause and effect, seems to have been one that did not lead directly to agriculture, however, though it set the stage for it. It is of interest to note that this plant knowledge belonged to a people who were Paleolithic in cultural level (that is, they did not have the bow and arrow, pottery, ground stone, agriculture, or any domestic animal except the dog).

The Australian situation suggests that agriculture had an exceedingly long prehistory, that domestication of plants was the work of women, and that they drifted into it perhaps quite unconsciously. If agriculture did develop in this way, it would help explain why basic domestic plants were already fully established when we first find firm evidence of the existence of real agriculture about 8000 years ago. In general, our domestic plants—such as wheat, barley, corn, and rice—are so different from their wild ancestors that we are unable to point to specific ancestral forms, only to the general plant family from which they are derived.

Other evidence that shows how women worked also suggests how their work could change plants. Among certain California Indians, the women gathered wild grass seeds by using a seed beater, an im-

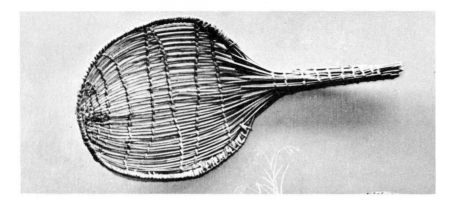

Seed Beater of the Type Used by the California Indians. *Smithsonian Institution.*

Indian Woman Winnowing Grass Seeds. The seeds are spilled a little at a time, letting the wind blow away the light straw. In this way the seeds are separated from the chaff. The amount of seeds that the Indian women gathered is indicated by the pile on the cloth. This is a Diegueño woman. Her tribe was one of the typical seed-gathering tribes of California. *Museum of the American Indian, Heye Foundation.*

plement that looks a bit like a small tennis racquet. The women walked through the grass striking the seed heads with the seed beater so that the seeds were thrown toward a large basket tray held in the other hand; the seeds caught on the tray were then dumped into a basket. Large quantities of seed could be gathered in a day in this way, depending on certain conditions: the grass had to ripen uniformly and it had to hold its seeds firmly and not shed them when any small breeze shook the plant. These conditions set the scene for the Indian women to make an efficient harvest. All this was fine for the Indian women, but just why should the grass have cooperated? If the Indian women got all the seeds, it meant extinction for the plant. Most grasses have loose seed heads, and they often have hair devices so that the seed will cling to passing animals. In addition, plants often ripen seed over a considerable span of time, adding to the survival chances of seed. Selection in nature encourages such survival traits. How then did domestic grasses that hold their seeds tightly, ripen uniformly, and have no devices for being spread about—such as wheat, barley, rye, oats, rice, and corn—come into existence? Did the Indian women select and encourage grasses for this quality?

Probably not. They simply gathered wild seeds; the method was vigorous but inefficient. Although they got a lot of seed, they scattered a lot also. The most that a heavy-seeded grass could hope to gain from a passing breeze was an inch or two of seed dispersal, while a brawny Indian woman striking the seed head a smart blow to break the seeds loose and send them flying toward her basket might well give the seeds a dispersal of a foot or two or three. If Indian women for thousands of years gathered seeds annually, there would automatically be a steady selection applied: the grasses that held their seeds firmly until the women came to disperse them might pay a price in some seed being caught by the women, but the rest of the seed would get maximum dispersal. Thus without any plan the plant and the woman would become increasingly dependent on each other. The plant would be modified in a direction that seemingly was not to its best survival interests in nature, but which actually was when women-with-seed-beaters were part of that nature. Not all women gathered seeds in this way; not all grasses would be so affected. In our uniform world, only in that area where the women worked out such a system would such grasses arise, and only there would parts of the physical environment be characterized by increasingly large areas of one kind of grass with these peculiar characteristics. Again, the activity of mankind would be altering the physical environment.

In California where the women gathered seeds from the wild grasses a striking thing happened. When the Indian women disappeared, the native California grasses nearly disappeared too. More than the disappearance of the Indian women was at stake, of course. The Spanish appeared, and later the Americans: they introduced cattle and subjected the native grasslands to heavy grazing, and they also introduced whole galaxies of weedy competitors for the soil and sun of California. Nevertheless, one of the factors of change was that the Indian women no longer annually gathered the wild grass seeds, striking the seed heads with their seed beaters and giving the seeds a maximum dispersal.

OTHER EXAMPLES OF THE EFFECTS OF CULTURAL CHANGE

There is an even clearer case of the effects of cultural change. In one part of Indonesia the matrilineal tribes live in forested areas and the patrilineal tribes live in grasslands. There is no appreciable climate difference between the two areas; according to the climate, both should have been covered with tropical forest. At first sight it may seem strange that counting descent from your father should discourage tree growth, while counting it from your mother should encourage the trees. The answer is found to lie in the way in which these two groups make their living. The matrilineal society is a farming society. The forest is their long-term rotation crop and is valued as such. The patrilineal people are cattle raisers. The forest supplies no sustenance to their animals: they want grasses, and young, new grass at that. At every opportunity, they burn the land, and the fierce fires running through stands of grass six-feet high kill trees that stand in the grassland or on its border. Slowly the forest edge is driven back, and the wet tropical forest gives way to grassland. Hence, even in Indonesia, in areas of uniformly tropical, rainy climate, farmers retain the forest while the cattlemen change the landscape to a grassland.

There is almost no end to the process. The attention of farmers is on rain and sun; expectedly, their religious rites would be different from those of the hunters. The hunter would have special words for the implements he used and the animals he hunted. The farmer too would have his own specialized vocabulary, for *clod* and *weed* are farmers' words, just as *scent* and *spoor* are hunters' words.

That changing activities can change language is amusingly clear in our own society. How many of these words can you define: *hame, breeching stay, lazy strap, trace, crupper?* Perhaps you are not even sure where these terms come from; nautical perhaps? No, these are terms for parts of the harness of horses. Fifty years ago it would have been unthinkable for anyone not to recognize most of them instantly. At the same time, we have also lost a rich and salty vocabulary filled with *royals, dolphin strikers, jiggers, top gallants,* and so forth. Of course, it has not been one-way traffic; our vocabulary is now rich with *carburetors, accelerators, distributors, spark plugs,* and a dictionary full of other terms that were unknown to our nonautomotive-minded great grandfathers. Divergence in way of life clearly does change vocabulary, and continued separation and more change also slowly penetrates the structure of language, its grammar. Changes could be far-reaching and thorough even on a uniform earth, and a vast diversity of languages could be expected.

Agriculture and Population Growth

The greatest changes, however, would come when the magical threshold of purposeful agriculture was finally crossed. Most of man's early activities led to economically limited ends. The hunting and gathering way of life can not maintain a large number of people on the earth. Gathering requires wide areas over which man can wander to gather first this wild harvest and then that. Hunting also requires large areas, for even under the best of conditions, there are only so many animals per acre of land. It takes not acres, but square miles of hunting territory to support people on this cultural level. Domestication and use of animals for herding as is done by pastoral nomads supports few more people per square mile than hunting does. The animals require food and therefore extensive areas for grazing.

The purposeful raising of plants changes all of this. With agriculture, permanent dense settlement became possible. All of the earth-modifying effects of man were multiplied as the number of men increased. Shifting agriculture in forested regions, with the trees used as a long-term rotation crop, is only possible so long as there are not too many people on the land. When the number of people grows beyond the critical limit of the ability of the land to recover its fertility under tree cover, then either the way of life must change or the area must be abandoned. The critical limit, of course, is the period of years that the land may be left idle. If it becomes too short, the trees no longer can re-establish themselves, choke out the grass and other weeds, and store up sufficient fertility to make the land yield crops again.

In a few places on the earth, men have solved this problem with the use of rice raised in water—wet-rice culture. This type of agriculture gave rise to the earliest, densest human settlement. When land became scarce, the rice farmers even terraced the mountain sides, thus changing the face of the earth almost as thoroughly as our modern subdivision builders often do.

The development of dense populations was long and slow. Agriculture did not immediately lead to great population growth and to vast changes in the face of the inhabited earth. At Jericho it is apparent that an agricultural, village-dwelling way of life became established just short of 10,000 years ago. It was more than 5000 years later before such ways of life reached into the comparatively nearby northern European area.

The point of our hypothesis should be clear by now. On a uniform earth, with neither human biology nor physical earth differences to serve as compelling forces to bring about change, change would still occur. Changes in way of life might be of several possible kinds. Some would alter the landscape in one direction, and others in quite another. Some would lead to no great changes of population density and would, in effect, be self-limiting. One of the ways of life, the agricultural basis of existence—springing from the lowly plant gatherers—would contain within it the potential that could lead to the dense populations, the specialization of human activity, and the basis of civilization as we in fact know it.

We do not then need a diversified earth to create variety in the ways of mankind. This does not mean that the actually diversified earth had no effect on the development of the many different ways of life that actually came to exist. The isolation of some areas, the dryness of others, and the great cold to be met with in still others all have had their effects. The purpose of the uniform earth hypothesis is not to deny these effects, but to put them into perspective. We are therefore cautioned to evaluate carefully the effect of the physical environment as a driving force.

2-Arid Lands

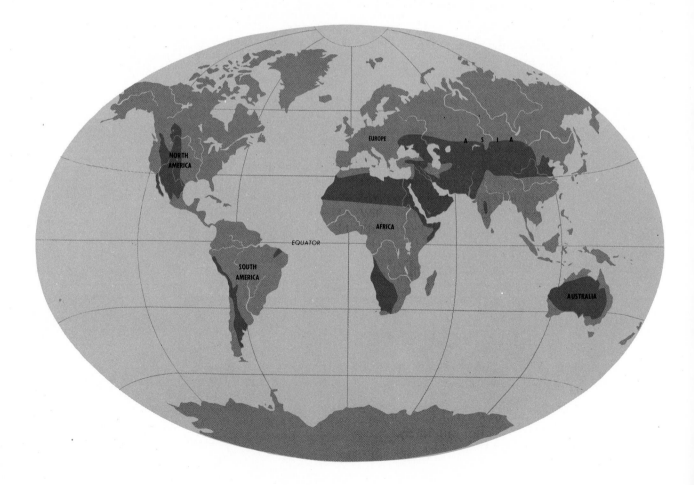

SINCE THERE ARE arid lands on all of the continents and they have been occupied by representatives of all the races of mankind, they present us with a case of a similar environment in variable locations inhabited by different varieties of mankind. This situation affords an environmental constant with numerous variations in both man and culture, providing us with an opportunity to study the roles played by race, culture, and environment.

Arid lands are those where there is not enough rainfall. The exact definition depends a little on what one chooses to measure. The climatologist would say that in these areas the amount of precipitation is exceeded by the amount of evaporation. From this point of view, there are many far-reaching results. For instance, there is no permanent water table at some small distance underground; streams do not run regularly; springs are rare. There is no fixed amount of rainfall. San Diego, California, with about ten inches of rainfall in a year concentrated in the cool winter months, is not quite a desert, although it is certainly arid. On the other hand, ten inches of rainfall in an area on the south side of the central Sahara, where the rainfall comes in the hot summer months, would be characteristic of a true desert.

A hydrologist thinks of the desert as an area where the depressions in the land fail to fill to overflowing with water. Drainage is therefore toward the center of these basins, and there are no permanent streams—except for those rare items such as the Nile and the Colorado that rise in high mountains or in adjacent moist areas and flow through a desert region on their way to the sea.

A geologist thinks of the desert with pleasure, for there is little bothersome vegetation to obscure the rocky structure of the region. The bedrock outcrops throughout the area except in the depressions, which serve as catch basins for the surrounding higher areas. The barren surface is ideal for seeing the effects of wind and water sculpturing the face of the earth. The soil scientist sees the aridity of the land reflected in the concentration of unleached minerals and in the thin and slightly developed soil mantle over most of the area.

The agriculturist sees the arid lands as regions where crops cannot be grown without irrigation. The desert is not attractive to him unless there is some exotic source of water, a large flowing spring or, better, a large flowing river; otherwise, for him occupation of the desert seems limited. The pastoralist, on the other hand, can use much more of the desert, for he does not need as large and regular a water supply but only water holes a few miles apart. The primitive hunters and gatherers could use even more of such an area, for they could carry the small amount of water they needed for a day or so and hence could range relatively far from water holes. This variable view of the usefulness and desirability of this one type of landscape is the principal theme that will concern us here.

Does the desert dictate a particular type of house? Since mud and stone are common in the desert and wood is scarce, will we find the mud house to be the "natural" response? Since most of the land is too dry for agriculture, is the pastoral-nomadic life to be expected in most if not all arid lands? Wherever great rivers flow through deserts, providing a year-round water supply and often, in the low-latitude deserts, nearly year-round crop-growing reasons, can we expect an Egypt to arise? There are no great world powers in the deserts today. Has this always been so? Will it always be so? And, no matter what the answer is to either question, just how, if at all, does the physical setting of the desert affect the answer?

THE PHYSICAL SETTING

The deserts of the world are found in certain regular positions on the earth. They are neither polar

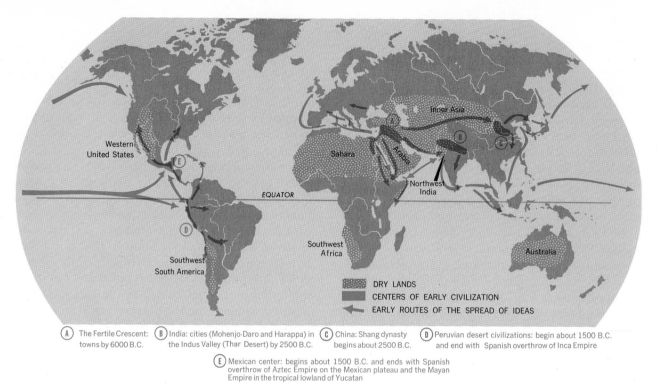

A The Fertile Crescent: towns by 6000 B.C.   B India: cities (Mohenjo-Daro and Harappa) in the Indus Valley (Thar Desert) by 2500 B.C.   C China: Shang dynasty begins about 2500 B.C.   D Peruvian desert civilizations: begin about 1500 B.C. and end with Spanish overthrow of Inca Empire

E Mexican center: begins about 1500 B.C. and ends with Spanish overthrow of Aztec Empire on the Mexican plateau and the Mayan Empire in the tropical lowland of Yucatan

Map 2-1   The Arid Lands in Relation to the Early Centers of Civilization and the Spread of Ideas

The sea routes reaching the length of the Mediterranean and up to Great Britain were functioning at least as early as 2500 B.C. About this time, overland contacts in the vicinity of the great bend of the Yellow River had begun to develop what was to culminate in Chinese culture. Sea routes led from Egypt down to the Red Sea, to the Indian Ocean, and thence to East Africa or India. Indian contacts reached into Indonesia, where they met Sinitic influences. We are just beginning to glimpse the importance of a trans-Pacific contact in stimulating cultural growth in native America, where one of the earliest centers lay in or adjacent to arid Peru.

In the arid lands of the world, there is a direct relationship between cultural status and location in relation to these centers of early cultural growth and the routes over which cultural ideas spread. Note that the arid land of Africa not only lies at the opposite end of the continent from early-developing Egypt, but also is off the main

routes of early contacts. Australia, too, is disadvantageously located in relation to early centers of growth and development. The arid lands of North America were relatively distant from the cultural center in Middle America, and were accordingly culturally retarded. In South America, a center of development lay in the coastal desert, while the culturally retarded areas were to be found in the adjacent humid regions.

The major dry lands of the world were in various stages of cultural development in A.D. 1500. Pastoralism and oases agriculture existed in the Sahara, Arabia, northwest India, and inner Asia; hunting and gathering, in Australia and southwest Africa. In southwest South America there was oasis agriculture in the north and hunting and gathering in the south. In the western United States there was oasis agriculture in the south and hunting and gathering in the north.

nor equatorial. They appear in mid-latitudes, mostly between 20 and 30 degrees. When they extend out of these latitudes, it is due to the shape of the land. Mountain ranges by blocking moist air may cause extensions of deserts. The strong north–south orientation and extension of the American deserts are due to this factor.

The greatest desert in the world is the Sahara and to some extent the adjacent Arabian desert and the Indian desert (the Thar) may be considered an extension of it. These are typical low-latitude deserts. This general desert region also extends northeastward into south Russia and over to western China, typical mid-latitude desert country. Desert extends northward here through the deep interior of Asia into which the moisture-bearing oceanic winds can penetrate only with great difficulty. Not only does the distance serve to limit the amount of moisture that can reach this area, but such great mountain barriers as the Himalayas block off the moisture also.

In North America in the same latitudes one finds arid northern Mexico and the adjacent desert regions in our own southwest. The North American dry region extends far to the north through the Great Basin and along the western edge of the Great Plains into southern Canada. This extension is clearly related to the north–south alignment of the mountain ranges in the West. These mountains block off the major air currents, which in these latitudes are flowing off the moist Pacific toward the land. This physical barrier creates situations such as are found in the states of Washington and Oregon where extremely high rainfall occurs on the western side of the mountains and extremely dry conditions prevail not many miles away on the eastern side of the mountains. The important extent of arid lands in the United States appears clearly on the map, for nearly one third of the country is arid.

In South America the east–west extent of arid lands is not great because little breadth of land exists there between 20 to 30 degrees latitude. The strong north–south line of the arid land is again due to the arrangement of the mountains in relation to the winds. On the Peruvian coast desert conditions prevail because the winds in this area do not blow onshore strongly and because along that shore line there is a major cold ocean current. The air moving toward the continent is cooled in its lower layers by this cold current and becomes very stable. Normally, to get moisture out of air, it is necessary to make it rise, expand, and cool. When the air has its heavy layers at the bottom, it is like a toy with a weighted base: it cannot be overturned easily. Hence, the air cannot be made to rise in violent uprushes such as occurs in thunderstorms. Such stable air is not a good source of moisture; therefore deserts are able to come right down to the edge of the sea where the atmospheric circulation favors drought and a cold current off-shore reinforces the effect. This is also the reason the desert comes to the shore in Lower California, in north and south Africa, and in western Australia.

The desert crosses over the Andes in southernmost South America. The winds shift in these latitudes; instead of being from the east as they are

Desert Landscape. View from Massada, Israel. *Embassy of Israel.*

Desert Mountains. Looking toward the Dead Sea in the Negev of Israel. *Embassy of Israel.*

in latitudes 10 to 30 degrees, they are from the west. The shift reverses the wet and dry sides of the mountains, and the effect of a mountain mass in blocking the prevailing winds is then easily seen. The area down wind of the mountain mass is the dry area and is said to be in the "rain shadow" of the mountain.

In South Africa, in the expected mid-latitudes on the west side of the continent—and coming to the margin of the ocean, which here also is cold for its latitude—the arid lands are extensive. Australia, its continental mass coinciding with the center of the desert latitudes, is largely arid. The vast arid interior is often spoken of as the dry heart of Australia. Very clearly, only the margins that have at least seasonally inblowing winds have much moisture.

Climate

The climatic characteristic of the deserts is that the amount of evaporation exceeds the amount of precipitation. For example, it was calculated that at Chacance, Chile, in 1918 the total annual precipitation was 0.04 inches. The potential evaporation was calculated to have been 182.5 inches. Needless to say, this is extreme desert. Deserts are also marked by great variability in precipitation. It is too often a feast or famine situation. Doorjabi in the Thar desert of northwestern India has an average annual precipitation of two inches. But one year thirty-four inches of rain fell in two days.*

Deserts have great ranges of temperature. On the basis of their temperatures they can be divided into

---

* I recall very clearly being caught in a great rain in the Imperial Valley in the Sonoran desert in the Southwest, where we were camped among sand dunes. For two days we just lay under our tarpaulins and waited for the downpour to stop so that we could go on with our field work. On the second night our air mattresses began to float! In many years of work in that area, I had only once before even seen a shower, but this time even the sand dunes were saturated and had lakes standing among them.

Rock-strewn Desert, Australia's Northern Territory. This landscape is much more typical of the desert than are sand dunes. *Australian News and Information Bureau.*

two types. The low-latitude deserts and the mid-latitude deserts. In both types the change from day to night can be extreme, varying on a very hot day from temperatures in the 90°s to a night with a temperature near freezing. This is due to the very clear, cloudless air, which not only lets the solar radiation come in freely during the day but also lets the earth radiation escape almost as freely at night.

The amount of rainfall that sets the boundary between the arid lands and the humid lands varies with the temperature and the season when the rainfall occurs. A little rainfall in the cool season wets the ground more effectively than the same amount in the hot season.

It is the low-latitude deserts that deserve the description "hot deserts." Even though such deserts can be cold on winter nights, during the period of high sun the weather can only be called continuously

hot. At Yuma, Arizona, during the middle of summer the average temperature is about 85° to 95° F. In one hot spell the maximum temperature exceeded 100° F. for all but one of 80 consecutive days. Death Valley has recorded maximum high temperatures in the low 130°s F. Azizia, Algeria, has a record of 136.4° F. Such heat must be experienced to be appreciated. It is possible to blister the skin by touching metal objects in the direct sun. Even objects in the shade are hot to the touch. Since the air is much hotter than the 98.6° F. of normal body temperature, the more air that contacts your body, the warmer you will be. Under these conditions it is best to wear clothing for insulation against the heat. Yet even in these areas in the low-sun period the temperature can drop surprisingly low. Campers in the bottom of Death Valley on winter nights may wake to find their sleeping bags covered with frost. Winter days may be pleasantly warm but the nights

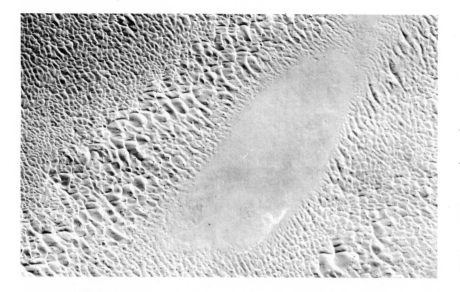

(*Left*) The Western Erg, Western Sahara Desert. This is one of the largest seas of dunes in any desert of the world. There is no comparable dune area in the American deserts. *American Geographical Society.*

(*Below*) Typical Rocky and Thinly Vegetated Landscape on the Edge of the Colorado Desert. Such vegetation cover as is seen here is more **typical of steppe conditions than extreme desert.** Here a riding party meets for breakfast in a landscape Americans avoided until recently. *Palm Springs Chamber of Commerce.*

can drop to the cool 40°s, while light frost is not unknown. High annual and daily ranges of temperatures in the desert are the rule. At Bil Milrha, in the Sahara, a low of 30° F. and a maximum of 99° F. were recorded within 24 hours.

Rainfall in the low-latitude deserts is meager. Cairo has 1.2 inches; Lima, Peru, 2 inches; Yuma, 3.3 inches. Such figures are not very helpful, however, for it may rain heavily for a few days, only to be followed by many months of virtually no rain. For example, Helwan, Egypt, once received 30 inches of rainfall, one fourth of which came in seven storms. These irregular heavy downpours are characteristic of the desert regions of our own Southwest, where they come in late summer and often send great rushes of water down the dry washes.

Dry washes with their smooth sand floors and meager vegetation often attract campers from the rocky and nearly vegetation-free desert surfaces. However, a sudden storm on a mountain range miles away may throw a flood of water into the head of the dry wash, and this flood can run for miles and strike the campers with sudden deadly force. This potential danger led the French Army at one time to forbid its troops to camp in the *wadis,* the dry washes of the Sahara.

The rainfall pattern of these desert regions is of course poor for agriculture: it is erratic in distribution over time, local in nature, and irregular in amount. Does this then prevent the agricultural use of the deserts? We will see that it does not.

Relative humidity in arid lands is usually low. This varies somewhat, however. Heavy dew can be experienced in the Colorado Desert, and the Yuma area can be very humid when air masses from the Gulf of Lower California move in. Generally, however, the high temperatures are accompanied by low relative humidity: evaporation goes on at a high rate and perspiration evaporates very rapidly, thereby cooling the body, with the result that 90° F. temperature is not felt to be excessively hot. Daily weather in the dry lands is, of course, sunny. There are exceptions along coasts, for example, in Peru and along the coast of Lower California—

where the offshore cold current creates a persistent coastal fog condition with the result a cool, foggy desert! But most low-latitude deserts are more like Yuma, where in June 97 percent of the possible sunshine is actually received.

The mid-latitude deserts are found in such areas as inner Asia, the Great Basin area and adjacent regions in the United States, and Patagonia in South America. Here the summers are better described as warm rather than excessively hot. The winters can be bitterly cold both because of the latitudes (40 to 50 degrees) and because of the continental interior position that places the lands out of reach of the ameliorating effects of the sea. Temperatures as low as 32° F. for the month of January and 80° F. for the month of July are experienced at interior locations in these deserts. As in the low-latitude deserts, both the daily and the seasonal ranges of temperatures are very high. There may even be some snow. Rainfall may occur in the winter, but in areas such as our Great Basin there is a tendency for a spring and fall concentration of the meager rainfall. With lower temperatures, there is a somewhat lower evaporation than in the low latitude deserts. Humidities are low, but wind velocity is often high and the frequency of wind above average.

The cool coastal deserts deserve a brief description because they are so different from what is generally thought of as desert. Examples are found on the coast of Peru, in the Atacama Desert in Chile, in Lower California, and in the Namib Desert of Southwest Africa. Here the land margins are much cooler than the interiors. Temperature gradients of one degree per mile are not unusual; temperatures of 70° F. on the beach, and in the 90°s twenty miles inland. This odd desert is a product of the movement of the great air and sea currents of the world. In the dry belt, the movement of the air is nearly parallel to the west coast. The offshore water is moving equatorward and is very cold for its latitude. The water a few hundred miles offshore is warm. The air over this warm water is also warm and has a high moisture content; when it moves across the cold water, it is chilled in its lower layers and con-

Steppe Landscape, Southwest Africa. *Bureau of American Ethnology, Gordon Gibson.*

Typical Vegetation in the Area of Summer Rains in Southern Arizona. The barrel cactus in the foreground and the cholla cactus in the background mark the edge of the desert in the United States Southwest. This would be considered rich grazing ground by the camel nomads of Arabia or North Africa. *Desert Museum, L. W. Walker.*

densation of the moisture begins, causing a fog to develop. The fog usually moves in over the edge of the land during the night and only slowly retreats during the day. Gray, overcast weather predominates on the coast, and it looks as if rain were certain within the hour. Instead, during the summer when this condition is most common, it never rains. The land is in fact extremely dry, even though there usually is a heavy dew each night.

Land Forms

It is difficult to say anything simple about desert land forms. Mountain masses are stripped of their weathered products; the rocky structures stand out; and the network of streams is a relatively coarse one, the streams themselves being dry except immediately after a rainfall. The slopes of the streams are very steep, tending to change abruptly upon coming out of the mountain mass. The weathered material brought down, often in violent floods resulting from the infrequent dumping of moderate amounts of water on the nearly bare rocks, is then dropped in vast quantities at the foot of the mountains.

The water rushing out of the mountain drops its burdens of boulders, gravel, sand, silt, and clay in that order. It piles these materials up in great fan- or cone-shaped masses at the mouths of the canyons, with the coarse materials at the apex of the fan. The clays are carried to the nearest flat area where the diminishing flow of water sinks into the soil. Everything is soon dry again. The wind then goes to work. The finer materials are moved around. The clay and silt-sized particles are small enough so that the wind can pick them up and carry them for great distances. The sand-sized particles the wind can lift only a few inches, or more often, can only bounce along the ground. The wind can blow out specific areas, leaving scooped-out hollows called "blow outs." The sand is sometimes piled up in dunes, but dunes are actually almost hard to find in most of the deserts of the world. Only the African-Arabian areas seem to have really large areas of them.

Vegetation

One reason there are fewer sand dunes than the Hollywood version of desert would lead us to expect is due to the surprising amount of vegetative cover found in the desert. Truly barren land is the rarest thing there is in the world's deserts. This varies, of course: on the coast of Peru there are sizable areas that are free of vegetation, and the Sahara has large barren tracts. The deserts of the United States, however, have some plant cover everywhere: creosote bush in the Colorado Desert and sagebrush in the Great Basin. The plants in desert areas are widely spaced and thinly leaved, but there are enough of them to make a sparse cover.

Two general kinds of plants must be distinguished, the annuals and the perennials. The annuals face the difficult task of living for long periods of time on very little water. They must have extensive root systems and small leaf systems, for roots gather water and leaves expend it. Some plants have no leaves, but specialized stems that take over the function of the leaves. Others have leaves at one time of the year, but none during the long dry periods. There are innumerable adaptations: corky bark, thick stems with hard exteriors to protect against sand blasting, resinous coverings to cut down on evaporation, pulpy interiors to store water. With all of these adaptations plants must still grow widely spaced so as not to compete too strongly for the little water available.

One might expect that desert plants, even the perennials, would be short-lived. In fact, they often prove to be relatively long-lived. Such things are learned in rather odd ways. The ironwood trees growing along the dry washes of the lower Colorado River were largely cut down toward the end of the nineteenth century to supply firewood for the mines then operating in the area. The large stumps are still there. The trees that have grown up in the past 50 years are much smaller; therefore, the stumps must have been made from quite old trees. At a famous paleontological-archeological site, Tule Springs in Nevada near Las Vegas, pictures taken

Omboa, or Thorn Bush. This plant is found in South Africa. *Smithsonian Institution.*

Pachypodium Lealii. This plant, found in parts of Africa, can grow to 15 feet high. *Smithsonian Institution.*

25 years apart have shown that even the little shrubby plants live for long periods of time, for nearly every bush around the site had lived through that period of time. A study of the growth rings of such plants has shown that some have lived for a hundred years. It is because the desert perennials are such highly successful adaptations that most of the desert areas of the world are better covered with vegetation than most people expect.

In addition to the perennial plants are the annuals. While the perennials can "take it" for decades, the annuals solve the feast and famine water situation of the desert in a totally different way. The cycle from seed through plant, flower, and back to seed is accomplished in one brief, almost fiercely rapid burst of growth. The seed stage is the dormant period. It matters little how long the environment is hot and dry, for the seeds are lodged in cracks in the ground, buried in the drifting sand, or hidden in cracks or under the edges of rocks. When rain does occur, the seeds will quickly germinate and repeat the brief life cycle. This burst of growth of short-lived annuals, often so short-lived as to deserve the term ephemerals, characterizes most of the deserts of the world. In the American Southwest, large areas may suddenly be carpeted with brilliantly colored blooms. The bloom is short-lived, however, and the areas of greatest color change rapidly. How can man use a plant resource as short-lived as this?

Animals

There are also numerous desert animals. Walt Disney's wonderful documentary film, *The Living Desert,* has given a misleading picture of the animal life there, however. It might be many years indeed before you would see a fraction of what is shown in that motion picture. There is life in the desert, but it is not as rich as that found beyond the desert.

It is easy to see why this must be so: animal life depends on the plant world for its food, and while the desert is not bare, it is sparsely covered with plants. There simply is less leaf, seed, and root material for animals to feed on. Accordingly, there must be less life.*

The desert animals, of course, are more numerous than the casual observer ever sees, especially while whizzing along in an automobile. There is evidence of their existence in the carcasses along the highway and the attendant ravens who harvest the slaughter. One of the oddest records of how many small animals there are in the desert is made by counting the number trapped overnight on freshly tarred roads. An impressive number of mice are so caught. As Disney correctly showed, these little harvesters of the seeds and leaves and roots of the desert are the base of the food chain. They feed the foxes and coyotes and the hawks—and of course could serve as food for man, and in times past actually did.

American deserts once had camels, horses, deer, antelope, and ground sloth. Indians hunted and ate all the horses, sloths, and camels, except in South America where the native camels survived, and modern Americans have virtually exterminated the herds of antelope that existed in the early twentieth century in the Southwest. Deer and mountain sheep survive in small numbers in remote desert mountains but elsewhere have been exterminated. This in itself is an interesting measure of the relatively low productivity of the dry lands. In the densely populated, humid eastern United States deer flourish, and game-management departments often worry because not enough of them are killed annually during the hunting season to ensure that the remaining deer will not starve to death due to overpopulation of the range. In the dry lands, far fewer hunters killing

* In many years of work in the deserts of America, I saw only two rattlesnakes, five coyotes, and one fox. Further, these were seen in part in areas so wild that two coyotes and the fox walked right into the camp looking for food. The coyotes came into our camp in Lower California. The fox came to call in the Death Valley region and stayed to take food from our hands. If animals in the mid-latitude forests were as tame, the situation would be similar to that of the bears in Yellowstone Park.

very many less animals per year have almost wiped out game-animal populations.

Early man in America did the same thing. There is no convincing reason for the disappearance of the ground sloths from the American deserts except that man killed them all. This was an irreplaceable loss: the ground sloths ate the creosote bush along with other desert vegetation; nothing else eats the oily creosote bush; when early man in America extinguished this slow-moving, bear-sized herbivor, the world lost the only animal capable of grazing on this otherwise useless vegetation that covers vast areas of our arid West.

Mule Deer at Desert Waterhole in Southern Arizona. Notice the stony ground and spiny vegetation; here the plant is the ocotillo. The landscape represents typical Sonoran desert. *Desert Museum, L. W. Walker.*

Domestic Animals

The early men of the Old World domesticated the camel instead of exterminating it. It is an amazing animal whose abilities are somewhat different from what is usually believed. For instance, while it is true that camels can go on for a long time without water, they have to be trained to endure this deprivation. Their humps are fat storage areas (incidentally, the American camels have no humps). Going without water for long periods of time under conditions of high heat, the camel can withstand a degree of dehydration that would kill a man. Then, given access to water, the camel in a matter of minutes can drink up to 25 percent of his body weight, almost immediately returning back to his normal state. Man cannot stand such dehydration, and any such water intake after heavy water loss would be deadly. As we mentioned earlier, such characteristics indicate that man is not a desert animal in his origin. The camel can drink the alkaline waters of the desert, eat its salty and oily shrubs, and walk over the slick rock surfaces or its soft sand surfaces on its tough, pillow-padded feet. It gives milk, has a fine wool, a useful hide, and edible flesh.

There is a decided difference in the vegetative cover of the Old World desert area of Sahara-Arabia and that of the rest of the deserts of the world. The Sahara-Arabia region is much more barren. Whether this is a climatic effect or in some way the work of man is problematical. The Sahara-Arabia desert is drier, and at first glance this seems to be sufficient cause to explain the difference. A look at the American desert, however, makes one wonder.

The effects of the introduction of domestic animals into the arid lands of our own Southwest show what the grazing animals can do to a landscape. The first written accounts of the Southwest do not describe it as a desert. There were good stands of grass along waterways; most of the valley floors were broad and flat; and water tended to spread over them after summer thundershowers, this natural irrigation of these valley bottoms supporting the grassy cover. After the pacification of the Indians and the introduction of domestic animals, there was a great increase in the number of horses, sheep, goats, and cattle. Shortly thereafter, huge gullies appeared throughout the country. The broad, flat bottom lands became trenched with deep, steep-sided canyons called *arroyos*. The water could no longer spread out over the valley bottom, but rushed down these narrow slots.

There has been bitter debate as to the cause of this condition. In the past, long before the Europeans erupted onto the scene, there were such arroyos. They had formed and healed a number of times. One great local storm can start such a gully. A long dry spell, by starving the vegetation cover and thus denuding the surface of the land, may start gullies over a whole area. What then is the cause of gullies: man or nature? This is probably not an either-or proposition, for either one can cause gullies. Long periods of good rainfall of low intensity allow much of the water to sink into the land. This type of rain supports vegetation; the runoff is slowed; and deposition (the collection of sediment) then occurs in the gullies. The process can lead to the healing of the land. A period of little rainfall with much of it concentrated in strong downpours, on the other hand, can lead to gullying, with or without incursions by domestic animals.

To overload the land with domestic animals, however, insures that gullying will result no matter what the short-range climate does. The explosive growth of the number of cattle on the land and the almost immediate appearance of very extensive gullying is so closely correlated in time and has so obvious a causal connection as to be a real example of the effect of man on the land.

This phenomenon seems to offer part of the answer to the very barren appearance of the Sahara and the Arabian deserts, with their much greater expanses of dune areas. Man has been using domestic animals in the American Southwest for a mere 100 years, and the landscape already looks tattered and torn. In the Old World the figure may be as high as 10,000 years and is certainly as high as 5000 years. If men with domestic animals can create spots

Grazing Comparison. The impact of overgrazing is shown by the contrast between overgrazed and well-managed bunch-grass range (*left*) and the broader view of the consequences of such mismanagement of land (*below*). Much of the Navaho reservation now looks like the overgrazed land shown here, although before the advent of sheep, goats, horses, and cows it was covered with bunch grass. Much of the good Mediterranean-climate land of North Africa and the Near East looks like this overgrazed land, and the steppe lands look worse. In general, human misuse can downgrade humid lands to steppelike conditions and steppe lands to a desertlike aspect. *USDA photos.*

of desert in good arid lands such as our Southwest in 100 years, how much could they do in 5000 years?

The use of domestic animals for harvesting vegetation—much of which is inedible for man—and then either eating the animal or using its products, such as wool and milk and butter, is just another way of using the land. This method allowed man to work more land more intensively than was accomplished by the simple gathering way of life. In turn, it altered the land, and it seems probable that the alteration is for the worse, ultimately limiting the usefulness of the land for man.

Domestic animals existed everywhere in the Old World dry lands before 1500, except in Australia and some parts of the South African area. In the New World in pre-Columbian times, domestic animals were either absent or unimportant (as in Peru). This leaves the question of why the man of the Old World domesticated animals; when and where domestication developed; and which animals were so used first. Actually we know very little about this subject with any certainty.

We know that the domestication of animals was carried out only in certain areas. We also know that this areal limitation had almost nothing to do with the availability of animals. The folklore that the American buffalo could not be domesticated or that the African elephant could not be tamed or that the American caribou could not have been used fully as easily as the Asiatic reindeer has no basis in fact. However, there seems to have been only one area in which the domestication of animals occurred early. This was in or near the great center of origins of ideas in the Near East. Animal domestication therefore would seem to be another idea we owe to this time, place, and people. Here the cow, pig, donkey, sheep, goat, and camel were probably domesticated, and marginal to this area horses, reindeer, elephant, chicken, geese, and ducks were domesticated. The only other area that had domestic animals was Middle America, and even this may have been due to ideas that originated in the Near East and reached America from across the Pacific.

Once the waves of pastoral nomads began their endless sweeps across the dry lands of the Old World, the total ecology of the land must have begun to change. Animals graze selectively, and the plants they prefer are therefore selected against and the "weeds" given a chance to flourish. The land thus stripped of vegetation can blow or wash, creating a differing ecological condition, one in which plants preferring disturbed ground increase at the expense of plants preferring stabilized ground. The animals from rodents to horses that depend on the vegetation must also change or perish. With the changing rates of runoff, the ground water table changes and springs come or go depending on these shifts. Man, dependent·on plants, animals, and water, must adjust his usage of the land to these shifts. It is important never to lose sight of the fact that very often man himself has created in part, and sometimes in large part, the very conditions to which he must then adjust.

OCCUPANCY OF THE DRY LANDS

A brief survey of the history of man in the dry lands produces a feeling that anything can happen there (see Map 2–1). In the Old World the great early centers of civilization were near the low-latitude hot deserts. Egypt, Mesopotamia, and the Indus Valley are examples of riverine oases. They are near the center of the growth of civilization, possibly the origin point of civilization for the entire world. At the same time, Australia and South Africa had primitive ways of life. The Australian natives were simple, unspecialized hunters and gatherers. The little pygmy Negrito people of the South African deserts were also hunters and gatherers but with a little more emphasis on hunting. In North America, the southern desert area and the Colorado Plateau had agriculturists, while in the Great Basin the people were simple hunters and gatherers. In South America the coastal desert of Peru had a series of city states based on the irrigated valleys: this was an irrigation civilization. In the Old World there was a vast belt of pastoral nomadic peoples in the dry lands of Africa, Arabia, and inner Asia. But such a way of life was totally lacking in Australia, and late to appear in the South African dry region and in the American dry lands. It is difficult to generalize these findings in terms of the compelling effect of the physical environment. If the environments are similar and if there are no great differences in the inherent ability of mankind, why then are there such great differences in the way in which the land is used?

OLD WORLD DRY LANDS: EGYPT AND THE NEAR EAST

Can we come to any conclusions from the fact that the birth of civilization seems to have occurred in the great riverine oases of the Old World? Egypt is often described in early geographical works as a perfect example of the force of the physical environment. Here was a land designed to force, or at least challenge, man and encourage the growth of civilization. The desert climate provided a year-round growing season, and the annual floods of the river renewed the soils so that there were no problems of soil exhaustion.

The floods were a natural means of irrigation. What was more natural, runs the theory, than to broaden the area touched by the flood waters a bit more, in other words, to begin to manage the waters and hence to drift into irrigation agriculture. With an agricultural base thus assured and the perfect protection of the desert expanses on either side to prevent easy access by enemies, how could it be otherwise than that the number of men should increase, that the good food supply should free some men to pursue learning, and that among the subjects studied would be the realm of the heavens—in order to establish a calendar for predicting the time of the flooding of the river—and the development of geometry—for the re-establishment of boundary marks when the flood subsided. Additional knowledge assured more food and, hence, both more people and more leisure and the differentiation among people—priests, kings, scholars, workers. And in the vast isolation guaranteed by the desert would grow up the distinctive Egyptian civilization. These are the familiar old explanations, but do they really explain the birth of civilization?

THE EARLIEST AGRICULTURE

It was once thought that Egypt was the earliest civilization and that all the other areas drew from her. Today this is being reversed. The earliest agriculture, the earliest villages and towns are being found in the area called the Fertile Crescent—that sickle-shaped area reaching from northern Palestine around through modern-day Syria and Lebanon into northern Iraq. This is not a desert region: most of the early agricultural sites found are in the 8 to 24 inch rainfall zone. Since these are areas of winter

Near Cairo, Egypt. The contrast between barren desert and the irrigated area is striking and typical of oases great and small. *American Geographical Society.*

(Opposite) Egyptian Contributions to·Art, Architecture, and Learning in Their Vast Oasis. This example of advanced art and architecture includes Egyptian writing, with its pictographic and pure sound (alphabetic) symbols. Notice the barren desert hills in the background. *Embassy of the United Arab Republic.*

(Right) Modern Egypt. Egypt struggles to rise again after 2000 years of outside domination. Modern housing rises in a land where most men through most of time have lived in primitive habitations. *Embassy of the United Arab Republic.*

rainfall concentrations, the climatically comparable areas in America would be from San Diego to San Francisco. It is only semidesert at worst, and in these areas the first agriculture now known is found. At present the earliest dates are about 10,000 years ago, but the well-established agricultural villages of that date suggest still earlier beginning dates.

This dating takes us back to the end of the glacial period. We know that at that time the climate was quite different in these regions: they were better watered than they are now. Far from agriculture having started in the desert, it seems to have started in the well-watered mid-latitudes; and far from starting off with irrigation, it seems much more probably to have started in the rainy hilly areas. If wheat and barley are the first crops of this part of the world, then we should have guessed that agriculture did not start in the flood plains, for if that were the case one would expect agriculture to have started with swamp plants such as rice. It now seems much more likely that agriculture started in the uplands and that the first agricultural villages were there, and that only much later did well-established agricul-

tural peoples gradually and probably very slowly move down into the valleys of the great rivers that flowed through the low deserts.

A glimpse of how slow this process may have been is supplied by such dates as we now have. In the Near East there were agricultural villages about 10,000 years ago, but it was not until 3500 B.C. that the "proto literate," or beginning-civilization stage, was reached. Egypt and China probably were influenced by the appearance of domestication in the Near East and followed along, Egypt, the nearer, getting started about 3500 B.C. and China about 2500 B.C. When it is considered that the date for the first agriculture is likely to be moved farther back in time while the beginnings of the cities and states and dynasties is less likely to be changed, it is seen that the time required for the spread of agriculture and the building of populations in this area was thousands of years. This is also portrayed in Map 2–2, where the slowness of the spread of agriculture is shown for Europe. The equivalent distance in the United States would be from Georgia to northern California.

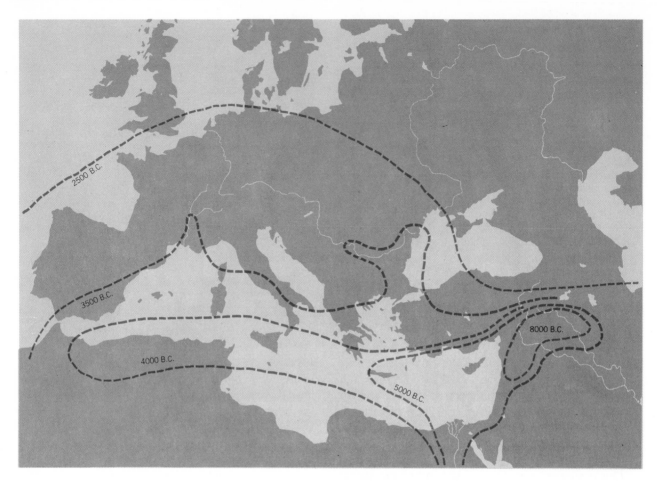

Map 2-2   The Spread of Agriculture into Europe

The earliest dates for the beginning of agriculture are in the Near East, where settled agricultural villages date to about 8000 B.C. As shown here, the revolutionary idea that food production could be controlled by man gradually spread into Europe. Several things show up clearly. The initial spreading out was very slow: note the relatively small area reached during the first 3000 years. Thereafter, the spread of agriculture was quite rapid, and there is a strong suggestion that it was greatly facilitated by sea routes: note the extension down the Mediterranean.

Finally, agriculture spread throughout the European peninsula, reaching the English channel about 2500 B.C. The distance is about 3000 miles, or about the distance across the United States. The travel time, in very round numbers, is half a mile per year. However, most of the spread occurred between 5000 and 2500, and a rate of about one mile per year seems indicated for this period. These are probably characteristic figures for the spread of ideas on comparable cultural levels.

Its Spread

If the beginning of agriculture was in the foot-hills of the northern part of the Fertile Crescent, then it spread east and west through subtropical humid lands and eventually northward into mid-latitude humid lands. While it early spread into the adjacent oases of Mesopotamia, Egypt, and northwestern India, the spread into Africa south of the Sahara was slow. In the arid lands of South Africa, even though men there had possibilities for irrigated agriculture, they never took even the first steps toward agriculture and civilization.

The domestication of animals begins with sheep about 11,000 years ago; the pig appears to have been domesticated about 8500 years ago; and domestic cattle appear about 7000 years ago. The domestication of animals seems to have centered in the humid area to the north of the arid parts of Mesopotamia. The use of arid lands by moving herds of animals about to harvest the sparse vegetation and then living on the animals must have been developed in the Old World sometime thereafter. The idea spread over North Africa and Arabia and throughout the arid interior of Asia from the Black Sea to China. The idea of cattle keeping spread slowly into South Africa and the arid lands there only belatedly came in part to be used by pastoralists. No other arid lands had a pastoral-nomadic way of life. Everything was there: the difficult dry environment, the potential domestic animals, and the human need for a more controlled food supply. However, only in those areas adjacent to the Near East did any such adjustment to the land arise. Seemingly, the idea arose but once.

The potential of this way of life is best exemplified by happenings in inner Asia. Here the horse, camel, goat, and sheep provided a nomadic way of life that supported large numbers of people in comparative luxury. Their numbers and mobility, when organized under great leaders such as the khans allowed them to use their central location to win control of central Eurasia. At times their political control extended into central Europe or into India

from a base in China. This manner of use of the arid to semiarid lands is then a potentially productive one. The failure of mankind to duplicate this particular use of land anywhere in the world beyond the reach of its invention in the Near East becomes all the more remarkable.

The arid lands of the Old World that were close to the Near East were for thousands of years the most productive of new ideas of any land in the world. Hot, low Mesopotamia and hot, low Egypt were long the great centers of civilization. From them, ideas streamed out to ignite the fires of civilization in the eastern Mediterranean and in China, and to greatly affect the growth of civilization in India. The low-latitude deserts have the highest summer temperatures in the world. If heat can inhibit human activity, especially mental activity, how can it be that these areas produced the wheel, the arch, mathematics, writing, astronomy, calendars, and a host of other inventions?

DECAY OF EARLY CENTERS OF CIVILIZATION

Later these areas lost their intellectual and cultural lead. After Graeco-Roman times Egypt and Mesopotamia recede to minor significance both politically and as sources for ideas. There is no great climatic change about that time; the land and sea and even the people remain as they were; it is the cultural world that changes. The centers of creativity move to Greece and Rome and Constantinople, and later, in one direction, to northwestern Europe. We tend to overlook the fact that there was also an eastward movement: China and India were functioning as major centers of creativity at this time, and civilizations were flourishing in America too.

The shift away from the ancient centers in the Near East is not easily explained. There is no obvious physical, geographical-environmental cause. The crossroads position of the Near East continued and still continues. The Arabs continued the trade between the Far East and the Mediterranean. The building of the Suez canal emphasized the importance of the area for the transfer of goods, men,

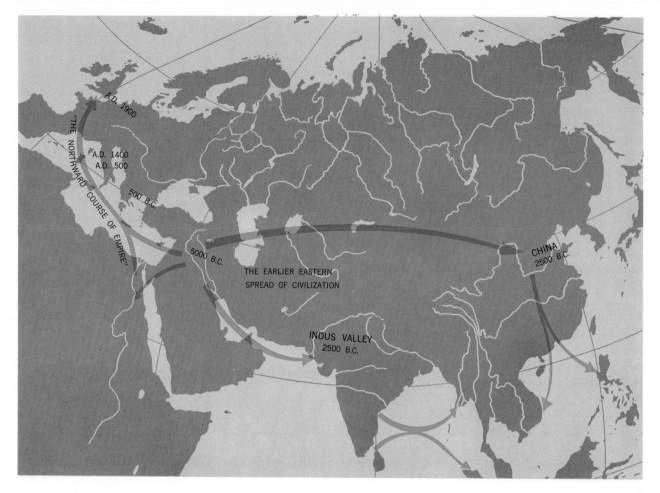

Map 2-3 The Spread of Civilization from the Near East

The beginning of agriculture in the Near East gave that region an enormous lead over the rest of the world. The later spread of ideas from this center has often been described as the "northward course of empire." This is indicated here in round numbers: 5000 B.C. for the beginning of cities and states in Mesopotamia; 500 B.C. for the flowering of Greece; A.D. 500 for the end of Rome; A.D. 1400 to mark the Renaissance in Italy; and A.D. 1900 for the period of greatest dominance of the North Sea nations.

One of the oddities of ethnocentric thought is the myth about the northwest spread of civilization from the eastern Mediterranean. While it is true that there was a spread to the northwest, there was also a simultaneous spreading out in northeastern, southeastern, and southern directions, as suggested on this map. The old explanation that the spread was primarily to the northwest because this was the zone of cool stimulating climates tended to overlook the spread into directions of quite different climates.

and ideas at the end of the nineteenth and first half of the twentieth century. Today the major airlines of Eurasia funnel through the area.

The reasons for the long decadence of the Near East and Egypt are far more subtle than mere shifts in climate, or even a shifting economic position. Even to say that the causes lie in history begs the question. The real causes lie in the spirit of men and nations, and this question has hardly been touched. What happened to the outlook of these people who once dreamed the mightiest dreams, conceived the finest art and architecture, and laid the basis for our modern science in the midst of the desert furnace heat in the semiarid foothills and in riverine oases that still dominate the land?

The geographer can state that the land is still there with the same climate, land forms, and soil. There has been some extinction of animals, considerable destruction of vegetation, and some soil erosion. But these are minor items. The same races of men are present that produced the inventors of writing, the codifiers of laws, and the architects of pyramids, and the lofty prose of the Old and New Testaments. The land remains in one of the crossroads of our earth. All that is required to make the great oases of Mesopotamia, Egypt, the Indus Valley, and the series of riverine oases between the Black Sea and Lake Balkash bloom again is the will to do so and the political and economic institutions to allow those who would to do so.

In the past, human energies in these areas were harnessed under some form of absolute rule, often combined with the idea of a divine priest-king, and the major economic base of society was agriculture. The early irrigation agricultures were efficient for their time, for they could produce a surplus of food to support a small percentage of the population in nonagricultural pursuits. Under the authoritarian governments of the day, this surplus went to the aristocracy and the priesthood, if different, and to the artists, architects, and scientists selected by the ruling group.

The group freed from the grinding daily toil was minute compared to the total population. Nonethe-

less, five thousand years ago it was a great advance. At least some men were freed for the pursuit of art, science, and philosophy. In the course of history, political shifts of power, shifting trade patterns, colonial status, and eventually the failure for some time in sharing in the industrial and social revolutions that were transforming the Western World—with their attendant freeing of larger percentages of people for learned pursuits, the growth of widespread education, and the potential extension to the mass of the people of the right to choose their own way of life and to produce to their limit of ability and energy—left these former seats of invention and learning to stagnate. As a rule, until now a farmer remained a farmer, and opportunity existed only for a few. Productivity of the land and of the people has remained at relatively low levels while areas formerly much less productive have become immensely more productive. The physical geographies have not changed; the set of men's minds have changed and the physical earth has produced accordingly.

Ruins in the Desert

Nevertheless there have at times been real, not just relative, declines in the productivity of the Old World dry lands. Inner Asia has a great series of ruined cities. Most of these lie along the rivers that come down out of the high mountains and head out into the desert. These abandoned cities early led to theories of climatic change as the cause of human accomplishment and failure. Careful study of the evidence of climatic change has not supported this theory. Instead, the growth and destruction of these ancient cities proves to be much more closely correlated with the political and economic happenings in the region. It has been more a matter of stability of governments and the flourishing of trade or the dominance of nomads that has determined the success or failure of the riverine oases people.

In the desert of southern Palestine there have at times been cities in the middle of the desert. There is no stream now there to support them. Seemingly they could not exist there in the present climate;

Ruins of an Ancient Church in the Negev, Israel. Such ruins are common in dry lands and are the usual source for the idea that there has been a climatic change. The Israeli redevelopment of the Negev illustrates the role of politico-economic forces. *Embassy of Israel.*

nor does there seem to be any reason for their being there. Since they are there, it is easy to conclude that there must have been a climatic change. A further look at the matter, however, indicates that this is not so. Study of the houses shows that every drop of water that fell was channeled into deep cisterns where the water was kept safe against evaporation and undoubtedly used most sparingly. The climate must have been as arid as it is now. The reason for the existence of these cities was trade, for at that particular time in history the Gulf of Suez was blocked for political reasons and trade from the Indian Ocean to the Mediterranean diverted into the Gulf of Aquaba, the goods being moved thence overland. It is one of the curiosities of history that current Egyptian-Israeli relations have recreated this situation and that the Israelis are considering reconstituting this ancient trade route. If they do so,

cities will again bloom in the desert, but they too will probably be abandoned with a change in the political situation.

Similar changes are found in North Africa. Before Roman times there were no camels in North Africa. Along the northern fringe of the Sahara in what is really the arid end of the Mediterranean, there were large flourishing settled agricultural colonies. Carthage was one of these. Later, Rome developed this land greatly: it was a granary, a source of olive oil and wine, a rich colonial area. Thereafter, it declined; cities dwindled or even were abandoned; areas that had been in olives or vineyards or wheat became just poor pastorage. Again the explanation often given has been that of climatic change. Certainly when land goes out of agricultural use and become a barren pasture, it *looks* as if the climate has changed.

(*Above, left*) **Camel Caravan in Algeria.** The barren desert appearance is probably greatly increased by the presence of camels, goats, and other herd animals for thousands of years. *French Government Tourist Office.*

(*Above, right*) **Biskra, Algeria.** An oasis town on the south side of the desert mountains, its location in relation to the Mediterranean climate, the sea, and the desert is much like that of Palm Springs, California. *French Government Tourist Office.*

(*Right*) **Bou Sada, Algeria.** This type of oasis settlement is typical of broad areas of the dry lands of the Old World north of the equator in pre-Columbian times. The building construction suggests more a cultural manifestation than anything the environment dictates. Compare the settlement at Palm Springs, the Navaho hogans, or the Paiute huts for the degree of variability that can be found in arid-land housing. *French Government Tourist Office.*

During Roman times the land was governed strictly: Romans enforced the peace and Roman law prevailed. The land was meant to be productive and disturbances that would reduce productivity were put down. Nevertheless, in later Roman times the land was going out of production, men were leaving the land, and the area was in an obvious decline. Was it the result of climatic change? Certainly not. Nomadic raids? Perhaps, but only secondarily so. A very good argument can be advanced that the cause was excessive taxation.

In early Roman times the tax was the *decumanae*, the "10 percent." Later it began to double, until it rose to about 40 percent. The tax was a combined land and poll tax. The people with the largest families paid more. If a farmer went bankrupt and fled the land, the payment of his taxes was divided amongst his neighbors. This meant that a farmer who was barely getting by when there were ten farmers in his district might face a 10 percent tax rise when one of his neighbors went out of production. This might be ruinous to him. But when he too went out of production, the remaining farmers had to add his tax burdens to theirs as well. This pyramiding of taxes seems guaranteed to drive men off the land or out of production of any kind, and exactly this happened toward the end of the Roman Empire. The abandonment of the land was general. It was not just the edge-of-the-desert lands that were exposed to climatic risks and to barbarian raids that were abandoned. All over the Empire, in the well-watered lands and in the heart of the Empire where nomads could not as yet raid, land was being abandoned.

Another Source of Change: Camels, Nomads, and Farmers

The appearance of the camel with the enormous mobility that this animal gave the desert dwellers did change life in the Sahara. This shift came surprisingly late. Camels were first introduced into Egypt about 500 B.C. Surprisingly, their use did not spread quickly over the Sahara. It was not until late Roman times that the camel came into wide use in the western Sahara. Prior to that time oxen and the little native elephants of North Africa were the pack animals used by the caravans. Expectably, the movement through the immense dry wastes of the inner Sahara was greatly limited, for neither oxen nor elephants are desert-adapted beasts. Prior to the time of the camel, the oases people had been dominant. Now men could wander farther over the desert, and greater numbers of men could live away from the oases. Furthermore, their great mobility enabled these men to concentrate sizable numbers in an attack on any single oasis. The balance of power shifted toward the pastoral nomad.

Settled people suffer from such pressure even without actual warfare. In the arid lands, olives and vineyards can be established in good spots by careful selection of the plots of land where water is concentrated during the occasional rains. It takes years to get vineyards and olives established and bearing, and the trees and vines are scattered over a wide area with some tucked in this canyon and a few at the mouth of the next, and some more around the corner of the hill where water is shed off a rocky expanse and concentrated onto a patch of good soil. The work of years can be undone in one night by a herd of camels. Camels browse; they have tremendously powerful jaws and teeth that can shear off a small limb; with the breakdown of law and order the pastoral nomad could wander into the edge of the settlements and do terrific damage with his herds before the settled people could muster the number of men required to drive him off.

If the settled people lost the struggle against destructive taxation and destructive nomads, the land that they abandoned would cease to produce wheat and wine and olive oil. It would become pasture land occupied by nomad herders living in tents. The aspect of the land would change in such a way as to suggest a climatic change. The causes, however, would be cultural. Just such changes occurred in the Sahara after the Roman period, and the result was the extension of arid-appearing conditions far into the zones that are climatically humid. Much of the North African margin is humid land that could well support a forest. Goats, camels, and man have re-

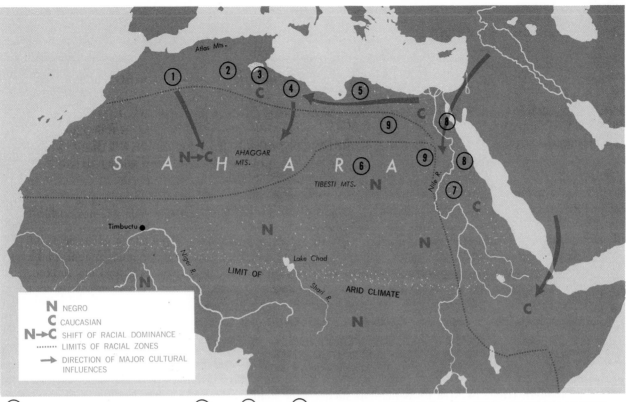

① AREA FROM WHICH ZENEBITES EXPANDED ② MZAB ③ THE SUF ④ AREA FROM WHICH GHARDAMIANS, WHO BECAME THE TUAREGS, EXPANDED

⑤ ARABIC EXPANSION ACROSS NORTH AFRICA ⑥ AREA OF SURVIVAL OF THE TIBU, REPRESENTATIVES OF THE ORIGINAL NEGROID POPULATION OF

THE SAHARA OASES ⑦ NUBIAN DESERT ⑧ ARABIAN DESERT ⑨ LIBYAN DESERT

Map 2-4 The Sahara

The Sahara is a vast dry area approximately the size of the United States. In the main it is low, but it does contain two large volcanic masses, the Ahaggar and Tibesti mountains. From these mountains minor amounts of water flow down into the surrounding basins and create oases. Larger oases are created by the streams flowing southward out of the much-better-watered Atlas Mountains. Such streams, even when they sink into the sand, often flow immense distances. Water also enters the Sahara in important amounts by the Nile, which flows through to the sea; the Niger, which enters the desert but turns back near Timbuctu; and the Shari, which ends in Lake Chad. The major cultural influences on Africa from Arabia into Egypt and Ethiopia, seem to have caused racial shifts comparable to that caused by the introduction of camels into the western Sahara in late Roman times. Possibly all of Africa was Negroid until late Paleolithic time.

moved most of the forest and made the land appear far drier than it really is. The "natural" vegetation can be seen today only in protected areas.

The shift of dominant peoples in the Sahara was complex. In the eastern Sahara, Egypt is an immense populous oasis with easy access to the narrow desert between it and the Red Sea. With large settled populations having ready access to this desert strip, the nomads were readily controlled. To the west of Egypt lies the immensely dry Libyan desert. The few nomads there could not muster large enough forces to upset the dense settlements along the Nile. Hence, in the eastern Sahara the farmers dominated the nomads.

In the western Sahara the conditions are reversed, no large oases exist in the desert there. The desert is vast and somewhat less formidable than the Libyan desert. The balance of power with the coming of the camel shifted to the nomad. Note that there the natural environment remained the same and that the change was dependent on the cultural shift.

The reversal of power changed the racial make-up of the Sahara. Prior to the introduction of the camel only the northern fringe of Africa was held by such racially Mediterranean peoples as the Berbers. It was into their territory that the Romans introduced the camel. Quite naturally it was these people that became the first camel nomads of the western Sahara. It is one of the oddities of history that a Jewish tribe, the Zenetes, not mentioned earlier in the literature of the area, appear to be the first camel nomads of that region. They appear in about the sixth century A.D. and spread into the desert area founding a string of oasis towns. Another group that obtained camels and spread into the desert were the Garmantians, a people identified later as the Tuaregs.

The spread of these mounted, nomadic, warlike peoples was at the expense of the previous occupants of the oases. These were a Negro people who had made their living by growing grain. Their entire way of life differed from that of the invaders. The Negroes grew grain, crushed the grain in characteristic grindstones that were totally different from the rotary querns of the invaders, and used the bow and arrow for hunting and war. Grain growing and flour was replaced by date growing and meat and dairy products. The rotary quern replaced the ancient grinding stones, and the spear replaced the bow and arrow. The change took a long time and in part is still continuing. In part, however, the region has come to a semiequilibrium.

The camel nomads dominate the area. They own the oases, and the oases people usually work the land for the nomads. The town-dwelling oases people are largely Negroid. This reflects two facts. First, the nomad considers the town-dwelling–farming way of life to be beneath him. Secondly, the oases are centers of malaria, and the Negro people as a race have more resistance to malaria than the white race. This resistance is associated with sickle-cell anemia, a blood type specialty characteristic of the Negro race. The result is that there is a steady elimination of the whites that do settle in the oases. A complex relationship has been established in which the nomads own and protect certain oases and the oases dwellers furnish dates, grain, and other materials for the nomads. In return they get not only protection, but meat, wool, hides, and milk products. Only in the most remote part of the Sahara, near the Tibesti Mountains, for example, do the Negro people still hold out in some purity of race and freedom.

This tremendous racial and cultural shift started, then, in later Roman times. It was made possible by the introduction of the camel and the highly mobile way of life that this created. Since the Mediterranean peoples took up this way of life, they were the ones that gained by it. The great push into the Sahara by the Mediterranean peoples was accelerated by the expansion of the Muslims, and its continuing spread is to a considerable extent fanned by the religious drive of Islam. It is typical of mankind that the Negro people clung to their grain farming, sedentary, bow-and-arrow–using way of life and lost control of their ancient homeland. In the American desert much the same thing happened with the settled Pueblo farming people when the warlike nomadic Athabascans invaded their territory. In the latter

Map 2-5 Egypt and the Nile Valley

Egypt is the typical great riverine oasis. The entire country has less than 4 inches of rainfall per year. The agricultural development is therefore concentrated along the narrow Nile Valley. Note the high rainfall at the headwaters of the Nile, and the frequency of cataracts in the river. The latter greatly inhibit the use of the river for transportation. *Adapted from* Focus—*The American Geographical Society.*

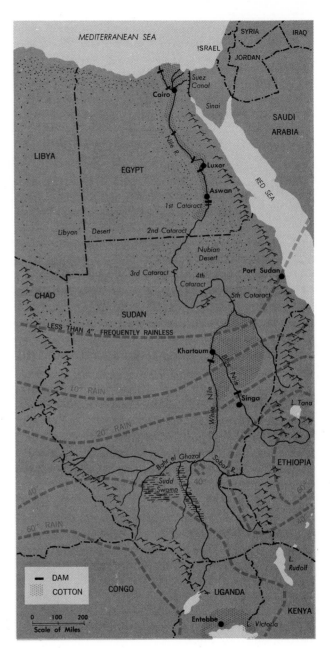

case there was no major racial difference, and the comparative cultural method thus cautions us against assuming that there was some racial causation in the Negro failure to shift to camel nomadism.

OASIS TYPES

There are more kinds of oases and more ways to live in them than one could at first imagine. In the great oases, such as the Nile and the Tigris-Euphrates valleys, villages and towns and cities and empires were constructed on the broad agricultural base that the large amounts of irrigation water made possible. In past times the produce of such lands was largely foodstuffs for the support of the local population. Today, as in Egypt for example, there may be large-scale production of materials for export. This production for export provides the necessary foreign exchange for the purchase of such commodities as tractors, automobiles, gasoline, and tires that are not produced within the country. Egypt's principal crops are rice, cotton, and onions, and they are also the principal exports. Egypt in many ways can serve as the typical "great oasis." The country is large (about the equivalent of Texas, Arkansas, and Oklahoma combined). However, only 2.5 percent of the land is presently useful, that is, irrigable. The other 97.5 percent of the land is desert with less than four inches of rainfall per year. Under low-latitude, hot-desert conditions, this is extremely little rainfall.

There are other types of oases. In the Shebka of the Mzab the Mozabites have worked out a way of life in a forbidding landscape. The Shebka is formed upon limestone. Mile upon mile of the desert land is a white, harsh, bare rock surface that has been cut into a maze of badlands. This surface is 2000 to 2300 feet above sea level. The limestone is underlain by marls, and springs appear where valleys cut through this material. Where the marl is not reached by the deep valley cuts, wells are dug in the bottom of the valleys to reach the water-bearing strata. The depths of these wells vary from 28 to 180 feet and there are 3300 of them. Since the water does not rise in these wells, it must be raised by buckets. Most of this work is done by men, but much of it is done by work animals such as the donkey. Since the water is used to irrigate the gardens, a vast amount of labor must be expended in raising enough water to keep the gardens alive.

Little rain is received; a rainy year may have two or three showers, while a dry year has none. Dams are built on the large, medium, small, and even tiny valleys to store the water that comes so infrequently. The crops are grown along the narrow valley bottoms in small plots of land that are more like gardens than fields, for the use of the land is intensive and fruit trees have vegetables or grains growing under them. Dates, figs, pomegranates, apricots, peaches, barley, beans, and grapes are all intimately intermixed. If a man works hard, he can win a modest subsistence and no more, yet the people cling to this way of life. Today many of the men spend their middle years outside the area, usually in Algeria, working as a merchant or banker and forming a separate, exclusive Islamic sect. It is the outside earnings that make possible the maintenance of the oasis. Life outside is only a means to gain the things that the oases could not supply. The social life, the sense of belonging, the nonmaterial things that these people value in life are found in their desert oases —lands that to us would be unthinkably isolated, barren, and laborious.

Everyone in this type of community plans to have two houses. One house is located at their gardens and may be far from the village; the second house is in the village or town, for social life is prized. The houses are made of limestone, and a mortar made of burnt limestone and gypsum is used to cement the rocks together. It is too facile a conclusion to say: "Of course, houses of rock in a rocky desert." A great deal of fuel must be used to burn limestone to cement; it could as well have been used to construct a wooden house. Indeed, why is so much emphasis placed on a house in a land where it rarely rains? Why not hollow out the limestone valley walls? If a tent is sufficient for the nomads, why do oases people need so permanent a house? And if a stone house is desired, why must it be cemented with mortar? Stone walls can be laid up without mortar, and in dry lands they can well be laid up with mud for mortar and will then stand for centuries. The people of the Mzab feel that life is best lived in a stone house with real mortar between its rocks and located in the bottom of a dry valley cut into an utterly barren rock mass in the midst of the world's greatest desert.

Near the Mzab are the people of the Suf, a great sea of sand dunes. Property here is not in land; there is an unlimited amount of that. It is not even in water, for water underlies vast areas of these dunes. Property is rather in date palms. The date palm flourishes if it has its feet in the water and its head in the furnace. The only practical limit on how many date palms a man may have in the Suf is the limit of a man's strength. Each palm is the result of digging down to the shallow water table, planting a palm, and then keeping any excess of sand from accumulating and choking the tree. Successful growth requires the constant digging away of the sand and places a limit on how many trees one man can maintain. To most people the area would look utterly useless; certainly without the date palm it would be much less useful. As it is, the people live in this great sand sheet following a way of life in which about half of the effort goes into nomadic herding and half into tending of the palm trees. The two activities are, of course, supplementary. Man cannot live on dates alone, but dates are an excellent supplement to the milk and cheese of the herdsman.

Given a vast sand sheet and a way of life centered on tending trees widely scattered over this dune swept expanse, what type of dwelling would seem most natural? Tents—as used by the pastoral fraction of the population—or palm-thatched houses with stout palm log frames? A thatched house would give excellent insulation and ventilation and in a dry area, would last indefinitely, and be cheap and easy to make of the available material. Yet the Sufis do not build that kind of a house. Instead, they mine calcareous cemented sand sheets from the sand dunes. Houses are built on a square floor plan, one square room at a time, each room being roofed with a dome of stone. Villages are large and may have up to a thousand of these square-shaped, dome-topped rooms. Here in the midst of the desert, then, one finds a fixed house utilizing one of the most advanced of architectural devices for the housing of a very simple society that is at least half nomadic.

In the belt sweeping from the Sahara through Arabia to China one finds that the land is occupied by a combination of oasis agriculturalists and pastoral nomads. Since European cultural roots are so deeply embedded in these regions, we tend to think of this as the natural way to use arid lands. This conclusion overlooks the fact that even in the Old World not all arid lands were always so used. Arid South Africa belatedly became partially pastoral, but had no oasis agricultural development. Australia had neither pastoral nor agricultural development. This should raise considerable doubt about whether oasis agriculture plus pastoralism is the natural or obvious way to use a dry land. Detailed studies of variations in ways of using the oases for agriculture or the desert for pastoralism show that there is less similarity in detail even within these systems than one might expect under a severely limiting environment. The delayed spread of the camel and the date palm, the variety of house types, including the nonuse of potential types (palm log and thatch, for example) suggest that man chose rather narrowly among a wide range of possibilities of land use. This can be made even clearer by shifting our view to the New World dry lands.

CULTURE AND ENVIRONMENT IN THE AMERICAN SOUTHWEST

An easy way to place into perspective these processes of developing advanced means of using arid lands is to move to an area where they either did not work, or did not have enough time to work, or depended on a people who were incapable of accomplishing the feat of taking a Mesopotamia or an Egypt and making a civilization out of it, that is, taking an arid interior and making it the pivot of a great empire. We can look at the American Southwest, and especially at the lower Colorado River valley, which to a considerable degree duplicates the Egyptian environment, and at our Great Basin and adjacent regions, which resemble the interior of Asia. Here we will find that the same rich opportunity that the people of the Near East capitalized on very early produced extremely little. However, at the present time while the Near East, in comparison, languishes, the American area forges ahead.

Egyptian development has been made to seem much more unusual than it really is. It is not the only civilization that flourished in a riverine oasis. Mesopotamia, the Indus Valley, and the rivers that drain northward toward the Caspian and Aral seas also had similar civilizations. In America there were a whole series of such irrigation civilizations along the desert coast of Peru, and like Egypt, these had their own marked cultural personality. Not all rivers flowing through deserts have developed such civilizations, however, for neither the Rio Grande nor the Colorado in North America, nor the Orange River in South Africa, nor the Murry-Darling system of Australia figured in such a process. The question becomes, then, why did some riverine oases foster civilizations and others not?

THE AMERICAN EGYPT

America has an area that is physically remarkably like Egypt. However, there is no resemblance in what happened in the history of the two places. If the environment is a powerful force in determining development, should we not expect two similar environments to provoke, stimulate, encourage, even demand similar responses?

The lower valley of the Colorado River is, like Egypt, a narrow ribbon of green stretching through formidable deserts. It is fed by a stream rising in high mountains a great distance away. Below the cataracts of the Grand Canyon the alluvial flood plain stretches to the sea. Like Egypt, there is a depression off to one side into which water sometimes flows naturally and which it is possible to irrigate by control of this natural overflow. In Egypt such an area is the Fayum; in America the comparable region is the Imperial Valley.

In Egypt, men took advantage of this. By 5500 B.C. agricultural beginnings are certain in Egypt; by 4000 B.C. there were cities occupying an area of two square miles and having all the commerce and specialized artisans and rulers that such a concentration of people always demands. By 3000 B.C. began the dynasties for which we know the rulers, for writing first appears at this time. Egypt was long protected by its isolation in the desert of North Africa, and unlike Mesopotamia, it was usually united under one ruler. The Egyptian civilization that developed is justly famous for its murals, its great buildings, its pyramids, its fine work in stone carving, and in numerous other arts. What we should notice is the time scale: 2500 years from agricultural beginnings to dynasties.

What happened in the nearly identical environment in America? At first glance the answer seems to be, *nothing*. The lower Colorado River valley was occupied by a group of people known as the Yumans. In fact, the Yumans were a whole series of peoples with a similar language who were strung out along the river. In the delta were the Cocopa; the Yumas lived near the city of that name; and the Mohave occupied the area near Needles. There were other tribes, but they were exterminated or driven out by these major groups shortly after the first Spanish contact with these people in the sixteenth century.

Yuman Agriculture

The Yumans lived a leisurely and simple life; they developed some agriculture, but they did not work hard at it. Before the annual flood of the river was due, they went out and cleared some small plots

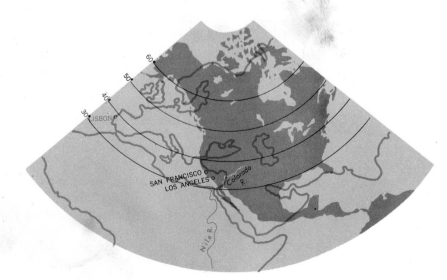

Map 2-6 Eur-Africa Super-imposed on North America

As the map shows, the mouths of the Colorado and the Nile lie in the same latitude. Both rivers rise in high mountains and flow through deserts to the sea. Both have narrow, flat-floored valleys that are subject to annual overflow by silt-bearing floodwater.

This map is also useful when considering other lands. Los Angeles, for example, is seen to be in the latitude of North Africa; San Francisco, in the latitude of Greece, Sicily, and Lisbon. For west coast marine climates, notice that Great Britain and Scandinavia are located in the latitude of the panhandle of **Alaska** and the **Aleutian Islands**.

of land in the river bottom. A good growth of arrow-weed was taken as a sign of good land. They cut down the arrowweed, piling it in stacks to dry, and just before the arrival of the floodwaters, they set the piles afire. It was considered good to time the burning so that the ground was still hot under the brush piles when the floodwaters reached the field areas.

When the floodwaters receded, the Yumans waded out in the mud and planted their crops. They had a small variety of maize, a specialized type of bean, and an unusual kind of pumpkin or squash. All of these plants were able to utilize the moisture in the wet ground to make a rapid growth under furnacelike heat, producing a crop very quickly. The corn plants only grew to heights of 2 or 3 feet, but they produced ears of corn about 5 inches long. By comparison, our modern-day 10 to 12 foot tall corn would yield ears 2 feet long. The beans also had the ability to absorb water very quickly and to sprout in about half the time that our modern beans do. They grew very rapidly despite the high heat, while modern beans drop their flowers and set no fruit when the heat is as high as is normal in the lower Colorado River valley in summer. The pumpkins, too, grew quickly and provided a quick harvest.

None of these plants were domesticated by the Yuma Indians. They borrowed them from their neighbors, the Hohokam people, who formerly lived in southern Arizona along the Gila and Salt rivers. They in turn had received their plants from neighbors to the south of them, in adjacent Mexico. Probably the whole set of plants they used were domesticated outside their desert areas, but the situation is not very different from that in Egypt. It is doubtful that the Egyptians domesticated any of their plants either. The homeland of wheat cannot be determined definitely as yet, but it is more probably in southwest Asia than in Egypt. The Egyptians, too, were borrowers.

Potential Resources

The Yumans, however, never tried large-scale production of food. A small clearing and a small crop were sufficient for them. If this harvest meant that during part of the year they would certainly go hungry—so regularly that one season was known as "the starving time"—this recurrent deprivation does not seem to have bothered them enough to make them get busy and clear more land. They did have other resources: each summer there was an abundant crop of mesquite beans. These nutritious beans, closely resembling large string beans, grow in large clusters on the mesquite trees that form immense thickets along the Colorado River. It was only necessary to be inured to being pricked and scratched by the claws of the mesquite tree in order to gather a huge harvest. The fleshy pods are stringy, but full of starch and sugar, while the seeds are very hard and must be reduced to meal to be utilized. The major way of using these beans was to put them down in a pit, well moistened, to let them ferment slightly, thus softening the fibers in the pods and converting more of the starches to sugar. The resultant material was then chewed, and the remnant of fiber formed a quid that, when well chewed, was spit out.

Apparently there was no attempt whatever to domesticate the mesquite trees. Why bother when they were so abundant? Yet why did *some* people in the world decide to domesticate trees? There was no selection for larger, sweeter, and less stringy beans among the Yumans, and the fermenting of the beans never led to making a fermented drink. Why not? Would not it have been easy for some Yuman to have put a few of the fermenting beans in a pot of water and forgotten them for a day or two only to find that the frothy water when drunk gave him a "heady" feeling?

Similarly, palm trees grow wild in the Sonoran Desert. They are found in little clusters in the canyons in the desert mountains. They have fan-shaped leaves and bear a round, fleshy fruit with an oily kernel. Elsewhere in the world, palms have been domesticated—for their sweet flesh in the North African–Arabian area, for their oil-rich meat in the Pacific area. However, these American palms were treated like mesquite trees. Even more interesting,

Date Palms at Palm Springs, Coachella Valley, California. The annual yield is over twenty million pounds of dates; these palms are the descendants of the finest strains of Palestine, Arabia, and Egypt, and were selected by scientists of the Department of Agriculture. *Palm Springs Chamber of Commerce.*

Arabian date palms were introduced into Lower California in the seventeenth century and flourished there. However, their cultivation did not spread, and not until the development of the Imperial Valley in the twentieth century did date growing finally take hold. Today, in the Coachella region of the Imperial Valley, ironically, near Palm Springs—which was named for the native palms growing there—there is now a sizable date industry. Palm trees were available there for thousands of years. Edible domestic date palms were introduced in adjacent California in the eighteenth century, but it

was 200 years later as an American enterprise, rather than Mexican or Spanish or Indian, that palm trees of entirely new introduction finally were used in the environment for which they are so well adapted.

Available grasses were not domesticated; tree fruits were not cultivated—whether it was the unlikely palm or the obviously rich and used mesquite. The world of the Yuman Indians is one where none of these things happened, while that of the Egyptians was one where such advantages of nature were tapped and made to supply a base for further achievements. Why the difference? The climates were equally hot, yet blisteringly hot summers did not stop the growth of culture in Egypt. The ideal winter weather, bright, sunny warm days followed by cool, pleasant nights, did not stimulate the Yumans. The landscape, the soils, the rocks, almost anything that one can think of in the physical environment were alike in both places.

Just as there was copper in the Sinai Peninsula adjacent to Egypt, so was there copper in adjacent southern Arizona. There was abundant granite and marble and limestone for monumental buildings and works of art. Asphalt was available in southern California, and so forth. No raw material of importance to Egypt was lacking in the areas immediately adjacent to the lower Colorado River valley. Why did a wealth of ideas take root in one area and not the other? Rather obviously, it was not the direct physical environment that was the causative agent.

Access to Ideas

Perhaps, then, it was an indirect environmental factor such as ease of access to ideas. After all, no people invents more than a fraction of their culture; instead, civilizations have largely been pieced together from the innumerable inventions and achievements of other peoples through time and over a vast spread of geographical areas. For instance, the paper in our books is a Chinese invention, and movable-type printing is also said to be a Chinese invention. Our writing is an adaptation made by a people on the shores of the eastern Mediterranean from a basis of Egyptian writing.

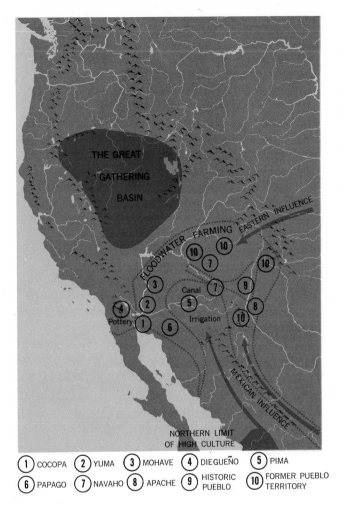

Map 2-7   Cultural Influences on the American West before 1500

Some of the cultural influences on the American West in pre-Columbian times are indicated here. Influences from the centers of high culture in Middle America were the most significant, reaching the Southwest in several waves and by several routes—and at differing times. Early introductions brought in agriculture that was dependent on rainfall, or on the natural concentration of floodwater runoff in certain favored spots. Some influences seem to have reached the Southwest by a route from Mexico to the Mississippi valley and then crossed the Great Plains to reach the Southwest. Finally, rather advanced ideas, including canal irrigation, probably reached the Southwest via a route on the west side of Mexico that had previously functioned to transmit such ideas as pottery and primitive agriculture.

Those areas far from the sources of ideas received the least stimulus. Thus canal irrigation stopped in Arizona, though it was fully applicable in adjacent California and Nevada. Floodwater farming spread a bit farther than canal irrigation, and pottery spread beyond the limits of agriculture. The Great Basin, which had the needed raw materials for pottery, possessed also the human needs for pottery and agriculture and a physical environment containing many oases—including rivers such as the Truckee that arise outside the desert and flow into it—but it was too far from the source areas for their cultural ideas to reach there early enough to take root and grow in pre-Columbian time. Given more time, such influences almost surely would have penetrated these areas, but the needed time might well have been measured in millennia.

① COCOPA ② YUMA ③ MOHAVE ④ DIEGUEÑO ⑤ PIMA
⑥ PAPAGO ⑦ NAVAHO ⑧ APACHE ⑨ HISTORIC PUEBLO ⑩ FORMER PUEBLO TERRITORY

Our breakfast coffee is of African origin. The tomato was first developed by the American Indians. Our use of the 360-degree circle is derived from the Sumerians, and so on. Perhaps the trouble with the Yumas is that they had no one nearby to borrow from.

However, this is not true. Eastward up the Gila and Salt rivers they had neighbors who had smaller streams to work with and used them to irrigate large areas. The Hohokam people raised not only corn and beans and squash, but also grew cotton—which they wove into fabrics. They traded with the Mexican Indians for copper bells and parrots, and did beautiful inlay work on shells they received in trade with tribes along the Gulf of Lower California. They

built great adobe compounds around very large, multistoried structures that had windows so located that they served for astronomical siting. Hohokam pottery was well made and tastefully decorated. The Hohokam people even knew how to use acids to etch designs on shells.

All these ideas and many more were available to the Yumans, for they were great travelers, visiting the Hohokam and learning of their accomplishments. Indeed, they had obviously borrowed their corn, beans, and squash from that people, for the varieties and species that the Yumans used were exactly the same as those of the Hohokam. Their pottery is even a poor imitation of the finer product of the peoples on the Gila and Salt rivers. The Yumans' travels also took them to the adjacent Pueblo lands, where they saw people living in snug stone houses with rooms set aside for granaries where a whole year's supply of corn was usually held in reserve for time of famine. Yet none of the things they came into contact with stimulated the Yumans to emulate such achievements.

Yuman Personality

They simply did not feel moved to work hard, dig canals, and irrigate large areas to be well fed. They did not feel any urge to build either great adobe compounds or even snug little adobe houses, much less strong and secure stone houses. The physical environment contained the raw materials for doing all of these things; and the ideas were available in adjacent areas. The Yumans knew those adjacent peoples and their way of life. They simply did not choose to live a kind of life other than the one that they had. This choice meant that food production was on a practically day-to-day level and that everyone had to participate in harvesting it. There was no dependable surplus, no political organization to channel a surplus to a creative few. The Yumans simply went along for thousands of years little changed in way of life. Perhaps, then, the Yumans were simply inferior genetically, mentally limited in some way. No one who has worked with these people in modern times has ever thought so, though. They are a lively, alert, often humorous, and intellectually curious people.

This leaves us with no apparent answer to the discrepancy between the development in Egypt and in its American counterpart. The physical environment is very much alike and able people occupied both areas for sufficiently long periods of time to have been exposed to earlier climates more favorable than the present one and to have undergone the stimulus of the great climatic change at the end of the glacial age—with accompanying rising sea levels leading to the filling of river valleys slowly with silt and thus creating broader and broader flood plains subject to annual overflow. In one area, the idea of agriculture was borrowed from adjacent people and on this agricultural base a great civilization was built. In the other, the idea of agriculture was borrowed, but very feebly developed, and very little progress was made toward civilization.

The Element of Time

Could it be that the development of the idea of agriculture takes a great deal of time? After all, Egypt did not spring into greatness overnight, and neither did any of the Mesopotamian centers. Widely over the Near East the beginnings of agriculture are being found to go back to about 8000 B.C. Agriculture-village ways of life existed for nearly five thousand years before the appearance of cities, states, and empires, and of arts and science and all the other marks of the growth of ideas and populations. Perhaps, then, the trouble in the American Egypt was that there simply had not been sufficient time of exposure for the ideas really to take root and develop.

The appearance of agriculture in the southwestern part of the United States is dated now as about 2000 B.C. This is the earliest find now known, and it is in southern New Mexico, a considerable distance from the Colorado River. Probably it was a good deal later that irrigation agriculture became established in the Gila and Salt river valleys adjacent to the Colorado River area. An informed guess would place this development about the time of Christ. Some time thereafter, the Yumans must have obtained their agriculture from the Hohokam people. The time lags may have been on this order: 2000 B.C. for the appearance of agriculture in New Mexico; 1 B.C. for the appearance of irrigation agriculture in the Hohokam area; and perhaps A.D. 500 for the appearance of agriculture on the Colorado. The Yumans are unlikely to have had more than a thousand years to develop the idea of agriculture before the Spanish first saw them about 1540, and the time may well have been shorter. It takes time for ideas to spread, to take root and grow, and the number of years involved here does not seem to have been enough time.

It is easy to find in history abundant testimony to show that ideas usually spread slowly. Japan, for example, as late as A.D. 500 lacked writing, despite its proximity to China where civilization had been flourishing for some two thousand years. Japan is an equally good example of the rapidity with which cultural change can occur in a given geographical setting when the set of the human minds in the area alters from resistant-to-change to avid-for-change. The problem for the American Egypt really finally comes down to the question, what was the set of the Yuman mind?

The Yuman Value System

The Yuman people were from our point of view of a peculiar turn of mind: they did not value the material comforts of life as much. As we have noted, they were courageous, curious, and humorous, but they seem not to have been at all avaricious. Since in the Yuman view of the world, material wealth did not count for much, men were not admired for the size of their houses, the extent of their fields, or for the accumulation of any kind of wealth. There was some respect paid to men of prowess in battle, but the greatest distinction—the thing most desired—among the Yumans was good dreams! The powerful dreamer was the fortunate man. It is difficult for us to understand their psychology, but their descendants have been equally at a loss with the modern Western obsession with material things. Part of what is written off as the Yuman "lack of progress" in the prewhite period, as well as in the postcontact period, is probably best understood as a result of their failure to fit into a pattern of progress that necessitates hard work to acquire more food and goods to support more people, who in turn both produce and require more goods and produce more people. It is almost as if the Yumans had looked at the consequence of stepping on the escalator that

leads to civilization and decided that it looked like a treadmill, and so decided against it.

There were features in their way of life that reinforced such a negative attitude toward the material aspect of life. At an individual's death, all of his property was destroyed with him. Since the Yumans practiced cremation, all a man's belongings were burned with the body—nothing was kept to remind the family of the deceased.* But why accumulate property if at death it is all to be destroyed? In recent times, fine horses were killed, and expensive saddles bought with half a lifetime's savings have gone up in smoke.

There was no very good reason to work hard at preparing large fields either. Property was largely communal. If you had a very fine crop of corn, you could expect all of your relatives and friends and neighbors to drop in to admire it and help you eat it up. The rules of hospitality demanded that you cheerfully supply all comers so long as the crop lasted. If there was to be no surplus for your family, no matter how hard you worked, what use was there in working hard?

The Yumans therefore went on living very much in the same simple economic way that their forefathers had lived for generations uncounted, gathering the wild roots and seeds and game that nature provided. Even though food was shared quite freely, there were very few people to share it with. The sharing with the one or two families that formed part of your band or branch of the tribe was a small burden whose compensation was the knowledge that when you were low in food and the other families had had good luck, you were automatically taken care of.

With innovation in agriculture, there was a potential increase in the number of people due to the

---

* If to you this seems contrary to human nature, your instinct is right. An old Mohave when telling me of this custom also told me of his mother's request that when she was gone they not destroy the metate, her grinding stone, on which she had ground the meal for the daily bread for her family all of her life. "Keep it to remember me," she said. In complete breach of tribal tradition, but in complete keeping with the universal human need for loving memory, her son had kept the stone.

potential increase in food. Increase in numbers would make sharing more burdensome, but better agriculture would also reduce the need to share. Nonetheless, the carry-over of old ways of life, combined with a generally unworldly, nonmaterial outlook slowed the rate of change. The cataclysmic arrival of the white man ended slow change and substituted the white man's ways. Had there been the time, it is possible that the lower Colorado would have seen the steady growth of population density, increased clearing of land, the addition of irrigation, the growth of communal effort in digging canals, the accompanying growth of political and social institutions, the appearance of genuine political leaders, and the slow growth from villages to towns to cities, and possibly to empire.

Would there then have been a duplication of Egypt in America had there been a period of perhaps five thousands years when the Yumans were left undisturbed to work out their own development of the application of agriculture in a river valley oasis? We can probably predict that there would have been growth of population and the appearance of cities and arts. We surely could not expect an Egyptian cast to the development, but rather something utterly different. Just what the social, political, and economic structures might have been and just what kind and development of arts would have occurred, we cannot possibly predict. This illustration can only show us that similar environments need not produce similar things; that the factors that must be considered are human, cultural, and historical, as well as physical; and that the time element is one of enormous importance. In the Yuman case, time was short and their degree of contact was slight. Perhaps their liking for warfare prevented adjacent advanced people from invading their territory and forcibly introducing new ideas. History would probably have been different if the Aztecs with their organized military might had lived near Tucson and Phoenix. But that is the point. It was not what the physical environment was, but what ideas existed in and adjacent to it that seem to have been the determining causes.

THE COLORADO RIVER VALLEY TODAY

What, then, has happened in the lower Colorado River valley, now that we have taken it over? Has it become another Egypt, a center of culture and population growth, of invention and of the arts? Where are the universities, the great monumental art works, the museums, the libraries? There are none in the lower Colorado River valley today, though there are some in adjacent Arizona.

The Southern California Desert

The American development of California centered on San Francisco and Sacramento, having been drawn there by gold. That area became the early center of population and here was located the capital, the state university, the first major city. It was the center of culture, learning, and finance. Southern California, until the twentieth century, remained a sleepy sun-soaked backwater of the economic and social currents flowing into California. The desert land of the Imperial Valley and the Colorado River was the backwater beyond the backwater. Central California boomed in the 1850s; southern California began its explosive growth after 1900; the desert land of California did not begin to boom until the 1950s.

The development of the land has been relatively slow. The base of development has been agricultural, with irrigation dependent on water from the Colorado River. Large stretches of the Colorado River valley were set aside as reservations for the Indians. The largest section of open land lay in the Imperial Valley, that great depression, 50 miles by 100 miles, with its floor 250 feet below sea level. When the white man first saw this area, the valley was dry and the low spot in the valley was covered with a deposit of salt. Modern evidence shows that only a few hundred years earlier the valley had been full of water as a result of an overflow of the Colorado River that had filled the depression with fresh water. At that time the Yuman Indians and others moved into the desert to live on the shores of this great lake. This we know from the remains of

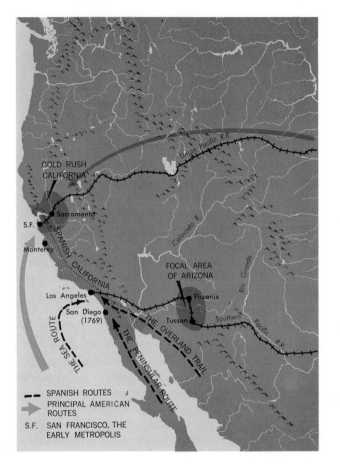

Map 2-8 Development of the Low Desert in the Post-Columbian Period

The Spanish reached California both by land and by sea. To them the Colorado Desert was a formidable barrier to be crossed hastily. Almost their only attempt at settlement in it centered on Yuma, where they wished to hold the strategic river crossing, and at El Paso and Tucson, frontier outposts guarding the route to Santa Fe. American interest early centered on the San Francisco–Sacramento area, the gateway to the all-important gold fields. Only after a century of contact has attention begun to shift toward the enormously productive and scenically attractive desert regions of California. Arizona developed in quite the opposite manner. The earliest center of settlement was in the hot, dry, low desert and steppe country around Phoenix and Tucson.

their camps found on the abandoned beaches in this desert area.

The first Europeans considered this area a dangerous desert that was extremely difficult to cross. For the Spanish and the Americans it was an obstacle to the overland route to California. Later the American railroads pushed across it, following a route around the salt flats at an elevation at times below sea level. The appearance of modern transportation changed the utility of the area; suddenly its products could be marketed. The first product was the salt itself, lying on the floor of the ancient lake, available for the scooping up and exportable by loading on the adjacent railroad.

At times of high water there was a weak flow from the Colorado River toward the Imperial Valley. This was just sufficient to fill the ancient channel of the river that looped south into Mexico and then turned northwest toward the valley. The flow was too feeble to reach the valley floor, but it was sufficient to support a grove of mesquite trees and some standing water in the southern end of the valley, at a place marked on the early maps as the "Blue Lakes." With the coming of the railroad and the growth of population in California at the end of the nineteenth century, and with a developing market in the East, men looked more appraisingly at the vast expanse of gently sloping alluvial land of the Imperial Valley and the almost frost-free climate. They saw it with the eyes of agriculturally minded, commercially minded people, for they now had the technical means to develop it and to move the produce to distant markets.

The natural path of the waterway was opened up, canals were dug, and header gates installed. Thousands of acres of land were soon producing crops under the desert sun. The intensity of solar energy, available almost every day in the year because of a nearly 365-day frost-free growing season, made it possible to produce many crops in great abundance. Winter crops could be followed by summer crops; sometimes the land could be made to yield three crops in a year. When the soil was put into alfalfa, it was found that ten crops per year could be taken off the land. To the men of our modern Western culture, this looked like a plant-producing situation of almost unlimited productivity requiring only transportation adequate to link it to the consuming areas. Once the productive areas of the East could afford the luxury of fresh vegetables in winter, and exotic fruits all year round, the Imperial Valley became a virtual bonanza. (See Table 2–1.)

Table 2-1 The Productivity of a Great Oasis: The Imperial Valley

(area under irrigation, 435,664 acres;
yield per acre, over $380)

Million-dollar Crops (in round numbers)

Asparagus	$ 1,500,000	Lettuce	$15,750,000
Barley	7,250,000	Onions	1,000,000
Cantaloupes	3,750,000	Pasture	2,500,000
Carrots	5,000,000	Sorghum	2,750,000
Cotton lint	23,000,000	Sugar beets	14,250,000
Cotton seed	2,000,000	Tomatoes	3,750,000
Flax seed	1,250,000	Watermelons	2,000,000
Alfalfa hay	20,000,000	Seed crops	5,500,000

Summary of Production, 1961

Field crops	$ 74,685,000
Vegetable crops	35,643,800
Livestock and poultry	48,888,620
Fruit and Nut	882,800
Seed crops	5,685,644
Apiary products	412,900
	$166,198,764

The wealth thus produced on the land did not stay in the valley, however; most of it flowed out. The development was one of large-scale properties, usually owned by men with considerable capital who employed others to manage their farms, which were run with a largely shifting labor population that was often foreign. The result was that there was little improvement on the land to show for the wealth that the land was producing. The fine homes were "on the coast" or "in the East." The valley was extremely hot in summer and dusty at all times and much of it was a dreary desert landscape that did not appeal to the recent emigrants from the beautiful, green, tree-filled land of the East. Consequently, no one felt an interest in promoting great universities, beautiful cities, or other evidences of flourishing civilization in the Imperial Valley.

Today, the desert has been "discovered." On the west side of the Imperial Valley lie such resorts as Palm Springs and Borrego Valley. Yuma, once considered unlivable, is now a fashionable winter resort. The bright, warm sunny days and cool, pleasant nights make it a most desirable area for winter resorts. The desert scenery, instead of being considered dreary, is now captured on canvas. The desert is eagerly sought after for winter homes, while air conditioning has become ever more prevalent and comfort in the area is no longer limited to the winter time. As men's ideas about the desert continue to change in the future, the vast oasis we call the Imperial Valley will change, too.

The future of the Imperial Valley will not, of course, be Egyptian, for the cultural background is American and features an industrial-type farm management, which makes a maximum use of machinery. In Egypt land is still concentrated in the hands of the few. There is an immense base of poor and uneducated, and hence unskilled, men on the land; therefore labor tends to be accomplished by unaided manpower. Further, Egypt has not yet become such a highly productive nation that it has a market for specialty crops. The lower Colorado River region, on the other hand, with an educated people with a high standard of living—and with increasing mechanization removing the drudge labor from farming—is likely to continue to attract, both for its productivity and for its scenery and winterless climate, a permanent settlement of families with good incomes who will demand schools and all else needed to make this a cultural center.

Aerial View of Palm Springs, California. Palm Springs bills itself as the winter golf and swimming-pool capital of the world. Its development has been that of a boom town since the warm, sunny climate and stark scenery of the desert gained in public appreciation in the mid-twentieth century. *Palm Springs Chamber of Commerce.*

The Southern Arizona Desert

The low desert, such as that found in the lower Colorado and Imperial Valley area, also extends eastward up the Gila and the Salt rivers of southern Arizona. These valleys were the home of the Hohokam people who used great canals to irrigate miles of the desert and were clearly many steps ahead of the Yumans. It is significant that they are closer to Mexico, in whose southern part lay one of the great centers of civilization in pre-Columbian America. Proximity to ideas, possession of the ideas for a longer time and greater receptivity to them—perhaps even colonization by a more advanced people—had placed these peoples much farther on the road toward civilization. Probably the most important factor was that they lay at the end of the Sonoran Desert closest to the center of cultural growth and stimulus in the Mexican area.

Some catastrophe, however, had greatly reduced these people just before the arrival of the Spaniards. It seems likely that the eruption of raiding, warlike nomadic peoples, such as the Apache and the Nav-

aho, had nearly destroyed them. Settled farming people always have difficulty with the nomads; one raid can destroy a year's work in the corn fields, and the nomads can melt into the surrounding desert leaving their victims faced with virtual starvation. Compare the conquest of the Sahara by the camel nomads. But some other cause may also have intervened; for example, a new disease introduced into an unprepared population can quickly reduce it to 10 percent of its original size. Had this happened sometime after 1520, the time of the Spanish arrival in Mexico, the dense population of the Hohokam area could well have been reduced to the situation that the first explorers recorded.

The Spanish evaluation of these same Southwestern lands tells much, for they did little with any part of them. They sent land and sea expeditions north from Mexico in 1540. The land expedition reached the Colorado River, but the land was not reported as offering great opportunity. It was a marginal land, far from the Spanish centers of interest in Mexico and Peru where there were large populations of civilized natives and great sources of gold and silver. The low, hot desert lands were only something to get across on the way to the frontier outposts of Santa Fe and Monterey, the mission frontier in California. Missionary zeal was the major driving force that led to settlement. The land in what was to become southern Arizona and adjacent New Mexico and on over to El Paso was viewed as no asset. It was too dry, too hot, and too far away; it remained a poor missionary and political frontier.

The early American view of the situation was not too different at first, occasional reports stressing the desert character of the land. Only a few of the people on the way to California during the gold-rush days of 1849 took the southern route that led to Santa Fe and then south through southern Arizona and across the desert from Yuma to California. The surveys for the railroads in the 1860s, however, found that there was a feasible low-level route through this southern country. A railroad was pushed through, linking this area with the East; that it also linked this southern Arizona desert country with the West was at the time relatively unimportant. The West was not populous, and it did not need to import agricultural produce or raw materials.

On the mile-high Colorado plateau of northern Arizona, not only were the winters cold, but the fierce Navaho and Apache were present. They were as great a block to settlement for a time, as were the Iroquois in the East in an earlier time. This temporary barrier left as the major open land at this time the southern part of Arizona. Here was a low-latitude desert, thinly settled by a peaceful people and marked by the lines of a great irrigation system some of whose abandoned canals could still be used. The arrival of the railroad made possible the shipment of the produce of such a land to the rapidly industrializing East. The productivity of the East allowed the purchasing of the type of crop that could be grown in this immense oasis, watered by the Gila and the Salt rivers. The physical geography had not changed a bit, but southern Arizona was no longer too far, too hot, and too dry to be an active and productive part of the nation.

For these reasons—the location of hostile Indians principally in the north and the arrival of the railroad on the irrigable plains located in the south— it was natural that the southern part of Arizona developed first. Arizona became a state in 1912; its capital was located at Phoenix in the center of the irrigated area, and the state university was begun at Tucson. It was southern Arizona that had become the center of population, government, productivity, and culture. There was less absentee ownership and less distant managership of the land than in the Imperial Valley. Southern Arizona with its populous and cultured oases on the Gila and Salt rivers, then, has an entirely different aspect to it than the oases of the Imperial Valley and the Colorado River valley, which are both far from the center of early growth and development in California.

What might have happened had the state boundaries been laid out differently? Suppose the southern California desert had been detached from the rest of that state and included within Arizona's borders. Suppose the western boundary of that hypothetical state had been along the ridge of the peninsular range just west of the Imperial Valley. Would the Colorado River valley and the Imperial Valley then have had a development more like that of southern Arizona? Would there have been a Tucson at Yuma and a Phoenix in the Imperial Valley? Would Yuma, as a location midway between the two great oases, have been chosen as the state capital; would it early have assumed an important social and political cultural role in the Southwest? This seems possible. Clearly, we cannot now know in detail what would have happened, but we can be sure that things would be different. The human assessment of the land and the type of growth and development there would have varied depending on how even the minor subdivisions within the national state were drawn.

So much then for the element of value judgment and the use of the low desert countries of the Southwest. The setting is not greatly different from that of the Fertile Crescent of the Old World. An Egyptian environment (the lower Colorado) lay at one end of the crescent. At the other lay a Mesopotamia with the Gila and the Salt taking the place of the Tigris and Euphrates. To the north of this "Mesopotamia" lay highlands, just as in the Old World. The physical setting, though on a smaller scale, is sufficiently similar to have provided the physical challenges that are found in the seat of the origin of civilization in the Old World. The differences, therefore, were not determined by the physical geography.

THE ARID WEST

If a larger view is taken of the arid West in America, a similar picture comes into focus. This is a vast region. It extends from the Sierra Nevadas to the Rocky Mountains and almost from the present-day Canadian border to far below the Mexican border. This is the American equivalent of arid inner Asia. Within the United States the northern part is called the Great Basin. It centers on the state of Utah but includes most of Nevada and parts of Oregon, Washington, and Idaho. This is an area of irregularly distributed, short mountain ranges, and the level of the land is high. South of the Great Basin lies the Colorado plateau country. This again is high land, less mountainous but characterized by such immense features as the Grand Canyon, making this a rugged land of great relief. The region's interior location, shut off from moist winds by the Sierra Nevadas to the west and the Rockies to the east, makes for aridity. Yet the differences of elevation are so great that it is a land of great contrast in short distances. It is possible to start in one of the broad basins in a condition of extreme aridity and by ascending one of the adjacent mountain ranges to pass from extremely sparse sagebrush-covered land into a zone of scrubby pinyon pine, then on into a zone of large Western yellow pine, and finally into an alpine meadowland with running streams, aspen, and rolling green meadows. Certainly not a desert situation! Sometimes sizable streams come down from these high mountains and create oases in the desert.

Pre-Columbian Life

In the Great Basin before 1500 the way of life was that of hunting and gathering. Small bands moved intermittently about the land gathering roots and seeds and catching small game. These people have been variously designated as seed gatherers, unspecialized hunters and gatherers, and as the Desert Culture people. All these terms describe much the same thing. The people who occupied most of this territory were living a very simple life, wandering in small bands, gathering wild seeds and roots and nuts, and doing some hunting. But their way of life was as unspecialized as possible. If they had any specialty, it was in the gathering of plant foods, hence the designation seed gatherers. They were very close to our theoretical man on the hypothetical earth. It is probable that their way of life was very close to that of all mankind in the early stages of man's development. We know that they had been living like this for tens of thousands of years. The people of the plateau region followed this same way of life until about the time of Christ. They then rapidly changed over to the agricultural town-dwellers way of life. The people of the adjacent Great Basin did not change.

Why in this vast area did man cling so long to so simple a way of life? Was it the difficult aridity, the high elevation with its numbing winter cold, and the summers with their hot days? But what about the stimulation of the greatly varied environments to be found from the desert basin floors to the alpine mountain environments? Why did people on the Colorado plateau suddenly change? Why did the wonderful oasis at Salt Lake City not seem as useful to these people as it did to the Mormons? And, after all, this area is not too different from the lands to the north of the mountains that divide inner Asia from southern Asia. Along the oases created by streams coming down from the high mountains and flowing toward the Caspian and the Aral seas and down into the desert heart of the Tarim basin, great cities flourished for thousands of years. Again the physical environment, forbidding as the desert stretches are, is an insufficient answer. If we brush aside the question of the potentiality of the human stock as unanswerable, what reason can we find? What could be done in such an area?

If we look at the rest of the world we see considerable range of possibility. In Australia in the period prior to 1500, a comparable area was occupied by people with a similar level of culture. In South Africa the same situation prevailed, for the cattle herding was clearly a relatively late introduction. In North Africa and Arabia and inner Asia settled people practiced agriculture wherever water allowed, and pastoral nomads moved herds about over the rest of the land. Why was there none of this in Australia and in North America and little of it in South America and South Africa?

It is notable that in all of these cases the distance from centers of ideas is of significance. South Africa was far from the active axis of civilization that stretched from Egypt to China. The inner Asian area lay on the routes that led from one of these areas to another. Australia lay completely out of touch with all of the activities of the developing civilization of the world, though as we will see, mere distance is an insufficient answer even there.

In America, the centers of growth lay in Middle America. Although northward extensions of this American civilization strongly influenced the Gila-Salt valleys and the Colorado plateau, they barely reached the Great Basin (see Map 2–7). The Great Basin people lay beyond the zone of effective reach of these ideas. Agricultural beginnings spread into the edge of the Great Basin, but about A.D. 1000 raiding peoples appeared and the farming folk withdrew. The people of the Great Basin remained hunters and gatherers because they were too far from any of the currents of ideas and change to benefit. Not that ideas never reached them, but the contact was not long sustained and meaningful enough for them to change their way of life, a long and slow business.

Moreover, mere environmental stimulus will not do. The people of the Great Basin faced extraordinarily stimulating conditions. During glacial times the Great Basin contained many lakes (see Map 2–9). Fish, waterbirds, and a host of aquatic plants were available to these people, and they used them. With the end of the glacial period the lakes dried

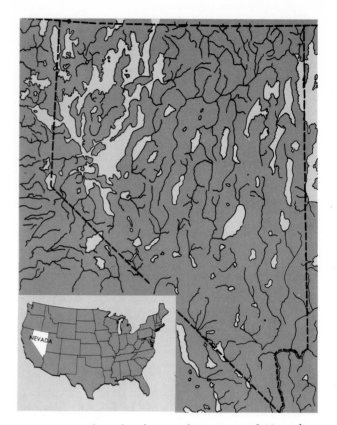

Map 2-9   Pluvial Lakes and Streams of Nevada

The magnitude of the changes that resulted from glacial-rainy periods in the arid lands of the world is demonstrated by this map of the lakes and streams of Nevada during such a period. The area is now one of America's driest. The Great Salt Lake in Utah, Pyramid Lake in Nevada, and Lake Tahoe on the Nevada and California line are the principal remnants of the water bodies shown here. The physical environment of this interior land must have been vastly different prior to the great climatic change that occurred about 10,000 years ago. *Adapted from compilation by Hubbs and Miller.*

up and the whole environment changed drastically. If necessity could compel a people to take up agriculture or change in some way to meet a challenge, these people surely should have changed. The record, however, is one of remarkably little change. Nor were these people subjected to this physical stimulus only once. There were several climatic fluctuations sufficient to change this lake environment greatly. Men were alternately subjected to good and poor environments. However, they ate up the potential domestic animals, such as horses and camels; they did not cultivate the nutritious local plants; nor later in time did they take up the already domesticated plants that their neighbors had. Yet there were numerous oases, and some of them were large enough to have supported towns or cities, even city-states. (Outstanding examples today are Salt Lake City and its adjacent cities in Utah, Reno and Carson City in Nevada, and Denver and Colorado Springs in Colorado.) Nor did these people domesticate any of the available animals. Sheep, elephant, horse, and camel were all present. They could have supplied the base of a pastoral nomadic way of life, but not even a beginning was made.

Agricultural Villages on the Colorado Plateau

South of the Great Basin, on the Colorado plateau and along the Rio Grande River, there are farming peoples. They live in towns and are called the Pueblo people, a name that is the Spanish term for town. The Pueblo people were originally seed gatherers or unspecialized hunters and gatherers wandering over the vast arid Colorado plateau in much the same manner as the people of the Great Basin were living in historic times. Ideas coming up from the south where agriculture had long been established reached these people sufficiently early and with sufficient impact to lead to their changing their way of life.

Earliest agriculture in the Southwest, unquestionably moving northward from Mexico, appears in the rugged mountainous fringes of the Colorado plateau, where increased elevation decreased the temperature and increased the rainfall and aided the possibility of agriculture. Corn cobs from a cave in New Mexico have been dated by radioactive carbon (C–14) as about 4000 years old. By careful site selection such an agriculture could have been spread almost indefinitely into the plateau and Great Basin regions to the north. Eventually this was done to a limited extent. It is noteworthy that

the earliest introduction of agriculture was not in the low hot lands that required the relatively advanced skill of irrigation with canal digging and all the population density and political organization that this monumental application of labor implies. Instead, the beginning was made in the foothill regions where the plots were small and little more than the natural rainwater need be used, enhanced in later time by the selection of field sites that natural run off tended to flood.

With the introduction of the idea of agriculture, a great part of the arid western United States be-

Paiute Woman Seated Outside Her Brush Shelter and Making a Basket, 1873. The racketlike implement on the shelter is a seed beater, and the large flat basket was used to catch the seeds. The small-mouthed basket is pitch-covered, and served as a water bottle. This crude brush shelter was in use in the same area as the Pueblo stone houses and Navaho earth-covered homes. *Smithsonian Institution, Bureau of American Ethnology.*

Navaho Woman at Her Loom in Front of Her Earth-covered Log House, about 1880. *Smithsonian Institution, Bureau of American Ethnology.*

came a potential agricultural region. Potentially this new idea could change the human geography. With agriculture, all the other ways of life could go on with little change. Only a more settled way of life for part of the people during the crop season was required. The return would be large: a relatively certain and large addition of food.

Yet men did not leap at the opportunity, for agriculture did not become established on the plateau region until after the time of Christ—there was a 2000 year lag. This situation is somewhat like that of the Yumans. There it is clear that a human decision was made; the environment certainly did not make it. Perhaps the weakest part of the discussion of the Yumans was the attempt to show that they are not inherently (genetically) inferior people: It could be said that since they never had accomplished anything it was evident that they could not. With the plateau people, however, we

can test such reasoning. For many thousands of years they had lived as hunters and gatherers; they were among the cultural laggards of the world. About 4000 years ago, ideas began to reach the area to the south of them, and for 2000 years the plateau people took no advantage of the new opportunity.

For some 2000 years, therefore, their refusal could well have been used to argue that there must be something genetically lacking. They then took up these ideas with such a spurt of energy that they shortly developed their own distinctive culture, rapidly changed in numerous ways, and went from among the simplest cultural people in the Southwest in pre-Columbian times to the culturally advanced Indian group known to us today as the Pueblo people.

Had our assessment of the geography and the people been made before 1000 B.C. we might have said that the environment of these arid high pla-

Walpi Pueblo, Arizona, 1879. This photograph shows the multistoried building of the Pueblos, with its ladders for access, its old-style doorways, and a rabbit-fur robe hanging near the top of the ladder. *Smithsonian Institution, Bureau of American Ethnology.*

teaus prevented the development of culture and the growth of populations, and that the one thing that would *not* develop here would be a town-dwelling society. Another person looking at the lagging status of these people might have suggested that they were simply inferior human types. Yet at 1000 A.D. town-dwelling societies with highly developed skills in agriculture and pottery and with a rich ceremonial life were flourishing in these very regions and among these very same people.

Parallels to this situation are numerous. The well-known case of the Japanese spurt in modern technological development in the late nineteenth century—a conscious decision to end their isolation from the advances of the West—is a good case in modern time of the role of human decision in accepting or rejecting ideas. The Europeans have also been excellent examples of peoples who were cultural tarriers at various times. The Greeks lagged behind the Egyptians, the Romans lagged behind the Greeks, and the Britons lagged behind the Romans. Yet each of these people learned from, and eventually exceeded, the people who had once been far ahead of them in cultural accomplishment. Even the 2000 year lag in the spread of agriculture in our Southwest from the area to the south of the Colorado plateau onto the plateau itself, can easily be matched. In Europe, cities were flourishing south of the Alps by 1000 B.C., but there were none north of the Rhine until almost A.D. 1000. Bronze, which appears in the Near East about 2500 B.C., took a full 1000 years to spread into northwest Europe.

There is no great climatic change at the time the Pueblo people took up agriculture. The shift from the glacial climates was then far in the past, and the extinction of the last of the great grazing animals, such as horses and camels, was also so far back in time that there probably remained not even a traditional memory of them. The arid to semiarid environment had long been fixed, as had the hunting and gathering way of life. Curiously, although agricultural ideas had been available to the south for 2000 years, agricultural beginnings appeared in the area where Utah, Colorado, Arizona, and New

Mexico share a common boundary point—the Four Corners region—300 miles to the north of the former agricultural boundary. If the impulse to begin farming came from the south, why does it first appear way up at the Four Corners region? Is this perhaps one of those accidents of history that we simply happen to have the earliest record here and have not found the still earlier one farther to the south? On this point we can get a cross check by looking at the plants that the people used.

Evidence from Domesticated Plants

To the south the agricultural beginnings were made with minute, primitive forms of maize. In the north the agricultural beginnings were made with a small but developed maize. In the south, the characteristic bean was the *tepary* bean; in the north, the bean used was the common bean. The pumpkin, or squash, also was probably different in the north and in the south. Such differences in plants used are difficult to explain; they certainly

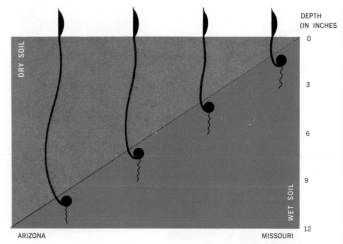

Figure 2-1 Depth to Moist Soil and Planting Depth. The decrease in rainfall as one moves westward from Missouri to Arizona is reflected in this schematic cross section. Arizona and Colorado are areas of weak winter and spring precipitation. The result is an increasing depth to moist ground at the time of spring planting. The gradual transition is of the type that would produce a plant adapted to floodwater farming on the semiarid high plateaus of the American Southwest.

suggest that the people in the Four Corners region were getting their agriculture from someone other than their southern neighbors. But where?

Again the plants are helpful. The corn that the people in the plateau region used had some very curious qualities. That used by the Hopi is perhaps the extreme example: this corn, when planted at a depth of 12 inches, is able to extend its shoot to the surface and make a normal growth. Normal corn planted at such a depth would be totally unable to reach the surface of the ground. In the arid Southwest, corn must be planted as deep as this, since at the beginning of the growing season that is where the moist soil is.

Somehow, somewhere, these plants were gradually adapted to conditions of increasing aridity that required their being planted deeper and deeper in the soil. One region that has just these characteristics is the Great Plains. On their eastern border the rainfall is about 40 inches. There is a steady decrease westward to about 10 inches. If agriculture spread slowly westward up the major river valleys of the plains, the plants would be grown under conditions of increasing aridity, and this would give a pathway leading toward the Four Corners region. Plants following this route would be gradually adapted to increasing aridity and eventually could supply the people of the plateau with plants adapted to the extremely difficult conditions of that area.

One might reason deterministically that the route from the Mississippi River to the foot of the Rockies formed a natural transition area, and hence that agriculture spread along this route; while the transition from the lowlands of the Sonoran Desert to the Colorado plateau is quite abrupt, and plants coming up against this barrier would have suddenly met a change in conditions for which there was no transitional zone. Although there is some fact in this, it is a deceptively easy explanation and is true only in part.

As a test case, one can take tepary beans from the low desert and grow them on the arid plateau. With careful selection of sites even without irrigation, all of the low desert plants could be grown in the oases throughout the Great Basin. It is less a matter of what the environment offered than which of the environmental offerings man chose to use.

Strong Influences Suggested by Great Change over a Brief Period

The change on the plateau was a dramatically sudden and far-reaching one. Up to the time of Christ, the people who were to be known to us as the Pueblo people were living in small bands, hunting and gathering in their ancient way. Shortly thereafter agricultural beginnings were made, pottery appears, and house types begin to change. The old crude shelters of grass and brush and the ancient semisubterranean houses are replaced by surface houses that are made of stone laid in mud for mortar. This is a larger change than is usually thought.

Houses on the Colorado plateau could be either semisubterranean or surface types and made of log, stone, or grass. The environment apparently demanded no one type. In an arid region marked by bitter cold in winter, the semisubterranean house would have had great advantages. It would be snug and warm in winter and if there were not too much moisture, it would stay dry. The log house, on the surface and well insulated with a thick layer of earth, would also be snug, dry, and warm. The least desirable in such a cold winter climate would be the grass-thatched flimsy shelter that probably was used throughout most of the arid West for tens of thousands of years.

The stone house that seems so "natural" to the arid regions was late to appear, developed rapidly, and included some odd features. The first stone houses are thought to have been granaries or store rooms built on the surface by some of the early agriculturalists. Soon they were being built in groups, and shortly thereafter they were being lived in. Little groups of small rooms linked together into "L" and rectangular shapes soon dotted the plateau region and were spread far north, well into Utah.

There were no stone houses among the Indian peoples to the west, north, or east of the Southwest, but stone houses *are* characteristic of Mexico. This suggests that the idea may well have been introduced from that direction rather than developed locally.

The plant evidence suggests early introductions both from the south and from the east. Later, it is clear there were large cultural introductions from the south. These included such things as the cotton plant, ceremonial ball courts, and such direct imports as copper bells manufactured in Mexico. It appears that after a long period during which ideas did not move into the plateau region at all, a critical point was reached and thereafter ideas flooded in. Once this initial change toward a settled way of life was made, the way was open to the acceptance of many ideas that had long been available on the southern edge of the plateau. The result was the Pueblo culture.

The Pueblos are composed of several people who are physically and linguistically distinct, but who share a common culture. They are to be thought of as much like the German-French-Italian composition of Switzerland, except that the Pueblos do not develop a national unity. The Hopi are a very small people physically and are Uto Aztecan in speech. Their relatives are in the Great Basin. The other Pueblo people are taller, and some of the Rio Grande people are related in speech to some of the Great Plains tribes. Like the plant evidence this suggests that men and ideas from the plains and from the low deserts met on the Colorado plateau and sparked the flame of culture change.

We know that ideas were coming in to the Southwest from the south where building in stone was a well-developed characteristic. Along with the ideas of agriculture, pottery, cotton, weaving, and related ideas reaching the plateau people by various routes, there probably was brought in the idea of building in stone. Then, when the raiding peoples appeared— the Navaho and Apache—the Pueblo people reacted by building larger and more compactly grouped stone dwellings until the classic Pueblo fortress apartment-house type of dwelling was evolved. The conclusion to be drawn therefore shifts from that of a direct reaction to a dry environment where it is natural to build in stone to an interpretation which suggests that the idea itself was the important determinant, and that secondarily the politico-economic situation was significant. The fact that the physical environment could supply large quantities of layered sandstone easily broken into bricklike shapes—and hence readily used for construction purposes—was accordingly only of tertiary importance.

Just how these arid-land seed gatherers were jolted out of their millenia-long wandering way of life, induced to take up agriculture in this difficult region, taught to build stone houses, and soon brought to live in towns has never been satisfactorily answered. From the evidence of slowness of change elsewhere, for example among the Yuma and the Great Basin tribes, one may suspect extremely strong influences from outside. Since the amount and rate of change are comparable to the changes that occurred in early Egypt under Mesopotamian influence, comparable influences seem likely to have been operative in the Southwest. And since the center of American cultural growth was in Middle America, these influences must have come from there by various routes.

The results were spectacular. Agriculture was begun about the first century A.D. Stone houses appeared shortly thereafter, and the houses almost at once are built in groups. By A.D. 1000 the plateau country had little agricultural settlements scattered all over it, and thereafter the area of settlement shrank southward and the settlements became larger, while the buildings became unified and fortified. Some of the best agricultural land in the Southwest was abandoned, and some of the remnants of the settled people, the Hopi for instance, ended up on very marginal land.

The Great Drought

This shrinkage, with migrations of tribes from place to place, is often attributed to the great drought that occurred at the end of the thirteenth

Tree Rings from a Douglas Fir from New Mexico. The great variation in ring width is related to growth conditions. In the Southwest, the critical factor is usually moisture. There was a period of great drought from 1276 to 1299, and a much greater drought between 1338 and 1352. *H. S. Gladwin.*

(*Below*) Specimen of a Tree (charcoal) from Gila Pueblo, Arizona, Dated by Its Ring Pattern at A.D. 1285. *H. S. Gladwin.*

century. This is a typically environmental deterministic explanation and deserves examination.

There was a drought period at the end of the thirteenth century; we know both the time and duration of this drought from the study of tree rings. Trees depend on the weather for their growth: for arctic trees summer warmth is critical; for arid-land trees moisture is critical, and as it turns out it is the winter moisture that is the most important kind for the coniferous trees in our Southwest. Good years are marked by wide rings; poor years by thin rings. Within an area experiencing similar weather, trees growing under similar conditions—preferably on dry hillsides where even small variations would affect the tree's growth—should show similar sequences of good and bad years by similar sequences of thick and thin rings. This analysis has been utilized to build a calendar for the Southwest that is also a record of past weather. Living trees provide a starting point, for their last ring formed the year they were cut. The rings of a 200-year-old tree can be matched at its early end with a log from an early building. Its rings can be overlapped onto a log from a prehistoric building, and so on.

Such a tree-ring calendar has been assembled that reaches back almost two thousand years. It shows many periods of drought, a notable one occurring during the last quarter of the thirteenth century. This was also a time of great unrest among the Pueblo peoples. Great Pueblos were abandoned and whole areas such as the Mesa Verde vacated. The conclusion is usually drawn that the great drought was the cause: Is this really so?

First, it should be noted that the drought at the end of the thirteenth century was broken by some good years. Second, there were other periods of severe drought in the past. Note in the accompanying illustration the severe drought at 1338 to 1352. Finally, the weather that is critical for tree growth in the Southwest is winter weather. Moisture at that time supplies the ground water for tree growth in spring. For the Southwestern Indian agriculture the critical rains are the late summer rains that must come if the corn is to make a crop. These two periods of rain in the Southwest come from quite separate weather systems. The winter rains come from cyclonic storms along the polar front. The summer rains are thunderstorms which result from in-drafts of air from the Gulf of Mexico.

These two air systems do not necessarily correlate: wet winters need not be followed by wet summers. Hence a wet winter that produced a wide ring on a tree might tell little or nothing about the summer rainfall that would determine the success of the Indians' corn crop. In the light of all of this, why is the idea clung to that the Great Drought caused the abandonment of much of the Southwest?

Man always seeks an answer to problems. He seizes quickly any apparent correlation as an answer. Once an answer has been advanced it tends to become *the* answer. New evidence and more critical treatment of the old evidence then has an uphill fight. It must displace an idea that already satisfies the need for an explanation. Mankind resists such change; for example, man resisted the ideas that the earth is round and that the earth moved about the sun. Each of these ideas had to displace an earlier idea that seemed to explain the given situation. The new idea was therefore viewed as an unnecessary intrusion into the smoothly operating set of ideas. This kind of resistance to change, even what is obviously to an outsider—change for the better, underlies the long periods of time during which most people have clung to their old ways of life.

When an old idea that has provided a seemingly adequate answer to a problem is displaced, a new answer must be sought. It is established as fact that the idea of an agriculturally based, settled way of life appeared in the semiarid plateau region and spread for nearly a thousand years. Thereafter, an immense shrinkage occurred. Vast areas that men had used for a farming way of life were abandoned. If it was not a climatic change, what then was the cause?

Nomadic Raiders

There are other things besides climatic change that can cause farmers to abandon areas of good land. Nomadic invasions that are beyond the farmers' organized ability to cope with would be one. The Pueblo people had no organization that welded them together; each town stood by itself. They were thus easy marks for an invading people. Any warlike nomadic people entering this environment would have found poorly defended small settlements sprinkled over the landscape, each producing abundant food in the widely scattered good patches of naturally watered land. Raiding these little villages would have provided food for such nomads with little more risk than the raiding of bee hives.

There are warlike, raiding, nomadic people in the Southwest, the Navaho and the Apache. Linguistically these people are Athabascans, and their origin lies in western Canada. The degree of differentiation of their speech from that of their Canadian relatives is not great; therefore, the amount of time that they have been separated from their northern relatives is probably not great.

The Athabascans are hunters. About a thousand years ago hunting or wandering or even driven into the Great Basin or Colorado plateau country, they would have entered a land sprinkled with tiny villages of farming people. If these hunters raided the farmers, the settled people would have been placed under terrible pressure. The unorganized villagers intent on tending their tiny, widely scattered fields could easily be ambushed on their way to or from work; or a raiding band could readily strip a field at harvest time and disappear into the surrounding vast area. Settled people are at the mercy of the hit-and-run tactics of nomadic people. Settlement must be so dense that the nomadic people must face superior numbers, or they will pick off the isolated groups one at a time. As we have seen, in Africa, Egyptian numbers were too great for the nomads, and the settled people dominated; while in the western Sahara, the small oases were dominated by the nomads.

In this type of situation there is an environmental causation of sorts at work. In the arid lands, agriculture can be practiced only on the scattered good spots. This was true in the Negev of Palestine and in the American Southwest, both areas once farmed and then abandoned. In America, land use was based on careful selection of those bits of land where water was naturally concentrated in rocky canyons and spread out over the alluvium at the foot of the hill or in sand patches that allowed little or no water to run off and little water to evaporate. Since favorable spots would be scattered, an agriculture based on such land use must have widely dispersed fields, and the farmers must scatter widely to work their land. In a sense, the environment determines this land use, hence this exposure to ambush. In fact, the land could be used otherwise: for example, irrigation works could be installed. Even minor ones would allow larger areas to be farmed, keeping larger groups of men together and thus lessening their vulnerability to raids. Or if the people had never taken up agriculture, they would not be "sitting ducks" for raiders. The choice lay with man, and the choice had consequences. The physical-environmental "influence" was dependent on man-made choice.

The Pueblo people reacted to the nomadic raids by concentrating into larger groups and by so arranging their houses that they formed a natural fort. Lower floors had no doorways or windows, and entry was by means of ladders that could be pulled up, leaving no easy entry for raiders. But much good land had to be abandoned, and even the biggest fortified apartments were vulnerable, for though the fortress might not be taken, the fields could still be raided. What use is a fort if the food supply cannot be protected? That it was not drought that drove the Pueblo people out of the lands that they abandoned is clear, for they abandoned some of the best lands. The town-dwelling Hopi were driven to settle on some of the poorest agricultural land in northern Arizona. If drought were the cause of abandonment of land, therefore, the Hopi would never be found where they are, and such well-watered lands as the Mesa Verde with its many great pueblos would never have been left to the raiding peoples.

Some Conclusions

In pre-Columbian times, then, the arid West can be seen in part as an area where the degree of development of culture can be viewed almost as directly related to the distance from the major centers where ideas originated in Middle America. The southernmost border of what became the United States had the most advanced culture, the adjacent peoples had lesser degrees of cultural development, and those beyond them were almost untouched by the stream of new ideas and remained simple gatherers. They all occupied arid lands. It was apparently not the aridity, but the access to ideas that was important. The geography of position was more important than the geography of the environment.

Modern-day occupation of the land has reversed things to some extent. The physical environment has not *changed,* but the focal points of cultural growth and stimulus have changed. The available technologies and the views on land use have also altered tremendously. Most of the land has gone from a local subsistence economy to a commercial economy based on specialized goods produced for the great consuming centers in the East. Ideas no longer come from the south, but from the east, and lately from the west. The arid West is no longer as marginal as it once was, but it is still a land of limited use. Is this situation physically determined? Within limits, the answer must be, yes. The shortage of water is decisive now—but it need not always be.

We are in the midst of a technological revolution. Chemistry is struggling with the problem of desalting the sea water at a cost that will make this inexhaustible source available, first for urban uses, and later for agricultural use. Simultaneously, the physicists dream of a solution to the release of atomic energy that may make this water available most anywhere. Should the physicists' dream materialize, the finest plant-factory areas of the world will prove to be the low-latitude deserts where the

Sea-water Conversion. Experimentation is now under way in California at this salt-water conversion plant built jointly by the state's Department of Water Resources and the federal Department of the Interior. This million-gallon-a-day plant near San Diego produces fresh water through a multistage flash distillation process. *California Department of Water Resources.*

growing season is almost 365 days long, the soils are loaded with nutrients, and the control of water through irrigation makes possible the maximum yields of plant materials that can supply the food and technological requirements of the world. The physical environment will not have changed, but our ability to use it will have changed.

The lessons from the American Southwest are these: ideas remain as the primary cause of change —our assessment of the world changes at least potentially with each new idea—and it is these ideas that determine the human use of the physical world, and not the physical environment that determines what man does.

SOUTH AMERICA

The history of the arid land of South America presents both similarities and contrasts with those of North America. The distribution of the lands is normal as to latitude, side of continent, and location in the rain shadow of mountain ranges. The arid area extends over the mountains and into northwest Argentina, where there is a rain shadow, dry land that resembles in many ways the basin and range country of the North American arid region. The shape of the land, however, has given rather special distributions to these dry lands. Thus the Peruvian-Chilean coastal desert is a long narrow ribbon running parallel to the coast and sharply limited inland by the presence of the high Andes Mountains. As with the mid-latitude deserts of North America and Africa, the desert comes right to the coast and there is a cold current offshore. In South America the cold current is very marked in temperature, salinity, and rate of flow, creating a special bioclimatic setting.

In terms of physical geography, the coast of Peru is more like the coast of Lower California and adjacent southern California than any other part of the earth. Points of similarity include a cool current offshore, a strong inversion formed over the cool current and blown onshore to give a high degree of cloud cover and much coastal fog, desert or semidesert conditions right to the coast, increasing sunshine and rising temperatures inland, and better-watered and cooler highlands farther inland. In South America almost all of these factors are heightened in intensity: the water is colder, the mountains higher, the desert lands barer. Nevertheless, the parallel is a close one. Comparisons between the northwest Argentine and the American Southwest are similarly close: both areas are interior dry lands with basins and ranges, hot summers, and cool winters. The question then arises: What has man done with these similar environments? In pre-Columbian America we are presumably dealing with one relatively restricted type of mankind in comparable environments, and are therefore able to hold these variables constant while we try to understand the role of each.

In contrast to the North American dry lands where all the developments that occurred must be viewed as marginal seepage from the Middle American centers of high culture, the South American dry lands of the coast of Peru and of the highlands of Peru and adjacent Bolivia had an advanced civilization. It was a civilization with a long history and many brilliant accomplishments in engineering, art, agriculture, and political and economic organization. The region in some ways is reminiscent of Mesopotamia: a dry land center of cultural and political ferment and growth.

Agriculture was developed in oasislike valleys watered by streams flowing down from the melting snow of the Andes. These streams were most skillfully utilized: the water was spread out over the valley bottoms through the use of canals, and when there was not sufficient land for the available water supply, canals were constructed that carried the water to areas where it could be used. In addition, water that flowed underground was tapped by digging tunnels into the slope: sometimes called horizontal wells. The building of long tunnels with frequent vertical shafts—through which the dirt was removed and which supplied ventilation for the workers—is a characteristic idea these people shared with the agriculturalists of the arid lands of the Near East.

In these valley oases, separated from each other by desert, city-states developed, and at various times one or another came to dominate considerable areas. Culture was also developing on the adjacent highlands, and city-states here too grew into empires. One early empire was based on the great city of Tiahuanaco on the Bolivian plateau. Tiahuanaco art styles for a time influenced much of the Peruvian and Bolvian area and testify to the dominance of these particular people. The situation of highland and lowland, of city-states and empires, of irrigation agriculture and great mud-walled cities is all extremely suggestive of the

Near East. Does this resemblance indicate the determining influence of the physical environment?

One school of thought holds that given this type of environment, as well as the idea of irrigation agriculture, such city-states with their whole structure of highly centralized political control will inevitably arise. It is argued that the building of canals and the control of water requires political control, and control of an absolute nature. We will return to the possible causes of growth of political structure presently. For the moment, note only that here such advanced ideas as lead to cities, states, monumental buildings, and irrigation were present.

In the similar physical geography of North America, none of these things existed. In the coastal desert of Lower California, with its mountainous relatively well-watered central spine from which streams descended toward the coast, a related race of men remained in a primitive hunting and gathering way of life, having virtually no clothes, no houses, no government. The contrast with the coastal desert of South America could hardly be more extreme.

THE INCA EMPIRE

When the Spanish arrived in South America they found the empire of the Incas, comparable in some ways to the Roman Empire. It was momentarily in the throes of internal difficulties resulting from a struggle over the inheritance of the kingship. The Incas were an obscure people who, beginning about A.D. 1000, began building an empire centered on the highland near Cuzco, Peru. The Inca empire was but the latest of a series of such empires in this region. They had a succession of able rulers, and in 500 years they had united the highland and the coastal lowland from southern Ecuador to northern Chile. This domain includes most of what is now Peru, Bolivia, and Chile, excluding the interior hot, wet lowlands and the cold, wet southern part of Chile. The north–south extent of this empire was about a thousand miles. It was connected by two systems of roads; one along the coast and the other lengthwise of the highlands. Messages could be sent great distances at night by a system of signal fires relayed from one mountain top to another. At regular intervals along the roads there were stations housing runners. Messages could be relayed by means of this system with great speed.

The Inca empire was an example of benevolent socialism, a planned society. In the Inca empire every person had cradle-to-grave security. They had an ever-normal-granary storage system that saved supplies in good years to tide the people over the inevitable lean years. They also had highly developed conservation practices that included periodic round-ups of the little wild camels—llamas and alpacas—of the region with selective slaughter to maintain the herds at levels desirable for the vegetation of the region. That a given range can carry only so much wildlife and that it is wasteful not to harvest the excess is often thought to be a twentieth-century wildlife management idea; however, in the planned society of the Inca, it was well-established long ago.

When a young couple married, they were allotted land at the annual division of land; when they had a child, their land holding was increased. The populace of a given settlement worked communally on the state lands. After those fields were tilled and planted, they then individually worked their own plots of ground. Harvest was organized in the same way. The government share was partly stored locally and partly transported to other areas where there might be need. It sounds like an ideal system, and in a way it was. However, there is a price for everything; in the planned society, the price is freedom. The individual in the Inca system had an absolute minimum of freedom. He could not freely choose his profession, where he would live, or whether or not he would be single or married. The state decreed that everyone should marry and saw that they did. A man was a farmer or soldier or roadworker as the state decreed.

This tightly organized state with absolute authority over life and death and all intermediate activities centered in one person, the Inca ruler. It achieved an immense development of the potentiality of this arid lowland and semiarid highland. Through the use of labor that could be put to work without any thought of cost, vast temples, palaces, canals, and land-terrace systems were constructed. Cities that were several square miles in extent were built; canals many miles in length were dug; whole mountainsides were terraced; and the population grew. Arts were encouraged and some of the finest work that the world has ever seen was produced in textiles and in pottery.

ORIGIN OF PRE-COLUMBIAN SOUTH AMERICAN CIVILIZATION

Why was this part of arid South America a center of great civilization and empires when its corresponding area in North America was virtually a cultural void? Why is this the only southern hemisphere dry land to achieve the level of civilization in pre-Columbian time? Since the physical environments are not so different as to supply an answer, a probable answer is to be found in a study of the culture of these people and in comparing their ways of doing things with those of peoples in other parts of the world.

To begin with an obvious comparison, the Incas kept their tax rolls, census rolls, and such records by tying knots in strings. It was a complex system, with the position of the knot determining the value of the unit; thus a knot in one position represented the unit 1; in another position, 10; and in another, 100. Both a decimal system and a place-value system are used, just as in our own system where the value of 1 is determined by how far it is from the decimal point. The zeros, of course, are just spacers to fix position.

Such a mathematical system is rare in the world. It appears in the Old World center of civilization, including India, and decimal systems are found in early China. China very early received from India the basis for the abacus, a system of beads on strings in a frame on which computations in a decimal system can be carried out rapidly. The Chinese annals state that before they had writing they kept their records by tying knots in strings. In the adjacent Pacific, Polynesian peoples kept their records by tying knots in strings and when the records were mathematical, they used a decimal system. The Polynesian and Peruvian records state that the Polynesians, at least occasionally, came to the coast of Peru. The probability that the Incas did sail out into the Pacific, as they say they did, has been greatly increased by Thor Heyerdahl's demonstration that the sailing rafts that they had were quite capable of the job.

Trans-Pacific Contacts

The evidence of such trans-Pacific contacts can be enormously extended. Only a few examples will be discussed here and a brief listing given of some of the items that support the notion that very early and very extensive voyages were made and that much of the civilization in the dry-land west coast of South America derived from Asia.

Much of the evidence on this topic in the past has been dismissed as interesting, but insignificant because man can obviously invent things and ideas may well have arisen in separate areas independently. Who can say that the idea of the zero is not a "natural" one that must arise as soon as men get to a certain stage of development and must use figures to deal with censuses and tax rolls, and so forth? Similarly, if pyramids are found in two different areas, how can this prove contact when a pyramid is one of the "natural" shapes for a monumental pile? If men draw similar-appearing mythical animals, how can this prove contact, since all men are basically alike and are apt to have similar hallucinations? Yet it is possible to turn to something that man cannot invent and that is also found on both sides of the Pacific, and find a complex idea, one with many parts that are not necessarily —that is functionally—related. Such things are found in games, for instance.

Domestic plants are an example of something that man not only does not but cannot invent. Man domesticates plants. He does not create them out of nothing. The plant is there; man modifies it. Of the domestic plants that were common to both the Old World and the New World, the most interesting is the sweet potato. This plant was widespread in the Middle American areas in pre-Columbian times and had a considerable distribution in Polynesia also. It is an American plant. It is the same plant in America and in Polynesia. Further, in part of the Inca empire, the name for the plant is the same as in Polynesia. In

the northern part of the Inca empire, the name is *kumar, umar,* or variations on them. In adjacent Polynesia, the names are *kumara, umara, umala, uwala.* The same plant used in the same ways and even known by the same name by peoples who each had traditions of contacts with the other seems about as close as we can come to absolute proof of contact.

Further information can be derived from this evidence. We have seen that people do not necessarily take up ideas quickly. In fact, that there may be a lag of a thousand years or more at times in the taking over of obviously useful ideas. We cannot assume then that one single, fleeting contact led someone to adopt a strange food plant. Rather there must have been contact over a fairly long time so that the receiving group could become used to the new plant, could come to like the taste of it, and so become interested in how it was grown and harvested, stored and cooked.

We are unlikely to know just how the first trip to America was made. It was probably accidental. Japanese fishing boats, disabled on the fishing grounds off Asia, drift to America automatically. In the nineteenth century they arrived with considerable regularity. When the European first reached the Indians of the northwest coast of America, they had Japanese fishermen as slaves. The sweep of the currents and winds is such that boats off the coast of America would have been carried down the coast of America to California and beyond. The people in America would learn from such landings that there was land to the west of them. Any castaway that won his freedom might well organize a return trip and be able to report the existence of a great land to the east of Asia. A South Pacific drift would also lead to America, just as any drift voyage from Middle America would lead to Polynesia and Asia.

Although we will never know the details of the first contacts, the plant evidence provides absolute proof that voyages were made. Sweet potatoes and cotton simply are not naturally dispersed across seas. Man is required to transport them. But if the contacts between the peoples on the two sides of the Pacific were enough so that they came to know and value some of each other's economic plants, they must have

Patolli (*above*) and Parchisi (*below*). These games, which are identical, were played in Mexico and in Asia in pre-Columbian times. The patolli drawing was made in Mexico in the sixteenth century by natives who had acquired some of the European idiom in drawing. The parchisi drawing shows the game as played in Persia. *American Museum of Natural History.*

exchanged other ideas also. There is abundant evidence that they did so.

The game of parchisi was known in Southwest Asia and in Middle America in pre-Columbian times. The shape of the board and all the rules of the game are the same. Mathematically the chances of independently duplicating such a game can be calculated to be between 100,000 and 1,000,000 to 1, depending on how many independent variables the game is assumed to have.

For those who are not mathematically minded, this can be put into familiar terms. If you were in a distant jungle land and saw a group of natives moaning, chanting, and swaying as they crouched in a circle on the ground, you would undoubtedly think that you had stumbled upon a primitive ceremony. When you came close, however, you would find that goods were changing hands. Gambling! "Ah well, natural to mankind," you might say. But then you would see that they were casting lots. "Naturally," you might think, "they have to invoke the laws of chance somehow." But the device they are using is a pair of cubes. Puzzling—it could have been a device for heads or tails or something else. However, cubes are a natural shape. Then you notice the numbering of the faces on the cubes with dots from one to six. Now why

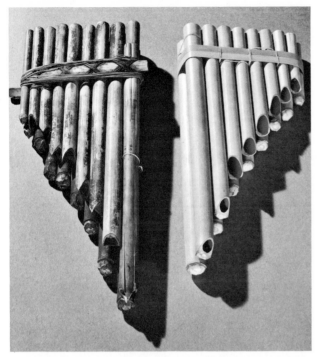

Pan Pipes from the Solomon Islands (*left*) and from Bolivia (*right*). The degree of similarity in these instruments on the two sides of the Pacific extends to the method of binding them, the scales used, and the religious-ceremonial notions associated with them. *American Museum of Natural History.*

dots? Among a jungle people, why shouldn't the six sides be marked by symbols for tree, monkey, parrot, snake, fish, or man?

By this time your suspicions are thoroughly aroused. Listening closely you find that you can understand part of the chant. As one of the men winds up to throw the dice he chants: "Come on Box Cars." Now, if you know anything about the American dice game, you will know that American soldiers have been in this jungle before you. There are entirely too many improbable occurrences of nonfunctional elements combined into an arbitrary game to have just happened by chance: this is what the earlier figures expressed in the precise language of the mathematician.

As an interesting aside, why do we mark our dice with dots instead of numbers? Do you suppose it is significant that dice exactly like those that we use today are found in Mesopotamia as early as 3000 B.C. and that in Mesopotamia the circle is divided into 360 degrees, just as we divide our circle today, and that much of our culture is derived from the eastern Mediterranean? This kind of evidence is proof that the roots of our Western European culture lie in the Near East. Similar evidence linking Middle America and Southeast Asia should be given a similar interpretation.

But if plants and games, what else? The list is long. Pan pipes are blown on both sides of the Pacific, and on both sides of the Atlantic, too. However, the pan pipes in America blow the same notes in the same scales as those used on the Asiatic side of the Pacific and have such improbable ideas associated with them as that pairs of pan pipes represent male and female. There are resemblances also in metal objects. A list of Asiatic cultural elements found in Middle America, indicating something of the extent of the parallels in ways of thinking and of doing things on the two sides of the Pacific, is given below.

Mathematics and Calendars
Time counting by permutations
The zero: early appearance in India and Mexico
Place numeral systems: India, Mexico, and Peru
Knot-in-string records (before script): Peru, Polynesia, China
Zodiac: Asia and Mexico

Music
Pan pipe: identical notes, similar scales, ceremonial ideas, including male-female concept for paired pipes and alternate notes
Nose flute
Conch-shell trumpet, with similar names and blown in similar ways
Hollowed-log drum with slit opening used for signaling in Middle America, Polynesia, Southeast Asia, and Africa

Art

Jade: highly valued in Mexico, especially by Mayan culture, and in China—similar concepts associated with jade in both areas

Chinese Chou dynasty art motifs duplicated in Maya area

Indian art motifs in Mexico: trefoil arch, sacred tree, tiger thrones, lotus staff, lotus panels with fish-vine-man-vine-fish elements, serpent-worship elements

Technology

Alcoholic and narcotic beverages prepared in similar ways and used in similar ceremonies

Metallurgy with similar alloys, weapon forms, and casting methods

The wheel: principle known and used on toys in America

Fore- and aft-rig sails used on centerboard rafts: Asia, Polynesia, Peru

Racial

Vivid portraits in pottery and stone of various races: Mongoloid, Caucasoid, and Negroid

Legends giving detailed descriptions of robed and bearded learned men visitors who came and went by sea

The Mayans have Chineselike palm prints

Many agricultural tribes have the Diego blood antigen that is also found in parts of Southeast Asia

Legendary

Peruvians claim to have crossed the Pacific

Chinese fifth-century document probably describes a missionary effort in Middle America

Polynesians claimed voyages to and from America

Numerous myths are alike on the two sides of the Pacific

Agricultural

Sweet potato, an American plant, carried with its name into Polynesia and probably carried by people from Borneo clear on to Africa well before A.D. 1500.

Numerous other plants probably carried between areas: coconut probably carried to America, cot-

Bark Cloth and Bark Beaters from Oceania (*left*) and America (*right*). Not only was bark cloth, or tapa cloth, prepared on both sides of the Pacific but the implements used in beating the soft inner bark into a feltlike material were also identical. *American Museum of Natural History.*

ton probably carried to America and later new forms from America carried into the Pacific

Similar types of agricultural terracing, irrigation systems

The Problem of Spanning the Pacific

The Pacific has been thought of as a great barrier. This seems to be because most of the people looking at it were landsmen and knew very little of the history of shipping. It is true that to pin down the history of ships in the period before writing is not easy, for wooden ships and fabric sails have seldom been preserved. There has also been a tendency to treat the first recorded ship as *the first ship*. This is a fundamental error that permeates thinking on almost all such problems: the first man found is the earliest man; the first stone implement found is the earliest implement. All this is probably wrong. The earliest

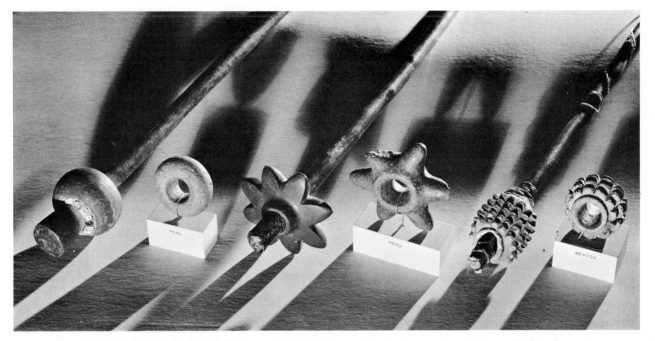

War Clubs of Melanesia Compared with Those of Peru and Mexico. Such similarity of form and function is virtually conclusive proof of the spread of ideas from one region to the other. *American Museum of Natural History.*

ship known is found in an Egyptian mural, and this is very often taken to be the earliest ship. It most probably is not.

Shipping was not even dependent on boats, as we too often assume, and it need not have used wooden boats, as we also tend to assume. The Eskimo and the Irish, to name only two, used skin boats and made notable voyages. The Eskimo repeatedly reached Great Britain in their kayaks, and the Irish traveled great distances in their curraghs, small ships capable of carrying up to 60 men. That the Eskimo had such boats—their umiak is the equivalent of the Irish curragh—suggests that such boats were within the technological ability of the Upper Paleolithic people. But even this possibility does not tell the story.

Any buoyant material may be bundled up and the bundles shaped and bound together to create a passable craft. Such craft made variously of reeds,

bark, bamboo, and similar material are to be found extremely early in history, widely distributed over the world and very frequently in the hands of marginal peoples. People of Middle Paleolithic culture level, such as the Tasmanians, used such craft to reach Tasmania, and their ancestors probably used such craft to reach Australia. All of which suggests that man was moving about the world across the broad waters of the oceans vastly earlier than we have thought. Middle Paleolithic level people, such as the Tasmanians and Lower Californians, used bundle rafts. Upper Paleolithic level people, such as the Eskimo, used skin boats. Plank boats may have been used as early as Neolithic times.

In Southeast Asia the brilliant solution of the sailing raft with the centerboard was invented early, but we have no means of knowing just when. The early mythological history of Japan does not mention boats, but rafts. The sailing raft able to sail windward, tack,

Brazilian Jangada. This vessel is used by fishermen in South America, including northeastern Brazil, Peru, and Ecuador. It is equally typical of fishing vessels in southern India today. The identical sail is still in use also in the Caroline Islands. *Brazilian Embassy.*

(*Right*) Prehistoric Centerboard from Peru, pre-Inca. The centerboard is a movable keel and enables a fore and aft rigged ship (opposite of a square rigged ship) to sail upwind. Both the fore and aft rigged sail and the centerboard employ the same principle of aerodynamics as the wing of an airplane. Furthermore, multiple centerboards can be adjusted to balance the forces of wind, sail, waves, and currents as desired and thus play the role of the rudder. This sophisticated piece of sailing equipment is ancient in the Pacific. The proportions of this ancient Peruvian centerboard are like those of centerboards used on modern racing sail boats. In Peru they are more than 1000 years old.

(*Below*) The Jangada of Brazil. This craft is certainly a relative of the sailing log crafts by which Asiatic peoples reached the shores of Peru. The raft is shown from the side and from above.

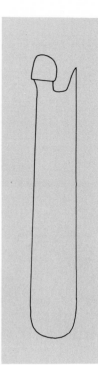

and perform better than a square-rigged ship made it possible for the Asiatics to move freely about the seas beginning in very early times. A number of students have pointed out that the sailing log raft used off the coast of Peru is an isolated phenomenon in America and that in many of its details—kind of mast, sail, use of centerboards—it is like Asiatic rafts. In Asia such craft are numerous and widespread, suggesting certainly that Asia is the homeland and America the area to which they spread. If the raft went, then men went on it: it would have been the means of carrying men and ideas and plants. It is probably one of the accidents of history that late in history the raft was replaced by canoes in Polynesia, thus helping us lose sight of the connecting links between America and the probable homeland of this ancient craft.

We can conclude therefore that the sailing raft probably has a great antiquity on both sides of the Pacific; that its probable home is Asia; and that its appearance in America shows up right in one of the areas where we suspect Asiatic contacts because of the appearance of Asiatic political forms, architectural

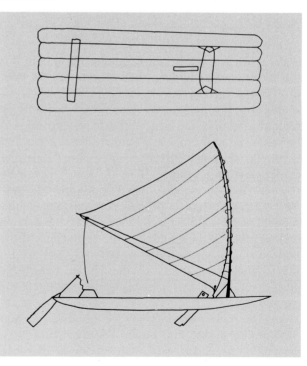

types, metalurgical techniques, and the like. The result of such considerations is that we cannot safely say that the similar developments in America are the result of similar men (all mankind being assumed to be similar) coming to similar conclusions when faced with similar problems in similar physical environments. Quite the contrary, it appears as if the similarities may be due to the wholesale importation of ideas.

Spread of Ideas versus Environmental Determinism

From the geographical point of view, such a conclusion presents us with a curious reversal. If the ideas of terraced and irrigated lands were imported from Asia, as is probable, then the ideas developed in the Old World for the growth of wet rice in a humid, forested land were adapted for use in America for the growth of entirely different crops in an arid land. Far from arid mountains dictating a scattered-field land use comparable to the Pueblo land use, the men of Peru remade the mountains to fit their concept of good land use.

This raises an equally interesting question. Why was rice not brought to America and grown on these terraces? Rice has a puzzling distribution. It was not grown in the Polynesian Islands, not even on the volcanic islands where the soil and water situation is favorable. Recent studies indicate that rice is a sub-tropical plant and very sensitive to changing lengths of day and night. It has only relatively recently been successfully adapted to growth under equatorial conditions where there is little variation in length of day. For example, wet-rice culture reached Malaya about A.D. 1000. If the contacts with America were early, then no equatorial-adapted rice may have been available and rice, if brought to America, would have failed. Maize, however, would flourish on irrigated "rice" terraces.

We are just beginning to gain some detailed insight into who and when these introductions were made by. The material listed in Table 2–2 included metal work from the south coast of China. Recently excavations on the coast of Ecuador have revealed deeply stratified deposits containing much pottery, including models of houses and furniture. The earliest

Temple Doorway, Cambodia. The use of such minor architectural details as the columnette ornament on both sides of the Pacific, taken together with the presence of identical games, mythology, mathematics and many other kinds of evidence, helps build up a picture of the spread of ideas in pre-Columbian times. *American Museum of Natural History.*

Terracing of Mountains in Peru. In pre-Columbian times, in the very areas where the art, architecture, and plant evidence suggests Asiatic influences, this nearly total re-making of the landscape for agricultural purposes was undertaken in just the same way that it was done in Asia. *American Geographical Society.*

House Types of Ecuador Indians and of Asia as Compared by Emilio Estrada. The pottery house models in the upper row were found in graves on the coast of Ecuador; they show features, especially in roof lines, typical of southeast Asian pagoda roofs. The pagoda roof line in turn is an old feature retained in sacred architecture in Asia. The lower row shows the roof lines of typical Asiatic houses.

of these materials have been dated to as early as 2500 B.C. The houses dating to about 200 B.C. are virtual duplicates of Asiatic house types. There are also models of wooden pillows, specialized burial traits, and special forms of pottery, all of which are characteristic of the coast of Asia. The coast of Ecuador seems to have been one of the centers of early settlement and colonial development by Asiatics who were sailing across the world's greatest ocean to begin the colonizing of undeveloped nations of America.

One of the confusing things found on the coast of Peru is a complex of traits that are more like the Near East than the Far East. This includes such items as mud-wall construction, lateral wells, and specific metal tool forms. It has often been pointed out that this tends to destroy an argument for the spread of ideas, since it is inconceivable that Near Eastern cultural traits would be transmitted to America. The argument rests on an assumption that ideas could not spread that far in early times, but this seems to be a false assumption. Toward the end of the Bronze Age, there was an empire in Asia that extended from the lower Danube to Indochina. This

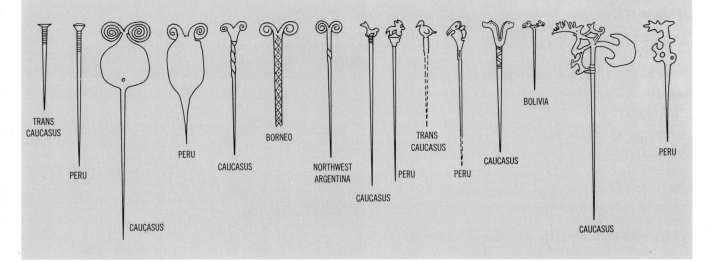

Metal Pins from South America and Asia. These pins, found on both sides of the Pacific Ocean, are only a few of the many objects from these areas that exhibit extremely close resemblance in form and function. Such pins are about the length of old-fashioned hat pins, and were used to fasten clothing. *Redrawn from Robert Heine-Geldern, "Die Asiatische Herkunft der Südamerikanischen Metalltechnik," Paideuma, vol. 5, 1954, pp. 347–423.*

empire, similar in extent to the empire of Genghis Khan, is known as the Dong-Son culture. It greatly influenced the growth of China and introduced many basic cultural traits, including a great deal of the art and technology of metal working in bronze. These same techniques and these same art forms appear on the coast of Peru in early levels of the local archeology.

If ideas about art forms and about metallurgy were transmitted, it seems very difficult to exclude the spread of ideas about building pyramids and city walls of mud, and digging wells laterally into hill slopes to collect water for irrigation, and all the other such ideas in Peru that are so much like those of the Near East. As is so often the case, the problem is not one of either or. The evidence suggests complex origins of cultural traits carried by different people over a long period of time. The result as seen in America is a mixture of Near Eastern and Far Eastern traits adapted to the arid environment of the coast of Peru and the cold highlands of Peru and Bolivia.

This view destroys the theme of crude environmental determinism. Instead of thinking of the dry lands of the Pacific coast of America as having developed their culture in isolation from the Old World, and hence giving us an example of man-reacting-to-the-desert-environment, we have instead the interesting case of Old World cultures of the time level of 2500 B.C. and later—for the contacts were continued over a long period of time—reacting to the dry land environments of America. The cities in the desert, with their adobe walls and pyramids, their irrigation canals and lateral wells, their divine priest-kingships—complete with such trappings as litters and umbrellas as insignia of rank—all are to be seen more as a direct importation of ideas than as responses to the environment. Such a flow of ideas was the real basis for the cultural growth and development that in the sixteenth century was the magnificent Inca empire.

THE SPANISH EVALUATION OF THE DESERT

The Spanish found this area to be a vast, organized empire, containing great cities, linked with foot paths, equipped with granaries, and supported by terraced mountain sides and irrigated desert oases.

There were also great temples roofed and lined and furnished with gold and silver, extracted from rich local mines.

The Spanish looted the temples, shipping back to Spain the vast wealth of gold assembled through centuries. Thereafter, the Spanish took over the mines and the precious metal became Spain's great source of wealth. What else could they take? Potatoes, one of Peru's great gifts to the world, could not survive a trip up the coast of South America to be transhipped at Panama and sent through the tropical Caribbean onward to markets in Europe. Besides, what European would eat so strange a food? So it was also with the other agricultural products of the New World. Only such things as gold, silver, gems, and sugar could last and pay the costs of the long trip.

The geography of location, the state of transportation, and the role of human values were each playing a role. Such factors determined that the general development of this part of the Spanish colonial world would be sacrificed to the support of the mines. Men were drafted for work in the mines, even though the coastal oases were thus depopulated, and the men of the lowlands died in the high altitudes where the mines lay. Even the distant grasslands of Argentina became an adjunct to the mines, supplying the needed mules, beef, and mutton. Under the impact of economic and political disruption, enforced labor in the mines, and unaccustomed diseases, the population in parts of the land was greatly reduced. Where great cities had stood there were now a few great, thinly populated landed estates. Where the land had once been used intensively to support many people, it was now used extensively to support a few. The pattern thus set has persisted to the present.

The dry lands of South America cross the Andes just south of 30 degrees latitude. Southward in the rain shadow of the Andes there is a long strip of dry land, lying principally in Argentina. In northwest Argentina the land resembles somewhat the Great Basin in North America, where streams descend from isolated, short mountain ranges into the dry basins between the mountains.

View of Part of the Ruins of the Great City of Chan Chan in the Coastal Desert Region of Peru. Such evidence is a measure of the degree of civilization and population that the area attained in pre-Spanish times. *American Geographical Society*.

In pre-Columbian times the use of this land greatly resembled that of the American Southwest. Town-dwelling people utilized these streams and other areas of water concentration for agriculture. They made pottery and built stone houses grouped together much like those of the southwestern Pueblos. Is this kind of geographical adaptation environmentally determined? At first glance it might seem so.

However, both areas are marginal to centers of culturally advanced areas: northwest Argentina to Peru; the American Southwest to Mexico. Location in relation to civilization is not raw physical environmental determinism; the first cause is culture. If northwest Argentina and the American Southwest were indeed alike in this early period, then we have the suggestion that the Mexican and South American cultures that influenced them shared certain basic values that gave rise to similar appearing cultures in arid peripheral areas. The basic relationships of the Middle American cultures is today increasingly recognized. When we explore details, we find such tell-tale similarities as T-shaped doorways associated with stone-house construction in the Southwest, Mexico, and the Andes. Such likeness seems indeed to stem primarily from a sharing in a basic stock of ideas and only secondarily from the sharing of a similar physical environment in which these ideas were worked out. In both areas cultural level declined with distance from the cultural centers. Beyond the farmers of the difficult arid lands were simple hunters and gatherers. It did not matter whether "back of the beyond" was the rich land of the Argentine pampas or the fertile valleys of California. If ideas did not penetrate effectively, these better lands lagged behind the relatively poor physical environments closer to stimulating centers.

Three Cultural Stages in Peru. (*Left*) Megalithic stone walls at Sacsayhuaman, Cuzco, are evidence of the great engineering ability and organizing power of the Incas. (*Below left*) A town mansion of the Spanish period, 1735. (*Below right*) The buildings of downtown Lima in modern Peru. *Embassy of Peru.*

Conquest of the Desert and Socio-economic Growth Stimulated by Mineral Resources. Talara in the coastal desert of Peru, because of the presence of oil, has become a town of 40,000 with 12 schools, modern homes, medical clinics, swimming pools, and other recreational facilities. All this development, maintained despite the fact that water has to be brought 25 miles by pipeline, is the result of investment by the International Petroleum Company—illustrating advances that foreign capital can help introduce into areas not yet fully participating in the industrial revolution. *Embassy of Peru.*

Native Dwelling, Southwest Africa. People in transition. Note the modern baby bottle, the old-fashioned dress, and the ancient house type. *Bureau of American Ethnology, Gordon Gibson.*

In the American Southwest, the cultural sequence after 1500 was from that of a marginal area to integration into one of the major economically, politically, and culturally productive areas of the world. In Peru, the change went from a center of political power and cultural growth to the status of a colonial dependency of a distant power, to ultimate independence, but as a small nation distant from the center of world power and not integrated into the adjacent region. The crude physical environment remained unchanged; the geographic position in relation to cultural forces had changed. The achievements of the men on the land paralleled those changes. While race changed considerably in the Southwest and culture advanced, race remained little changed in Peru and culture declined. It seems clear that the causes are not racial, however, for both the Peruvian natives and the Spanish have records of great achievements in former times. But so do the Indians of the American Southwest. Both race and physical environment are therefore inadequate as explanation, especially for the arid lands of South America.

The arid coastal lands of Peru and northern Chile are not poor. The irrigated land is a rich potential; the problems are those of finding and marketing material desired in the world market. At present production centers on cotton and sugar cane. Development of the adjacent highland areas, perhaps as industrial centers, could well lead to a shift toward the production of locally desired food, for the coastal desert oases of Peru and Chile could in a productive, industrialized society play the same role as the Imperial, Colorado, and Gila-Salt oases do in the American economy. The cold offshore ocean current is one of the world's richest fisheries. The Andes are mineralized and rich in copper, gold, silver, and other metals. The limited development of arid South America is not due to environmental poverty; rather, it is a measure of the continuation of a preindustrial society and economy into the twentieth century. There is nothing remarkable about this, for the same thing can be said of most of Asia, all of Africa, and most of Latin America—examples from virtually every climate and every race.

AFRICA AND AUSTRALIA

In the southern hemisphere of the Old World the course of history in the dry lands was very unlike that in the northern hemisphere of the Old World. Indeed, we have the odd reversal that in the Old World great civilizations arose in the northern dry lands, but the southern dry lands remained in most backward stages of development. In the New World it was the southern hemisphere dry lands that were the more advanced culturally, while the northern dry lands languished.

SOUTH AFRICAN BUSHMEN

In the South African dry lands there were two ways of life, cattle raising and hunting and gathering. The ancient one was that of hunting and gathering, still the characteristic way of life of the Bushmen, who shift their habitations from one water hole to another depending on the location of game and the

seasonable abundance of vegetable crops. As is common with such people, the women are the gatherers and the men are the hunters. The woman's characteristic tool is her digging stick; the man's is his bow. There is no pottery; ostrich egg shells serve as cups; and except for the ostrich shells, the way of life is that of the gatherers of the Great Basin—and by omitting the bow would do well for the natives of Australia.

The Bushmen are an interesting racial variant of mankind. They have a triangular face with Mongoloid slanted eyes, yellowish skin, and extremely kinky hair. The women have a tendency toward extreme fattiness of the buttocks and thighs combined with slender shins and upper bodies. These characteristics are neatly portrayed in their distinctive art.

The Bushmen have sometimes been described as a product of the Kalahari—a specialized form of man

Native Housing on the Outskirts of a Town in Southwest Africa. Except for the children, this scene could be duplicated in numerous places in Latin America, North Africa, Arabia, India, and elsewhere. It records a cultural stage and an economic condition rather than either an environmentally or racially determined status. Compare Talara or Palm Springs, both much more arid than southwest Africa. *Bureau of American Ethnology, Gordon Gibson.*

fitted for the desert. First, it is notable that no other desert produced such a physical type; next, that the remains of Bushmen have been found over a very wide area in Africa and that cave paintings in their art style have been found as far north as Spain. Most of Bushman history probably was spent in the better watered, forested areas of Africa from which they have been displaced in relatively recent times by the larger Negro peoples. Why the Bushmen developed their peculiarities remains unknown. Yellow skin and kinky hair are well suited to the high humidity and moderate heat of the tropical forest; small body size is useful in any hot area; while fat storage is useful to any people lacking assured food supplies and is especially desirable for mothers who may have to

nurse infants through starving times. But much of mankind faced similar needs without developing equally marked racial traits. Isolation and genetic drift as well as selection must have been at work.

The Bushman habitat, scrubby thorn forests with bunch grass between the widely spaced trees, with much bare ground between clumps of trees, is much like the landscape in the mesquite and grass-covered areas of the American Southwest. In South Africa there are giraffes and even elephants in such country. This was in fact true of the American Southwest also, for such large animals as ground sloths and elephants have been dated as present and hunted by man as late as 8000 years ago. It is one of the curious and unsolved phenomena of the world that in the New

Native Group, Southwest Africa. Life in the open in the summer shade. The girl kneeling in the foreground is grinding seeds on a metate, the ancient grinding implement of the seed-gathering people. The girl at the right is crushing the seeds preparatory to their being ground into flour. The scene could virtually be duplicated on the native level in Australia, in much of the Great Basin (see p. 79 ff.), in Lower California, or in much of arid southern California. The scene and the activity define a stage of cultural and economic development. *Bureau of American Ethnology, Gordon Gibson.*

World the great animals became extinct while in the Old World and especially in Africa they survived in a much larger number of areas. The point here is that in similar climatic situations where men lived in similar ways there were similar landscapes. The South African dry lands, used by men lacking pastoral animals, look very much like the dry lands of the American Southwest, which also were used by men lacking pastoral animals. The North African and Arabian and inner Asian dry lands, used by men with pastoral animals, have a much more arid aspect. The North American dry lands are becoming much more arid appearing as the impact of the modern usage of domestic animals bears down on them and strips the vegetation, letting loose the forces of erosion.

On the margins of the South African dry lands, the cattle-using Hottentot people have been moving in on the Bushmen and introducing another way of life. In Africa the use of cattle for pastoral life is clearly an idea that has been working south from origins in the Egypt-Ethiopian civilizations. The farther from the center of the origin of ideas, the more primitive the culture. From an Egyptian center of civilization there is a drop in level of advancement toward the south, and the most primitive use of the land has persisted in the far south.

MODERN PROBLEMS IN AFRICA

South Africa today remains a land of lesser opportunity. In addition to the problems inherent in the use of any arid land, South Africa is distant from centers of high productivity and hence ability to pay for any expensive consumer crops that might be raised there. The arid areas of South Africa have no special advantages, such as political union with any large consuming area. This situation of course, is in direct contrast with the American arid West where the warm oases of the Sonoran Desert are politically and physically linked with consuming areas of high productivity in the eastern United States.

Africa now is in a period of chaos, and its future is unpredictable. South Africa's future may well depend very largely on what happens in the rest of Africa: it could become another American Southwest; or it could be another Chile. The problem is less a matter of physical environment than of cultural development. Change cannot come rapidly, for even in this day of advanced technology it would be nearly miraculous if a major change in the educational, economic, and political outlook of the people could be achieved in three generations. It is certainly unlikely to proceed at this rate without outside assistance and tutelage. This problem is not peculiar to Africa or Negroes. The same situation faced the Yumas; it faced the early people of northwest Europe; and today, as exemplified by Puerto Rico, it faces much of Latin America. Africa's problems are unusually great because more of her people are in a stage of illiterate tribalism than is true over most of the world.

South Africa does not lack physical-geographical assets. Although the Namib Desert is extremely dry (under four inches of rain per year), rainfall increases steadily to the east. There is from 10 to 20 inches of rain in the semidesert of steppe area of the central part, and 30 to 50 inches on the east side. This last part is, of course, humid forested highland. It is significant for the arid lands to the west, for the Orange River rises within 120 miles of the Indian Ocean in these humid highlands of southeast Africa and flows 1300 miles westward to the Atlantic. Water flowing through the desert presents enormous opportunities: in the desert north of the equator in the Old World such opportunities were regularly developed, but south of the equator they never were. The equator is not the important factor, however; for as we have seen in America, the deserts were irrigated both north and south of the equator but most intensively south of the equator.

ABORIGINAL CULTURE IN AUSTRALIA

Finally there is Australia, which has often been described as having a desert heart, for the one half of the interior land is desert or semi-desert. For the human geographer, Australia is of extreme interest. In pre-Columbian times, it mattered little what the

The Simpson Desert from 10,000 Feet. This desert, about 180 miles east of Alice Springs, Northern Territory, Australia, is devoid of water and all signs of life. *Australian News and Information Bureau.*

climate was; the culture level remained much the same. The entire continent including Tasmania was in the hands of people who lived on a hunting and gathering level of existence. Australia in pre-Columbian times was inhabited by a short-statured, bearded, prognathous, dark-skinned, beetle-browed type of man that, in many characteristics, falls between the Negroid and the White race. These people are probably best considered as a separate variant of mankind that arose in Australia through very long isolation. They had no agriculture, no pottery, no ground stone tools, and no domestic animals except the dog. By these terms the aboriginal Australians were all living on a pre-Neolithic level: They were survivals of the ancient way of life that once characterized all of mankind for the longer part of our existence and that can be called the Paleolithic way of life.

In Australia there are many climates in which this way of life was practiced. In the north there is a season of great rains in the summer, followed by a very long dry season in the "winter." Winter in northern Australia, of course, is not to be thought of as a time of cold. The east coast of Australia ranges from a wet tropical northern coast to a subtropical rainy central coast, until in its southern corner the land has a distinct winter and the mountains have a heavy snow cover. Southwest Australia has a "Mediterranean" type of climate, such as is found around the Mediterranean, at the tip of South Africa, in California, and in central Chile. Tasmania, inhabited by a people related to the Australians and having an even more simple culture, has a cool marine climate like that of Great Britain and the Pacific Northwest coast of America. It did not matter what the environment was, the level of culture remained that of simple gatherers and hunters. As elsewhere in the world where this way of life is found, the digging stick was the woman's chief tool and her duty was the gathering of roots, seeds, and berries. The men hunted, and the throwing spear was their chief implement.

Housing was virtually nonexistent. A shelter that cut the wind but did not cover them was as much as they built. Clothing was also practically nonexistent. In the cold nights of the mid-latitude deserts a family curled up about a fire with a brush shelter to windward and slept on the ground while the thermometer dropped to the freezing mark. In the morning the natives would be almost torpid. It has been found that they have the remarkable ability to adjust to such rigorous conditions by lowering their body temperature, especially in their limbs, retaining vital heat in their body cavity. When the sun comes up and they resume exercise, they regain their normal body temperature and go about the daily business of hunting and gathering. If need could drive men to clothing and housing, surely these people should have felt the need. One would expect these unclothed and unhoused natives to have been stimulated, encouraged, or driven by the physical environment to do something about their "needs." But they apparently felt the cold without "feeling the need" to do something about it. Until 1500, when the Europeans began to spill across the whole world, Australia lay outside the orbit of the world of ideas, and these simple folk were left alone to follow their own bent—which did not include "progress" in the sense that we think of it.

It is easy to conclude that there must have been something wrong with the Australians as human beings, but there is no evidence of it. Were they mentally deficient? No one can say that they were, or are. They simply did not take a great interest in the material things that so concern us. On the other hand, they had interests that we largely ignore; in particular, they kept close track of family relationships. It is a peculiarity of our society that we are poorly equipped with names describing the types of family relationships that exist. We lack any term to distinguish between those of our aunts and uncles that are our father's brothers and sisters and those that are our aunts and uncles through our mother's side. We only have the single term cousin to distinguish between the large number of relationships that exist in our own and several other generation levels. We feel the need of kinship terms and extend the titles "aunt," "uncle," and "cousin" to people to whom we are related only distantly. All of this would seem ridiculous to a native Australian,

and he would think something to be wrong with a people who were so concerned with houses and clothing that they did not even take time out to get a good set of kinship terms established so that the most important thing in life could be kept track of.

The Australian lavished attention and inventiveness on his kinship system. He also lavished time on a vast system of secret societies, organizations that were like some of our modern fraternal orders in being characterized by a long series of grades. Advancement from one level to the next was dependent on age and on learning the extensive ritual and mythology that belonged to each. In this way an illiterate people carried an extensive literature of mythology that would seem to be quite out of keeping with their low economic stage. The Australians were like the Yumans in that their interests in life were not turned toward the material things that are so important in our society today but turned instead toward such immaterial things as the importance of relationships and the achievement of status in the secret societies, and through this the maintaining of the traditions of their people. The physical environment was nothing more than the stage on which this play was acted. It did not matter to these players whether the stage was tropical woodland, temperate forest or desert scrub. It was the plot that counted.

Why should Australia have lagged so long at this cultural stage? Was it isolation? This seems an obvious answer at first glance. However, New Zealand is even more distant, yet it had the more advanced Polynesian Maori culture complete with agriculture. Northern Australia is close to the outlying Indian civilization that centered on Java. The Asiatic people had known of Australia for a long time. However, it offered them little incentive to take over, for there were no settled, productive people there. How could simple hunters and gatherers be seized, made subjects, and taxed? One could not trade with them, for they produced almost nothing and desired almost nothing. Yet one could not simply move in and occupy the land for, primitive as they were, they held the land and were fiercely possessive of their hunting and gathering territories. The type of decision made by peoples of advanced cultures when faced with such a prospect is well illustrated in the discussion of the Spanish reaction to a California occupied by a people of similarly low culture level (see Chapter 4).

BRITISH AUSTRALIA

Modern Australia is one of the latest of the European colonial developments. Just as in the United States, the British found a land occupied by a people at a much lower level of development than their own. In Australia there was even more marked a contrast than in the United States, for in the eastern United States the Indians were mostly farmers and in our South many of them were town dwellers. The British "solution" in both America and Australia was the removal of the native population. The causes and reasons given for this policy and the history of attempts to get along with the natives are a complex matter. In reducing the numbers of aboriginal Australians, the role of outright warfare has been overemphasized and indirect destruction through the introduction of European diseases to which the native population was totally unaccustomed, underestimated. The effects of such diseases can be gauged by examining episodes in the extermination of some American Indian tribes. The Mandan went from 2000 to 200 people in one winter simply as a result of the introduction of small pox. The remnant joined adjacent tribes, and the Mandan as such ceased to exist.

In Australia, after their initial settlement in the humid lands of the east coast, the British soon found the dry interior of the continent. Rapid exploration showed the vast extent and the extreme aridity of much of this land. The colony needed products that could be sold to the mother country and that could stand the rigors of a long ocean voyage, both in terms of cost and in resistance to deterioration. Although the hot dry lands of Australia could well produce watermelons and lettuce for the British market, there was no point in this in the nineteenth century when there was no way to get such perishables to the potential market. While it is now possible by jet to put such products on the world market, the cost of such transportation is prohibitive. Australia could not play the role of an Imperial Valley to Britain's need for vegetables in winter.

The British solution for products from the arid lands had to be in terms of nonperishable products in demand in the home country and of sufficient value to stand the transportation costs. Wheat, the staff of life for the Europeans, can be grown on the margin of the arid lands. It is a relatively nonperishable product and of relatively high value for its bulk. Sheep can be grazed in the arid lands and moved about to take advantage of the shifting of useful areas that results from the uneven distribution of rainfall in arid regions. The wool had a high demand in the mother country, could last the long trip, and therefore was profitable to send through the tropics and nearly half way around the world to the market.

Both wheat and sheep are traditional uses of the land in the British Isles, but British wheat and British sheep are not necessarily the best kinds for Australia. After all, Britain is a cool, moist country of nearly perpetual green. Arid Australia is a tawny yellow country of great heat and frequent drought. Although the idea of growing wheat and raising sheep for wool was natural to the British colonists, the transfer of these ideas to a new and totally different physical environment was not a "natural response to the physical environment." Instead, the potential market led these men to develop such land-use possibilities almost in spite of the physical environment.

Arid Australia remains a land of thin settlement, of very extensive use of the land (as contrasted with intensive use), and is constantly struggling with the problem of water. At the present stage of technological development, it may be said that the use of this great dry heart of Australia is severely limited by the lack of water. The land, the chemically rich earth materials, and the hot sun are all there.

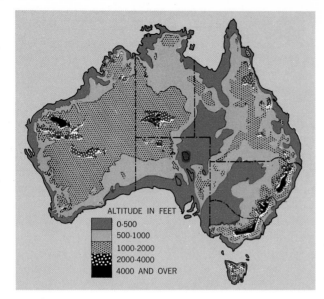

Land Form

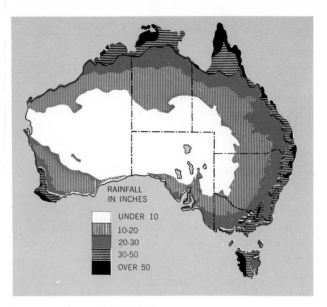

Average Annual Rainfall

Map 2-10   Australia and Tasmania: Land Form, Rainfall, and Land Use

The general low altitude of Australia is clearly indicated by the very small areas over 2000 feet and the very extensive areas under 1000 feet. It is a land of extensive plains and low rolling uplands with small areas of moderate-size mountains.

The range of rainfall in Australia is very high: from more than 50 inches in some regions to less than 10 in others. The values of these rainfalls are also variable. Fifty inches on the tropical north coast coming during a period of heavy rainfall gives rise to flood conditions that in the succeeding period of little rainfall under tropical sun soon give way to severe drought. Fifty inches of rainfall in south Australia creates a much wetter situation due to less evaporation. The 20-inch rainfall line approximately marks the zone of transition from agriculture to cattle and sheep raising, from farming to ranching. The area with less than 10 inches of rainfall is desert of very low productivity.

The importance of rainfall in the utilization of Australia becomes clear when the rainfall map is compared with the land-use map. Very little land with less than 20 inches of rainfall is used for crops, except in the area of winter rainfall in the south. Equally interesting, however, is the extent of untilled land in the areas of high rainfall in the north. The land-use map shows how small is the area under cultivation. The large, almost unused arid interior stands out strongly in contrast. The nonintensive level of land use is well indicated by the broad areas of cattle and sheep ranges, which are almost all on natural unimproved pasture land. *Adapted from* Focus—*The American Geographical Society.*

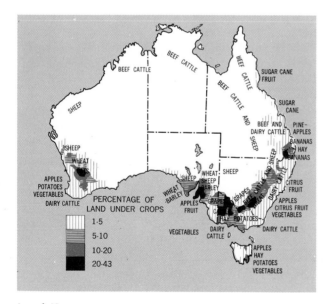

Land Use

Only the magical element of water is needed to make of this vast area an enormous plant-production area. Should the release of energy now being explored in atomic physics give us almost unlimited cheap power and should the chemical industry learn to desalt sea water cheaply, then such arid regions may yet come to be viewed as major-resource areas of the earth. No one can say whether these things will happen, but they may. Every new idea, every technological advance could (or should) lead us to assess anew the potentiality of the earth. The physical environment's usefulness changes every time a new idea is born. It is the idea that is the ruling element.

SUMMARY

To summarize, the dry lands present the following picture. They have a limitation placed on them by the shortage of water, but they have a great potential in their abundance of sunshine, the long growing season in the low-latitude dry lands, and in the chemical wealth of their unleached soils. Where water from adjacent humid regions is concentrated in these areas, there are rich oases in the desert. These may vary from tiny oases about small springs to extensive ones such as the Nile and the Colorado river valleys, or such other potential Egypts as the Orange River of South Africa, or the Murray-Darling river system of Australia.

What happened in each of these dry lands of the world was entirely different: ranging from great civilization and empire in Egypt and Peru to the simplest hunters and gatherers in the American Southwest, in Australia, and in South Africa. In the Old World there was a development of pastoral nomadism that had no counterpart in the New World or in Australia. In the Old World, the stage of development of culture can be seen to be rather directly related to access to ideas stemming from the great cultural hearth in the Near East. In the New World, the spread of ideas radiated from a Middle American center, and there was some symmetry to the spread of the ideas from this center and in the effects that these ideas produced in the arid lands that they reached. Thus, on the margins of the civilized center of Mexico lay the simple town-dwellers of our Plateau region (the Pueblo people), and on the margins of the civilized center of Peru a similar culture existed in northwest Argentina. Beyond these regions were simple hunters and gatherers untouched by advanced ideas.

In post-Columbian times the use of the arid lands has had a varied history. The greatest changes have occurred in those areas where the land at European contact was in the hands of the least culturally advanced peoples, who were largely dispossessed. The change in Egypt is slight compared to the change in Australia. The spread of domestic animals as a useful means of harvesting the arid lands, and thus replacing the simple gathering folk with pastoral or ranching people, has been nearly world-wide. No great civilization or empire is now based on the dry lands, or any major oases. The bases of power that once lay in such dry lands as Mesopotamia, northwest India, Egypt, and Peru, now lie in utterly different climates. These changes have all occurred in a time of relatively constant conditions of the physical world. The causes cannot then have been the physical environments.

3-The Wet Tropics

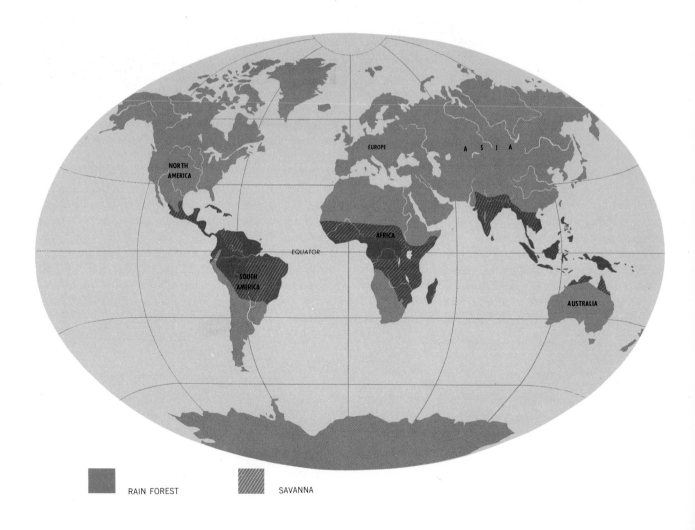

RAIN FOREST   SAVANNA

NO OTHER CLIMATIC REGION has so much folklore associated with it as the wet tropics. This land, straddling the equator in an irregular belt of 20 to 40 degrees in width, is distinguished from all the other regions of the earth by the lack of substantial seasonal variations, particularly by the lack of winter cold. Instead, the difference between day and night provides variation in climate greater than between winter and summer. The coolest months average about 65° F., and such trees as palms mark the landscape. These lands occupy 20 percent of the land surface of the earth.

THE PHYSICAL SETTING

Tropical lands must be subdivided. The tropical rain forest has no dry season; the savanna has a distinct dry season, and drought lays a firm hand on the land; while the monsoon climate has a dry season, but the rainfall during the wet season is so great that the effect of the drought is much less. Mountains interrupt the tropical belts, and above 3500 feet the temperatures fall below those typical of the tropics.

Tropical Rain Forest

The tropical rain forest is characterized by uniformly high temperatures with heavy rainfall well distributed through the year. It is typically located astride the equator and extends poleward approximately 5 to 10 degrees of latitude. The length of day changes not at all on the equator, and very little near it. The noonday sun is always nearly vertical in the sky, so that the amount of sunlight or insolation is at a near maximum throughout the year, varying little. The results are annual average temperatures of about 77° to 80° F.

Many cities in the United States have summer-month temperatures higher than this, but in the tropics these temperatures vary little through the year. The annual range from the hottest month to the coldest month is less than 5 degrees. For instance, Belem in Brazil and Singapore in Malaya have an annual range of 3 degrees, although the daily ranges are much greater than this and may run from 10 to 25 degrees. Bolobo, in the Congo, has a daily temperature range of 16 degrees and annual temperature range of only 2 degrees. Even the absolute ranges are not great. Santarem in Brazil, for example, has had a maximum of 96° F. and a minimum of 65° F. Compare Baltimore's 107° F. maximum and −7° F. minimum and some of the imagined horrors of the tropics begin to disappear.

However, the wet tropics are humid, and humidity increases the body's reaction to heat. The nights too are humid, and cool off relatively little. It cannot be said that the tropics are cool, but the question of discomfort must be kept in perspective. The heat load is considerably greater during a heat wave in Chicago, St. Louis, or Washington than it ever is in the tropical rain forest.

Rainfall is heavy and regular, and a great deal of it comes in the form of hard thundershowers. Although there is no dry period, some months are less wet than others. At Belem it rains on 90 percent of the days in the rainiest season, but on only one third of the days in the "dry" season. The amount of rainfall is heavy, but often varies considerably. For instance, at Colombo in Ceylon the wettest year on record had 139 inches of rain, and the driest, 50 inches. The wet tropics also have spots such as Cherrapunji in India that compete for the wettest place on earth, with such rainfalls as 400 inches per year, 900 inches being recorded in 1861.

Monsoon Regions

The monsoon regions, most typically developed in India and Burma, are intermediate between the rain forest and the savanna climates. They have the heavy rainfall of the former and the dry season of

Banks of the Amazon. Typical selva vegetation appears here except that the river forms an opening that allows light to reach the forest floor and hence there is a growth of vegetation near the ground that would not be found 100 yards in from the bank. The cultural poverty of the Amazon is also illustrated by the poor housing clinging to the bank of the stream. Yet this is one of the world's most navigable rivers running through one of the greatest rain forests there is. *American Geographical Society.*

Daule River, Ecuador. Savanna-type landscape in the seasonally wet-and-dry tropics is shown here. The steep banks and low position of the landing stages indicate that this is the dry period. *International Bank for Reconstruction and Development.*

the latter, and are usually found along tropical coasts backed by mountains, where the seasonally onshore winds spill heavy loads of moisture. Total rainfall is often high, and is markedly seasonal. The range of temperatures is greater than in the rain forest climates, annually varying some 12 to 14 degrees. The highest temperatures generally come just before the rainy (summer) season begins. With the approach of summer the sun mounts higher in the sky, the parched land gets hotter and hotter, until finally the rains come. Then the moistened ground and the spreading green under the increasing cloud cover bring the slightly lower temperatures that continue until the rains cease and the sun moves to lower elevations, when the warm, dry period (winter) begins.

Savanna Climates

In the Savanna climates there is more seasonality of rainfall and less rainfall than in the monsoon climates. The forest that characterizes both the rain forest and the monsoon regions gives way to a tree-studded grassland that merges toward the poles with the low-latitude dry lands. This is the transition between the desert climates and the equatorial wet climates. Tropical rainy summers alternate with desert dry winters. Rainfall is strongly concentrated in the summers but usually amounts to only 40 to 60 inches per year. In these hot regions, this is not a great deal of precipitation, for rain falling on hot earth and under an intense sun evaporates quickly. In the cooler mid-latitudes this would be enough rainfall for a forest cover!

Where the onshore winds on the tropical east coast of continents bring both evenly distributed rainfall and stable, oceanic temperatures to the shore there are extensions of the tropical climates to mid-latitudes. Such areas extend up the east coast of Central America to Yucatán, down the east coast of Brazil to Rio de Janeiro, and down the east side of Madagascar.

Vegetation

Each of these climatic regions has its characteristic vegetation. The rain forest has trees 100 feet and more in height and is very exacting in its requirements: there can be no prolonged dry season, and there must be at least 60 to 80 inches of rainfall per year. Elevation brings cooler temperatures and the tropical rain forest generally does not go up to more than 2000 feet elevation. Few areas meet such conditions; the Amazon basin, the Congo basin, and the

Cattle at a Water Hole in Brushy Savanna-type Country of Venezuela. The greatly mixed types of cattle indicate the relatively undeveloped state of cattle culture. *Embassy of Venezuela.*

equatorial inlands from Sumatra to New Guinea are the principal rain forests.

The tropical rain forest is composed of layers of trees. The forest giants reach up 130 to 160 feet and their tops protrude from a green sea of foliage. Trees of 100 to 130 in height form a continuous umbrella of green and intercept much of the insolation. Beneath them is an understory of trees 50 to 80 feet in height. These layers leave little light to reach the forest floor and consequently there is little vegetation on the ground. The trees are straight trunked, shallow rooted, and stand on mats of surface roots and prop roots that form buttresses. The trees are bound together by strongly growing vines, or lianas. Epiphytes, nonparasitic plants that use trees for support, are numerous, the orchid being an example.

The savanna varies greatly in its plant cover. On its equatorial boundary it is nearly semi-desert; these are grassy savannas where greatly varied grasses range from 1 to 12 feet in height—elephant grass sometimes grows to 16 feet high! There are also wooded savannas where the trees are moderately abundant; such an area is sometimes called a "park forest." Trees in savannas may reach a height of 50 feet and often have thick bark. There is considerable controversy over the origin of the grass savannas—as there is with the grasslands (see Chapter 6). Are they natural, or did man help to create them by setting frequent fires? That a woody cover of the land is a "normal" situation rather than a grass savanna is suggested by the dry deciduous forest that often forms the transition between the rain forest and the dry lands. The dry deciduous forests are stunted-tree and thorny-bush areas. Rainfall ranges in the wooded savannas from 15 to 45 inches per year, but the dry season is very long, sometimes lasting up to nine months. Again, the rain comes in the summer when evaporation is high.

Such woody plant cover is common in Queensland, Australia, and is found on the Pacific slope of Mexico south of Lower California down to Panama. There are large areas of this type of vegetation in Africa, especially in the Sudan and East Africa. In Brazil this type of savanna is very extensive and has

the special name of "caatinga." It covers 300,000 square miles of northeastern Brazil and is present over large areas to the south. This vast, scrubby tree forest is deciduous: in the dry season, it is a barren, gray area looking like a mid-latitude beech forest in winter; with the onset of the summer rains, it puts out a profusion of colorful blossoms and rapidly becomes green.

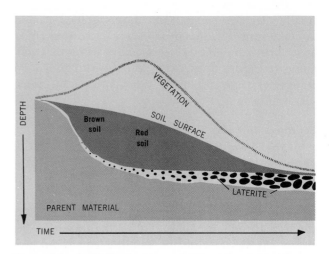

Figure 3-1 Soil Weathering and Time. Starting with unweathered material of any kind, the soil-weathering process can be illustrated as shown in the diagram, which reads from left to right. Any material subjected to surface weathering will at first improve in ability to support vegetation, and then gradually it will lose fertility as the weathering releases mineral nutrients that are removed from the soil by the rain water that percolates through the soil mass and drains away. Simultaneously, the surface of the land is being lowered by erosion, and redeposition of minerals is going on at depth. Iron and its related minerals, manganese and aluminum, accumulate at depth, and in time this accumulation may produce a heavy slag-like iron layer: laterite. When the land surface erodes down to this layer, an almost sterile land surface is the result. Characteristically, soils change color through time. Those starting from nonred materials are first gray, then brown, then red. Reddish soils normally are older soils and poorer than brown soils. Since heat and moisture speed weathering, tropical humid soils tend to age rapidly. Nevertheless, it normally takes one-half to one million years of stable weathering conditions to reach the stage of greatly impoverished soil with an immense laterite layer.

Tropical Soils

The soils of the tropics are one of the limiting factors in the agricultural use of the land. The process of weathering of rock that produces soil is a complex one and goes on through time (see Figure 3–1). The weathering is directional, that is, there is a continuing breakdown of the rock material into simpler and simpler compounds. In humid regions the soluble materials are constantly being removed by the percolating waters. The chemical action of the rain water is greatly increased by the organic compounds resulting from the decay of the vegetable material derived from the forest cover of the land. In the rain forest regions, the immense forests produce a huge amount of vegetable material, all of which eventually falls to the ground and decays, providing humic acids and other organic compounds that aid in the chemical breakup first of the solid rock, then of the rock fragments, and then of the finer particles. The end of the process can be an accumulation of the insoluble parts of the rock,

with most of this material being quartz. Such material is of no use for growing plants. Since this weathering process goes on through time, it is clear that the longer any land area has been left undisturbed subject to humid tropical weathering, the poorer the soils on that area will be. This tends to be true in all humid areas, but since the speed of chemical reactions increases with temperature, the result of impoverished soils is achieved more rapidly in the hot, wet tropics than elsewhere.

Tropical soils therefore tend with age to become poor. The old flat lands of the tropics tend to have ancient, deeply weathered covers of leached out and therefore very poor soil materials. Where young volcanic materials cover the landscape, or where fresh alluvium is deposited, or on steep slopes where erosion removes the weathered products and exposes fresh rock materials, the soils are good. It is a curious fact that what much of the low, flat tropical areas need is an accelerated case of erosion to strip off the 50 to 100 feet of weathered and impoverished materials that overlie the fresh rock that could

Mount Bromo, Java. Active young volcanic materials keep the soils fertile, and even the streams coming down these volcanic slopes carry much nutrient material in solution. *Embassy of Indonesia.*

supply the nutrients that plants must have for adequate growth and production. Yet it is just the flat areas that are not subject to erosion.

There is a seeming contradiction in all of this. The tropical rain forest is the highest, densest, most varied forest on earth. If tropical soils are so poor, how can this be? No forest can grow luxuriantly on a soil that cannot provide nutrients. In areas of utterly impoverished soils in the tropics, despite optimum temperature and rainfall, the vegetation is desertlike. There have been areas where luxuriant forest grew, but which when the forest was cut down, were found to be unable to maintain any crops whatever. Furthermore, once the land was abandoned, it could not be brought to support a forest again either.

This interesting situation arises because the tropical forests are cycling the nutrients that exist in their soil and plant system (see Figure 3–2), and there is very little leakage out of the system. The minerals taken from the soil go to form branch, leaf, and fruit; these ultimately fall to the ground, and there decay. As fast as their minerals are returned to the ground, the waiting network of roots takes them up and reuses them. Since the plants are using carbon

Figure 3-2 (*opposite*) Cycling of Nutrients in a Tropical Rain Forest. The complex cycling of nutrients in a tropical rain forest is diagrammed in simplified form here. Except for the continuous action due to lack of seasons in the tropics, this cycle applies to vegetation in the seasonal climates too. The plant utilizes water and nutrients drawn from the soil and then utilizes solar energy to combine them to form wood, leaf, and fruit. Leaf, fruit, and branch falling to the ground decay, and the nutrient materials released, minus leakage to the ground water, are taken up by the tree roots and reused. Nutrients are also gained from the decay of rock material. As weathering progresses, the amount of weatherable rock minerals near the surface decreases, and the depth to relatively fresh rock increases. Eventually, the depth to fresh rock exceeds the depth of penetration of the roots. When this occurs the system is precariously balanced, for the plants are running on the material in the cycle. Any large loss, such as would occur if the forest were burned, might bankrupt the system.

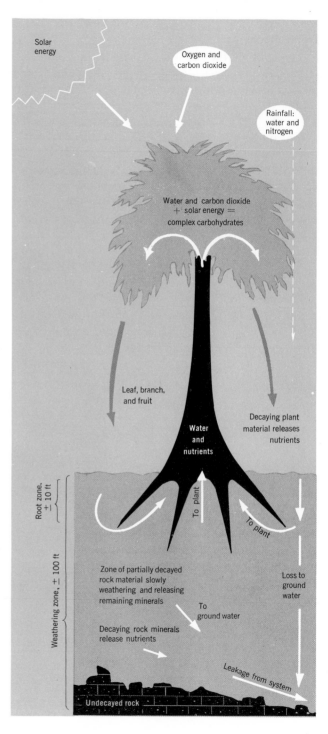

dioxide taken from the air to make carbohydrates, and combining these carbohydrates with minerals, there is a slow enrichment going on that tends to balance the slow leakage of nutrients through the weathering process. Such a system can run for a long time, delicately balancing the losses and the gains, but imperceptibly running down as the rocks are weathered to greater and greater depth and the surface mantle of weathered materials come to contain less and less weatherable material that can release the minerals needed by the plant cover.

When man enters such a critically balanced system and cuts down the trees and burns the woody and vegetable material, he destroys the balance. The immense tonnage of woody, organic compounds is converted to gases that go off as smoke and flame; the ashy residue is largely washed down through the soil mass and drained away in the ground water. Little is left except the insoluble end products of weathering, and little can be grown in this; the forest cannot re-establish itself.

This imbalance, of course, represents the extreme case. In most tropical rainy regions, the forests tend to accumulate the organic and mineral materials and cycle them in the way described. Usually the soils have not gone to so extreme a situation of weathering. Consequently, when the forest is cut and burned, there is enough fertility to grow a crop or two, and still enough fertility for the forest to regenerate and begin accumulating organic materials again.

LAND USE

There are many ways of using the tropical forest lands. The simplest and undoubtedly the earliest was that of simple hunting and gathering, a way of life that can be practiced in every environment with the possible exception of the arctic. There are a few people left in the world that still utilize the tropical lands in this way, for example, the Veddas of Ceylon, the Pygmies of the Ituri forest of the Congo,

Hilly Land on the Island of Sumba. Treeless, grassy areas in the humid tropics are not uncommon. They frequently are caused by shifting agriculturalists having driven out the trees by too frequent clearing and burning. *Embassy of Indonesia.*

and the people of the Yellow Leaves in northern Siam. They wander through the forests, gathering fruits and honey, catching small animals, and getting some fish, but most of the tropical forest people of the world have long left this way of life, and turned to farming. There are several kinds of forest agriculture, but they can be treated under two headings: shifting agriculture and permanent agriculture.

Primitive forest agriculture has always used the forest as a long-term rotation crop. The land is allowed to rest under forest cover for 5 to 20 years, during which time a large stock of material is accumulated in the plant cover on the land. Burning releases this material and the ash provides a dressing of mineral fertilizer. The forest cover also shades out all the weeds. In a year or two, when the weak fertilizer effects have worn off, the land is again allowed to rest under its 5- to 20-year rotation into forest cover. This is a way of land use, of course, that dictates that there be 5 to 20 times as much land in the rotation reserve as is necessary for sustaining the agricultural needs of the inhabitants. Students of tropical agriculture generally agree that this type of land use is an efficient way for primitive agricultures to use a rain forest. While it seems wasteful of timber, this product itself has no market. The patchy forest clearings create little erosion risk and disturb the ecology of the land the minimum amount. But what is the determining force here: the physical environment or the cultural one? Could a tropical forest area be used otherwise?

There is a built-in potential crisis in the shifting agriculture pattern of land use. If the population grows, a point is reached where the land can not be allowed enough time to recover between periods of use. Then the weeds get established, the soil becomes run down, and the situation deteriorates rapidly. At this point, new land must be found, or the population must be reduced, or some new and more intensive way of using the land must be found. Few peoples have discovered new ways of land use and the population density of most of the tropical forest lands of the world has therefore been fixed by the amount of forest available for rotation.

The Wet-rice Solution

A way of developing a denser and more permanent settlement on the wet-forest land was worked out in Southeast Asia. The rice plant was found to be capable of growing in standing water and of making a crop on soils so poor that they would not yield a return under any other circumstances. We are uncertain of the origin of rice; it does not belong in northern China or northwestern India and is surprisingly late to appear in the East Indian islands. Since its cultivation depends upon changing lengths of day, that is, seasons, rice can not be an equatorial plant. Perhaps its homeland was southern China, in some area such as the Yangtze River valley.

Rice is an amazingly versatile plant, for different kinds can grow under a great variety of conditions. One type can be planted in hillside forest clearings and grown without irrigation; another can be planted in shallow water, will elongate its stem as the floods raise the water level, and will develop a rice crop while floating like a rooted pond weed. This rice is harvested when the flood waters recede and the land is dry again. There is rice that will mature a crop in 120 days and rice that needs more than 360 days. In addition to the elongated rice grains familiar to us, there are both longer and more slender grain types and shorter and thicker types right down to nearly round grains. Such a variety of adaptation—long to short season, swamp to dry field—gives man great opportunity to select ways of handling his crop. Is this great variability something man found in this plant and utilized, or did man take this plant and develop this wide range of uses? Probably it was a little of both.

Only Asia developed a grain plant to grow in a swamp! Although it is difficult to see just how this was done, it seems more likely that man started with a swamp plant than with an upland plant. It is conceivable that he then extended the swamp environment by simple dikes and ditches, eventually making whole flood plains and even mountainsides into artificial swamps for rice growing.

Wet Rice Fields, Java. Notice the terracing of the slopes leading down to the streams. The clumps of trees, mostly around house and village sites, completely hidden by the trees, are all that remains of the tropical forest. *Embassy of Indonesia.*

Preparing a Wet Rice Field with Water Buffalo in Java. *Embassy of Indonesia.*

This development has made possible a dense permanent settlement on land that could not otherwise continuously yield a harvest, because the wet rice draws a good deal of its sustenance not from the soil but from the water. A rice paddy is a bit like a balanced aquarium, only more complex. In the rice field there are fish, frogs, insects, micro-organisms, and birds and animals to prey on them. In the warm shallow waters, these many life forms all live and die and the rice plant profits thereby. It draws some sustenance from the often poor soil, some from the air, some from the water, and some from the by-products of the rich plant and animal community that shares its pond.

Sometimes the paddyfields are simply wafflelike, catching only the rain water that falls. Rain water is not pure water, but contains measurable amounts of impurities, especially the important plant nutrient nitrogen. Other fields are fed by streams, whose waters carry dissolved nutrients; and streams from young volcanic mountains, especially those from basic volcanic areas, may carry relatively large amounts of desirable nutrient materials. It therefore pays the farmer to irrigate his fields even though there is an abundant rainfall to supply the water needed to keep the paddyfields flooded. In Southeast Asia, Java is a conspicuously densely settled area, and some, though by no means all, of this density is due to the fact that Java is largely composed of active, basic, volcanic mountains. Its streams are an extremely dilute but highly valuable liquid fertilizer because these young basic volcanic rocks yield measurable amounts of chemicals under active tropical humid weathering.

The extremely great population densities from India around to China are agriculturally based, in sharp contrast to those of Europe and North America, which are based on commercial developments. We know that the Indian population is an old one that as early as 2500 B.C. had city-states rivaling the Mesopotamia area. China's beginnings are thought to have been in the north, outside the tropics, and Chinese and Indian influences seem to account for later developments in the area between them. The question, therefore, is: Who developed the intense agricultural system that we associate with wet-rice culture? If China, was the invention made outside the tropics and irrigation techniques developed in dry lands, carried into the wet lands, and there applied to rice growing? If India, was this new way of using the land invented in the dryer parts and extended into the wet lands? Is wet-rice farming an extension of arid-land irrigation into the wet tropics? Or did wet-rice farming lead to the discovery of water control and this in turn lead to irrigation of dry lands? Or were the two ideas discovered quite independently? These are important questions. Until they are answered, how can one draw conclusions about man's response to his environment?

Wherever and however discovered, the wet-rice method of using tropical lands is important, for it made possible permanent dense settlement on a scale not seen in the rain forest before this time. It is potentially useful in much of the world, but notice how little of tropical Africa or tropical America grows rice. Yet by utilizing Asiatic methods, these areas too could support similar agriculture. As always, each new idea potentially remakes the world, and as always, the potential is exceedingly slow in being developed.

Mechanization of Rice Production

It is often said that rice growing requires coolie labor, and that its spread is therefore not desirable. Rice growing methods in the United States refute this. Rice growing began quite early in colonial America, where the low swampy land on the eastern coastal plain was well suited to this crop. The lands were diked and the crop produced with the use of much labor, as in the orient. However, the scarcity of labor and limited European markets as well as the higher return for other crops such as tobacco and cotton led to the decline of rice production.

Note here the negligible role of the physical environment. For thousands of years the eastern United States coastal plain existed as it does now, but the Indians did not grow rice or any equivalent

Harvesting Wild Rice on the Vermilion River, Minnesota. One person poles the boat through the rice beds while the other pulls batches of rice stalks into the boat with a stick in one hand and knocks the ripe rice into the bottom of the boat with a stick in the other hand. This is precisely the method used by the Indians to harvest rice in earlier times. Although this grain will bring about 50 cents a pound as harvested and from 3 to 4 dollars a pound in the stores, no one is rushing to put production on a rational basis. Thus we repeat the foibles of other peoples in other times in the realm of plant and animal domestication. *USDA photo.*

crop there. Nor can it be said that such a plant was not available in North America, for there is a plant here called wild rice. It is a grass of a different genus than rice, but its growth pattern is like the Asiatic wet rice. The American Indians harvested it, but never cultivated it; this is doubly interesting since they did cultivate corn. They had the idea of farming, but in the eastern United States, where they harvested both corn and wild rice, they lacked the idea of irrigation. Hence even in an ideal environment and with a ready-made plant, whose use they fully understood, they failed to accept "the environmental invitation." There was no invitation, of course. The possibility lay mutely before them, and they saw it not.

The American colonists had contacts directly and indirectly with Asia, and from this source came the ideas. The environmental possibility for the foreign grain was seen. The ideas came in a package: Asiatic wet-rice cultivation with Asiatic rice. The colonists did not use the American plant, probably because the idea never occurred to them. They certainly

would have had marketing difficulties if it had, for people are very resistant to new foods. Who would take up a strange new grain? Only recently has the American "wild rice" found a limited market as a luxury, "specialty" food.

In America a transfer of methods occurred where the rice-growing area of the lower Mississippi met the wheat growers of the Middle West. Once the wheat farmers had mechanized their own production, they looked at the laborious hand methods of the rice farmers and saw a wheatlike grain, grassy straw, and the price of rice. If they could handle rice with their mechanized cultivators, seeders, harvester, and threshers, they could produce rice cheaply. The wet soil was a problem. They proceeded to control this by cultivating the land when dry, drilling the seed in, then flooding the land by use of pumps. Harvesting was done by drying the land and utilizing slightly modified wheat combines and threshers pulled by tractors. By these methods it was found that rice could be produced cheaply enough to compete with the "cheap labor" of the

Harvesting a Vast Rice Field in the Sacramento River Valley, California. The extreme of mechanization is represented by airplanes sowing the seed, spraying for weed and insect control, and frightening away wild ducks. Harvesting is accomplished with giant combines as shown here. *Agricultural Publications, University of California.*

Rice Growing at Humpty Doo, Northern Territory, Australia. The vast northern part of this territory, over half a million acres of vast, flat, virtually unoccupied land, is equal in size to the states of Washington, Oregon, California, Nevada, and Arizona combined. Each year 4 months of heavy to moderate rainfall are followed by 8 months of drought. Experimentation with rice finally promises a solution to the problem of an economic use for this land. *Australian News and Information Bureau.*

Asiatic area. Rice is now grown in the United States in a number of areas, including the desert oases of the Imperial Valley and the San Joaquin Valley of California.

An example of how these ideas can be applied elsewhere is found in Northern Australia. This tropical savanna area has been a problem of the Australians. It is distant from their population centers; transportation has been meager; and the seasons are so extreme that during the dry season the streams cease to run and the grass withers away. It is poor land for cattle or sheep, or wheat or oats, but it is good rice land—flat, alternately flooded and dry—immense tracts available at very low cost to provide rice in demand in the world market.

With adequate capital, and with Australian governmental blessing, test plantings are now being carried on. If they prove successful, large-scale development will follow. A 10 percent increase in world rice production is planned. Again one sees the importance of ideas. The Australian environment has changed little in the past 10,000 years. Irrigation rice farmers have lived in nearby Asia for per-haps 5000 years and on the adjacent Indonesian islands for at least 1000 years. Europeans with abundant knowledge have occupied Australia for 150 years, and have looked for some way to use "the north country" for at least these past 50 years. Yet the final putting together of man and land and ideas comes only in the 1960s.

Should Asia now revamp the use of its rice lands and put tractors and harvesters to work instead of men? Perhaps, but surely not suddenly. The Asiatic rice paddy is a small field, adapted to a bullock, and to work by hand labor. The fields are not laid out for tractors. The whole scale of the Asiatic operation is small, the labor input is great, and the yield per acre is large. The American system is the reverse. It could not be introduced into Asia without reshaping the land, reorienting the people, and almost totally changing the social and economic structure of the countries. Such changes can be made only gradually.

In Japan today the mechanization of small rice fields has begun with the introduction of heavy-duty rototillers. These are a one-man garden tool com-

Preparing a Wet Rice Field with a Power Tiller in Japan. This implement represents the current step toward mechanization of hand agriculture of this type. *Consulate General of Japan, N.Y.*

Tea Plantation in West Java. An example of the conversion of the naturally mixed forest to a forest of a desired economic species. *Embassy of Indonesia.*

parable to a power mower but designed to stir the soil of the flooded fields. They are relatively light, cheap, and can be operated by one man on his traditionally small fields. Already they have increased yields up to 40 percent. This innovation should release manpower from field labor, and this manpower can then be employed in Japan's growing industry while being fed from the greater amount of rice produced by fewer men on the land. Not every nation is ready for this step, for there must be growing industry to absorb displaced farm labor. Also, there must be a farm-labor force ready to accept, care for, and use wisely the new machinery, which is relatively expensive and complicated compared to either the old hand tools or the simple plows used with water buffalo.

We have been through a change somewhat of this kind in the United States. To use rough figures: 100 years ago this was a land of small farmers who produced a small surplus by using horses for power. There were 10 farmers for every city-manufacturing-commercial worker. Today this is a land of increasingly few, mechanized, large farms producing such high surpluses that our people are now about 90 percent urban workers and 10 percent rural. Asia

could, and probably will, make a similar shift in the next 100 years. The Communist regime in China is attempting to force the change in a tenth of this time, but the price being paid in human values is incalculably high, while the outcome so far has been catastrophic declines in both agricultural and manufacturing production with resulting famine.

The Plantation System

Another way of using tropical lands is the plantation system, the application of capital and skilled direction to the production in the tropics of a product destined to enter the world market. Examples of such products are sugar, bananas, coconuts, palm oil, and rice as produced in northern Australia. The origin of this system is often credited to the Portugese, who produced sugar on the islands off West Africa by taking advantage of the tropical climate, using slave labor, adding their managerial and commercial skills, and profiting by the sale of the product in the European market. The Portuguese carried this system to Brazil, where they produced sugar under these same conditions. Other examples of the development of tropical crops under the plantation system have been the growing of bananas by the United Fruit Company in Central America, the British and Dutch production of rubber in the East Indies, tea production in India, palm oil production in West Africa, and copra production in Polynesia. In each case the impetus (ideas, capital, and organization) came from outside and put the natural resources and native labor to use to produce a product for the world market.

The plantation system has acquired a bad name in this century because it has been linked with economic imperialism and identified with the use of slave labor. Like any human institution, of course, it can be and has been abused. The United Fruit Company in Central America is often cited by those who dislike big business and plantations as an example. Yet the United Fruit Company today pays high wages in the areas in which it works. It builds railroads and docks, brings about improved sanitation, and increases the national income of the nation within whose territory it operates. A company can not succeed with sick and ignorant labor and cannot afford to have its skilled management die off; in its own interest it must sanitate its area and build up its labor force. Tropical development results from such efforts. Productivity is necessary if tropical peoples are to have the adequate housing, sanitation, medication, and education that are the prerequisites of making these regions the potentially useful regions of the world that they could be.

Since the tropics are natural tree areas, it would seem that the best thing to do with them is to use them to produce tree crops. There are many of these, and the plantations have seized upon some of them to supply industrial materials, food crops, or textiles. For example, palms supply many kinds of oils that are useful either as foods or as industrial materials, for example, as the basis for soaps. There are many tropical tree fruits, of which the banana, citrus, and avocado are but a tiny sampling. With the explosive increase in facility of transportation there is little reason that tropical fruits should not enter world trade. Tropical nuts are already popular: the cashew and brazil nut among others. There are also many tropical vegetables that come directly from trees,

such as leaves that are like spinach and flowers that are like cauliflower. Even textiles are available: not only is Manila hemp a tree crop (a banana), but cotton is naturally a perennial shrubby tree that we have converted into an annual. In the tropics it yields continuously for years.

Modern efforts to use the tropical forests have not been marked by much wisdom in the early stages. When tropical forest crops such as rubber were first grown in plantations in Indonesia, the land was cleared, the trees planted, and the ground kept free of weeds and cultivated just as it would be in a mid-latitude orchard. The result under tropical heat and high intensity rainfalls was enormous erosion and great loss of fertilizer through leaching down through the soil. Belatedly, it was learned that the proper way to grow a tropical rain-forest tree was to grow it under tropical rain-forest conditions. Today the approach is never to break the forest cover.

Tapping a Rubber Tree, Java. *Embassy of Indonesia.*

A new plantation is set out by going into the forest and making a tiny clearing, perhaps felling one or two trees, and planting the sapling of the desired tree in the spot of light on the forest floor that was so created. With such clearings spaced 100 feet apart, and with gradual cutting back of the adjacent trees as the economically useful trees grow, the transition can be made from a forest of many varieties of trees of little economic value, to a forest of trees of high economic value. The transition can be made without ever breaking the continuity of the forest and the end product is a forest growing under seemingly natural conditions, but differing from a natural forest in the great concentration of economically useful trees. It needs no cultivation; it has no erosion risk.

The Ford Rubber Experiment

The limitations of tropical land forms—and their characteristic soils, plants, and climate—can be illustrated by the experience of the Ford Motor Company in its attempts to produce rubber in the Amazon some years ago. The Ford Company was trying at that time to establish its own supply of rubber, and hence to be free of the virtual monopoly in the East Indies under British and Dutch control. What was more natural than to turn to Brazil, the home of the rubber tree?

Brazil was glad to cooperate. The Amazon basin had become virtually nonproductive after the British and the Dutch rubber plantations in the Far East had driven Brazilian wild rubber out of the world market with their cheaper and higher quality production. If Ford wished to redivert some of the millions of dollars in the rubber business into Brazil, its government could only be delighted.

Ford was therefore given almost carte blanche in choosing land in the Amazon basin. Its first mistake was to choose a tract of gently rolling, nearly flat, upland back off the floodplain of the river. Under tropical weathering conditions, lands that are level and not subject either to erosion—which would expose fresh rock material—or to deposition by flood waters—which would add fresh alluvial material—will be steadily impoverished by the weathering process. These flat, forest-covered, uneroded, uplands—free from river deposition—had been subject to the processes of tropical weathering for geological lengths of time. Such a site was guaranteed to produce poor soils. The second mistake was made when large areas of land were cleared, the wood burned, and the loosened and torn-up soil exposed to the tropical downpours and the strong tropical sun. The downpours started immense erosion; the hot tropical sun, beating on the soil that had for millennia been shaded by layer upon layer of forest trees, oxidized the remaining organic materials. The temperature of the soil was raised to heights so much greater than normal that the micro flora and fauna of the soil were virtually exterminated.

The third mistake was to plant in this desert—bare soil and blazing sun—seedling trees adapted to making their start under the shaded, moist, hothouselike atmosphere of a rain forest. It was like planting a hothouse plant in the Sahara. The result was large losses of the transplanted trees.

The plantation struggled along with poor soil, erosion, soil impoverishment, and seedling losses. When the mistakes were finally realized, it was decided to start afresh. The Brazilian government remained cooperative. A new tract nearer the river mouth and on better soils was selected, and the trees were set out in forest clearings. But further difficulties developed: the trees that yielded such large amounts of rubber in the Far East, because they had been carefully selected for high yield by the Dutch and British, suffered tremendously from diseases when they were reintroduced into their homeland. Why should this have occurred?

The original trees shipped to the Far East had been seedlings, and the seed had been carried to Great Britain, where they were started in Kew Gardens. The diseases normal to the rubber tree in its homeland, and to which the trees had a high resistance, were all left behind when the trees were then sent on out to the Far East. The selection of trees over the succeeding years was for high yields, and since there was no disease load, there was no selection for the continuation of resistance to the plant diseases of Brazil. As a result, the trees were generally no longer immune, or resistant. When then they were reintroduced into the environment where the diseases that had been associated with rubber trees for millions of years were very much a part of the scene, these nonresistant strains were rapidly struck down.

It would seem here that the physical environment was at last determining something. Man had to use his ingenuity now. The quality desired was the ability of the rubber tree to yield a large amount of latex from the trunk of the tree. The disease attack concentrated on the roots and the leaves. The solution, therefore, was to grow a native tree, graft onto the native root a high-yielding strain, and when this strain had produced a stem capable of carrying a graft, to graft onto it a top of one of the leaf-blight resistant native strains. This tripartite plant then had a disease-resistant root, a highly productive trunk, and a disease-resistant top. Man had thus manufactured a plant to meet the disease problem in this particular environment. He could have done it by other means, too, but selecting and breeding high-yielding strains of the naturally resistant native trees would have taken longer.

Yet, after overcoming all the problems of soil, disease, and climate, the Ford plantations still failed; the causes were social, economic, and technological. There is almost no labor supply in the Amazon: population density is extremely low, and the region has an evil reputation. Under boom conditions in the past manpower had been dragooned into the area and cruelly exploited, and the loss of life under conditions of inadequate sanitation, housing, medical care, and income had been immense. Ford set out to avoid such mistakes. Good housing, pure water, medical care, and adequate food at moderate cost, combined with wages well above national averages, were counted on to attract a labor force, but to no avail. Workers were reluctant to enter the Amazon, a death trap for labor forces of the past. Perhaps given a longer time, the successful operation of the Ford plantations would have convinced workers of the superior living conditions provided there, and there might have developed the type of stable labor force that a plantation requires. But a technological revolution intervened.

Synthetic rubber was brought into production at cost levels that made it clear that natural rubber was going to face increasingly steep competition, with the probable eventual elimination of natural rubber as the major source of supply. At this point, the Ford Company cut its losses. After decades of effort during which they had learned a great deal and had invested many millions of dollars, the Ford Company turned its plantations over to the Brazilian government and withdrew from its experiment in tropical agriculture. It would be very easy to use this as an example of the impossibility of accomplishing anything in the tropics; however, the errors made and the great costs and delays that resulted could equally have been made in any other region. The technological change that led to the final decision to abandon the effort could equally have occurred in many another field. Another example of the problem is the Dutch monopoly in quinine produced from the cinchona tree (also a native of America taken to Southeast Asia and there improved), which was virtually destroyed by the production of a synthetic malaria drug that was as good as quinine in suppressing the symptoms of malaria and had fewer distressing side effects. Change and displacement due to technological advance is not limited to impacts on tropical agriculture, of course, though it may seem so because of the importance at present of plantation agriculture in the tropics.

CULTURE AND CIVILIZATION IN THE TROPICS

Clearly, there is a considerable variety of wet to semiwet tropical lands. The problem of man in the tropics has to be discussed with this variety in mind. If the wet tropics are defined as having at least a mean monthly temperature of 65° F. and sufficient rainfall for agriculture without irrigation, the hot, wet climates have an area of 14.5 million square miles.

Areas of Hot, Wet Climate	Square Miles
Asia and the East Indies	3,000,000
Melanesia, Oceania, Australia	750,000
Africa	5,750,000
America	5,000,000

In the main these are thinly populated areas. In America, the average density of population is about 2 per square mile; in Africa, between 2 and 3; and in New Guinea, less than 1. Average figures can be deceptive, of course, for areas like Central America have spots of dense population in the midst of large empty regions. Yet it remains true that these hot, wet regions are virtually empty in America, and are only thinly populated in Africa. Outside Asia these regions have only 8 percent of the world's population on 12 percent of the earth's land surface, and generally speaking, the people are food gatherers or simple cultivators.

In the hot wet parts of Asia, on the other hand, one quarter of all mankind is crowded onto 8 percent of the land surface of the earth. Despite this crowding, these people are higher on the scale of civilization than those in the more thinly occupied parts of the tropics. At first glance, it would seem that what much of the humid tropics needs is some vigorous population growth; however, it is commonly held that the tropics are unhealthy—too unhealthy to support large populations.

PHYSIOLOGY OF MAN IN THE TROPICS

One of the commonest beliefs is that white men cannot live productive lives in the tropics. This implies that there is a direct effect of the hot, wet climate on man, and that in particular it affects the white race. The usual implication is that both general health and mental activity are influenced. A brief review of man's physiology with special reference to heat seems the proper way to approach this problem, and it might be noted first of all that we have no data showing any significant differences between the various races in their reaction to heat and humidity.

Life processes are dependent on chemical changes; our bodies burn food to produce energy. A fair analogy is the internal combustion engine in automobiles: the heat produced must be dissipated or we rapidly run into difficulties. The general term for this consumption of energy by the body is metabolism, and basal metabolism is that energy needed for bare existence—the working of the heart, lungs, and so forth—even when we are at rest. Some energy is used even in digestion, but we use the greatest amount when we work; and 90 percent of this energy appears as heat.

We must normally maintain our body temperature at about 98.6° F., for increasingly great variation from this is accompanied by discomfort, distress, and eventually death. Hence, when we work, we must lose large amounts of heat to our surroundings. If we are unable to do so, physiological failure will result just as surely as an automotive failure if the engine's cooling system fails. It is common experience that autos overheat more often when working hard, as on mountain grades or at high speeds in hot weather. We can expect the human body to react similarly, so we must first consider the human cooling system.

Heat loss can be looked at in terms of simple physics. Heat can be lost or gained by radiation. You feel the warmth of a stove without touching it, for it is warmer than your body and you are gaining heat from it. If it were filled with ice, you could lose heat to it by the same process—a process independent of the temperature of the air. If you sat in a room filled with warm air, but whose walls were cold, you could become thoroughly chilled by radiation heat loss to the walls, a not uncommon experience in winter in mid-latitude houses that are not sufficiently insulated.

Sunlight also acts like radiant heat. Its effect is quite complex because the different parts of the light (ultraviolet to infrared) have different qualities for penetrating the layer of the atmosphere or the skin, for reflection and absorption in relation to colors, and so forth. Solar radiation is heating, and in the tropics the nearly vertical sun makes its effect intense. Added to the already warm and humid air, solar radiation increases the heat being added to the body, which already has the problem of disposing of the heat that it is generating. Wide roof overhangs, large hats, and parasols are all sensible cultural reactions to this heat load. How many people native to the tropics had them? Relatively few.

Heat may also be lost by conduction and convection. Heat is carried by the blood from deep body sources to the skin; the warm skin can then lose heat by contact with the surrounding air, provided that the air temperature is below the skin temperature. Since skin temperature is lower than body temperature, when the air temperature is about 95° F., this cooling process ceases, and at higher temperatures the body is heated rather than cooled. Conduction is not a very efficient cooling process. The heat transfer is from the skin to a thin layer of air in contact with the skin, which soon becomes skin temperature. Air movement facilitates the heat transfer by bringing new air in contact with the skin, accounting for the cooling effect of breezes and fans. If the air temperature were higher than the skin temperature, however, the effect of a breeze would be to increase the heat added to the body. But in most of the tropics the average monthly temperature is well below 90° F. and the highest temperatures ever recorded, at Panama and Singapore, are well below those annually experienced at such places as St. Louis, Chicago, Baltimore. This is only part of the story, however.

Our most effective cooling system is based on evaporation, heat being dissipated by using it to evaporate water. In dry regions, simple air conditioners work on this principle. Since we lose moisture through our skins and from our lungs and the temperature of these areas are fairly constant, the rate at which they can lose moisture is most nearly measured by the absolute amount of moisture in the surrounding air. This process, like the conduction loss, goes from the skin surface to the layer of air in contact with the skin. Rapid replacement of this contact layer of air ensures a new absorbent layer to replace the saturated layer. Breeze, then, greatly increases the efficiency of this system, and the dryer the air, the more moisture it can absorb and the more efficiently the evaporative cooling system can operate.

The body is equipped to use these methods. Blood volume, the water content of the blood, and the amount of blood sent to the surface areas are all increased as the heat load on the body increases. This process brings more moisture to the skin surface, where moisture loss occurs in two ways. There is simple evaporation from the moist surface, or perspiration. In addition, man—though not all animals—has special glands that can greatly increase the amount of water brought to the surface of the skin to evaporate: the sweat glands. The lungs are also areas of water loss from the body, hence a cooling zone. Under warm conditions, people breathe a little more deeply, thus increasing the ventilation in their lungs. This also tends to increase the oxygen content of the blood, an important function, for the diversion of blood to the skin areas can decrease blood flow to such vital areas as the brain. Even a slight decrease in oxygen supply there will result in discomfort, lassitude and headache and, if continued, could lead to greater distress.

Man reacts largely automatically to heat load. We do not have to think about our blood volume or perspiration, and even our deeper breathing is automatic. Just as we curl up to keep warm when cold, we stretch to cool off: the principle involved is that of increasing or decreasing the area from which heat will be lost. Behavior changes too; people rush around in the cold and slow their movements down in the heat. Can we say, then, that tropical people tend to move slowly and are less vigorous, or would it be more apt to say that they are simply making a normal efficiency adjustment? Observers report that tropical workers move more slowly but more efficiently. They get the same amount of work done with less energy output and hence less heat is generated.

This raises the problem of how to evaluate the degree of strain imposed by heat and humidity. Stretching out, slowing down, breathing deeply, sweating, and eating less (you need less for energy for heating and gain a radiation advantage by being lean) are all perfectly natural adjustments. By sweating, the body can be kept cool for long periods even under the extreme conditions to be found in the wet tropics, just as long as the water intake is kept up—and water is available in the wet tropics. Only when these changes have failed to meet the heat load requirements can we say that a strain has been put upon man's physical make-up.

If the body cannot lose sufficient heat, a stress is set up. If too much dilation of the capillaries of the skin causes a lowered blood pressure, the circulation will be impaired, and a deficiency of oxygen supply can occur. The first area to feel this is the brain, where a slight change can produce a large effect. Judgment slips, lassitude occurs, then headache, then nausea, and finally unconsciousness—and, rarely, death. The milder forms of this—inertia, irritability, mental fatigue—are the things that tropical people are accused of. But mid-latitude summers are as hot and humid, or hotter and as humid, as weather in the tropics.

Physiological climatologists state that under conditions likely to be found in the shade in the tropics, the capacity of healthy acclimatized people is not likely to be strained. They report also that troops in the tropics with the heaviest and most constant work to do are the fittest and most contented so long as they feel that their work is of direct military importance, which brings us back again to the matter of attitudes discussed in Chapter 1. Experiments and experience have indicated that attitude often determines comfort or discomfort.

Military units in tropical areas that showed "tropical deterioration" also showed signs of neurasthenia. The men complained of backaches, loss of weight, sleeplessness, and the like, yet physical examination showed nothing physiologically wrong. Doctors' offices in all climates are filled with such cases.

The wet tropics have their problems. They have many times the number of plant and animal forms that the mid-latitudes have. These include plants and animals that attack man and man's works. There are fungi and bacteria and parasitic worms and termites in profusion. The constant sweating often leads to prickly heat, and this leads to scratching, and this opens the road to infection.

However, the main idea developed here is that when we look at man's physiology in relation to heat, we find that man is well equipped to deal with the kind of heat load to be expected in the humid tropics. Since this is the probable area of origin of man, this seems reasonable. We must look then at the cultural record with these facts in mind: man should be well adapted to heat and humidity.

WHITE SETTLEMENT IN THE TROPICS

An interesting way to look at the problem of the white man in the tropics is to see what has happened to some of his settlements there. What we learn is probably applicable to all of mankind, for we have no evidence of differences between the major races in climatic responses.

After 1500 Europeans spread over the world, but the way in which they settled differed from place to place. In Asia, relatively few Europeans settled permanently; they came as traders, managers, and civil servants. The great masses of people already there supplied the labor force. In India in 1921 there were about 160,000 Europeans and over 300,000,000 Indians. In the Netherlands East Indies there were less than 250,000 Europeans and over 60,000,000 Indonesians. This lack of large-scale permanent settlement on the part of Europeans has often been said to be an effect of the tropical climate.

It is true that a number of the Europeans going to these areas began to drink to excess and to live with native women. Single men sent to outposts remote from their own society found solace in such means of "escape" no matter what the climate was. This phenomenon was more a matter of personal maladjustment, of course, than it was of climate, and to some extent, resulted from a defeatist attitude about the tropics. The European whose life had been lived in cooler climates felt that the intense solar radiation might damage his central nervous system; he therefore never stirred without his pith helmet. Some even wore a strip of red flannel down their back to protect the spinal column from excessive radiation. Everyone "knew" the climate was "bad." Everyone "had" to go home for six-month vacations to stave off "tropical deterioration."

Many missionary groups provided the contrast to this point of view. They lived in the hot, wet tropics with their wives and children and took only infrequent, short home leaves, and they suffered no apparent tropical deterioration. Their motivation was sufficient to help them adapt to their new environment.

In the New World, tropical settlement took a quite different course. For various reasons (new diseases, warfare, political and economic disruptions), the native populations were virtually swept away in many areas, many of which had been only moderately too thinly populated to begin with. At times Europeans settled on the land, but in part the needed labor supply was imported from Africa. As the New World recovered in strength, there sprang up a great mixture of races, with the European strain generally in a minority position. Was this due to climate?

THE WEST INDIES AS A TEST AREA

If we look at the West Indies, we find a laboratory of human experiments. The physical environment is relatively constant, for most of these coral-fringed islands lie in a tropical sea between 25 and 10 degrees

Map 3-1 The Caribbean: January Average Temperature

The Caribbean is shown with isotherms for the average temperature in January. All of the Caribbean area is warmer than the southernmost tip of Florida. Most of the Caribbean islands have January temperatures close to 75° F. This is the average summer temperature of the belt of states from Maryland to Missouri. Panama, with 80° F. temperature throughout the year, is comparable to summer in the Gulf area from Louisiana to Florida.

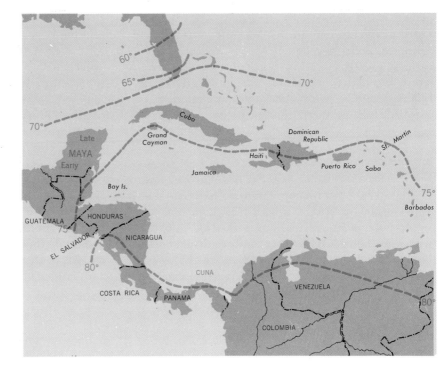

Highlands of Barbados. In the Chalky Mountain area one sees deforestation and erosion resulting from cultivation of steep slopes.

north of the equator. In this area the impact of the European political conquest with its economic dislocations, plus the shock of entirely new diseases to which the native population was apparently totally unaccustomed, at first swept native populations away. Into this vacuum the Europeans poured.

British Colonial Barbados

By 1502 the Spanish had 12,000 Europeans on Haiti; later the British population on Barbados numbered 40,000, or 200 per square mile. Land was held in plots of 5 to 30 acres and was worked by white men with white helpers. This was a family settlement of the land and it flourished. After 1642 due to civil war in England—*not* a tropical climatic factor—immigration ceased. Thereafter the North American colonies were more attractive and an inflow of "undesirables" began in Barbados.

The new immigrants were white servants, indentured men, kidnapped men, and political prisoners from the Puritan Rebellion, and they were all treated worse than slaves. After all, an African slave cost his owner money and worked for him as long as he lived. An indentured man or political prisoner served out his time and had to be freed. His contract often called for giving him clothing and a set of tools at the end of his term of service. Financially, it was desirable to maintain the African slave, but to be less concerned with the fate of the European servant. Under these conditions, the European working class left the islands, and more and more Africans were brought in. But what role did race and climate have to play in this development?

Actually the list of cultural forces at work is a long one. All of them worked against the small European land holder: high taxes hampered him, and wars ruined the economy of the whole islands, at the same time creating such opportunities in buccaneering and pirating as to drain off much of the active manpower. Only large planters survived, and absentee ownership of large estates became common.

Taxes, navigation acts, all patronage in the hands of the kings' ministers, troops quartered on the people—all of these things combined to drive the white settler off the land and out of the islands. None of these are physical-geographical forces or peculiar to the tropics.

Further, it cannot be said that the British settlers lived what would be called a wholesome life. Their houses were poor, damp, and infested with vermin. They wore heavy British clothing, well-suited to the damp, cool British Isles, but not at all suited to the humid tropics. They ate heavy food in large quantities, and since they did not need so large a food intake, they added fat, thus decreasing their ability to lose heat. They also drank heavily of the available liquor, which was rum, a byproduct of the sugar cane production, the major industry of the island. This raw rum was near to being poison. As a result, the death rate ran ten men to every woman. There is no climatic-physiological basis for such a difference; the women simply drank very little, as was the accepted cultural pattern. A clear example of the forces at work is found in military statistics. In 1796 nearly 20,000 men were sent to the British West Indies; and 17,000 died within five years! One could make a devastating attack on the tropics with such figures. However, look at cultural setting. The men had been recruited from the poorly nourished slums of the British Isles and therefore represented poor physical stock. No attention was paid to hygiene and diet; they ate Old World rations—salt meat five times a week—and drank as much raw rum as they could lay hands on. The men lived in crowded quarters, ideal for spreading disease, and they wore the traditional heavy European uniform, bathing rarely. Would it have mattered much if they were in Florida, Washington, or Boston?

That none of this was inevitable is suggested by a description of the planter aristocracy in the British West Indies at the end of the eighteenth century. Significantly, the people were said to be taller and more slender than their British ancestors. The Jamaican historian who gave us this description knew no physiological climatology, yet he described a change toward the slender form of greater advantage for heat dissipa-

tion. This is reported in Australia in the twentieth century, and is probably a nongenetic change. The body is fairly plastic and can respond to some degree to environmental forces, as we see in our society today where children are normally taller than their parents due to improved nutritional standards, especially in infant feeding.

These planters were also said to be graceful and agile, men less liable to local infectious diseases than newcomers. Their women lived calm, even lives, but as a result of little exercise they were also pale, spiritless, and languid. Their children were said to develop early, especially in mental ability, but to fail to keep pace later, a statement that turns out to be more myth than observation whenever closely studied. In fact, there is little in this contemporary account that indicates evidence of any climatic effect. Except for some desirable minor shifts in body form, the tropical environment had left these aristocratic planters untouched after two-to-three generations of living in the tropics.

Today Barbados has a population of 230,000 and the blacks and browns outnumber the whites by better than 10 to 1. The whites as well as the colored population, are riddled with hookworm and malaria. The people are caught in a vicious circle of poverty and resulting diseases. Wells are polluted, and plumbing facilities in homes or schools are rare. Lack of sanitation loads the ground with hookworm and bare feet pick it up. The disease-weakened people lack the strength and will to earn shoes and dig privies. This deadening cycle was once true of much of our South, but there the climate is not tropical—except in summer, when it is super tropical.

In the United States hookworm is still prevalent. In 1950 in one area of 5000 school children, more than half were found to be infected. Recent figures show 2 to 20 percent infection rates in eight southern states. These are much lower than figures obtained in the early part of the century when the rates ran from 25 to 60 percent. In this very period, 1900 to 1950, temperatures have in fact on the average risen slightly in the South, yet hookworm has declined. The improvement is the result of cultural factors such as better educa-

Two Scenes from the San Juan Area, Puerto Rico: a Shanty Town (*above*) and the Namesio Canales Housing Project. Slums are too often attributed to the physical environment. Puerto Rico presents dramatic evidence of changing cultural outlooks in an unchanging physical environment. *Puerto Rico Information Service.*

tion and sanitation and a rising economy. They are clearly the more powerful influences.

Puerto Rico

A further survey of the West Indies shows more of this type of complex interplay of politics, economics, and history in a limited area of similar geographic setting. Puerto Rico, for example, is a rugged island with volcanic mountains in the interior and corraline limestone formations on its edges, forming a narrow coastal plain. On the coast the average annual temperature is about 76° F. In the mountains it is cooler, from 74° to 68° F. Originally it was thickly settled with Indians, but they vanished very early. The Spanish were primarily attracted to the mainland where the gold and silver and great empires lay. Only a few of the less adventurous Spaniards and an even smaller number of Spanish women settled on the island. Negro slaves were soon brought in as laborers and the result was a Spanish-Negro-Indian mixture. Later, Portuguese, English, and American settlers came, especially after 1815 when the island was opened to commerce. During the revolution for independence from Spain early in the nineteenth century, many wealthy Spanish families fled the newly created countries on the mainland to settle in Puerto Rico. They brought education, enterprise, and capital.

The development of the island was almost purely agriculture. In 1845 Negroes and whites were almost equal in numbers; since then, the number of Negroes has fallen steadily: 1802, 52 percent; 1860, 48 percent; 1920, 27 percent. These figures probably reflect at least in part a shifting race classification, but they surely do not indicate any failure of the white race in the tropics.

The population increased 50 percent from 1900 to reach 1,500,000 in 1930 and by 1960 was over 2,350,000. Birth and death rates are high. Tuberculosis, malaria, and hookworm are prevalent, and the diet is poor: primarily dry beans, corn, salt fish, and polished rice. Under United States influence the importance of sugar in the economy was intensified to virtually a monoculture, which led to seasonal unemployment and undesirable corporate relationships with too much wire pulling and interference with government. This rich tropical land had to import food.

In the first half of the twentieth century Puerto Rico was known as a "slum of the Caribbean." The explanation was simple: it had no resources. Its economy was primitive and its population mostly illiterate and impoverished. Yet in the 1960s the island has a rising living standard; one third of the entire population is going to school; the illiteracy rate and the average personal income are the second highest in Latin America; and a middle class is developing. The climate, the physical geography, and the geographic location both physically and in relation to the shifts of world power and development have not changed—the social outlook has.

Puerto Rico has an advantageous political status. As a self-governing commonwealth associated with the United States, its people are American citizens, but do not have to pay United States income taxes. The island has embarked on a plan to attract private industry and capital, including a ten-year exemption from local taxes for desirable firms and the possibility of government financial aid. The tax impetus, combined with a stable government, a location within the United States political orbit, and a large supply of low-priced labor has drawn large amounts of capital to Puerto Rico. More than 350 million dollars of private United States capital has been invested in recent years. Since there are less than three million people on the island, this amounts to an investment of more than 100 dollars per person. Currently an average of two new factories start operations each week. Meanwhile, the Communist takeover in Cuba has destroyed the lucrative tourist trade of that island, and this profitable business is now flowing into Puerto Rico. In 1959, 250,000 mainlanders spent 50 million dollars in Puerto Rico. It is estimated that this business could increase eightfold by 1970.

The results are spectacular. San Juan is described as a boom town: supermarkets, shopping centers, and housing developments for workers are being built. These are measures of the growth of masses of people who can afford to buy what we consider the ordinary necessities of life, but which for most of undeveloped Latin America have been unattainable luxuries.

This has been a planned development. The kind of factory attracted and supported has been carefully screened for fitting into Puerto Rico's characteristics of few raw materials and a large unskilled labor force. The aim is to get away from monoculture: sugar, sugar, and more sugar, with a little tobacco and coffee. Clothing industries and electrical and electronic industries have been attracted. In 1959 the island exported about 400 different products valued at 500 million dollars—more than double the figures for ten years earlier. The average weekly income of factory workers nearly doubled from 1954 to 1959—from $15 to $28. In average personal income Puerto Rico is now second only to Venezuela. Venezuela's figures are influenced by its immense wealth in oil, an exhaustible resource, while Puerto Rico is building a productive system that is potentially inexhaustible. The resource it is developing is its people.

As income has risen, food consumption has gone up. Puerto Ricans now eat twice as much meat and dairy products as they did 20 years ago. The government is pushing farm production in an attempt to make the island much more productive of fish, grain, poultry, and meat. As the growth picks up headway, as education spreads out and incomes rise, there are increasing opportunities for economic enterprise.

All is not easy and rosy, of course. Change and growth and development are never accomplished without pain. Unemployment is still high; new factories have not yet soaked up the pool of labor. The factories tend to draw the villager into the big city. Here the often unskilled and illiterate poor form large slums. Some of the unemployed have flooded into such centers as New York City, where their low standards of literacy, hygiene, and differing customs have created problems. Nevertheless, the Puerto Ricans in New York are only repeating the experience of many another minority group that has come to our great eastern cities for economic opportunity and gained education and technical knowledge.

There has now begun a return flow of these people to Puerto Rico, bringing still more new outlooks and abilities into their island. With the current program of schooling for everyone, a stable government aiming at attracting private capital, and governmental aid in the growth and development of health, education, and industry, Puerto Rico is experiencing a revolutionary development from the "slum of the Caribbean" to the "showcase of the Caribbean." The climate has changed, it is true, but it is the social climate, not the physical climate.

Puerto Rico's present economic status still leaves it poorer than any state in the Union, and the economic situation is not expected to overcome that level before 1990. Thus a revolutionary rate of change, starting from an advanced status (not a tribal situation) and aided by political and economic ties with the United States is expected to take at least 50 years to achieve a bare United States minimum. This may be very close to the optimum rate of change achievable. It is significant that the changes here have been carried out under a program of governmental control, but with encouragement of private capital and enterprise, and that under these conditions a good supply of private capital has come forward. For our inquiry into the future of the tropics, and of the white man in the tropics, it is apparent that the races and race mixtures in Puerto Rico seem capable of arousing from centuries of "tropical lassitude" to "tropical energy" when given political and economic freedom and opportunity. The physical-geographical potential has always been there; it has been the economic, political, and historical forces that have varied, and the use of physical resources has changed accordingly.

Other Caribbean Cases

Continuing on around the Caribbean, we find variations on this theme. A striking example of the ups and downs possible in one physical environment is found on St. Martin's Island in the Lesser Antilles. At Simpson's Bay a group of 160 English-speaking whites living on the island slid down the isolation-poverty-disease road until they reached the most primitive level of existence. The Dutch built a bridge to the island, conducted a hookworm campaign by supplying shoes and digging privies and enforcing the use of both. They also supplied medicine to ameliorate the more common tropical disorders—for example, quinine for malaria—and compelled the use of these drugs. They dug wells to ensure pure drinking water. Within three years there was a virtual economic revolution: The people were well instead of three-fourths incapacitated at all times. They had the strength to work; they could get enough fish both to eat well and to sell some. What had been a classic case of tropical deterioration simply ceased to exist.

Saba, a five-mile square volcanic island, offers the opposite story. White colonization began in the early seventeenth century. By 1665 there were 87 Dutch, 54 British, and 85 Negroes and Indians. It became a prosperous little planting community. In 1800 it had fifty European families holding 150 slaves; yet today, the island is increasingly Negro and the whites are mostly impoverished, sickly, and unproductive. Climate? No.

On Saba the Dutch emancipated the slaves, and the young white men elected not to stay on the land. The island was small, rugged, and practically roadless, and it had no harbor. Without slaves its economy wasted away, a fate that might have occurred anyway during the nineteenth century as large-scale commercial production in the world left it behind. The withdrawal of the young vigorous men and the reduction of the whites to peasant farmers merely brought on stagnation more rapidly. Today the Negroes predominate. Farming is limited to the few flat spots, and men carry loads over terrain that a donkey cart couldn't manage. The diet of the whites is poor: biscuit, bread, tea, salt fish, canned goods, and very little use of green vegetables. Yet the men work hard and are healthy. Their women do not work and are nervous, sickly, and pale, probably a holdover from former times when the domestic work was done by slaves. The group of whites doing the poorest are on the highest, coolest part of the island. In general the Negroes stay, while the whites leave, especially the men, leaving the white women to outnumber the men two to one. There hardly seems to be any climatic determination in all of this.

Another example of a white settlement that failed is found on Jamaica. In 1835 about 500 German settlers moved there. They were above average in skills, capital, and enterprise. Some super salesmen convinced these folk that a tropical paradise awaited them in the beautiful, bountiful Caribbean. Many died on the trip over, but this was usual whether the boat was headed for New England or the equator. The land on which they were settled has an average annual temperature of 77° F. and a rainfall of 80 inches. It is low country, and the people were soon loaded with hookworm and malaria; on this isolated island their skills were wasted, for there was no market for them. Some gave up and left, while the remainder mingled with the Negro population, losing identity of race, language, and culture. Much later, other Germans looked into the fate of their countrymen. A priest was sent out, and economic aid followed. The people were resettled on their own land and continued to live on it as industrious peasant agriculturists. They are now better housed and have attained a higher economic standard than their Negro neighbors. Since these settlers fared both ill and well on Jamaica, their environment itself can not be held responsible for their histories.

The Grand Cayman Islands were settled by the British from adjacent Jamaica about 1700. These people already had some previous experience of settlement in the tropics. Today the whites are chiefly shipbuilders and mariners, and their wives do their own housework. Houses are well built and set up off the ground to let air circulate under them. The diet consists of breadfruit and yams, turtle meat and fish, wild fruit, and American canned vegetables; the principal beverage is cocoa. The people are tall and well built, and their intellectual standing is very good despite poor educational opportunities. Yet the annual temperature is 80° F., the rainfall is 60 inches, and the humidity is high.

Just off the north coast of Honduras are the low, hot, humid Bay Islands. The people are English-speaking whites of uncertain origin but quite possibly the descendants of seventeenth- and eighteenth-century buccaneers. The islands have something over 4000 people about equally divided between colored and white. The whites maintain a strict color line. Their principal livelihood comes from the sea, for they build schooners and carry fruit to Gulf ports—and in the past they have not hesitated to add to their income by gun running. The whites remain handsome, healthy, and well built, so here again there appears to be no tropical deterioration even after 200 years.

Panama

Everyone knows something about Panama and the building of the canal, but usually only a little. Panama is a perfect example of a tropical rainy location at 9° N. latitude. The heat equator does not coincide with the true equator and passes through Panama, where the average monthly temperature stays at 80° F. through the year. The annual rainfall is 130 inches, but February and March are relatively dry. The area is low and swampy. (See Table 3–1.)

This area was once known as the "pest hole of the world." In 1903, the official description was "one of the hottest, wettest, and most feverish regions in existence. Intermittent and malignant fevers are prevalent, and there is an epidemic of yellow fever at all times. The death rate under normal conditions is large." In 1931, the description ran: "formerly a permanent regional focus [for yellow fever] because [it] existed at some place in it at all times; and from such infected places other places in the region were infected from time to time."

We know relatively little about the pre-European settlement of this region, but there are some indications that the Indians considered it a good land. Panama is characterized by a special style of art work in gold, while nearby people, the Cuna, had a form of writing. Agriculture, metallurgy, and writing all point to a developed society.

The Spanish record here, however, is one of terrible mortality. Colonies were attempted but failed, and many officials died in attempting the brief crossing of the isthmus to reach their posts in Peru. The California Gold Rush brought floods of people surging across the isthmus, and the loss of life was fantastic. A railroad was then planned, but the 1000 Negroes imported to build it were all dead in six months. Chinese were brought in and they too died within six months. As though in a laboratory experiment, each race tried and failed, none proving to have any special racial resistance to tropical heat, humidity, and disease.

Then came the French to try building a canal, for they had succeeded at Suez. They lost 16,000 men from malaria, yellow fever, dysentery, and small pox. Despite tragic heroism, the French failed. The "climate" could use up men faster than they could pour

Table 3-1 Climate of Panama

Station	Latitude	TEMPERATURE (° F.)			Relative Humidity* (percent)	Rain (inches)	Wind (miles per hour)
		Mean	January	July			
Balboa	9° N.	78.6	78.2	78.7	83	68	7.6
Colón	9° N.	79.8	79.8	79.9	83	128	10.5
Yuma	32° N.		54	91			
Miami	26° N.		66	81	78	60	8.9

* Relative humidity taken in early morning—lower during heat of day. Note that Miami in summer is hotter, almost as humid, and no breezier than Panama. New Orleans, from June through August, is hotter and almost as wet as Panama (temperatures of 80.6°, 82.4°, and 79.2°F. and rainfall about 6 inches per month). Balboa on the Pacific side is slightly cooler, drier and less humid than Colón on the Caribbean.

them in. But was it climate, or was it disease? Or do the two go together?

Then how did Indian civilization survive there? Interestingly enough, few of these fatal diseases were present before the Europeans brought them: both malaria and small pox were imported into the New World. They are an excellent example of how man changes the environment, for without them the tropical lowlands of the New World would be much healthier. It is a mistake, moreover, to think of them as "tropical" diseases. Malaria once scourged the United States up into New England; its disappearance here is due mainly to better housing. Yellow fever and small pox are also not limited to the tropics; they are held down in mid-latitudes by public-health measures.

Finally to Panama came the American effort. The role of the mosquito in transmitting yellow fever and malaria had been isolated and unlimited funds were made available. A zone ten-miles wide was drained, sprayed and screened, and sanitary facilities and innoculations were instituted on a grand scale. The health level quickly approached continental United States levels: the "tropical" diseases were practically eliminated.

In the building of the canal the test of various ethnic and racial groups continued. Southern Europeans (Spaniards, Italians, and Greeks) were used in large numbers, and although they worked hard in any weather, they were difficult to discipline. Those that obeyed the sanitary rules remained healthy; those that did not became "victims of the tropics." Negro labor was also used in large amounts. Large numbers from the West Indies were brought in, but at first their efficiency was extremely low. As the effects of medical care and good food began to show, however, their work improved. The key to the situation again seems to have been neither racial nor climatic.

Three generations of Americans have lived in Panama, for there is a strong tendency for those who have worked there for years to stay there, and for those raised there to go to work there. Children thrive. They wear sun suits and go bareheaded and the tropical sun somehow fails to "strike their nervous system." Most childhood illnesses prove to be mild,

and some are lacking. All of which suggests no tropical deterioration.

The Canal Zone remains today a sanitary band across Panama, with reservoirs of disease in the native populations on either side. Health and vigor at Panama is related to knowledge and will power: the value of good hygiene must be known to be practiced, and knowledge of its value aids in the will power to keep up the necessary measures. The Canal Zone shows that the white man can succeed in the tropics, and it supports no racial selection for tropical life. It emphasizes again the ability of man to modify his environment. Europeans introduced diseases that made this the "pest hole" of the world; their descendants cleaned up a strip of it and showed that it could be a healthful, pleasant, productive part of the world where any race could flourish.

CIVILIZATION IN THE TROPICS

We can turn now to the problem of civilization in the tropics. There have been and still are civilizations in the tropics, India being one of the oldest in the world. Today India is not a great power, but it exercises considerable influence both in Asia and in international councils. About the time of Christ, the Indians began to colonize to the east and their civilizing influence created a series of kingdoms in Burma, Siam, Cambodia, Sumatra, and Java. These areas have at various times and in differing combinations been sizable kingdoms with their own art, literature, architecture, and wide trading spheres. It may be objected that they have not endured, but no empire in history has ever endured, no matter the climate.

The Mayan Civilization

In discussing tropical civilizations, the Americas are sometimes overlooked. In pre-Columbian times, *all* civilization was in the tropics: some in the highlands, and some in the lowlands. The classic example is that of the Maya. The Old Empire of the Maya was in the tropical rainy area of Honduras, and the New Empire was erected in the similar climatic area of Guatemala and adjacent Mexico. Within this area

Art Forms in Asia and America as Compared by Osvald Sirén in *A History of Chinese Art, the Prehistoric and Pre-Han Periods* (London: Ernest Benn Limited, 1929, plate 21). This art historian was impressed by the similarity of masklike figures in early Mexican Indian art to the classic t'ao t'ie masks of early China. He also noted that similar forms often had similar designs, as in *A* and *B*. *A*, Early Chinese; *B*, Maya; *C*, Early Chinese t'ao t'ie head in marble; *D*, Maya vase with similar mask; *E*, Early Chinese t'ao t'ie head in terra cotta; *F*, Figure on Mayan stela, Quirigua, Guatemala.

there is actually considerable range of climate. Northern Yucatán is dry bush savanna; central Petén is a wet savanna; and the rest of the area is rain forest.

Leaving aside the question of ultimate beginnings, by the time of Christ the Old Empire was flourishing in a rain forest. For the next 600 years there was extensive cultural and territorial growth. Great civic centers were built, sculpture, painting, architecture, astronomy, and mathematics flourished. Thereafter came the Middle Empire, from A.D. 600 to A.D. 700, often described as a period of consolidation. Then came the great period from 700 to 900, when the arts and the empire flourished. Thereafter came the New Empire in the Yucatán savanna area, 900 to 1200, and the period of Mexican influence, 1200 to 1500. The Maya were still literate, monumental city builders—perhaps best equated with Egypt in one of its great periods—when the Spanish arrived.

The Mayan empire crashed under the Spanish impact. There was conquest, destruction of written records, disruption of the priestly, learned, and ruling classes, and a melting away of the people. It is easy to understand the disintegration of a culture whose traditions are smashed and records destroyed. Cultural declines have occurred in history for lesser reasons. The melting away of the people has received less attention, but we have already touched the probable reasons: plague, dysentery, malaria, yellow fever, small pox, measles, and the dozens of other new diseases that proved devastatingly destructive in all latitudes undoubtedly did their deadly work, but are less well recorded than such onslaughts that came later in time. What small pox alone could do to a non-immune population is illustrated by its effect on the Mandan Indians of North Dakota (see page 111).

How remarkable were the Maya achievements? They knew and used skillfully the corbelled arch, the only arch used by most of the world east of the Mediterranean at their time. They built vast pyramids on which they erected architecturally notable buildings, and their religious-civic centers rival in beauty and layout those of Egypt, Mesopotamia, Greece, and

Palace at Sayil, Yucatán, Mexico. This reconstruction drawing gives some idea of the monumental nature of the Mayan buildings. In numerous details, such as the use of columnettes (lower left corner), the stepped pyramidlike structure, the broad central stairway, and the use of false, or corbelled, arches, these structures duplicate similar monumental architecture in parts of southeast Asia that came under Indian influence. *American Museum of Natural History.*

Rome. Their pottery was tastefully decorated and they did beautiful work inlaying and carving stone, bone, and wood.

The Mayan achievements in mathematics were equal to Egyptian efforts in Ptolemaic times. They had several calendars of very great accuracy. They knew the 365-day year which they divided into 18 units of 20 days each plus a 5-day period. They also had a sacred year of 260 days, with 13 units of 20 days each. This sacred "year" they permutated with the natural year to create a 52-year cycle. If this most general description of a very complex calendric system sounds intricate, it barely indicates how far advanced these peoples' astronomic and calendric knowledge was, for they also had moon calendars, Venus calendars, and fully understood the interrelationships of all of them. Using the moon calendar, a date could be fixed in the "long count" (as opposed to short-term reckoning) that would not recur for 374,440 years.

They considered the length of the year to be 365.2420 days. It is actually 365.2422 days, though our own calendar is based on a 365.2425 day year. They had astronomical observatories, predicted eclipses and the heliacal rising and setting of Venus, knew the period of Venus' revolution, and were aware that their calendar had an error of 8/100 day every 584 days.

The Maya wrote in an ideographic form which in degree of development resembles Chinese. They carved dates we can read and accounts we cannot read on their monumental buildings. They had books of paper, but few of these have survived and we cannot read them.

What we have here then is a record of political, economic, and cultural achievement of the highest order maintained in a tropical rainy area for longer by far than many other cultures in the world survived.

The Problem of Mayan Agriculture and Population

The Maya have long posed a number of problems. How could a simple, forest, shifting agriculture ever have supported such a civilization? How could such an agriculture be continuously maintained on the thin soils of a limestone plateau in a tropical rain forest? Was the great shift in location between the Old Empire and the New Empire—and the several spurts in development during the Mayans' long occupation—due to changes in agricultural practices and to the abandonment of areas that had exhausted their soil fertility or been overrun by weeds such as grasses?

Studies of shifting, forest-type agriculture suggest that it can support about 100 to 150 people per square mile, and perhaps this is enough to account for the Mayan civilization. However, there is some indication that the population may have been much larger than this. At Uaxactún, not one of the major cities, a survey made through the jungle around this center revealed so many house sites that if all of them had been occupied at one time a population density of 1000 people per square mile would be indicated. If only one fourth of them were simultaneously occupied, the density of population would have been well beyond the possibility of simple, forest, rotation agriculture.

The agriculture had to be efficient, for it had to support not only the people on the land but also great numbers of men at work producing the monumental buildings and the works of art as well as the scholarly and priestly classes who did governmental work. Further, the population figures given above are of a secondary civic center. The great cities of the Mayan area must have had larger populations and even denser settlement on the land—all of which indicates that there must have been a much more intensive land use in the Mayan area in the past. An oriental pattern of husbanding is suggested—all waste materials being returned to the land combined with all possible organic material from the adjacent lands, with the careful composting of this material to maintain the fertility of the fields. The question then arises: Once achieved, why would such an agricultural way of life be abandoned?

Intensity of land use is related to population density. Not only is increasing density of population accompanied by increasing intensity of land utilization, but decreasing density of population leads to decreased intensity of land use. A classic example occurred in colonial North America. The colonists came from areas having advanced agricultural techniques developed for utilizing the land intensively. This included crop rotation, the use of animal manures, the use of vegetable matter for composting, and the beginning of the use of mineral fertilizers. In North America when the colonial population found itself with a huge amount of land and very little capital or labor, they substituted extensive use of the land for the other two factors. This led them to practice a shifting, forest-type agriculture that their European cousins always described in utterly scandalized tones because of its weedy, impermanent, primitive nature.

If, then, something had happened to the Maya that suddenly shifted the relation of the population size to the land available, it would be expectable that they would change their manner of land utilization. Quite clearly a catastrophe struck the Maya in the appearance of the Spanish and the European diseases. Between wars and disease the Mayan population fell from a minimum of 100 per square mile, and from a possible high of 1000 per square mile, to about 1 per square mile, its present status. It seems inevitable that under these circumstances the agricultural methods would shift radically toward a simple land-use system where the laborious maintenance of land in permanent production would be abandoned for the much easier clearing of a new patch of forest where natural processes had restored the soil fertility during the period that the land was allowed to rest and to grow up to a forest cover. It seems probable that a catastrophic loss of population in the Mayan area led to the shift in agricultural practices toward the primitive extensive land use that marks the land today. The more difficult thing to understand is the failure of the Maya to rebuild a population density above the present figure of 1 per square mile. Probably this is an example of the dangers inherent in destroying a social fabric. With the disappearances of learning, tradition, and religion, accompanied by a loss of life of enormous magnitude, a whole way of life disappeared and a new way of life with the drive to increase and be fruitful has not yet arisen. Explanations that lean on soil exhaustion, weed infestation, or climatic change seem unnecessary to account for the record.

THE NEW WORLD TROPICS

A survey of the wet tropical regions of the New World must keep in view, what was, what is, and what could be. Our view of the future is necessarily very limited. We cannot see all the present possibilities and probably have virtually no notion of future possibilities.

In the Americas the center of Pre-Columbian achievement lay in the wet tropical regions. Civilizations existed in Middle America, and village agricultural settlement characterized most of the rest of tropical America. We know little about the densities of population in these areas except that they must have been high even by modern standards. Outside the civilized city-state areas, population densities were lower, possibly somewhere between 10 and 20 persons per square mile. Shifting agriculture can easily support even greater populations. The disruption of the European conquest and the devastation of the new diseases so thoroughly removed the people from the land that we probably underestimate how many people there once were even in the areas of shifting agriculture.

The American tropics today are underdeveloped lands of great potential. As the Panama experience shows, they can be made healthful living areas. There is a cost involved, but we tend to forget that there is a public health cost in mid-latitudes also, and that without such expenditure we would first face a great loss of life and then a continuing loss through inefficiency caused by the drain of debilitating illnesses such as hookworm, malaria, dysentery, amoebae, small pox, diphtheria, plague, and leprosy.

The situation in the wet tropics of the New World, all of which are in Latin America, can be summarized in several ways. The whole area is one of largely agricultural and mining production; manufacturing is limited, and most manufactured goods are imported. This situation is an economic stage of development not physically and geographically determined, and applies to all of Latin America, whether it is wet or dry, high or low, tropical or subtropical. Latin America has a Mediterranean tradition and a colonial background of exploitation. This cultural inheritance has given it a particular outlook on landownership, and a social structure that has inhibited the development of free enterprise that has characterized the economy of the United States and some states of Western Europe, and, belatedly, is leading to development in parts of southern Europe (see p. 195 ff.) and even in a small tropical country such as Puerto Rico—in spite of shortages in coal, petroleum, hydroelectric power, and basic metals. We will later compare the United States and Brazil to put the American accomplishment in better perspective (see p. 254 ff.).

The wet tropics of the New World can be reviewed sectionally.

TROPICAL NORTH AMERICA

The wet tropics of southern Mexico and Central America are savanna and rain forest. Most of the people are subsistence farmers, clearing patches of forest and moving as the soil fertility declines. Corn, beans, and squash are the great staples, but other grain and root crops are grown. Cotton grows as a perennial. There is much fruit, and commercial production of cotton, bananas, coffee, and chocolate supply important exports. These are grown in plantationlike systems that vary from relatively small holdings in the El Salvador coffee area to the very large corporate developments of the United Fruit Company's holdings. In addition, Mexico has continued since colonial times to be an important producer of metals, especially silver, and more recently of petroleum.

Many of these lands are largely Indian. Mexico is about 15 percent white, 55 percent mixed, and 30 percent Indian. Since much of the classification is social rather than racial, it is probable that a considerably higher portion of the population is actually Indian. Guatemala, El Salvador, and Honduras are about 80 percent Indian and 20 percent mixed. Nicaragua and Panama are Indian, European, and Negro, in that order. Costa Rica is predominantly white in race. Over most of this area, the men on the land are Indians living very much as they did at the time the Spanish arrived and often still speaking their own languages. They have been stripped of their native civilization, and the European civilization has not yet rooted and flourished. Although European domination has caused everyone who can to claim to be European, growing appreciation of the Indian accomplishment in art, architecture, agriculture and government is beginning to remove these pressures.

The Caribbean area we have reviewed. Depending on the vagaries of colonial history, the major islands are largely white, as in Puerto Rico and Cuba, or largely Negro, as in Jamaica or Haiti. Again, there is no climatic basis for such differences. In the Caribbean the pattern is largely subsistence farming for the mass of the population with plantation-type production of sugar, coffee, tobacco, cacao, and bananas supplying the export crops. Imports are typically fish, rice, flour, cloth, iron and steel, machinery, and vehicles.

The way to development is being demonstrated by Puerto Rico. Destruction of an economy is being demonstrated by Castro in Cuba. The hindering of development has been demonstrated in the past in Mexico, where dissatisfaction with foreign control of their petroleum industry lead to governmental seizure of these properties. Instead of increased profits accruing to the Mexicans, the result was a decrease in efficiency, a slow down in the development of new wells, and a declining productivity. With the exclusion of the knowledge, skills, and capital of the major oil companies the whole industry declined. Further, investment capital in general was discouraged from undertaking development in such politically unstable lands.

TROPICAL SOUTH AMERICA

Tropical South America presents somewhat the same picture. Population density, on the average, is low. People are concentrated on the rim of the continent. Here there are areas of dense settlement and modern cities with populations over a million. The interior is thinly occupied by primitive Indian tribes and some mixed groups. The people on the edges are similar to the Central American area in their racial make-up: Negro, Indian, mixed, and European. The largest Indian populations in South America are not in the wet lowlands, but in the Andean highlands. Brazil is approximately 60 percent European, 15 percent Negro, 20 percent mixed, and has a tiny Indian population. Venezuela is predominantly mixed; while the Guianas are mixed Indian and Negro. In all of Latin America, population declined under the impact of the Europeans and a low point was reached around 1800. There was then only some fraction of the peak population that the land had once supported—quite probably only half as many people, possibly only a tenth. Since then the population has been growing rapidly. It doubled between 1900 and 1950 with the major growth appearing in the European and mixed groups.

The peripheral location of population in South America is striking. It is an excellent indication of the direction in which the colonial settlers looked. They reached the coast first. Since land transportation was nonexistent, their contacts, markets, and sources were all in the Old World, and the sea was their highway. Quite naturally they stayed near the coast and looked overseas. This inheritance still marks the land, and is only slowly changing.

Venezuela has been hampered by poor government in addition to the usual Latin American problem of extreme unevenness of landownership, masses of uneducated people, and the absence of a free-enterprise system. The vast oil resources of the Maracaibo basin and the further productive areas in the llanos, the extensive plains, have proven to be a

Map 3-2   Venezuela

Venezuela has highlands in its north, and a disproportionate part of its population is concentrated in them. The vast Guayanan interior is nearly empty. The great low-lying well-watered interior, the llanos, is thinly populated. Such population concentration in a few areas is typical of much of Latin America. The major resource now being exploited is petroleum, with iron reserves also becoming important recently. Such resources are bringing in a flood of money, some of which is going into the development of the country. The network of roads is unusually good for Latin America. The growth of the capital city of Caracas has been extremely rapid and has drawn people away from the land. Paradoxically, in this tropical land, well watered and rich in plains, not enough food stuff is produced to feed the population. This is a classic case of the human tendency to ignore the obvious resources of the physical environment. *Adapted from* Focus— *The American Geographical Society.*

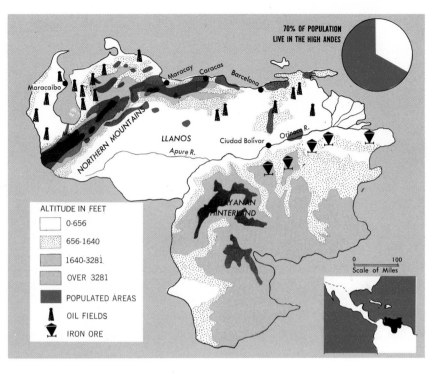

70% OF POPULATION LIVE IN THE HIGH ANDES

Maracaibo · Maracay · Caracas · Barcelona

NORTHERN MOUNTAINS

LLANOS   Ciudad Bolívar   Orinoco R.

Apure R.

GUAYANAN HINTERLAND

ALTITUDE IN FEET
- 0-656
- 656-1640
- 1640-3281
- OVER 3281
- POPULATED AREAS
- OIL FIELDS
- IRON ORE

Scale of Miles   0   100

The Old and the New in Venezuela. The thatch roof and walls of mud packed between wooden poles accompany a dirt floor. Though the thatched roof is good for insulation, it is also a reservoir for vermin. The cement block walls and iron roof accompanies a concrete floor. Even if the sheet-iron roof is less than perfect heat insulation under a tropical sun, the advance is enormous. Notice the screening for privacy and against tropical sun that has been simply but effectively supplied in the major window area. Compare this approach with the more elaborate screening used in modern Brazilian architecture, page 152. *Embassy of Venezuela.*

Caracas, Venezuela. The complex problems of the industrial revolution and urbanization place great strain on many countries in the world. Great masses of people with little education flock into the urban centers of countries that are as yet not sufficiently industrialized to employ their people in highly productive enterprises. These 20 low-rent, 15-story-high apartment buildings contain churches, schools, shopping centers, theaters, and clinics. The concept of a "city within a city" is an experiment in city living. Venezuela is in a good position to carry out such works because of its large income from petroleum. *Embassy of Venezuela.*

mixed blessing. Too great a dependence on these sources of income has led to an unbalanced economy with this agriculturally rich land importing food stuff and having one of the world's highest living costs.

The vast, grassy llanos could be made a major cattle-producing area and an attempt was once made to develop them. A modern slaughter and freezing plant was built on the northern edge of the country. Cattle driven in from the plains were to be prepared there for export to the meat-hungry European market. However, intervention by a dictator who was at that time virtually running the country as his private monopoly so discouraged the foreign capital that the plant never operated. A potential industry giving employment to many, bringing in needed foreign exchange, and leading to a useful development of a large relatively empty area was throttled by one man's greed. But greed is not a product of the physical environment nor specifically

of hot and humid climates, or even peculiar to Latin America.

Brazil is larger than was the forty-eight state United States, and contains half of the area and people of South America. However, 80 percent of its 50 million people live on or near the Atlantic Coast, and this leaves the vast interior extremely thinly populated. Imagine the United States with 45 million people living along the east coast and only 5 million spread over the rest of the country, living on a primitive subsistence agricultural basis. Brazilian settlement has emphasized one particular vegetation type, the semideciduous forest of the tropical rainy southeast coast. Now that that type of land is about used up, they are on the brink of putting into use other types of land. This tendency to use one type of landscape to the near exclusion of all others is a common human approach to the land and will be seen again in the grassland discussion (see Chapter 7).

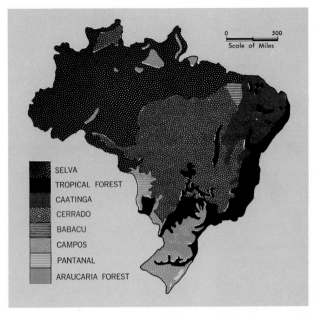

Natural Vegetation

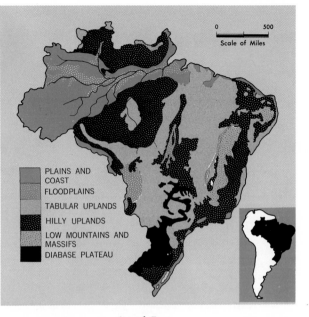

Land Form

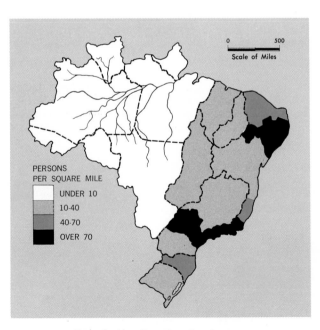

Population Density, by States

Map 3-3 Brazil: Vegetation, Land Form, and Population

Some of the botanical wealth of Brazil is suggested by the number of vegetation types used here. The selva and tropical forest are rain forests. The caatinga, cerrado, and babacu are scrub and thorn forests. The campos and pantanal are grasslands and the araucaria forest is a midlatitude forest.

The vegetational boundaries tend to cut across the land forms. The population is strongly centered in the uplands along the Atlantic coast. Note the absence of population in the interior and northern hilly uplands. *Adapted from Focus—The American Geographical Society.*

Brazilian Contribution to Tropical Housing. This modern apartment building is marked by balconies with sun screens that combine privacy with control of the radiant heat from the sun, a major problem in tropical lands. *Brazilian Government Trade Bureau.*

Brasilia. Bold architectural innovation characterizes Brazil's new capital. *Brazilian Government Trade Bureau.*

Brazil is now showing many signs of a coming burst of human energy. She has been leading the world in modern tropical architecture and has been producing artists, musicians, and scholars of note. Centering on São Paulo there is an aggressive development spirit that resembles the burst of growth that came in the United States in the second half of the nineteenth century. Railroads, power plants, factories, and roads are being built. The capital of the country has been resolutely transplanted to a new city built in a near wilderness in the interior of the country. If Brazil now looks to her rich vast interior and sets free the energies of her people, that is, experiences a change in her human climate, her tropical climate is likely to prove to be no handicap. If, however, Brazil bogs down in inflation and political chaos, it is difficult to see why this should be attributed to climate.

The rest of humid tropical South America presents a similar picture. In Colombia 80 percent of the people live in the western third of the country and most of them in the mountains, and thus out of the tropics. The principal products are agricultural—coffee for export and corn for consumption at home. The principal imports are manufactured goods. Ecuador too has most of its people in the mountains. It exports rice and chocolate to the world market and imports manufactured goods. In both countries much of the population is Indian. Paraguay is an interior lowland area with a climate only slightly more tropical than the American South. Although as large as California and having a much larger percentage of potentially useful land, the population only totals about one and one-half million. It is mostly Indian. Again, it is neither race, nor climate, nor even interior location that is the cause of an almost totally stagnant culture. The American Indians have maintained civilizations in tropical climates. Interior location has not handicapped the Swiss unduly. On the other hand, Paraguay does not have productive advanced nations for neighbors, a stable government, or an educated people. None of these is physically or geographically determined. The rich soil and long growing season—an area where oranges can grow wild—suggest potential agricultural wealth.

THE OLD WORLD TROPICS

AFRICA: THE PROBLEM OF CULTURAL LAG

Africa south of the Sahara is Negro Africa, often thought of as a vast tropical forest inhabited by a culturally retarded people, and the inferences drawn are usually that the tropics prevented development or that the race is inferior—or both. We must then consider environment, race, and accomplishment.

The wet tropics of Africa are not as extensive as is usually thought, for North Africa is mostly desert and steppe, as is Southwest Africa. Only about one fourth of tropical Africa has dense forest, and large areas are covered with scattered scrubby trees set in brushy and grassy landscapes. In part this scrub area is due to the action of man through his long-continued practice of slash and burn agriculture, but in part it reflects the fact that much of tropical Africa has only about 40 inches of rainfall—not a large amount for a tropical climate.

Much of tropical Africa is highland. The structure of the continent is such that a short distance inland there is a rapid ascent to a plateau-like upland. This upland averages 1000 feet above sea level even in the Congo basin, and in East Africa there are large areas of 5000 feet elevation or greater. Since the normal temperature decrease with elevation is 3 degrees per 1000 feet, many equatorial African stations are 6 to 15 degrees cooler than their latitude would suggest. Launde in the Cameroons has average monthly temperatures ranging between 70° and 74° F., and Entebe, Uganda, right on the equator, has a range of 68° to 71° F. for its coolest and warmest months.

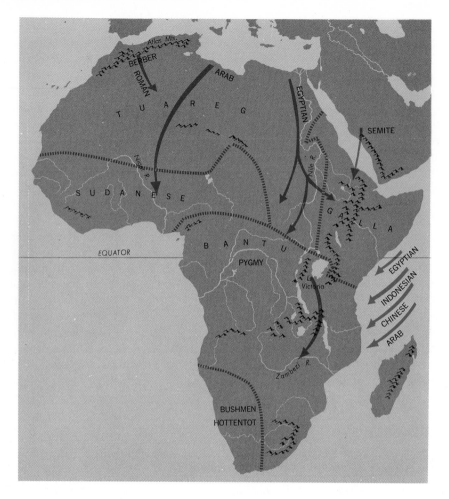

Map 3-4 Africa

The location of the major peoples of Africa is shown here, together with arrows suggesting movements of people and ideas. The Bantu expanded southward relatively recently, and had not yet reached South Africa when the Europeans landed at Cape Town. The extent of early sea trade with East Africa on the part of Egyptians, Indonesians, Chinese, and Arabs is just becoming recognized.

These are April, May, and October temperatures at New Orleans, and much cooler than the five hot summer months of that "subtropical" city.

Water power potential is very high because of the tropical rainfall on high mountains along the eastern side of the continent and because all the rivers have to reach the sea by descending from the plateaulike interior. This creates water falls and some of these are among the world's largest potential sites for hydroelectric development. Resources of coal are small, and oil prospects in tropical Africa are little known, but the central Sahara oil could of course

easily be piped into tropical Africa. Mineral wealth is known to be great, for Africa is already a major producer of antimony, chromite, cobalt, copper, manganese, tin, industrial diamonds, and vanadium and in times past has been a major producer of gold.

Tropical soils are often poor, and in this Africa does suffer. The relatively level land has allowed old soils to develop with the associated extreme weathering and leaching. Nevertheless, Africa has large areas of good soils, and coffee, sugar, palm oils, and other plantation crops have already been most successfully grown there.

Tanganyika, Africa. The landscape would be much more tree-covered were it not for the clearing of land for agriculture and the grazing of domesticated animals. The remaining trees are largely baobab, which the natives left when they cleared the remainder of the vegetation. *American Geographical Society*.

Zulu Family Group in South Africa. The stupendous task of bringing a people from this way of life to the mid-twentieth–century Western European standard is too often assumed to be readily accomplished. Notice the woman grinding grain on a stone slab, the metate. This implement once had a world-wide distribution among primitive people, surviving through biblical times in the eastern Mediterranean. *Information Service of South Africa*.

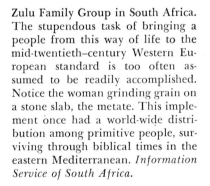

One cannot from this description make much of a case for Africa as a geographically handicapped area. Even the tropical climate, if this were considered a handicap, is modified by elevation, and great civilizations have flourished in hotter, wetter, and in some ways poorer environments than this. Further, in Negro Africa there are many kinds of environments; hot, wet lowlands; warm, well-watered uplands; and cool, moist highlands; grasslands; wooded and grassy savannas and rain forest; plains, plateaus, and mountains. It is a rich and varied environment well stocked with useful plants and animals. One may well ask why the Negroes have done so little with so good an environment, but first one must review what they have actually done.

All of Africa was held by people of Negro race until toward the end of the Paleolithic period, at which time Europeans appeared in northernmost Africa. Small, brown-skinned people of the Bushman type seemingly held much of Africa originally, but have been progressively displaced by the expansion of the large, very dark skinned Negroes, especially the Bantu, after A.D. 500. Migrants into the region were the Hamitic people who entered Egypt from Arabia and Semitic- and Hamitic-speaking people of European race who entered Ethiopia. There was also a minor racial influence from Indonesia that introduced Mongoloid race types to the east coast of Africa.

Cultural stimuli reached Negro Africa principally from the north and the northeast. As early as 1500 B.C. states modeled on the Egyptian–Near Eastern pattern (priest-king, absolutist rule, with courts, harems, nobility, and so forth) were developed by the Negroes in Nubia, and despotic states of typical African type derived from these models began at this time to appear along the northern border of the western Sudan. After 1000 B.C. maritime trade across the northern Indian Ocean led to the introduction of Malaysian and Indian food plants into East Africa, where they were combined with the Near Eastern plant domesticates and the West African domestic plants to greatly strengthen the African agricultural base. People from Indonesia, principally Borneo, established settlements along the East African coast in order to engage in trade with Negro Africa. After A.D. 1 the empire of Ghana arose in the western Sudan, and the new food plants introduced from Malaysia allowed the growth of dense populations in the Guinea coast area, where the Bantu people had their homeland. It was the expansion of these people with their new food plants that thereafter progressively reduced the areas held by the smaller peoples of Africa: the Pygmies of the Congo forest and the Bushmen of East and South Africa.

Between A.D. 1 and A.D. 500 Semitic traders displaced the Indonesians in the East African trade, and the Indonesians moved to the island of Madagascar, establishing their speech there, and remaining even today as a major part of the racial stock on that island. After A.D. 500 milking belatedly began spreading into Africa from the north, following the much earlier introduction of animals used only for meat and hides, a situation parallel to that of China, where cattle keeping was introduced without milking. This is also the time of the establishment of Zimbabwe and similar great stone fortifications in East Africa by Cushites of European race and Muslem Arabs who were entering the area in search of gold.

After A.D. 1000 the pastoralists who practiced dairying and the Bantu both continued their expansions, mostly at the expense of the small Negroid peoples, most of whom had remained in the hunting and gathering stage of development.

States, empires, and kingdoms continued to rise and fall in West Africa, the Sudan, and East Africa, the areas most influenced for the longest time by developments in areas bordering the Mediterranean and Indian oceans.

Progress in tropical Africa can then be summarized as follows: With the introduction of agriculture from the north between 4000 and 3000 B.C. a steady cultural growth began. Within 2000 years states and empires appeared on the northern margin, and under continuing stimulation through trade across the

Indian Ocean an agricultural and population base was laid for the expansion of these culturally advantaged northern people at the expense of the non-agricultural smaller Negro peoples. The picture is little different from that of the spread of ideas among the American Indians: those having most access to ideas reached the stage of empires and states, and those too far from the areas of stimulus remained in the stage of hunters and gatherers, with those hunters and gatherers near the centers of development who did not change being overwhelmed by the increasing numbers of the peoples that did change.

While one may well ask why a people that was reaching the stage of empires between 2000 and 1000 B.C. did not go on to ever greater heights, it is only just to recognize that the course of events in Africa is little different from that in most other areas, for no race has maintained an even course ever onward and upward.

Africa is geographically so close to the center of growth and development in the Near East that it would seem that ideas should have reached the area in sufficient number over a long enough time to have promoted greater cultural growth. Africa does have some difficulties, however. The Sahara is a vast barrier. While it has never stopped contact entirely, it has greatly reduced the flow of men and ideas from the Mediterranean to Africa south of the Sahara. If cultural growth is in proportion to the length of time and the intensity of cultural stimulus, then the Sahara must be seen as having greatly reduced the intensity of contact. Unusual amounts of time would expectably be required to compensate for this. While the vast desert west of the Nile River with its long and difficult oasis routes reduced the flow of men and of ideas to a trickle, the Nile valley seems, unexpectedly, to have been little better as a corridor for transporting ideas. In part this was because the Egyptian civilization spread only slowly up the Nile, and in part because cultural stimulus along so thin a thread must become a pin prick instead of a shove. Again the expectation would be that more time would be needed for a situation such as this, where

contact is on a narrow front, than would be required where the contact is on a broad front.

Africa's contacts have been punctuated by stormy interludes. If we start with the latest happening and work backward, we can see what the effect of changing contacts can be. When the Europeans entered the Indian Ocean just after A.D. 1500, they found a rich trade flourishing between East Africa and India. They disrupted it so thoroughly that they can best be described as having killed the goose that laid the golden egg. Production of gold and ivory and other such products stopped, and not only did the trade die but contacts for the people of interior Africa was cut off. Thereafter came a long period of confusion and isolation. Only after nearly three centuries did the Europeans penetrate the interior of Africa and begin the full-scale development of the area through the building of roads, railroads, mining operations, and so forth. If each such shift in the dominant group trading with Africa was accompanied by similar setbacks, then Africa's slow progress despite the long-continued Indian Ocean trade becomes more understandable. The succession of Egyptians, Indonesians, Yemenite Arabs, Muslem Arabs, and finally Europeans suggests that roughly every 500 years a violent setback occurred.

To these disruptions of external sea-borne contacts one must add comparable disruptions in overland contacts and equally great cultural setbacks due to internal explosions. For example, the expansion of the Bantu from West Africa and in part the expansion of the cattle-oriented culture of the mixed race groups from northeast Africa were partially at the expense of culturally advanced people whose agriculture was marked by irrigation of terraced hillsides in a manner reminiscent of the irrigated rice terraces of southeast Asia. The course of culture history is punctuated with such events, for the parallel to the farming–cattle keeping people overrunning more advanced cultures would be the outpouring of the Germanic tribes and their overwhelming of France, Spain, and Italy, with a consequent cultural collapse so deep as to be called the

Dark Ages. The course of events in Africa seems, then, to follow normal patterns, and the locale and race are only variations on a theme. The Africans were more isolated and lacked a Byzantium to keep the cultural flame bright while adjacent areas fell back into the darkness of barbarism.

Africa does have some handicaps, notably in tropical diseases. It is suspected that this may be the home of malaria, for the Negro race is the only one that has a specific resistance to this disease, which suggests long exposure and the development of a partial immunity through a blood abnormality called sickle-cell anemia. Africa is also the focal area of sleeping sickness, carried by the tsetse fly. This disease attacks man and his domestic animals. The wild animals are not killed by it but are infected with it and supply a reservoir of infection from which the disease is constantly reintroduced into human settlements. Most of the other tropical diseases are also present. Has the disease burden been unusually high and has this been a contributing cause of Negro Africa's failure to advance? Other areas have had similar burdens.

The sleeping-sickness problem has been attacked with vigor by the colonial powers, but with very little success. Great, organized slaughters of wild animals have been carried out in the hopes of reducing the host population. These have all failed, for the wild-animal populations rebuild, and the domestic animals continue to become infected.

Here we have an example of man plodding ahead in the face of vast difficulties instead of trying to make the means at hand accomplish the task. The idea of domestic animals has not been generalized. Domestic animals are cows, pigs, sheep, goats, ducks, and chickens. Giraffes, African elephants, zebras, gnus, antelope, and deer are not only not domestic but are generally said to be nondomesticable. If these animals could be domesticated, Africa would have sleeping-sickness resistant "cattle." This idea seems not to have been seriously considered.

When the "nondomesticable" notion is examined, it is often found to be untrue. The African elephant is as domesticable as the Indian elephant, and the facts have been in the records for 2000 years: the Romans and the Carthaginians had and used domesticated African elephants. More recently, elephants in the tropical rain forest were tamed and trained as work beasts. Probably the goatlike antelopes and gazelles, the striped horses, and numbers of other African wild animals are potentially useful domestic animals that the "environment" displays before mankind, but man in his usual unimaginative way clings to imported animals that are nonresistant to disease.

The plant world is treated by mankind in much the same way. Africa is rich in plants but has supplied relatively few domestic plants to the world. The watermelon and the grain sorghums (milo maize, kaffir corn, and their relatives) are Africa's major contributions to the world's agriculture. Vastly more has been gained in recent times: maize and cocoa from America; bananas and rice from Asia. Two other African plant contributions, coffee and cotton, came not from wet-tropical Africa but from highland Abyssinia. The record of Negro Africa looks poor, but the record for Europe is no better, and for America north of Mexico, much poorer. When it is considered that most of the peoples of the world contributed nothing to the agricultural heritage that is the real basis of all great cultural accomplishment in the past 10,000 years, the Negro contribution of some plants takes on added significance.

There are of course other Negro contributions. Negro art and music are greatly appreciated by some, but this is a difficult field with highly variable judgment. Of greater interest, perhaps is the Gada republic, a unique political invention found in Negro Africa. In addition to primitive family-band democracy common to much of mankind and the despotic states stimulated by contact with the Near East and Egypt, the Negroes invented an age-graded political structure not found elsewhere in the world. In this structure duties fell upon age groups, and men progressed through the various groups (warriors, councilors, governors) and then were retired. As elders, they were respected and listened to but they had no official duties. Few peoples in the world can claim so unusual an invention. It is on the same level of originality as the Chinese invention of civil service examinations.

This review, then, should remove the picture of Africa as a vast tropical forest, occupied from time immemorial by a backward people. Instead, a picture emerges of considerable accomplishment by the Negro people, and the localization of this accomplishment in just those areas where proximity and contact would lead one to expect it. The only criticism of Negro achievement possible would seem to be that, given all the contact, more should have been accomplished. The explanation seems to lie in the fact that each hopeful beginning by Egypt, Rome, Indonesia, Arabia, and Europe was cut off before the inertia to mass cultural change was overcome. The cultural history of much of the world has probably proceeded in a similar fashion but the large number of abortive starts in Europe, India, China, and Middle America are now lost to us in the darkness of unrecorded history, while the struggles of tropical Africa go on before our eyes.

Modern Development

When modern development of tropical Africa began, its pattern was much like that of Brazil. Coastal areas were the focal points to which produce came to be shipped overseas. With this outward look, transportation systems developed as short-line routes feeding the nearest port; areas were not linked together; and there was and, except for the air lines, there is today no transportation network. In part the flow of heavy goods such as the copper of Katanga has followed national lines rather than natural routes to the sea. In the present national fractionization of Africa, there is unlikely to be either the will or the immense capital necessary for the construction of a rational rail network. This is not due to the physical geography, however, for the African terrain is not a difficult one for railroad construction.

Most of Africa remains today in the mixed economy of subsistence village dwellers who are just being drawn into the orbit of the world of commerce. Under colonial rule, the extractive industries were started; mining began on a modern scale, with metals other than the precious ones sought. Agriculture was expanded into commercially valuable crops such as chocolate, palm oil, cotton, tea, coffee, and peanuts. The native populations typically had to be urged into production of crops of commercial value, for in the main their outlook was comparable to that of the Yumas, that is, no incentive existed to produce for the world market. However, this attitude is typical of all noncommercially oriented peoples, and only when desires for the amenities of the civilized world develop do they become willing to work for wages, to produce materials they do not themselves consume.

Tropical Africa has both advantages and disadvantages in the modern world. Agriculturally there is little that cannot be grown there, for the area ranges from coastal lowlands to highlands, from old acid soils to rich young volcanic soils, from high rainfalls to low ones, and from constant rains to seasonal showers. Perhaps the greatest disadvantages are the large extent of old soils with the characteristic accumulation of iron and low amounts of soluble nutrients, and the broad belt where the tsetse fly makes cattle keeping impossible and human living risky because of sleeping sickness. Yet agricultural chemistry can enrich soils, though at a cost, and it is not unthinkable that modern science can eliminate the tsetse fly. In the modern world of instantaneous communication, of spreading education, and ever-growing commercial connections, Africa cannot remain isolated, and despite predictable political travail, growth and development there will be.

INDIA AND SOUTHEAST ASIA: LAND AND PEOPLE

Wet tropical Asia includes most of India, Southeast Asia, Indonesia, and southern China. This area holds representatives of all the major races of man. The people of northwest India are dark-skinned members of the Mediterranean race, while those to the southeast are Dravidians, a darker-skinned people often called Australoids. Probably all India was

Map 3-5 India:
Population, Land Form, Rainfall, and Crop Yield

This series of maps is focused on the population problem. The total population is large; it exceeds 1000 persons per square mile over considerable areas, and is growing rapidly. In the densely settled parts of India, the land is supporting two, three, and at times four persons per acre. Comparison of the population-density map with the land-form map shows that the high densities are on the margins of the Deccan Plateau. The rainfall graphs show rainfall through the year. Those of cities in the plateau area indicate that it is relatively dry. All the graphs show the strong seasonal concentration of rainfall that is characteristic of monsoon climates. The enormous seasonal concentration and amount of precipitation at Cherrapunji is noteworthy.

The crop-yield graphs portray another side of India's problem. Although it is an agricultural nation, yields are low. In the few cases where India's yields approach those of other nations graphed here, there are other reasons that leave India in poor relative position. The United States grows sugar cane in Louisiana under great climatic difficulty. We grow wheat in semiarid lands with extensive mechanized handling. This results in low yields per acre, but at very low cost per bushel. Note India's poor position in cotton or maize growing compared with Egypt. India's agriculture is, then, quite inefficient, and its food problem is, in large part, a measure of the primitive state of this aspect of its primary production. *Adapted from* Focus— *The American Geographical Society.*

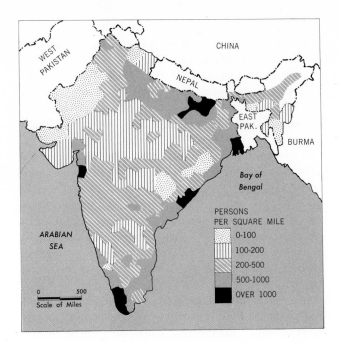

Population Density

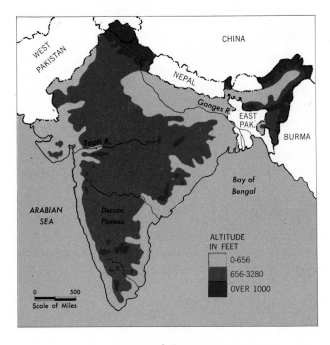

Land Form

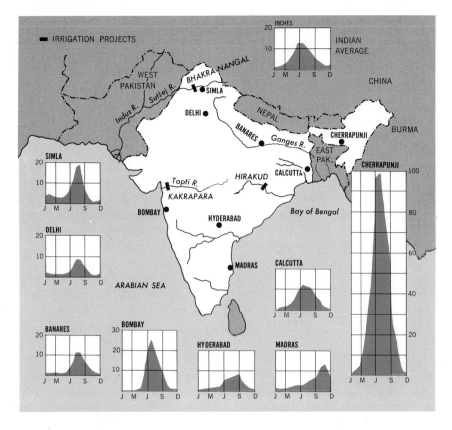

Average Annual Rainfall, by Month

(Below)
Yield per Acre of Major Cereal and
Cash Crops Compared with Yields in
Various Other Countries

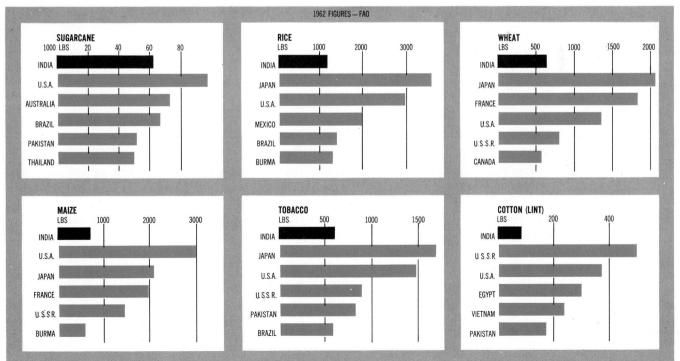

1962 FIGURES — FAO

SUGARCANE
1000 LBS   20   40   60   80

INDIA
U.S.A.
AUSTRALIA
BRAZIL
PAKISTAN
THAILAND

RICE
LBS   1000   2000   3000

INDIA
JAPAN
U.S.A.
MEXICO
BRAZIL
BURMA

WHEAT
LBS   500   1000   1500   2000

INDIA
JAPAN
FRANCE
U.S.A.
U.S.S.R.
CANADA

MAIZE
LBS   1000   2000   3000

INDIA
U.S.A.
JAPAN
FRANCE
U.S.S.R.
BURMA

TOBACCO
LBS.   500   1000   1500

INDIA
JAPAN
U.S.A.
U.S.S.R.
PAKISTAN
BRAZIL

COTTON (LINT)
LBS   200   400

INDIA
U.S.S.R.
U.S.A.
EGYPT
VIETNAM
PAKISTAN

originally Dravidian in race, and Caucasoid people entering the area from the northwest modified the original situation (see Map 1–2). The Burmese, Siamese, Anamese, and Chinese are Mongolian in race. The people of the islands between the mainland and Melanesia are called Malays or Indonesians. They are an intermediate group, perhaps more closely related to the Mongoloid race than to any other. From New Guinea to the Fiji Islands, the people are Negro. Why there should be two centers of Negro people in the world, one in the Pacific and one in Africa is one of the mysteries of the origin of the races of man. As suggested earlier, possibly a continous distribution of dark-skinned people has been broken by relatively recent expansions of the Caucasoid and Mongoloid peoples. For comparative purposes, it is useful to have all the races of man in one climatic type of environment in one corner of the world. Southeast Asia, with adjacent Indonesia and Melanesia, holds nearly half of all mankind. These people are very unevenly distributed: parts of India, southern China, and Java are densely settled, while the rest of the land varies from moderately to lightly settled.

Monsoon India

Monsoon India is largely Hindu. The Muslims occupy mainly the dryer northwest, although they have an outlying group in the Ganges delta, which became the basis for forming East Pakistan during the tragic splitting of India at the time it gained its independence in 1946. That the Muslim religion is strongly associated with dry lands is one of the accidents of history. Muhammad was an Arab, and his followers spread principally through the adjacent dry lands, to some extent perhaps because they were accustomed to and knew how to cope with such lands. However, the Ganges delta is a very wet land, and Muslims are numerically important not only there but also in such hot, wet lands as Indonesia and the Philippines, where the currents of world trade carried their influence. The existing pattern of religion, race, and climate reflects the movements of trade and conquest through a large expanse of time. Muslim history began in the dry lands and spread widely through them, but as India shows, it also spread into wet areas when opportunity offered.

Monsoon India is sometimes called a subcontinent, although it is only about one third the size of the United States. It is set off from the rest of the world by the Himalayas to the north, by deserts to the west, and by seas on its other sides. The Ganges-Brahmaputra plain in the northeast is a major area of fertile well-watered land. Peninsular India is a triangular plateau with mountains on two sides. These bordering ranges intercept the seasonally reversed wind flows and are areas of high rainfall; the areas between them are surprisingly dry. The phenomena of winds blowing in nearly opposite directions in two strongly marked seasons is called the monsoon. It is most strongly developed in Asia because this greatest land mass of the world extends here from low to high latitude, and on so great a land mass the seas can have little tempering effect. In the winter, the interior becomes extremely cold, and the cold, dry air flows outward, bringing a dry season; in the summer, the continent becomes extremely hot, and moist air masses from over the warm tropical seas flow in over the land, bringing heavy summer rains.

The population of India is strongly concentrated in the Ganges River valley and on the well-watered sides of the Deccan Plateau. The drier interior part of the plateau averages about half the density of the wetter, lower, flatter parts of monsoon India. This is a geographically determined population location *if* one properly understands it. India's major population density is based on wet-rice agriculture, which demands abundant water and is most easily irrigated on flat lands. It is primarily this choice of a wet-rice agriculture that dictates the population concentration where the land and climate are most productive. If their major crop were sweet potatoes or some other crop with requirements different from rice, the maximum population density would undoubtedly be elsewhere. As it is, India produces six times as much rice as wheat. Jute in the East Pakistan area

Jaipur, India. The cottage industry of today was characteristic of the advanced nations of the world before the industrial revolution. Here the dye is being prepared by the couple in the background and material is being hand block-stamp printed by the man in the foreground. *Information Service of India.*

of the Ganges Delta and cotton on the Deccan and in the dryer upper Ganges valley are the next most important crops.

India faces chronic malnutrition and recurrent famine—and it is said that it is an unsuccessful famine that does not reduce the population sufficiently to alleviate the hunger of the survivors. With population increasing at the rate of three million per year the situation is seemingly hopeless, but such things are seldom as simple as they seem.

First of all, India has twice as many cattle as the United States. Their chief use is as draft animals that produce dung, which can be dried and used as fuel. Further, although devout Hindus cannot eat beef, a cow eats a great deal of feed, much of which could serve as human food. At best a cow is an inefficient converter of plant material into protein, but if the cow's protein is not used, the loss is total. In addition, the cattle dirty the city, injure people, and create a traffic hazard; yet man here elects not to use the

major potential of this animal, but on the contrary to carry it as a heavy economic burden.

Secondly, it is difficult to say of any land that it is overpopulated; it is more realistic to view the people as underemployed. Indian peasant agriculture is inefficient: tools are light, scarce, and poor; and human energy levels are low. India's great political leader Ghandi is reported to have said that India's greatest handicap is the almost unconquerable inertia of her people. The will to accomplish something does not fill the ordinary Indian, and until it does, the land will remain overpopulated in the sense that the people will not make it productive.

Many of the reasons for India's nonproductiveness are attributed to her caste system. While this is unquestionably a major factor in its low productivity, India is in many ways a typical underdeveloped country. The mass of her people are illiterate, subsistence farmers; while her rail transportation network is only fair compared to Europe or the United

States. In order to raise the Indians to a better standard of living, a whole series of changes must be made. The man on the land must improve his efficiency to the point where he can support several families in industry, commerce, and transportation. This more efficient farmer will need a larger farm. The people displaced from the land in this process must be absorbed by a growing industry. Industry demands more and more skills as it becomes increasingly mechanized, so the people displaced from the land must be educated if they are to be useful in the city industries. Capital must be found to build up such industries; marketing channels and skills and transportation networks must be set up to distribute the goods and services created. In other words, what is required is generations of education, growth, and development. One cannot take a vast mass of people, wave a wand, and have simultaneously a revolution in attitudes, education, transportation, production, population distribution, and standards of living. If this can be said of relatively advanced India, how much more difficult the African problem!

England went through extremely difficult times when it industrialized early in the nineteenth century. The United States today is struggling with the impact of automation in the factories and mechanization on the farm. Even with our enormously developed economy and society we are suffering from the resulting dislocation. Why then do we think that a few glowing phrases and a few billion dollars can accomplish what only time and desire can really bring into being?

This is not to say that India cannot become again a great world power. In the remote past the Indians have been great creative producers; hence, by the severe test of high accomplishment, they are an able race. Out of this hot, wet land have come such great inventions as the mathematical concept of zero and our numeral system. Our numbering system is called Arabic because the Arabs brought it to us, but they borrowed it from the Indians. Without it, even simple arithmetic is nearly impossible: try multiplying the Roman numeral XIV by XXX rather than the "Arabic" 14 times 30.

India is rich in resources. She has coal, iron, nickel, manganese, graphite, and other valuable industrial resources, and she is rich in people. If these were more gainfully employed, they could make her a great productive center. Her problems are not tropical, not physical-geographical; they are human-geographical: her outlook on man and land are a bit like that of the Yuma Indians.

The Human Factor in Southeast Asia

In Southeast Asia, India for the past 2000 years or more has exerted a great influence on Burma, Thailand, Cambodia, Vietnam, Malaya, and Indonesia. The arts (architecture, dance, music, and the like) show this strongly. Southeast Asia is a land of forested mountains and seasonally flooded plains. Rice is the major crop although in Malaya rubber equals it in tonnage, and in Indonesia cassava exceeds it. Both rubber and cassava are American Indian crops.

It is sometimes said of this region that here cultivation means constant struggle with the environment. Where is cultivation any different? It is also alleged that this area has the ideal climate for the rubber tree and thus became the world center of rubber production, yet the causes were quite otherwise. The rubber tree is a native of the American tropical rain forest: it would grow equally well in any similar climate. Africa, Melanesia, any of the American rain forest areas, and vastly more of Asia than actually grows rubber are equally well suited by physical geography. Indeed, if there were such a thing as a natural rubber-tree climate area, one would think that its American homeland would qualify.

Rubber is growing primarily in Southeast Asia, rather than in America, for political-economic-entrepreneurial reasons. The British and the Dutch, applying plantation methods combined with botanical knowledge and colonial control of areas well populated with sedentary, skilled agricultural people,

Influences from India in Indonesia. (*Above*) Bas reliefs from the temple of Borobudur, Java, built in the eighth century. (*Left*) Balinese woman doing a temple dance; these posture dances are specifically Hindu. *Embassy of Indonesia.*

A Holy Bull in a Temple in Central Java (*left*) and the Use of Indian Humped Cattle as Draft Animals in Central Java (*below*). These are examples of Hindu influence in Indonesia, which was especially strong between the eighth and twelfth centuries. Art, architecture, religion, and numerous other traits show strong Hindu influences. *Embassy of Indonesia.*

took advantage of a rich market potential. The production of rubber from stands of wild trees in Brazil was inefficient, costly, and limited. Plantation agriculture was more efficient and less costly because of the closer spacing of trees, the better control of labor and production methods, leading to a high quality of material, and the skilled plant selection of varieties yielding much more rubber than the natural trees. There were many physical environments where this could have been done; the human factors placed it in Southeast Asia.

In some areas the human factors have led to further complications. In Malaya the tin mining and much of the plantation work has been done by Chinese. The native Malay did not choose to do this work; hence Chinese labor was imported. Many Chinese have stayed on, and much of the wealth of the country (factories, plantations, mines, banks, stores) is now in their hands. In Singapore, they make up 80 percent of the population. There would seem to be no racial difference to account for this, for the Malays are a more tropical people than the Chinese. However, the Malays are less commercially motivated, and the hard working, money-minded Chinese easily gained economic leadership. This situation is due neither to race nor to climate, but to culture.

In the period of colonial expansion after 1500, all of monsoon Asia went under the control of European powers except Siam (present-day Thailand), which lost Cambodia to the French but managed to maintain its independence. Today all of these lands are independent, and the problem now is how to maintain their freedom. These countries were all more advanced than any of tropical Africa, yet literacy, a sense of political unity, and an understanding of the processes of government were not common in the masses of the people. At this crucial time in their national development, they are caught in the international struggle between the Communist world and the free world. They are in a precarious position with only a fair chance to maintain law and order and build up productivity and unity in their respective areas while remaining free from the Com-

Influences from India in Indochina. Monuments to cultural influences from India are preserved in Cambodia at Angkor Thom (*upper*) and Angkor Wat (*lower*), capital cities of the Khmers in the period between the eighth and eleventh centuries. The false, or corbelled, arch in the gateway at Angkor Thom and the steep stairway to the first pavilion and the spool-shaped ornaments in the windows at Angkor Wat are features that reappear in Middle American civic-center type architecture in early pre-Columbian periods. *Embassy of Cambodia.*

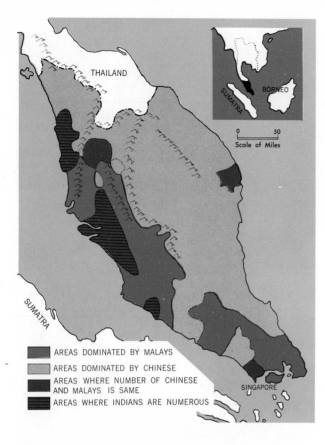

AREAS DOMINATED BY MALAYS

AREAS DOMINATED BY CHINESE

AREAS WHERE NUMBER OF CHINESE AND MALAYS IS SAME

AREAS WHERE INDIANS ARE NUMEROUS

Map 3-6   Major Ethno-linguistic Groups in Malaya

The Malays have been reduced to a minority position in parts of their country by the inpouring of Chinese, primarily, and Indians, secondarily. Indians are numerous in areas on the west coast; in these areas the Indian population and Chinese fraction are 40 to 60 percent of the total, often making the Malays there a minority group. The Indian- and Chinese-dominated areas coincide with the rubber- and tin-producing regions since it is these activities that have attracted these groups.

munist bloc, which desires to become the new colonial world power. Yet most of the former colonies of Southeast Asia, aware of their recent colonial past at the hands of the West, do not see clearly their present danger of a much worse colonial future.

The Delta Lands of Peninsular Asia

Burma, Thailand, and Cambodia are three delta regions of Southeast Asia. Burma is set off from India and Thailand by mountain ranges. The country has two major valleys, and on these flood plains and especially in the deltas, rice is grown. Since the population density of the country is only about 70 per square mile, there is a rice surplus, which is exported to India, Ceylon, and Malaya, in part to feed the plantation workers of those areas. Southeast Asia is a region of great population contrasts, for moderately populated Burma is separated by only one mountain range from the densely populated Ganges valley of India. In fact, the mountainous part of Burma, the larger part of the country, is quite thinly populated.

Thailand repeats the Burmese picture: the dense population is in the lowlands, and the major product is rice. Cambodia, a part of the lowland between Indochina and Burma, was long a part of Thailand and the whole area was long under Indian influence. A series of petty kingdoms came and went; at times the area was united, but more often it was not. The area is one of curious cultural combinations. The religion is Buddhism, derived from India—where it has almost ceased to exist; yet the speech of the area is Sino-Tibetan, a language related to Chinese. Indian influence, however, has long been the strongest one, as art, architecture, and many customs clearly show. This complex situation is a good measure of the cultural crosscurrents that have long marked this region.

In Thailand as in Burma most of the population lives on the delta plains and few people inhabit the mountains. The agriculture of the plains is a wet-rice one, that of the mountains is "forest rotation," the familiar cycle of clear–burn–cultivate–abandon. One of the products of the mountain

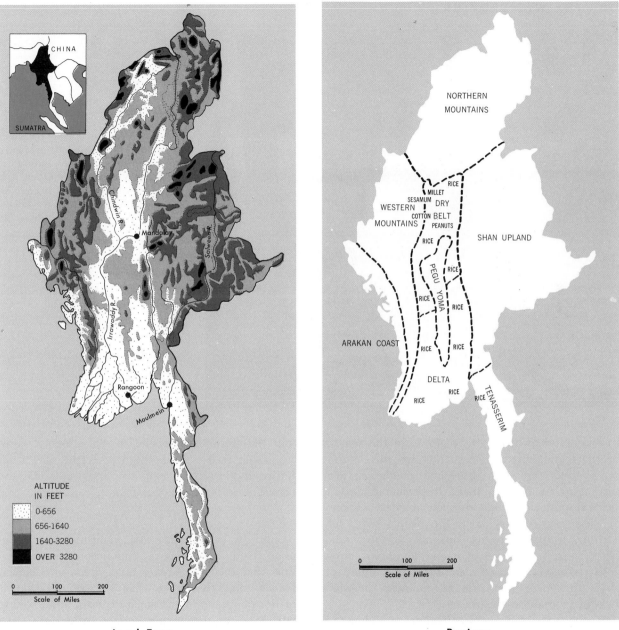

Map 3-7   Burma: Land Form and Regions

Burma is a mountainous land. Most of the people and most of the agricultural production
are in the delta or in the dry belt, while the fewest are on the Arakan coast and in Tenasserim. The Delta, the Arakan coast, and the plain at the northern end of Tenasserim
are the rice-producing areas. In the dry belt, caused by the enclosing mountains trapping
the moisture-laden winds, the principal crops are sesamum, cotton, peanuts, and millet.
Adapted from Focus—*The American Geographical Society.*

Tropical Housing. Thatch roofs give good insulation. Widely overhanging eaves provide shade and shelter from heavy downpours. Open style allows maximum flow of breeze. All of these characteristics are advantageous for tropical conditions. *Embassy of Indonesia.*

area is opium, which can be grown in the remote clearings undetected. The market for this contraband product creates a value high enough in proportion to its bulk to make it profitable despite the transportation costs through roadless regions. In these back-country areas the people wear silk clothing, a luxury to us, but not to those who can raise, spin, and weave it and to whom cotton cloth represents the expenditure of money—of which they have too little to squander on what they can produce themselves.

In the Chiengmai delta region of Thailand "floating rice" is cultivated. The land is planted when the rains begin; the house, hay stack, and cow all sit on rafts; and as the floods come, the rice grows and the entire farmstead begins to float. The water gets six feet or more deep, and the rice develops long, limber stems and the leaves float on the water surface; flowers form and the

grain develops. At the end of the summer rains, the water recedes and the rice settles down on the ground, which is soon dry and hard, and the harvest can be gathered in.

Indonesia

Contrasts in Southeast Asia continue into Indonesia. Here Java has a population density approaching 1000 per square mile. Sumatra, Celebes, Borneo, and the other islands have very much smaller population densities, with large areas having only 5 to 10 people per square mile. Java, like Burma and Thailand, was strongly influenced by the Indian culture. However, Indian colonies that grew to kingdoms, complete with elaborate capitals, well-developed trade, and literate classes, marked this whole Southeast Asian area for more than 1000 years. When it is considered that Indonesia lay between the two ancient culture centers

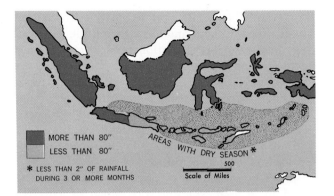

Average Annual Rainfall

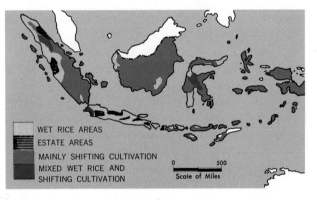

Agriculture

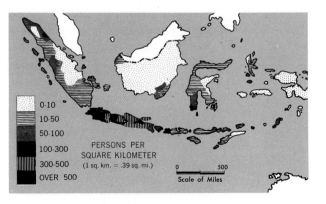

Population Density

Map 3-8 Indonesia: Rainfall, Agriculture, and Population

The relatively limited areas of wet rice cultivation are notable. That this situation is not determined by physical geography is easily seen by comparing the agriculture map with the rainfall map and considering that all the islands are mountainous and many of them are volcanic in origin. It is a clear record of the relatively late arrival of wet rice culture. Population density declines toward the marginal areas, as does general cultural level. *Adapted from* Focus *—The American Geographical Society*.

of Asia and was powerfully influenced by both for more than 2000, and perhaps for as long as 4000, years their level of achievement is not surprising. These influences had built up a moderately dense agriculturally based population that produced high-value, low-bulk materials such as spices for world trade. The long, slow process of building a civilization is well exemplified by its modest success here over a long period of time, in an area well located to receive influences from more advanced neighbors.

Thus the Europeans who colonized Southeast Asia stepped into a "going concern." The population was settled on the land. They were accustomed to producing material for the world market. There were established governments, tax systems, capital cities, and so forth. The Europeans powers simply took over the controls. These people had been in contact with traders from both East and West for thousands of years. They had already been exposed to most of the world's known diseases and did not melt away following contact with Europeans. There was no empty land for Europeans to move into, and there was no need to import black slave labor. As a result, Southeast Asia remains Asiatic, and the people are mostly descendants of the original inhabitants—with the exceptions we have noted of the Chinese in Malaya and Singapore, where the influx radically changed the picture.

The effects of the colonial developments were very uneven. The Dutch on Java stopped the local wars, improved health and sanitation, and developed a

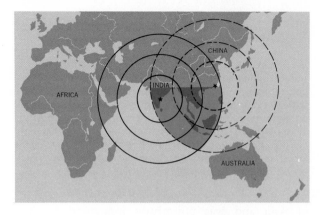

**Map 3-9   Indonesia in
Relation to China and India**

From centers on the coasts of China and India, circles 5°, 10°, and 15° of longitude in radius have been drawn. The area equidistant by sea from India and China is indicated by shading. This includes Burma, Siam, Cambodia, Indochina, Indonesia, and the Philippines. These are the areas of culturally advanced people. Beyond this zone of double influence lie Australia and Melanesia. Melanesia, the closer, received agriculture; Australia did not.

All simple correlations of this sort are, of course, suspect. Chinese trade goods reached East Africa in quantity but no comparable trade developed with closer Australia. Indonesian people became culture bearers in their own right and settled Madagascar across the Indian Ocean in one direction and greatly influenced developments in Polynesia in the other. Nevertheless, the role of location in relation to culture centers seems clear here. That the contacts in this zone were early is suggested by evidences of sea trade between the Persian Gulf and India about 2500 B.C., and between India and Ethiopia about 1500 B.C. Coastwise trading is probably considerably older than this. The Indonesian cultural growth seems then to be the product of joint influences of India and China over a period of about 3000 years.

series of export crops. They brought in American rubber and cinchona trees and developed highly productive strains. The efficiency of their management allowed them to capture a large part of the world market, in the quinine market (derived from the cinchona bark) they had a near monopoly. They also developed sugar, tobacco, pepper, and coffee.

Programs of land use that left native populations undisturbed in their land ownership while still drawing them into the plantation production system as a labor supply were put into effect. Under Dutch management, at first cruelly exploitive but later increasingly benevolent, the populations and productivity of the Netherlands Indies expanded greatly. The population of Java for instance went from 20 million in 1880 to 28 million in 1900, and to nearly 50 million by mid-century.

Java's great density of population is in part related to its rich, volcanic soil. Much of Java is a string of active, or recently active, basic volcanoes. The young volcanic materials assure fertile soils. However, this is not sufficient to explain the difference between densely packed Java, moderately settled Sumatra, and nearly empty Borneo. All of these areas experienced early Hindu influences, all have good alluvial plains, and most have some young volcanic soils. Distance is not a negligible factor in Indonesia (see Maps 3–9 and 3–10); however, Sumatra is closer to India than is Java, so distance alone is not a sufficient answer. The concentration on Java is probably the accidental result of a number of human decisions focusing attention here rather than elsewhere.

Indonesia is now an independent nation. In the past, the area achieved some unity under the Hindu Majaphit princes and then again when conquered by the Muslims, and most of the people there today are Muslim. However, 25 different languages are spoken, and the culture level varies from civilization in parts of Java to head hunters in unexplored interior areas of Borneo. Density of settlement varies from 1000 per square mile on Java to under 10 per square mile. Illiteracy is high; technological knowledge slight; and capital extremely limited. Production is nearly all in primary materials such as quinine, pepper, kapok, rubber, copra, palm oil, tea, and tin. The costs of administrating a nation composed of islands strung across one eighth of the earth's equatorial circumference is enormous. In the face of all these difficulties, the Indonesians are accepting Russian aid with its associated difficulties

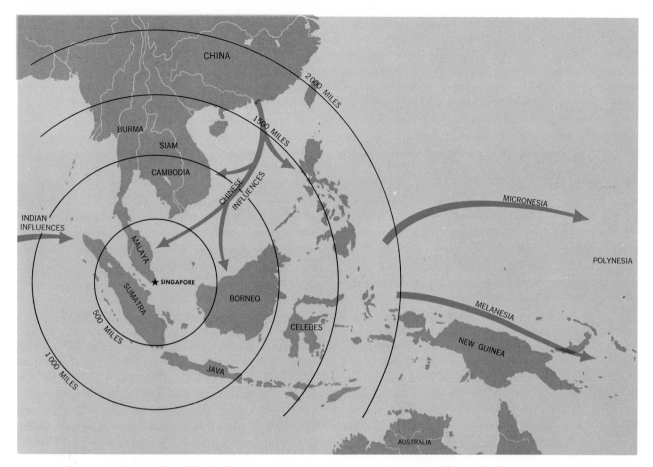

Map 3-10   The Indonesian-Malay Area as a Center of Cultural Influence

Considering Singapore as central to this region, arcs mark distances at intervals of 500 miles. At 2000 miles from Singapore, the transition is made from rice farmers with metals and developed trade and towns, to nonmetal-using villagers in New Guinea and to nonagricultural people in Australia.

and have taken over the Dutch portion of New Guinea, an area neither culturally nor racially related to them. This will be a costly burden for a nation that needs every penny for internal development.

At this time it is increasingly possible through air travel and radio communication to make a unit out of lands spread over a vast sea area such as Indonesia, but the development requires a technological development that Indonesia does not now have. To gain these skills an educational program is required. Educational programs are both costly and take time. The first generation of effort educates some and produces technicians and teachers to make possible a bigger effort during the next generation. The third generation can expect to begin to reap the harvest.

All of this assumes governmental stability and steady economic growth. The forecast for growth and stability in Indonesia is not optimistic.

Therefore, because of these socio-political factors, not the physical environment, the excellent start toward productivity on Java and Sumatra achieved under Dutch control is likely to stagnate. The development of the outer islands such as Borneo, Celebes, Ceram, and many others is likely to lag even further. The evenly distributed rainfall combined with unlimited growing season that made these the fabulous spice islands of old can be expected to be used only in a limited way. They will remain relatively empty lands on an earth crowding with people.

The uneven distribution of population is nothing new. Densely populated Java has not sent out floods of people to the adjacent thinly populated islands. Under Dutch management, although people were encouraged and aided to move to the less populous islands, the movement was small. The primary resistance was social. The Javanese villagers did not want to leave their kin and their settled existence in their beloved village to go and live among strangers in a strange land. The immense contrasts between Java with 1000 people per square mile and Borneo with about 10 were much more socially determined than physically determined.

Borneo, although divided politically, is a large mountainous island with plains more extensive than on Java. Because of standard geomorphic processes, mountains cannot have soils of great age; hence, young, relatively rich soils exist. The same can be said for the rest of the islands of Indonesia. Sanitated on the Panama plan, put into production with Dutch plantation efficiency and with energetic and educated people to fill the land there would be no natural limit to the potential of the area.

The Philippines

The Philippines provide an example of how difficult the process of change can be. The Philippines are another island chain scattered over a vast area of the Pacific. The total land area is 115,600 square miles and the population some 22 million, or a density of about 187 per square mile. Compare the United States, which has about 53 per square mile. Like Indonesia, these islands are mountainous and their coastal plains are generally small. Chinese influence reached the islands early.

Numerous other people reached the Philippines and influenced their development, notably the Muslims, with the result that before A.D. 1500 the islands presented a great variety of peoples of differing cultural levels. In the mountains, there were Negrito peoples living a hunting and gathering existence. In forested regions, there were simple farmers practicing the ancient shifting agriculture so well adapted to thin settlements. There were also rice growers who had carried the Asiatic terracing of mountainsides with them and put the land into permanent, densely settled, intensive agriculture.

When the Spanish reached the Orient, the Philippines became their base of operations. They sent out Mexican silver via the Manila galleon from Acapulco and obtained spices, porcelain, silks, and other oriental luxury goods. Building a capital city at Manila, they controlled the islands from a few key points, developing the land relatively little. They did introduce the Spanish language, Christianity and a pattern of large-scale landownership that has been called "the Iberian curse." Perhaps the most lasting Spanish achievement was in making this a Christian nation for they managed to convert about 90 percent of the people.

When the United States took over these islands in 1898, the American educational system was instituted, and an attempt was made, in a limited way, to break up the large land holdings. The great mass of illiterate tribesmen in the interior, however, remained relatively untouched. The Americans did encourage the production of such crops as sugar, manila hemp, and copra, and began the exploration and development of mineral resources. The Philippines are major producers of iron, chromite, and gold, even though the land is still poorly explored for mineral resources.

Catholic Church, Morong, Rizal Province. Spanish influence in the Philippines is exemplified by this church with its architecture typical of the Iberian peninsula of colonial times. *Embassy of the Philippines.*

The importance of the time factor in cultural-change situations is well illustrated. The long non-intensive Spanish period of contact was followed by the more intensive contacts of the American period. Yet the American period lasted only from 1898 to 1946, some 40 years, and World War II stopped much of the progress that had been instituted. This was too little time for extensive change even when the vast resources of the United States are deployed.

The Philippines, independent since 1946 and given preferential treatment in the United States market, are struggling to build a modern nation. In a sense they have everything. Like Britain, on an island "protected from invasion" but far richer in soil and minerals and not hampered by short growing seasons or drought, surrounded by a sea rich in fish (which they still harvest to only a limited extent), and culturally enriched both by the Orient and Occident, they need only move ahead. It will not be easy. In a sense they, as so many other undeveloped nations motivated by understandable pride, cast off their tutors too soon. Education takes time; 40 years is not enough for the development of a broad educational base. If the Philippines do not advance as they might, beware the cry that the "tropical heat and humidity got them down."

The Negroids of the Pacific

Melanesia is the appropriate name for the group of islands stretching along the equator from New Guinea to Fiji. These lands are occupied by the Oceanic Negroes. In fact, there are a variety of Negroid races here: Negrito peoples, Papuans, and Melanesians. They represent three waves of mankind that moved into this area at various times in the remote past. The Asiatic-Indian-Malay occupation of Southeast Asia and Indonesia probably came after the Negro movement. The presence of remnants of a Negro-Negrito population in Southeast Asia—for example, on the Andaman Islands, in the mountains of Indochina, and in the mountains of the Philippines—supports this displacement theory, but it must all have occurred extremely long ago.

Melanesia is culturally a low spot in the wet tropics. Nowhere did the people exceed an early Neolithic, agriculturally based way of life. Political organization remained on the village-tribal level: metallurgy was nonexistent, writing unknown, cities unheard of. Why? It cannot be the wet, tropical climate. Civilization flourished nearby in similar climates. It cannot be soil or land forms, for these were extremely varied. Indeed, the land forms include everything from temperate highlands to broad lowland flood plains, from volcanic high islands to low coral islands. Ideas rolled up to Melanesia and died away, or surged past. Advanced political and religious ideas, elaborate trade networks, and skilled navigation techniques swept past Melanesia into the scattered islands of the vast Pacific. Even Easter Island had a form of writing, which they clearly owed to some cultural impulse coming ultimately from India.

It is impossible to answer the question of why Melanesia failed to progress. It was not the land or the climate that was at fault, for the land is rich and the climate wet tropical to cool highland. It would be easy to say that since ideas were available for a long period of time, the race was at fault. But how could one be sure of this? If the cultural outlook of the Melanesians was such that the cultural currents were repelled, then the effect would be the same whether the inherent ability of the people was great or small. Only the turn of the wheel of time is likely to resolve the question of whether the Melanesians are culturally or racially inhibited. The flow of ideas that clearly penetrated the Pacific and reached America carrying the germ of civilization largely bypassed Melanesia. This is not an unusual happening. If early contacts developed nothing of extraordinary value, the land would be avoided, and its cultural lag intensified. This is a chain reaction; thereafter, because they were cultural laggards, they would continue to be avoided. Note, for instance, that the Spanish, Portuguese, and Dutch avoided New Guinea but fought for possession of the spice islands. The ignoring of the big undeveloped land for the small productive unit is a commonplace in history. The choice in the past often was between developed economies and primitive economies. In a sense it still is; by far the greatest amount of trade and travel and contact is between the developed countries of the world. Such routes often bypass undeveloped areas for centuries. At least we can be absolutely certain that the physical environment is the least likely reason for the lack of advance in New Guinea. The most likely reason is the pattern of high culture avoidance of primitive areas.

SUMMARY

The wet tropics show every stage of social development. There are simple hunters and gatherers, simple agriculturists, advanced agriculturists, and nations of advanced development. It cannot be said, then, that the physical environment has determined what happened. Why do we have the notion that the wet tropics depress human achievement?

Several unsubstantiated views led to this conclusion. First, it has been too long taken for granted that the heat and humidity act directly on man to decrease his activity, and that the white race in particular is subject to this direct influence. But two sets of facts counter this notion. If the origin of man indicates his probable adaptation, then he should be more at home in warm, humid climates than outside them. In addition, the hottest parts of the world are not the equatorial wet regions, but the low-latitude desert regions, and seasonally, the lower mid-latitude areas—and both of these hotter regions have been the scenes of notable human achievement. While the effects of extreme heat and humidity are undeniable, the record simply shows that they are not at their maximum in equatorial regions, and have not deterred man even in the areas where these maximums are reached. As for the white race's ability to work successfully either physically or mentally in the tropics, the record clearly suggests that the white race can achieve in the tropics. Failures of white settlement are usually due to social, economic, and political factors. The achievements of both white and yellow races in the tropics exceed that of the black races. Whether the causes of this are racial or cultural-historical is at present not demonstrable. In general, such differences have proven to be cultural rather than racial or physical-envrionmental. The limited data available suggest that the Negro race is slightly better suited to the tropics than any other race.

It is worth emphasizing that the leading nations of the world have at times been in tropical, humid regions. The center of pre-Columbian civilization was in the equatorial area, and included lowlands from Yucatán through Panama. India has at times been a world center of civilization, and her colonies in Indonesia were advanced nations in their time. We see the world at a moment in history when the tropical regions are "undeveloped." The conclusion we must reach from all we know is that this probably is a momentary situation, and not one causally connected with the tropical climate.

Could we really predict a possible development of the wet, tropical regions to positions of world leadership? Could Brazil, for example, rise to the level of a great power? The answer must be affirmative. "Enervating climate" is largely a myth. Disease is a controllable part of the environment, as was demonstrated at Panama under the most adverse conditions. New materials make tropical deterioration less of a problem. Air-conditioning, simply the reverse from mid-latitude heating, is increasingly efficient.

It should be noted that neither heating in mid-latitudes nor cooling in low latitudes is necessary for human achievement. Most of mankind's great advances were made by northern Europeans in housing that we would consider frigid under winter conditions and by Indians, Near Eastern peoples, and Egyptians in housing we would consider intolerably hot. We may be overvaluing the relationship between comfort and achievement today.

Of the tropical liabilities, the greatest may be that of soils. Large areas have undergone extreme weathering, and the remaining materials are poor in nutrient chemicals. This is true of large areas in the Amazon basin, in parts of Southeast Asia, and in the Congo. As we have seen, wet-rice culture is one answer to this. And there is no need for wet-rice culture to be peasant agriculture; it can be mechanized. Further, we may have missed obvious solutions to improving soil fertility. Our tendency has been to add concentrated fertilizers, perhaps ground-up fresh rock is a better answer. We tend to think of cleared land and root or grain crops, perhaps tree crops are a better answer. We already harvest many trees—coconuts, oil palms, avocados, oranges, coffee, cacao, cotton—and the list can be extended to include nearly everything needed by man. Trees are the natural plant cover in humid lands; they reduce the cultivation costs to very low levels; and they reduce the erosion problem to a minimum.

The tropical problem is largely in our minds. We are a nontropical people; the tropics were and are strange lands to us. We have overplayed their difficulties and underestimated their advantages: the lack of seasons is *not* a disadvantage, it can be an advantage.

4-The Mediterranean Climate

THERE ARE FIVE small areas on the earth that have what is called the Mediterranean climate. These are around the Mediterranean Sea and parts of California, Chile, South Africa, and southern Australia. Most of the earth is either continuously wet or dry, or if it has a seasonal maximum of rainfall, it occurs in the summer. In the Mediterranean lands, however, summer is drier and winter is wetter. Not only rainfall sets these lands apart: their summers may vary from hot in the interior to mild on the coasts, but their winters are characteristically mild and sunny. They receive high percentages of the possible sunshine, summer and winter. For example, Los Angeles (presmog) received 90 percent of the possible sunshine in summer and 60 to 70 percent in winter. This combination of mild winters and much sun makes these Mediterranean climates winter resort areas today.

THE PHYSICAL SETTING

Typically these lands are located on the tropical margin of the mid-latitudes between latitudes 30 and 40 degrees and usually on the western sides of the continents. In these areas the seasonal shifts of the climatic belts of the earth place the land alternately under the desertlike conditions created by the subtropical high pressure systems in summer and the variable weather systems of the westerly wind belt in winter. Thus they have constantly sunny, hot, dry weather all summer long, with alternating sunny and rainy weather in the winter season. One can think of the Mediterranean Sea as having a Sahara climate in summer and a cool English or French summer for its winter climate.

The absence of cold weather is striking. Summers are warm, averaging from 70° to 80° F., but winters average only 40° to 50° F. The annual range of temperature is therefore small, and in some coastal areas where the sea helps to hold the temperature constant, the range may be only about 10 degrees.

Inland, the temperature range may be higher—that is, much hotter in the summer and somewhat colder in the winter. Classic examples are found in California where San Francisco normally has a cool and foggy summer with temperatures in the 70°s, while Sacramento, 90 miles away in the Central Valley, in summer may experience temperatures above 110° F. In winter San Francisco has much bright, sunny mild weather between spells of rain, while Sacramento may have spells of freezing weather. This variation is typical of the Mediterranean climates of the world. Summer temperatures on the coast are mild, inland hot. Winter temperatures on the coast are mild, inland cooler, but still warm for their latitude and with plenty of bright sunny days. The nearby oceans moderate the climate, and often high mountains such as the Alps or the Sierra Nevadas cut off the outbreaks of cold polar air that reach areas of much lower latitudes elsewhere. As a result, frost is rare in many Mediterranean areas. Its rarity tempts men into growing exotic plants, and when frost does come, it is often extremely damaging to such tropical crops as oranges and avocados.

Rainfall is generally less than moderate in Mediterranean lands, averages varying from 15 to 35 inches. Fifteen inches of rainfall is low for agriculture, except at great risk of drought. However, winter rainfall is efficient. If it came in the summer, during high temperatures, the losses through evaporation would be so high that such rainfall would do little good. In the winter, on the contrary, evaporation is slow and a great deal sinks into the ground where it is useful to the plants. This winter concentration may be quite extreme; for example, at Los Angeles 78 percent of the annual precipitation comes between December and March. Rainfall increases steadily from the equatorial, dry edge toward the polar edge of these climates. San Diego has about 10 inches, Los Angeles 15 inches, and San Francisco 23 inches of rainfall. Such changes are typical along the coast of Palestine, from North Africa northward along the coast of Portugal, and in Chile from the equatorward end of the Mediterranean climate toward the polar end.

Most Mediterranean climates have mountains, and these profoundly modify the rainfall pattern. The air rising over the mountains is forced to drop much greater amounts of moisture; thus very high rainfalls occur and the streams from these areas are important to the much drier lands below them. Snowfall, so rare on the lowlands of the Mediterranean climates as to be newsworthy when it occurs, is common on the mountains. A typical scene in many Mediterranean lands shows orange trees and palms on the coastal plain with snow-covered mountains in the background. These snow covers are of great value, not only for vacational skiing, but also for the period when the drought is greatest on the plains and the water most valuable to the crops.

In this unusual climate the vegetation is also unusual. The plants in the drier areas are dwarfed, often thorny, and usually evergreen in the Mediterranean and in California and the evergreen oaks have stiff spiked leaves similar to the holly plant. California has a scrub oak that never makes a tree, but only achieves a tall bushy form. It forms a part of the brush-covered landscape typical of the drier part of the Mediterranean areas.

The seasonal rhythm of the Mediterranean plants is different; growth starts with the winter rainy season, and flowering and fruiting take place in the early spring at the end of the rainy season. Plant adaption to the summer drought is found in relatively light foliage, thick bark, and small leaves with hard and leathery surfaces. This type of shrubby growth dominates large areas in the Mediterranean and in California; it is called maquis in Europe and chaparral in California.

Poleward and on higher mountain slopes, the increasing rainfall leads to decreasing brush cover, and to increasing dominance of trees. Thus along the coast there is a progression from treeless San Diego to a region of scattered trees and grassland beginning at Santa Barbara and finally to the wet redwood-forest belt about San Francisco. Ascending the Sierra Nevada mountains east of Sacramento carries one from dry grassy valleys, into brush-covered (chaparral) foothills, on up into oak and pine mixed forest, and finally into heavily pine-forested, high mountain areas. Similar plant distributions are found all around the Mediterranean and in Chile and South Africa. Around the Mediterranean, however, man has so seriously modified the vegetation that the land looks drier than the rainfall would suggest: formerly tree-covered areas are often reduced to brush.

In these mountain-backed areas, lowlands and plains exist to only a limited extent; the exception is western Australia, where mountains are lacking. The largest areas of lowlands in these regions occur in the central valley regions of California and Chile. Elsewhere most of the land is sloping to steep or even to rugged. Rivers rise in the mountains and often follow short and steep courses to the sea, bringing down gravels and sands and depositing them in great alluvial fans along the foot of the mountains. These are ideal for irrigation purposes, both because of the natural delivery of water to the apex of the cone-shaped land form and because of the expanse of good alluvial soils that they present. There are problems, of course; rivers in Mediterranean regions are subject to great fluctuations in volume between the desertlike summer, the mild, wet winters, and the spring periods of snow melt.

It is difficult to generalize about soils in Mediterranean climates. The rugged land forms can have little soil stability, and hence must have thin young soils on them. The small alluvial plains and valleys may have rich alluvial soils. In general, the low rainfalls tend not to wash out the nutrients of the soils rapidly, but in Mediterranean lands there are many soils that are older than contemporary climates and that have been strongly leached in past times of much wetter climates. Thus on the coastal plain about San Diego in southern California nearly 50 percent of the soils had their dominant characteristics determined prior to 10,000 years ago when the glacial climate brought much greater moisture to this area now at the dry end of the Mediterranean climate. Such climatic change must have affected all of the Mediterranean climate areas, and many of them have old, acidic red soils that probably date to pre-modern climates.

One of these soils that is frequently mentioned is the terra rossa, or red soil. Strictly speaking, this is a type of soil developed on hard limestone. It is red, friable, permeable to water, and of modest fertility. The term is very loosely applied to reddish loess deposits in some areas, for example, in North Africa, for like many soil names, terra rossa has different meanings in different places. Most of the Mediterranean soils are brown soils with well-developed horizons, with lime accumulating in them at modest depths, and they are moderately rich soils.

The five areas of Mediterranean climate are, then, much alike. Their similar climates have caused similar soils and vegetation to develop. While the details of their geology differ, all except Australia present a steep coast with a narrow coastal plain to the sea. For the student of cultural geography, they present a neat group of similar environments in which he can study the differing reactions of men. If the physical environment is the dominant cause of human behavior, there should be striking similarities in the ways of life in these regions. If not, then we must turn to other causative factors. In the investigation we should learn a great deal about how the various factors interact to create the differing ways of life that men lead in the various regions.

THE MEDITERRANEAN OF THE OLD WORLD

Some of man's earliest and greatest achievements occurred in the Mediterranean basin of the Old World. Here the Greeks wrote great literature and led the world in philosophy and arts. Here the Romans built a great empire. And here was the homeland of the Judaeo-Christian religion. Just how and why did this all happen? Was it because of the favorable climate that great men brought forth great thoughts? Was it because of the sheltering sea and the many islands that navigation and trade started so early and became so important? The answers given to these questions in the past have often been "yes," and the impression given that the favorable physical environment virtually created the cultural achievement. What is this environment like—and what happened in it?

The Mediterranean Sea, literally the sea in the midst of the land, is divided into two basins. The western basin, lying between Italy and Spain, is the more open one; the eastern basin, lying between Sicily and Palestine, has bordering seas to the north, the Adriatic, Ionian, and Aegean. The latter two seas, bordering Greece, are filled with islands. The Mediterranean Sea averages 5000 feet deep, but the depth at the Strait of Gibraltar is only 700 feet deep. Within this nearly closed basin tides are almost absent. Winds, however, are often violent, especially in winter.

Around this basin the Mediterranean climate is found on the Palestinian coast, on the coast of Turkey, throughout Greece, extending up the Balkan coast of the Dalmation Sea, and covering all of Italy—except the Po plain to the north, which has too much summer rainfall to be classified as a Mediterranean land but which will be included here as a part of Italy, which is predominantly Mediterranean in climate. The climate extends along the south coast of France and follows the coasts of Spain and Portugal, but does not include the interior of the Iberian Peninsula, which is too dry and in winter too cold, due to its northerly latitude and its high elevation, to be classed as a Mediterranean climate. Mountainous northwest Africa, coastal Morocco, Algeria, and Tunisia are also Mediterranean in climate. These last lands are to be thought of as the equivalent of southern California in climate, while northern Portugal is to be thought of as like San Francisco.

Acropolis, Greece. Greek greatness in the arts is symbolized by the Acropolis. Greek architecture is still copied, as in the Supreme Court Building in Washington, D.C. The Greek heritage for Western culture goes deeper than architectural style, however, for Greek philosophy has established a way of thinking that we still follow. *Royal Greek Embassy.*

CULTURAL ACHIEVEMENTS AND THE SPREAD OF IDEAS

Within these varied but similar areas bordering on one inland sea, what has happened in human history? This is a very ancient homeland for man. Stone tools belonging to some of the earliest of human cultures have been found in the desert areas of North Africa. Early types of fossil men have been found in Italy, Palestine, and Turkey. Some of the early great art of the Upper Paleolithic age has been found in caves in Spain. Most significantly, one of the possible homelands of agriculture lies at the eastern end of the Mediterranean, where the earliest known agriculture in the Old World is dated at about 8000 B.C. This is a most interesting date, for it falls right at the end of the glacial period and right at the beginning of the time when we can be sure that we are dealing with climates more or less like those that we presently know in this area.

Our discoveries thus far pose two interesting problems for us. Is this the beginning of agricul-

ture? Or is it simply the earliest agriculture yet found? The plants show that they are already greatly changed from what probably were their ancestral forms. The processes of domestication, then, must have gone on for a considerable amount of time prior to the 8000 B.C. date, for it takes some length of time to domesticate a plant. This dating places us over the recent-glacial boundary line, which is quite precisely placed now at 11,000 years ago, and means that there must be a complete readjustment of all environmental thinking, for during the glacial period the climate of the Mediterranean basin and its neighboring regions was greatly changed. This glacial change has sometimes been expressed as having brought the climate of France into North Africa. Much of what is now desert in North Africa, southern Palestine (the Negev), and Arabia must have been at least well-watered enough to have been called Mediterranean in climate during the times of glacial accumulation in the north. Does this mean that agriculture may actually have started in what is now desert but was then Mediterranean in climatic type? At present, we do not know enough to do more than raise the question.

For our present purposes we will do well not to try to start too far back. Our knowledge becomes much too thin, and speculation comes to play too large a role. We can better focus on such facts as the beginning of town-dwelling and farming ways of life by 8000 B.C. in the Near East. Out of this grew city-state civilizations and, relatively quickly, empires and dynasties. By 4500 B.C. Mesopotamia was well on the way to civilization; Egypt was clearly on its road to greatness by 4000 B.C. From these great centers of early accomplishment, ideas radiated outward to adjacent lands.

The beginnings of civilization, then, were not in the Mediterranean climates, but in the adjacent hot and dry lands. The spread of ideas, populations, and techniques was from these lands into the marginal lands, and quite naturally to the edge of the Mediterranean Sea nearest the centers of the origin of ideas. Thus the Phoenician trading states became established on the coast of what until recently was called Palestine, and is now Israel, Lebanon, and Jordan. This does not make much of a case for the mild Mediterranean climate as the stimulator of ideas and accomplishment. Nor does further pursuit of the idea add much point to the physical-environmental argument.

By 3000 B.C. there was a civilization developing on the island of Crete. The roots of this brilliant early center lay in the trade in grain, olive oil, and luxuries that flowed from the raw-material–producing areas on the north side of the Mediterranean to the centers of civilization to the south and east. The people on Crete sat in a protected island location, in the midst of the stream of traffic, but their protected position lasted only until another group of people acquired an equal or better sea power. It was the stream of traffic that made the island an advantageous location.

The Spread of Agriculture in the Mediterranean

The earliest expansion of agriculture seems to have been along the coast of Turkey and Pales-

tine, into Egypt. Very early it was carried to the adjacent islands of the eastern Mediterranean, a phenomenon that clearly implies a well-developed maritime culture—and this is further indicated by its early spread to the region of the Atlas Mountains in northwest Africa. In general, it seems clear that there was a relatively rapid flow of agricultural ideas carried largely by sea down the length of the Mediterranean. This is an interesting example of the priority

The Gate of the Lions, Mycenae. Greek accomplishment was enormous but it built on the learning of others. The Mycenaeans represent one of the early (about 1400 B.C.) flowerings of culture resulting from contacts with Crete and other Near Eastern centers of learning. *Royal Greek Embassy.*

of sea routes over land routes for the long-distance spread of ideas. While every 20 miles on the land might place a traveler in jeopardy from a new group of people or a new tax collector, once clear of the land on the high seas he could go hundreds of miles with complete freedom.

The Cretans gained ideas from both directions, and wealth from the trade. Their cities had indoor plumbing and many civilized features that were to disappear from the earth for some thousands of years after the fall of these early civilizations. The Minoan civilization of Crete spread to the adjacent mainland of Greece, where it is called the Mycenaean. The inflow of ideas formed the basis for the city-states that grew up in the peninsulas and islands that make up the favored land of Greece.

Ideas from the Asiatic end of the Mediterranean Sea also formed the basis for the beginning of civilization in Italy. The Etruscans and the Romans used as building blocks for their civilizations such ideas as the alphabet, which shows clearly its origin to the east. They developed later than Greece, which was later in time than Crete. Beyond Italy lay Spain and Portugal and the north African Mediterranean lands, but they remained outlying colonial regions, suppliers of raw materials, during this early period. The picture is almost deceptively simple: distance from the center of the origin of ideas, growth, and development in the Near East was reflected by progressively later development to the west, and by a dying out of the impulse as the distance exceeded certain limits. The map of cultural diminution as distance from the focal center increases is much like that for the American Southwest, where the Middle American area played the role of the center of growth.

THE GREEK GOLDEN AGE: CLIMATE, GENIUS, OR CULTURE?

The problem of accounting for the tremendous accomplishments made in Greece between 500 B.C. and about the time of Christ has interested scholars for centuries. How much was due to physical geography? How much to race? How much to culture?

First, notice that race probably changed little from 1000 B.C. to the present, while culture rose to great heights and receded. Race would therefore not seem then to have been a critical factor. Second, it is clear also that climate changed little, if any, in this time period; and the mountains, seas, rivers, and similar physical features all remained about as we see them today. It is hard to see these unchanging factors as causes of a truly immense cultural rise and fall. What did make Greece great? And what part, if any, did geography play in this?

For a time in history Greece was located very close to the centers of the greatest growth of knowledge then occurring on the earth. Ideas from these centers reached her shores by means of traders, colonists, and, quite probably, conquerors. Agriculture, at first simple but increasingly complex, brought a more assured food supply, and population grew. Men from the great cultural centers reached her shores by boat; shipping was thus introduced, and with it the idea of trade. Trade brought wealth and also an increased number of contacts with other peoples, and hence more new ideas.

Sitting in a crossroads position, with new ideas flowing in from contacts in all directions and with wealth accumulating through trade, the Greeks were enabled to increase in numbers and wealth. Wealth makes possible some leisure. It is probably important that the Greeks were not organized into a great superstate and that they had a class of free men with a degree of leisure because they were supported in part by a slave class. Since the neolithic revolution, with the great growth of population and the appearance of kingdoms and empires, such freedom for groups of men had been rare. In Egypt and Mesopotamia, only a tiny fraction of the population had had leisure, freedom, and education. In Greece a significant percentage of the people had these gifts. How were these people to use their freedom?

Their interests were only partially deflected into intellectual activities. City fought city; tyrants came and went. The Greeks were forced to defend themselves against incursions by the Persians, and they finally fell before the onslaught of the Romans.

Through all of this, however, there ran a constant interest in ideas and a theme of individuality.

The Greeks did not put their efforts equally into all realms of knowledge. They were philosophers concerned with the nature of reality, but their religious thought was a confused, unsystematized collection of everything current. They were mathematicians skilled in certain kinds of geometry, but did little work in arithmetic and algebra. They were artists of extreme skill in certain kinds of architecture, but hardly used the arch at all. The startling thing about Greece is the appearance of so many men of first rank in accomplishment in so small an area in so short a time, and in a few fields of thought.

Greek achievements in early classical times were in these fields:

Philosophy Plato and Aristotle, 400–320 B.C.
Science Euclid and Archimedes, 320–220 B.C.
Medicine Hippocrates, 420 B.C.
History Thucydides, 420 B.C.
Arts Sophocles, Aristophanes, and Phidias (the Parthenon), all about 450 B.C.

Did the climate with its hot, dry summers lead to long, leisurely hours in the shade with discussion wandering through all the ranges of the human mind, and with the consequent foundation of philosophy? Nothing like this happened in the other Mediterranean climates, which have equally hot summers. Did the strongly seasonal climate encourage men to work hard in one season and during the resting season to use their leisure for mental activities? It did not happen elsewhere. Only in this one place at this one time did this particular cultural development occur. Why?

It does not seem too mysterious after all, for the the contact with ideas was there. A particular social setting was there: leisure for an unusually large part of the population spread the opportunity to produce intellectually. But most important was the value placed on ideas in their culture. But not just all ideas, only certain kinds of ideas.

Could you predict the particular field of high accomplishment for the United States in the period from A.D. 1950 to 2000? I would try, with some confidence. Today in many a university the freshmen class is addressed by representatives of various departments. The physicists, mathematicians, and chemists can say to these men selected for mental ability, "If the brightest of you study with me and go on to take an advanced degree, the sky is the limit in your potential financial reward. You will be able to pick and choose between jobs in terms of where you prefer to live and the particular work that you wish to do. You can expect to start with a handsome salary." And although this is not said, it could be added that as an atomic physicist, or physical chemist, or mathematician, the populace will honor you. Man's ego craves honor.

On the other hand, the representatives of such fields as philosophy, art, poetry, history (all fields in which the Greeks were well represented) can say to these same young men: "Come and study with me and take an advanced degree. We can probably get you a job, but you will have to go where the opening is. You can expect to start at a low wage, and advance slowly. You will be viewed with a sort of tolerant and kindly respect for your work, but you can expect no adulation or admiring recognition. Further, no matter how good your work may be, most of you will have to settle for a lower monetary reward than men in the sciences."

Under these circumstances where do you think that the best minds go? Most, not all of course, are deflected into the fields having not only high material premiums, but also high public esteem as part of the reward. There is also the attraction of being in the leading field, in the area of the greatest discovery and greatest public attention, the most exciting field. Just which area of learning and discovery is the most exciting in general and scientific esteem varies from generation to generation. The best minds are then deflected into those fields, and those of the best minds that have the greatest natural gift for work in this particular field will then accomplish the maximum; and such men we call geniuses.

To be a genius, it is necessary to be born with the right gifts, in the right age, in the right place. Had Socrates been born in Greece in 10,000 B.C., before the growth of ideas had made possible his philosophizing, he would have been lost to history. Were Socrates living in Greece today, would he be noticed? Probably not. The Greek location at a particular time in history, together with a particular bent of the Greek culture made possible the flowering of a particular set of minds. Had a man with a mind suitable for handling modern higher mathematics been born then, he might have perished unrecognized. The tools of his trade, the setting of ideas, the permissive tendency of the society was not ready for him.

So, for our society, it seems predictable that the twentieth century, especially the second half of it, will be marked by a flowering of genius in the physical sciences—and the climate and soil will have nothing to do with it. Our location in the world in place and time and the orientation of our culture sets the pattern for this.

LOCATION AND PROGRESS

It has often been noted that the center of civilization shifted northwestward through history: from the Near East, to Crete, to Greece, to Rome, to France, to northwestern Europe. This is of course a partial view. The spread of ideas from the Near Eastern heartland was going in several directions: northeastward to China, eastward to India and Indochina, and ultimately to America (see Map 2–3). From each new center there were secondary radiations. The course of the spreading out was somewhat radial, and it was somewhat simultaneous in all directions. While ideas were spreading from Crete to Greece to Rome, they were also spreading from the Near East to the Indus Valley to India and beyond. The northward course of civilization is a one-sided view arising out of an overemphasis of the Western European on his own cultural history.

The last in time of the great Mediterranean powers were the Iberian states of Spain and Portugal. The maritime skills of the Mediterranean, the commercial tradition of the peoples of that sea, and the slowly increasing knowledge of other lands with exotic products of great value, all came together in these lands in the fifteenth century and set off one of the most explosive cultural changes of the world. But note the immense time lag: 2000 years later than Greece; 1000 years after Rome.

A great deal has been said about the importance of the location of Portugal and Spain on the Atlantic and of the shutting off of the trade routes to the East. There is a good deal of truth in this, but it must be seen in the right perspective. First, the position did not change, the historical situation did. The position remains pure physical geography; the situation is human geography. Neither is an absolute determinant, but it is clear that it is the situation that is the ruling one.

For a time in history the Mediterranean Sea was the "lake" at one end of which Western civilization was growing. Later this sea was the highway for transportation of goods, and the area along which ideas spread westward and northward. The turning outward into the great oceans is often thought of as having changed the historical pattern in such a way as to have left the Mediterranean powers in a position of great disadvantage. The focus was now on the Atlantic. All of this is true as far as it goes.

It is interesting that with the opening of the Suez Canal in 1869 the Mediterranean again became a crossroads of the world, but that there was no resurgence of the Mediterranean powers. Italy did not seize upon her central position to control the Mediterranean Sea as of old, and to become the dominant power of the world. Simple geographical position is not enough. Portugal, Spain, Italy, Greece, and Egypt, all great powers in the past, still occupy their ancient geographical position, and again sit at the crossroads of the world. Control of the critical geographical points in the Mediterranean, Gibraltar, Suez, Cypress, Sicily, and Malta, fell into the hands of the Atlantic powers, however, and the ancient Mediterranean powers lagged behind. Perhaps it is better to say that because they were lagging, the critical control points fell into the hands of others.

Today the growing importance of air travel continues to focus attention on the Mediterranean area, yet the Mediterranean powers still lag. It is often argued that their geography is against them; that for modern developments coal and iron and oil are required. That this is not necessarily true is shown by the economic development in such countries as Belgium, where there is very little coal and iron but a very extensive industry. Japan after 1900 is an even better example of what a country can do in spite of a poor environment, if human energy is channeled in productive lines.

It is easy then, to overestimate the physical-geographical position of the Mediterranean at any time. It would be of no value if there were no people there; it would be useless if there were people there of the cultural level of the natives of Australia. Only when Portugal and Spain were occupied by an aggressive, commercial-minded, and adventurous people who had sufficient mastery of sailing and an idea to drive them to attempt great voyages did the raw fact of the physical location of the Iberian Peninsula come to have any great importance. Even then the importance of mere physical location seems almost accidental. As history shows, colonial empires around the world were also founded from other Atlantic states, such as France, Belgium, Holland, and Great Britain. All these people shared a cultural background that included shipping skills, commercial developments, and a taste for the luxuries of the Indies. It was these factors more than geographical position that drove these peoples to their overseas movements. This is not to say, of course, that the seaside position had nothing to do with the whole matter. The Swiss and the Poles and the Austrians did not take to the sea and found vast overseas colonial empires. However, seaside location only leads to colonial expansion overseas for those

people that have such notions in their cultural pattern. It was not of such significance to the shore dwellers of California, Australia, or South Africa.

In the Mediterranean lands of the Old World we have the interesting example of an area where it has been clearly demonstrated that the human material present is of the very highest caliber. The achievements of Greece, Rome, Spain, and Portugal, and of earlier peoples at the eastern end of the Mediterranean and at Carthage in North Africa show that gifted peoples could, when motivated, make of these Old World Mediterranean lands great centers of creative thought, productivity, and world power. The same race is still there; the lands have changed but little. Perhaps the land is somewhat the worse for wear in some places, but in other places the endless labor of ages of farmers has terraced and irrigated the land until it is better than it ever was. The travel patterns of the world have shifted back and forth: the means of transportation has changed from the sea to the railroad to the air, but the sea has always remained the basic bulk carrier of the world. In this area at the crossroads of the world, a gifted race has been resting on its oars. It is a clear example of a good environment with a tested race that is now relatively unproductive. Physically these are not the richest lands, but neither are they the poorest. Economically they are all now underdeveloped. They have not shared in the industrial revolution.

PALESTINE AND THE ISRAELI EXPERIMENT

Palestine (present-day Israel, Lebanon, and Jordan) is much like southern California. San Diego is the equivalent of Tel Aviv and Los Angeles is located at Beirut's latitude. As in southern California, the narrow coastal plain is backed by a mountain range, beyond which lies a trough whose bottom extends below sea level, the Dead Sea: this is like the Salton Sea. Jerusalem is located somewhat like the little town of Julian in southern

American Sisal Planted in the Negev. The desert becomes productive with the application of knowledge, capital, and will power. *Israel Office of Information.*

Experimental Farm at Avdat, Israel. Ancient farming methods are being reintroduced. Notice the long ditches arranged to catch the water from the barren slopes and concentrate the runoff on the field areas. *Embassy of Israel.*

Dimona, Israel. New homes are under construction; a textile plant is in the background. The barren hills express the aridity of the country, yet with a vast input of capital and skills, prosperity is returning to this ancient land. The effort at Dimona is one of many such experiments. Should the Israeli political experiment fail, there would again be ruins in the desert. *Embassy of Israel.*

California, perched on the mountains above the great, deep, arid trough to the east. The coast of Palestine is somewhat rainier than southern California, but the two areas are alike in having a steady increase in rainfall toward the north. Palestine's soils and forests have been used and abused by agriculturists and pastoralists for more than 5000 years, southern California's for less than 200 years. More arid California, therefore, has more vegetation and soil on its hills and more forest on its mountains than rainier Palestine.

Shifts of economic and political power at the end of the Middle Ages began to leave the Arab world aside. Soil erosion and deforestation impoverished the physical base for an agricultural-pastoral way of life, and the level of development sank very low.

The Jewish nation of Israel has now been established in this area. It is a relatively small expanse of land, about the size of Vermont, but much of it is desert, the Negev. Israel, therefore, is discussed both here as a Mediterranean land and earlier as a dry land. The old, worn land, however, is being revived by the application of capital and skills from the Western world. Jewish refugees from Europe brought a flood of skilled workers and professional people. The Jewish community of the world has contributed capital. Hills are being reforested and plains irrigated, and even the Negev is being studied for resettlement. It is estimated that the area once held five million people. With modern technology, it should readily support this many again; with industrial development it could support many more. The critical shortage is water, for both industry and population require large amounts. The interesting point is that even a terribly abused land can be brought back into production; that with will, skill, and capital any land can industrialize, even if it lacks basic minerals and fuels.

Unfortunately, the world is in turmoil, and the Arab world views the Jews as intruders. The future of Israel will depend, not on physical geography, but on political geography. What the Jews are demonstrating meanwhile is that the area here called Palestine could be another southern California.

Fishing Boats, Greece. Greek dependence on fishing and the destructive effects of deforestation and misuse of land over a 6000 year period are illustrated here. Greece has an excellent rainfall compared to southern California, but an equally barren, rocky scene in California can only be found in the desert. *Royal Greek Embassy.*

GREECE

Greece, the seat of such immense mental achievements, is a mountainous set of peninsulas extending southward into the Mediterranean Sea. Greece is the size of New York plus Rhode Island, but the population of somewhat more than 8,000,000 is less than half that of these two states. There are few good alluvial plains. The latitude is approximately that of San Francisco. The rainfall is somewhat greater than for central California, but the climate is much like California's. Temperatures in summer are hot, but the winters are mild with frost being infrequent on the plains, though snow may blanket the mountain tops. The land is rough, hence only about 20 percent of it is arable. Another 20 percent is in forest, 20 percent is waste lands, and the remaining 40 percent is pastureland, used by sheep and goats.

On this meager physical base one half of the population make their living: a fair measure of the lack of industrialization—compare the United States figure of about 10 percent of the people in agriculture. The industry is mostly on a small scale and dispersed among such items as chemicals, rugs, textiles, leather, cigarettes. Wheat and flour, petroleum products, machinery and most manufactured goods are imported. With half their population in agriculture, they still do not feed themselves, but they offset this by such agricultural exports as grapes, olives, and tobacco. These exports command sufficient price on the world market to make it profitable to sell their labor through these specialty crops and buy wheat they need.

No nation in first rank today is primarily an agricultural producer. Greece's problem is to increase her industrialization, despite her limited amounts of iron, silver, copper, nickel, lead, and zinc. There is no fuel of significance in the country, but petroleum is widely available today, and some of the major producing fields of the world lie adjacent to Greece. The greatest need is for education, organization, and capital: with these, there is no apparent limit on what Greece could produce.

One may well ask why a nation that once led the world in so many artistic and intellectual fields, including such practical ones as mathematics, is now in a state of eclipse? The answer lies in history. While Rome reduced Greece to a vassal state, Greece continued as an important center of culture under Roman control. The Goths, however, devastated Greece twice; and thereafter, with the fall of the Western Roman Empire, Greece was left in the outer periphery of Byzantine culture. Then came frequent conquest and changes of rule: Slavs, Crusaders, Byzantines, and then the Turks swept down on Greece. After centuries of incursion and the devastation that alien occupation and wars ensure, Greece finally emerged as a nation again in 1832. But it was a poverty stricken, internally quarreling, foreign-dominated nation. Greece has been struggling ever since, with further setbacks in World Wars I and II. Perhaps one should ask how any people could have even managed to survive under such a load of misfortune, rather than, What is wrong with Greece? It is a good land with a good people who have been burdened with 1500 years of invasion, occupation, and destruction. It is a small unit and would function better as part of an economic union; the developing European Common Market therefore offers Greece an opportunity to play an important role in the world once more.

ITALY

The Physical-Economic Base

Italy is a long, slim mountainous peninsula, about 850 miles long and 150 miles wide. Plains make up about one third of the land surface, and the valley of the Po (Lombardy), the only large plain, is about two thirds the size of California's Central Valley. The mountains are relatively high: peaks range from 6000 to 9000 feet. Since they rise at rather short distances from the sea, they are marked by steepness, and give Italy a rugged aspect. They also give the typical Mediterranean winter scene of snow-capped peaks rising within sight of the warm blue sea. Such snow- and rain-catching mountains are of great importance in a land of summer drought. The mountains get increased precipitation, and feed the streams that descend to the coastal plains; they are also areas of potential hydroelectric power developments.

A mountainous land more than 800 miles long must have a variety of climates. Southern Italy is warm in winter, while the Po plain is very cold. Summer temperatures vary not only with altitude, but with location on or away from the coasts and the ameliorating sea breezes. Rome is so hot in the summer that all who can, leave for the cooler hills. Only tourists visit Rome in the summer. The vegetation varies as the climate does. Southern Italy has the olive, orange, palms, figs, and pomegranates that one would expect, while northern Italy is much too cold in winter for subtropical trees. The mountains are oak and chestnut forested at the lower levels and pine-covered on their higher levels. Despite its mountainous land, Italy is poor in basic minerals and resources: oil, coal, and iron are scarce. Other minerals, except for mercury and sulfur, are not present in large amounts.

Italy can be compared in many ways with California. Italy is 116,224 square miles and California 158,693 square miles in area. They are almost exactly the same length, but California is a little wider in extent. Italy lies farther north than California: Sicily is at the latitude of San Francisco, while Rome is near the latitude of Eureka in northernmost California. This gives Italy much better rainfall than California, but considerably colder winters also.

With this small and rugged land the Italians have done an astounding amount. They support nearly 50 million people on less land than California uses to support about 16 million. The Italians, with only one third of their land in plains, have made about 55 percent of it arable by means of terracing a great deal of steep and sloping land, or otherwise managing it in such a way as to bring it into agricultural use. California, with a greater extent of plains, has only 11 percent arable land. In Italy

Land-use Pattern of the Po Plain, Italy. Compare this rectangular grid and the large holdings as shown for America (page 362). *American Geographical Society.*

Erosion Control in the province of Cosenza, Northern Calabria, Italy. This elaborate terracing in preparation for reforestation marks modern Italy's determined drive to improve the often deteriorated landscape. *Italian Information Service.*

more than 20 percent of the population is engaged in agriculture, yet not enough grain is produced to feed the population, and wheat flour is one of the major imports. Wine production is so high that Italy accounts for nearly 20 percent of the world's production. In olive-oil production Italy is second only to Spain, for vines and trees can be grown on steep slopes if hand labor is used. It is this kind of land use that raises the percentage of Italy's "arable" land. While not enough grain can be raised to feed the population, wheat and corn are major crops.

Past Greatness

In the past, Italy has been the center of cultural and political achievements of first rank. It may well be argued that in the preindustrial past the geographic base did not need to be so large, and that the shortage of mineral resources was not as critical. While this is certainly true, it is less than a full explanation.

In part the success of nations has to be seen as a sort of study in comparative advantages. At the time of Christ, Italy was a significantly large unit, with an agricultural base that supported a dense population for its day. Italy was then also one of the technologically advanced nations of the world. Great Britain, the center of the nineteenth-century equivalent of the Roman Empire, is approximately the same size as Italy and has approximately the same population as Italy. True, Great Britain has coal and iron, while Italy has little. But despite coal and iron, Great Britain has now lost her empire and pre-eminent position. All that would be needed to complete a test of the approximate freedom from environmental control of these variations in accomplishment would be for Italy now to rise to an important position again.

The fall of the Roman Empire can hardly be blamed on Italian geography. The empire was built on population and organizational force based on

The Colosseum, Rome. The power of Rome is epitomized in the Colosseum, which illustrates the Roman adaptation of the arch to architecture, the enormous productivity that made possible expenditures such as that required for the construction of this amphitheater, and the organizational and engineering genius that underlay the empire. *Italian Information Service.*

The Strozzi Palace, Florence. Italian renaissance greatness, seen here in architecture, is evident also in painting, sculpture, and literature. *Italian Information Service.*

Italy. By 265 B.C. the Romans had won control of all of Italy, and went on from this base to build their immense empire. Thereafter came a long history of conquest abroad accompanied by shifts at home from a republic (265 to 33 B.C.) to dominance by emperors. By A.D. 476 a series of barbarian invasions had brought the empire to an end. The causes of the fall of Rome have been endlessly debated. Whatever they were, they were not due to climatic change, movements of the land, or even of soil erosion. The physical geography remained unchanged. Rome became corrupt internally, and there was a loss of the organizational driving force that had built the empire. The most conspicuous change was the shift from a republic, with elected heads of state limited to one term of office, to an empire ruled by virtual dictators.

The breakdown of the republican form of government was hastened by such generals as Sulla, who in 83 B.C. used his troops to defeat the popular party and to seize his opponents' lands, which he then distributed to his veterans, who often ne-

glected them. Thus productive lands went into lowered production, or even went out of production. The tax situation in later Rome accomplished the same thing. Land was taxed and if some land went out of production, the tax on the rest of the land was simply increased. This drove more land out of production. The material wealth of a nation is measured by its productivity, some of its strength is supplied by the number of its people, but its greatest source of power comes from the moral forces that check public and private immorality. Scholars agree that both public and private morality declined throughout the history of the empire. They describe also a weakening of the state as the republican vigor of the Romans declined. This process seems to have been related to the corruption that led to a lessening of production, this in turn to increased taxation, and this in turn to lessened production. But there is very little physical-geographical determination in this cycle of disintegration.

The weakened empire finally collapsed and the Germanic tribes ravaged it from end to end. Production and population fell to still lower levels. Italy fell into a period of history in which there was no unity: city-state fought city-state; neighboring countries contended over various parts of the peninsula. Spain, France, Austria, and others fought over and divided Italy again and again. During a momentary lull in the squabbling in the fifteenth century, the Italian state achieved greater prosperity and a measure of stability, a period that gave rise to the flowering of genius known as the Renaissance. At this time Italy was the foremost country of Europe in learning and the arts. Thereafter, the dreary recitations of wars, conquests, and the inheritance of different parts of the land we call Italy by various dynastic houses of Europe resumed. In the early nineteenth century, following the American and French revolutions, a movement toward Italian national unity gained momentum. It was not until 1861 that the first Italian parliament was convened, and ten years later before there was a united Italy.

Italy had not stood still through all of this time. The various city-states had been active centers of trade and wealth and culture. Venice, for instance, was a city-state of immense importance in the Mediterranean, with sufficient power to have overseas possessions of its own. But if Italy is considered small for a modern state, how much less adequate would a peninsula divided into city-states be.

Unified Italy entered belatedly into the acquisition of a colonial empire, obtaining parts of northeast Africa late in the nineteenth century. After World War I, Mussolini established his Fascist dictatorship, and the Fascists worked hard at the material buildup of Italy: reclamation of wasteland, modernization of agriculture, building of highways, modernization of ports, and the encouraging of industry. Under extremely centralized dictatorial control, the development was meager, only to be reduced further by depression beginning in 1929. To give his countrymen foreign exploits to take their minds off their misery, Mussolini led Italy into its conquest of Ethiopia, an activity that placed Italy more firmly on the side of Hitler's Germany and

opposed to the French and British. This in turn led to Italy's disastrous role in the North African campaigns during World War II and the eventual destructive campaigns in Italy itself. The peace treaty at the end of the war stripped Italy of its African colonies and saddled it with severe reparations charges, for example, $100,000,000 to Communist Russia. The country thus emerged in 1945 wrecked by warfare, internally torn by strife between the Fascists and the Communists, and with little unity in the opposition.

Against such a background, the question might well be asked: What has the geography to do with the fact that since the end of the Roman Empire Italy has been one of the weaker nations of the world? However, the question could be turned around: Given a modicum of unity and stability could Italy accomplish anything in the modern world? Or is its land too small, too poor, to support its people? Must it continue endlessly to suffer from poverty and must its people be exported as surplus?

Industrial Renaissance

Since 1945 there has been a nearly miraculous change. The industrial revolution is finally reaching Italy. As a result, Italian engineering and business techniques are being exported all over the world. Italians are building pipelines from Russia to four satellite states in Eastern Europe, a power plant in Pakistan, roads, port facilities, and power plants in Colombia, Ecuador, Honduras, Mexico, Peru, and Uruguay, and engaging in similar engineering enterprises around the world. This kind of activity brings in needed income for development at home. It is also a measure of a high level of human achievement.

Production in many lines of endeavor—heavy industry to women's *haute couture*—has increased to the extent that sales abroad jumped 30 percent from 1957 through 1960. Between 1955 and 1960 industrial production increased 33 percent; auto output more than doubled; auto exports tripled; machine tool exports went up 45 percent; and office machin-

Oil Refinery at Portomarghera, near Venice. Italy's mid-twentieth century renaissance is exemplified by plants such as this. Other multi-million-dollar installations are appearing all over Italy. *Italian Information Service.*

ery exports doubled. Italy's merchant marine, practically destroyed during the war, had meanwhile been rebuilt to fourth place in the world, and Genoa is now the Mediterranean's busiest port. Over-all industrial production doubled in the decade between 1950 and 1960.

This kind of explosive growth has resulted in Italy's having strong gold and dollar reserves— 3.2 billion dollars in 1960. This was more than Britain had at that date, and was second only to the United States and West Germany. As an index of financial strength, the stock market has been rising. American investment in Italy tripled in three years, and in 1960 amounted to $300 millions. This has brought in United States firms, and American methods are reaching even into such activities as scientific chicken-raising and ice-cream factories.

This swift growth of industry has begun to change Italy. Italians eat twice as much meat as they previously did. There are now more than 2 million private cars in circulation, and about 4 million motor scooters. This is not all advan-

tageous of course, as traffic jams, noise, air pollution, and the need for many new costly highways accompany such growth. On the other hand, more cars and more roads, mean more work for more people who can then buy more cars which will need more roads. However, Italy's difficulties are not all over. There are still at least 1.7 million Italians unemployed, and the distribution of the industrial boom is not even. Northern Italy, long the industrial heart of the nation, is the most prosperous region; Sicily is the poorest. Italians still have a lower standard of living than French, German, Belgian, and Dutch workers. However, the large labor pool in Italy is an advantage. Italy has been relatively free from crippling strikes, and the cost of labor has been held down, while the productivity of industry has shot up. The Western European countries are running into labor shortages. With the growth of the European Common Market, there will be increasing mobility of capital, and more industry can be expected to flow into Italy to take advantage of the pool of low cost, stable labor there. This will inevitably lead to rising standards of living and increasing labor costs as the Italian worker pulls abreast of the standards of expectations of the rest of Western Europe.

Natural gas has been found in the Po Valley, and is an important supplement to the hydroelectric power for that region, which has been fortunate in being able to draw water power from both the Alps to the north and Apennines to the south. Southern Italy has now also found natural gas, and combined with its labor force there is no reason that there should not now be an industrial development there.

Even Sicily, one of Italy's most depressed areas, has in its combination of good land, rich fisheries, large sulphur desposits, and a large reservoir of labor a real potential for industrial development once the free flow of capital and goods within the Common Market combines with the now stable government and beautiful location.

Italy has curious advantages in this mid-twentieth-century growth she is now experiencing. Her lack of coal is of slight disadvantage, for petroleum is available nearby and easily transported by tanker. Coal is a depressed industry in other countries, where it can be obtained at less than cost because governments are subsidizing its production. Meanwhile technological developments in the mineral industries are making the use of coking coal less and less important. Even the absence of colonies has proven to be a blessing. The other Western European nations are losing their colonies, often along with all of the investments that have been made in them or, as in the case of France, after having unsuccessfully poured out immense sums to attempt to hold them. It does not seem far fetched to predict that in a unified Europe, and Italy is already a member of the Common Market, Italy can readily come to be one of the dominant states. The old geographic analysis that emphasized the lack of basic minerals, the limited amount of land, and the crowding population as the basic causes of Italy's impotence will once more have been confounded by the decisive force of the human geography.

THE IBERIAN PENINSULA

Spain and Portugal are the man-made political divisions of one of the most obvious, natural physical geographic units in the world. The other such natural area is Scandinavia. In each case the division is the more remarkable in that the people are racially, linguistically, and culturally similar. The principal discussion of the Iberian Peninsula will be found in the mountain-land section, with attention focused on Spain. A few comments on the Mediterranean aspects of this peninsula are included here.

Coimbra, Portugal. This is the style of architecture the Iberians carried with them into whatever climatic type they settled in America. *Casa de Portugal.*

Intensive Land Use in Portugal. Terraced land for maize. *James J. Parsons.*

Cork Oak Trees, Iberian Peninsula. These trees supply wood, cork, and acorns for hogs. *James J. Parsons.*

Harvesting Olives, Portugal. A crew of nine men is at work here, knocking the olives onto sacking placed under the trees. This use of much labor is one of the reasons the olive oil industry is located in lands where labor costs are low. *Casa de Portugal.*

Stripping the Cork from Oak Trees. It is typical of the low intensity of land use and the low cost of labor in much of the Iberian peninsula that hand labor can be used so extensively to produce a relatively low-value material such as cork. *Casa de Portugal.*

Harvesting Grapes in Portugal. While the general landscape shown here could well be in California, the men, their costumes, the extensive vineyard on a steep hillside, are typically Old World Mediterranean. In California the vineyards have mostly been moved from the hill slopes onto the flat irrigable bottom lands. Quantities per acre are higher by the California method, but the quality is higher by the Portuguese method. *Casa de Portugal.*

The Iberian Peninsula is rainy in its northwest corner, arid in its center, and only Mediterranean in climate on its borders. It is in the southern, sheltered, lowland valleys that the typical Mediterranean crops, such as citrus and off-season fruits and flowers, are produced in winter to supply northern European markets. Both Spain and Portugal are large exporters of olive oil, wine, citrus, textiles, and cork. Both are importers of wheat, petroleum products, and machinery. Both possess mineral wealth, which they export largely as ore, and import as finished machinery. In this they reveal their lack of industrial development. Their situation is no different in principle from Greece, nor is their possibility for revolutionary economic growth any poorer, indeed it is in some ways better, than Italy's. For a fuller discussion with the focus on Spain, see Chapter 8.

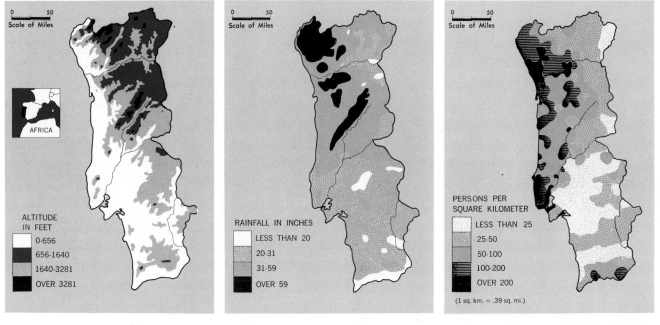

Land Form   Average Annual Rainfall   Population Density

Maps 4-1   Portugal: Land Form, Rainfall, and Population

Portugal's highest land is to the northeast; its greatest rainfall is in the northwest. Its population is densest in the rainier areas. Rainfall in Portugal is high for a Mediterranean climate. Even the south, with 20 to 30 inches of rainfall—which comes in the cool season and hence is very efficient in wetting the ground—is well watered by California standards (San Diego, 10 inches; Los Angeles, 15; San Francisco, 20). The drier south of Portugal produces cork, wheat, and olive oil; the northwest produces wine and cattle. *Adapted from* Focus—*The American Geographical Society.*

NORTH AFRICA

Northwest Africa, the Atlas Mountains and the adjacent coastal strip, is also a land with a Mediterranean climate. The coastal part of Morocco, Algeria, and Tunisia is a piece of land 1200 miles long and about 150 miles wide, or twice as large as California. Its location is comparable to that of southern California, and the rainfall is also comparable: being annually 10 to 20 inches. The area originally had much forest cover and undoubtedly was well mantled with good soils. The mountains are high enough

to be good precipitation catchers and are often snow-covered well into the summer. In an area of summer drought this is an enormous advantage.

Located at the extreme end of the Mediterranean, far from the ferment of ideas at the eastern, Mesopotamian end, only a few ideas—agriculture, cattle keeping, and irrigation—reached the area in pre-Roman times. A Neolithic way of life with agriculture and pottery and domestic animals, but lacking metals, was established. It has persisted with aston-

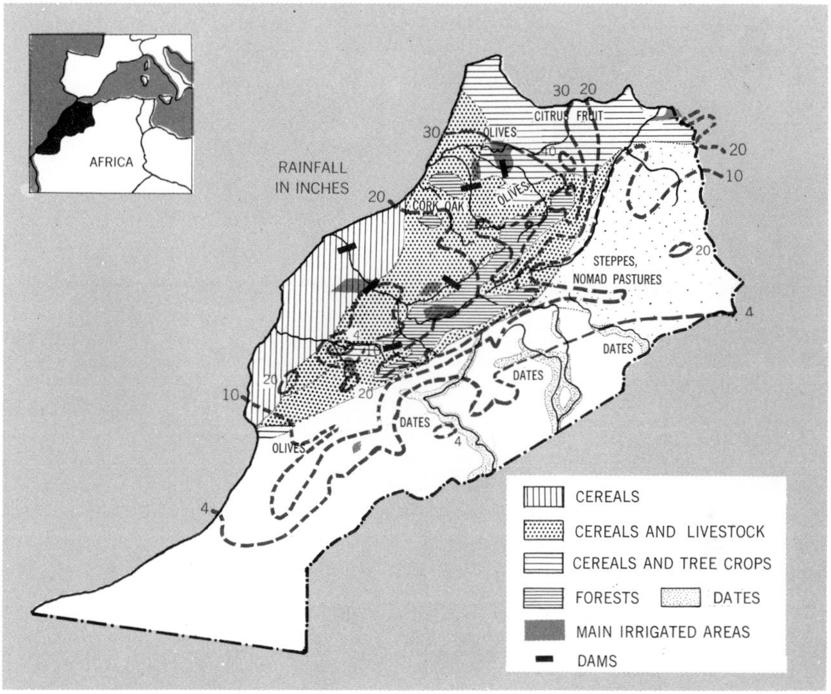

Map 4-2 Morocco: Agriculture, Rainfall, and Irrigation

The monarchy of Morocco is larger than the state of California and has a population of 11,500,000 people. Its location is similar to that of southern California. The comparison extends to a steady increase of precipitation from south to north and a sharp increase toward the mountainous interior, followed by a sharp decrease into a desert interior. In California one half the population is in the southern areas with 12 inches of rainfall or less. In Morocco most of the population is in the areas of 20 inches of rainfall or more. As in California, crops include cereals, citrus fruits, vines, olives, and dates. Morocco has the climatic advantages of southern California, but lacks the politically and culturally determined locational opportunities of the New World area. *Adapted from* Focus—*The American Geographical Society.*

RAINFALL IN INCHES

CITRUS FRUIT
OLIVES
CORK OAK
OLIVES
STEPPES, NOMAD PASTURES
DATES
DATES
DATES
OLIVES
DATES

	CEREALS
	CEREALS AND LIVESTOCK
	CEREALS AND TREE CROPS
	FORESTS DATES
	MAIN IRRIGATED AREAS
	DAMS

ishingly little change to the present. The Carthaginians based themselves on a few favorable spots on the sea coast and little utilized the inland region; they therefore had a minimal influence on the native peoples there, the Berbers. The Romans held a slightly deeper coastal area, but again left the Berber tribes relatively untouched. Even the French and Spanish occupations of modern times have altered the old ways of life extremely little. The French impact of the nineteenth century was much greater because they moved thousands of colonists into the coastal strip of Algeria and greatly increased the productiveness of their coastal land.

The Spanish, with less to work with, barely touched the hinterland of Morocco. The land with its enormous potential is not empty; the population of Morocco, Algeria, and Tunisia is 15 million— nearly equal to that of California, but only half that of the Iberian Peninsula. It is a rapidly increasing population, which formerly faced starvation in times

of drought, and continues to exert a heavy pressure on the land as it increases.

The use of the land is largely agricultural. The most heavily settled lands are in the hill regions where irrigation and terracing form a way of intense land utilization. Domestic animals include cows, sheep, goats, and camels. The vegetation, formerly largely forest, has been immensely impoverished. Wood is cut for charcoal to supply household needs: every home has a charcoal fire for cooking and for making tea, and it has been estimated that much more charcoal is used in tea making than in cooking. Wood is also used in house construction. It is destroyed by fires that are used in land clearing, and are sometimes deliberately set, and sometimes "just happen." Finally, the grazing animals, especially the goats, greatly deplete the remaining vegetation. Clues as to what the land might once have been are found in areas around shrines and holy places where the vegetation is left untouched and

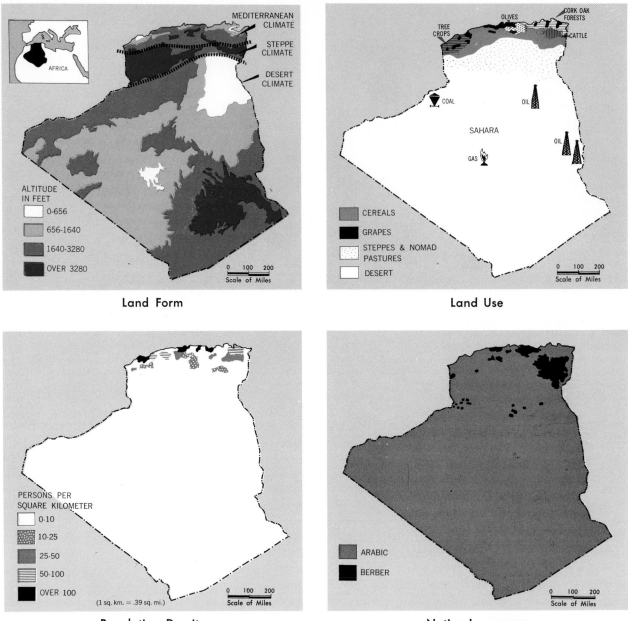

Land Form

Land Use

Population Density

Native Languages

Map 4-3   Algeria: Land Form, Land Use, Population, and Native Languages

Algeria is two-thirds desert. The steppe and Mediterranean climate areas are larger than Texas, much larger than all of California. Its ten million inhabitants are mostly in the better-watered areas. Significant recent developments include the discovery of vast oil resources in the desert interior and independence from France, with the loss of about one million Europeans. The discovery of oil may lead to considerable economic development, but the flight of 10 percent of the population—the part with the highest percentage of literacy, the most capital, and the greatest enterprise—is a great loss. *Adapted from Focus—The American Geographical Society.*

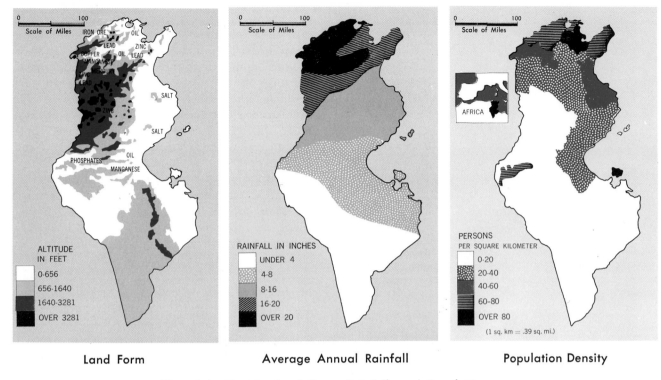

Map 4-4   Tunisia: Land Form, Rainfall, and Population

These maps show the relationship of relief, rainfall, and population for this Mediterranean climate area in North Africa. Notice the abundant mineral resources, the very good rainfall, and the presence of mountains with their potential for water storage and hydroelectric development. *Adapted from* Focus—*The American Geographical Society.*

forms islands of beautiful forest in a sea of scrub. The arid and impoverished aspect of much of the land is an artifact: something made by man.

Agriculture is carried on with primitive tools, and the work is almost entirely done by hand. The plows are little better than the light Roman plows of 200 years ago, and the olive presses are like the ancient Roman presses. There is little mechanized agricultural machinery, except in a few recently developed European areas; and grain crops are planted, harvested, and threshed by hand. There is little hydroelectric development and a general state of economic undevelopment. This is a land that has stood still, or nearly still, for the past 4000 years. Cultural ad-

vance has been slight and has probably been more than offset by the deterioration of the land through deforestation and soil erosion through poor land management.

North Africa is not a poor land; it is well suited to grain, vine, olive, citrus, and fruit production. It is not mineral poor, for it is a major exporter of iron and phosphate, and it is not a land that must remain poor. But divided as it is, it is handicapped by internal dissention and lack of capital for development, and is unlikely to attract international capital while plagued with internal troubles. The immense pools of oils found in the Algerian Sahara and in adjacent Libya, combined with modern pipeline

Roman Ruins in Algeria. The grass-covered hills somewhat resemble parts of southern California, where the climate is similar. *French Tourist Office.*

movement of oil, now creates the possibility of industrial development. Abundant, potentially cheap mineral fuel offers a substitute for charcoal in home cooking, and this in turn could relieve the heavy pressure on the forest resources, which in turn could help to reduce floods and soil erosion. The problems are not primarily in the physical environment, they rest in the millenia-long, fiercely independent and unchanging outlooks of the Berber and, more recently, the Arabic culture of the muslims.

The location of North Africa gives it a great advantage in relation to Europe. It could play much the same role as California plays in the United States. Its subtropical location could be utilized to produce off-season fruits and vegetables that the highly productive industrial societies of northern Europe desire and could pay for. North Africa could be developed as a winter resort area for adjacent Europe. Physical geography demands, urges, offers these opportunities. Seemingly these possibilities will be very long in being realized. North Africa is Muslim in religion and culturally and politically oriented toward the Arab world. It is fiercely anti-colonial and nationalistic, and it is therefore most unlikely that it will enter the European Common Market and share in the economic growth of Europe. In spite of its physical geography, it seems destined to lag yet a while in a preindustrial stage of development.

THE NEW WORLD MEDITERRANEAN CLIMATES

Two of the five Mediterranean lands of the earth are very much alike in their physical structure. These are California and central Chile. The central parts of both areas have similar climates, similar temperatures through the year, and similar soil and vegetation types. In both lands there are coastal ranges that rise steeply from the sea leaving little coastal plain available, yet the mountains are so disposed that they are not entered by the sea so as to create many harbors. Inside the chain of coastal mountains lies a great trough or central valley. Behind this trough rise truly high ranges of mountains: the Andes in Chile and the Sierra Nevadas in California. These mountains are great continuous chains in both countries with relatively few passes through them. They are snow-covered in winter and in spring the melting snow provides great floods of water to the depression lying between the higher interior and the lower coastal mountain ranges. One of the few differences between the two countries is that the Central Valley of California is drained by two rivers that run from the two ends toward the middle, and join to go to sea through the great system of bays at San Francisco, while in Chile there is no such unified river system. Rather, a series of rivers cross the central valley at right angles to its axis and reach the sea by separate mouths. This is a minor difference, in comparison to the large number of similarities to be found in the two countries. Given this remarkably comparable pair of countries, how similar are their histories? And if physical environment is similar, what of race and cultural setting? These can be profitably studied in two periods: before 1500 and after.

CALIFORNIA: THE INDIAN PERIOD

In California, which is now viewed as a golden land of vast opportunity and into which more millions seem to be destined to crowd each decade, what was the situation before 1500? Instead of a cultural center complete with great universities, immensely productive acres, and industry, there was to be found one of the most culturally backward areas of the Americas, and indeed of the world. The Indians of Mediterranean California were called "Diggers" because they were gatherers of roots and seeds and hunted relatively little. There was plenty of game: deer were abundant; buffalo, elk, antelope, and grizzly bears—as well as brown bears—were all present in moderate to large numbers, but this resource was relatively little used. Such small game as rabbits, quail, and squirrels were more important to most of the people.

There were many tribes in California, and it has been said that there were as many speech families in California as in all of Eurasia. A speech family is a language division for which there is no known relationship to any other language. The degree of difference can be grasped by recalling that languages as different as English, French, German, Latin, Greek, and Sanskrit are all closely related in the view of linguists. It is startling, then, that in California adjacent valleys may have entirely separate languages. Is this the result of numerous separate peoples entering the area over a considerable length

of time, each having an entirely separate language? Or is it the result of differentiation within the state over a period of time due to the isolation of the tribes in their separate valleys?

Since the similar situation did not create separate language families in Greece or North Africa, it cannot be simply isolation in valleys. If it is the result of entry of different peoples, where are their language relatives? Only a few of the California tribes have any known language relations. This leaves the time factor. It is thought to take about 20,000 years for languages to diverge to the point that linguists are unable to distinguish any relationship. It is probable that the multiplicity of languages in California is the result of several of these factors. Differing peoples, over a very long period of time, drifted into California, settled in limited areas, where they remained with little movement and where they maintained their own way of life unchanged.

Mediterranean California was an area of great cultural lag. There were only three spots of minor cultural advancement. Two of these are so clearly the result of stimulus from the outside that the very strong suspicion is raised that the third may be so also. The influences that we have traced from central Mexico reaching northward to the Pueblo country and to the Yumans along the Colorado River barely reached into southern California. In San Diego county along the Mexican border, the Indians spoke a Yuman Indian language and shared a few cultural traits that clearly point eastward across the desert to the Yuman and the Hohokam, and through them to Mexico. These include such things as pottery making and cremating the dead and putting the ashes in funerary urns. Agriculture failed to make the trip, although it could have if the idea of irrigation had come with it. The gathering people, however, were not receptive to the idea of farming. Why plant when nature provided an abundant harvest? Their whole way of life was geared to moving about the countryside gathering the crops that came into ripeness with the differing seasons.

On the eastern side of San Diego county, through which area the idea of agriculture would have come,

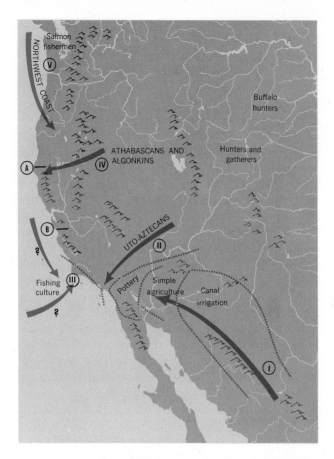

Map 4-5 Cultural Influences in Pre-Columbian California

Five lines of influence are suggested here. There certainly were more. I, The flow of ideas coming up from Mexico, bringing irrigation to southern Arizona, floodwater farming to the lower Colorado, and pottery to southern California. II, Influences coming in from the Great Basin, indicated in southern California by the presence between San Diego and Los Angeles of a group of people speaking a Uto-Aztecan language. III, The isolated occurrence of a fishing people equipped with hook and line, nets, spears, and plank boats in the Santa Barbara region. Many of their traits suggest relationships with either the Pacific Northwest or Polynesia. IV, Small groups of Athabascans and Algonkin-speaking peoples in northern California show that the drift of peoples into California went on for a long time. V, Influences from the advanced cultures on the northwest coast of America brought such items as the plank house and the dugout canoe to northwestern California. The southern limit of the dugout was about Cape Mendocino, *A* on the map. The finest possible boat-building tree, the redwood, continues to grow along the coast as far south as Monterey Bay, *B*.

the people had a particularly rich and varied range of harvests. In the spring the yuccas sent up their enormous asparaguslike shoots, covering the mountainsides. They were baked for 24 hours in an earth oven—a pit dug in the ground, filled with fire wood, and burned till very hot. When the fire died out in such a pit, it was filled with yucca shoots and covered to give slow baking. This produced a product that was very much like candied sweet potatoes. Later the mesquite bushes at the foot of the mountains yielded their immense harvest of beans. Still later, the Piñon pines on the tops of the mountains produced their abundant harvest of oily nutritious nuts. The coast ranges and valleys were sprinkled with oaks that supplied a heavy harvest of nutritious acorns. On the coastal areas there were also wild grasses and edible roots and bulbs and shoots. Why plant when the natural harvest was so varied and abundant and provided by nature? Why disturb the ancient family band organization that had made this a happy and easy way of life in a pleasant land for time beyond counting? The question is less, Why did agriculture fail to spread here? We should rather ask, "Why did people ever take up agriculture?"

Another area just beyond Mediterranean California that felt the wind of cultural advancement was northwestern California. Here there were good dugout canoes, not huge sea-going types, but good river boats, well shaped and useful. In northern California, too, there were some houses built of planks. These are traits highly developed to the north in coastal Oregon, Washington, and British Columbia. It is of utmost interest that such boats and houses disappeared in northern California long before arid, treeless southern California was reached.

Boats disappeared even before the great San Francisco Bay and the immense marshes at the juncture of the Sacramento River and the San Joaquin River were reached. In this vast delta, known as the Suisun Marshes, there was a whole world of reeds and channels filled with fish and water fowl and with acres of starchy roots of the cattail ready for harvest. In this watery land a boat was needed, and a dugout would have been a most valuable thing. There was plenty of suitable timber in the adjacent hills and along the natural levees of the rivers running through the country. The ideas were available nearby in northwestern California where good dugouts were in use on the Klamath and the Eel and the Trinity rivers. But almost as if the Mediterranean climate were a deterrent to progress, these useful ideas failed to penetrate into the Sacramento–San Joaquin system. Instead the ancient primitive reed-bundle raft was used. It could, of course, be thought that a reed boat is the natural response of men living in a reedy swamp. A survey of the boats used in the world will quickly show that this is not so. There are many reedy areas where only wooden boats are used, and some areas of scarcity of reed where only reed boats are used.

The third area of California that showed a spark of change from the simple hunting and gathering way of life was the island world off the coast of Santa Barbara. In 1500 there was found on these islands and part of the adjacent coast a maritime culture that had good boats built by sewing planks together, that used nets and lines for deep-sea fishing, and that had through these developments built up a sizable population. Although their arts were simple, they were definitely more advanced than those of the gathering folk of the mainland. They carved artistic animal figures in the round, and made tasteful inlays using shell on stone and bone.

Why was there this sudden appearance of a maritime skill in the California scene? Is it significant that

Redwoods, Found from the Northern Border of California to San Francisco. The long, straight, soft wood logs are ideal for dugout-canoe construction, but were so used only at the northern end of their range. *Redwood Empire Association.*

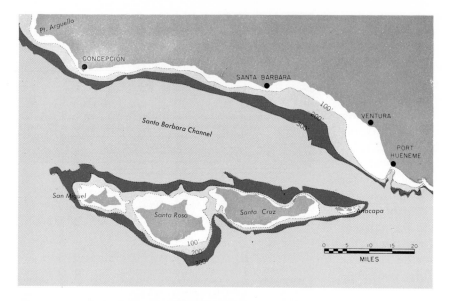

Map 4-6   Santa Barbara Islands

The three large islands plus Anacapa off Santa Barbara are shown here. The shading indicates the location of the shore line if the sea level were lowered 100, 200, and 300 feet. A lowering of at least 300 feet accompanied the accumulation of ice on the continents during the last glacial period. The islands were then linked into one large land mass, and a channel of little more than five miles in width separated it from the mainland. Man probably crossed to the islands when they were easily reached and played an important role in exterminating the little island elephants.

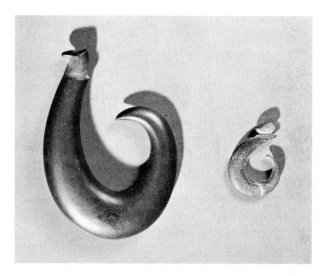

Fishhooks from Easter Island (left) and California (right). The appearance of a specialized fishing culture on the islands off the coast of California poses interesting problems of cultural history. That this culture may not have been a simple response to the environment is suggested by the appearance of a number of specialized items duplicated by the highly skilled seafaring people of the Pacific. These fishhooks represent one such parallel. *American Museum of Natural History.*

it appears right where an island habitat made this desirable? Are we looking here at a natural response by man to an ideal habitat? These people had shell fishhooks, made in the same way that the shell fishhooks of the Polynesians are made, compound fishhooks, also much like those of the fishermen of the Pacific, and good nets. Boats, which we know they had in historic time, must have been present earlier to make some of this gear useful; and carved stone replicas of boats have been found, indicating that boats were indeed being made. It is an open question whether this culture developed here in response to the special environment, or whether the plank boats, the shell and compound fishhooks, the peculiar pestles, and other Polynesianlike items indicate that a Polynesian people or one of the Asiatic peoples, such as the Japanese or people from the northwest coast of America reached these islands. If so, they came without bringing a whole society, and influenced a group of California Indians in such a way as to initiate a maritime culture on this coast, which was otherwise lacking any use of the sea beyond bare shore line gathering. When one considers that for tens of thousands of years men had lived on the Mediterranean coast of California without making a move toward going to sea, but did make such changes around the time of Christ when it is known that the Pacific was being peopled by sea-going fisherfolk, then the possibility that influences from the Pacific may have reached California seems not too unlikely.

California before 1500 remained, however, a backward area. The blessings of virtually no seasons, of mild winters and moderate summers, beautiful scenery, rich soils, water from the mountains available for irrigation, gold to be had for the taking, and oil to be had for the drilling, all were wasted in the culture world of the pre-Columbian Far West. Only at its southern end had the last gasp of Mexican influence stirred the cultural quiet; a similar faint ripple stirred northern California; and from some source the beginning of a maritime culture was introduced into the Santa Barbara region.

SPANISH CALIFORNIA

It is almost as striking a failure that the Spanish did so little with California. California, after all, had a climate like the Mediterranean shores of Spain. The landscape of rich valleys with large evergreen oaks, of mountains covered with brush in the foothills and pines on the highlands, and of streams coming down to the warm valleys, all should have looked attractive to the Spanish. And the Spanish did look at it. In 1540 their explorers entered the beautiful, finely sheltered bay of San Diego, one of the few natural harbors on the coast of California. The Spanish explorers described the river running into it, the sheltering wooded headland, and the large expanse of sheltered water. They also noted the wild-seed gathering Indians living there. They then explored up the coast, reporting on the islands off Santa Barbara and the fishing Indians there, people who had fine light boats. The Spanish went on up the coast, missing San Francisco Bay but finding Monterey Bay, whose values they overestimated.

Yet California was not attractive to these Old World explorers. There were no civilized Indians among whom they could settle and whose produc-

tivity would support them. There was no gold to be looted from the natives—the coastal expeditions had seen no evidence of the wealth of gold that was later to be found in the interior of the state. There was evidence of petroleum as tar on the beaches, on the land in tar pits, and on the sea as great oil slicks. But the technology of Europe was still three centuries away from appreciation that this was a "resource." To the Spaniards, California was a distant land with little to recommend it. Of course, they could grow wheat, raise cattle, and cultivate citrus and grapes there, but they had sufficient land for that at home or in closer places where production was already organized and where they did not have to transport such products half way round the earth. When there were empires in Mexico and Peru with gold to be had for the taking and with more gold and silver in the mountains to be had for the mining, why bother with a remote, undeveloped country? (This is the kind of world view that probably best explains cultural lag in such places as Australia and New Guinea, too.)

The Spanish might well have left California untouched indefinitely had it not been for potential rivalry with Russian incursions into the area. Russian explorers had for centuries been reaching across the subarctic world following the source of furs. They reached the Pacific and followed on across to Alaska in 1740. Among the valuable furs they found was that of the sea otter, and pursuit of this animal led them south into California and down to the islands off Santa Barbara. In 1812, to support this distant effort, they established a fort to the north of what is now San Francisco. Fort Ross on the Russian River marks this farthermost outpost of Russian expansion.

Spain's settlement of California, therefore, came about as a reaction to this appearance of the Russians in territory that Spain claimed, for only occupation could make good Spain's claim. But two centuries had already elapsed before the threat of Russian occupation moved the Spanish to settle in California, and during that time the Indians had been left to follow their own simple way of life. In those 200 years the great Mexican and Peruvian empires had been conquered, looted, their rich mines exploited, and the pattern of Spanish colonial America had been blocked out. The developed and productive lands were all in the central part of the empire. The margins in both North and South America were the poor lands: New Mexico, Louisiana, Florida, Argentina, and Chile. Since there was little profit to be gained from such regions and from California, few chose to settle an undeveloped frontier where hardship and danger were the principal rewards.

But there was one group eager to go: the missionaries, who sought souls to save, rather than wealth. In the true meaning of "all men are created equal" they considered the souls of the Indians as important as those of any other men. Therefore, while the motive of the crown was political, the motive of those who came to settle was spiritual.

The Spanish effort was well planned in light of the information on hand. Since it was known that California could be reached by land around the head of the Gulf of California, a land expedition with great herds of animals was sent by this route. It was also known that a good harbor was to be found at San Diego, and according to the Spanish records of the exploration of 200 years earlier, there was another fine harbor at Monterey. Since the settlement was planned as a check to the Russians, it was ordered that the capital be placed at the northern frontier where the enemy could be more readily watched. From San Diego north, missions were to be placed about a day's journey apart. A ship's expedition was sent by way of Lower California, where supplies were picked up from the earlier missions settled there, and then went on to San Diego where the first new mission settlement was made in 1769. A presidio (garrisoned place) was built on the first height of land near water on the bay, but it was a poor site, too far from the harbor entrance to protect the harbor and too far down the river to assure abundant water for agriculture, and the mission soon moved up the valley ten miles to a location more accessible to an assured water supply. Although the presidio remained where

it was first established, the harbor defenses were moved out near the entrance.

A string of missions was quickly established along the coast leading to Monterey, which was found then to be an open bay that afforded very little protection for shipping. The virtual inland sea of the San Francisco, San Pablo, and Suisun bays remained undiscovered until a party of hunters from the presidio at Monterey topped the hills to the east and looked down on this vast sheet of water. The role of environmental determinism and of "cultural determinism" here had an interesting test. The immense sheltered system of bays with the Sacramento and San Joaquin rivers entering into them gave perfect protection for shipping and excellent waterway access to desirable lands without the cost of building roads. Instead of a capital on an open cove on an isolated coast, the San Francisco Bay area offered a location for a capital at the focal point of a waterway

California missions at Santa Barbara (*opposite*) and Carmel, on Monterey (*right*). Such missions represent Spain's last major effort at colonial expansion in the New World, a response to a political threat leading to the reluctant occupation of California. This effort was accompanied by the incidental transfer of Spanish architecture to a like climate and a triumph of spiritually motivated accomplishment in teaching stone-age natives preindustrial revolutionary arts and crafts along with their religion. *California Mission Trails Association, Ltd.*

Map 4-7   Spanish Missions in California, 1769–1823

The first missions in California were at San Diego, 1769, and Monterey (Carmel), 1770. Within fifteen years there were 9 missions. By 1823 there were 21. They were located along the coast about a day's journey on horseback apart. The coastal location was selected because the principal contact with Mexico was by ship rather than overland. Their distribution reflects the limited occupation and development of California achieved in the Spanish-Mexican period that ended in 1848. The breakdown of the colonial economy brought on by the confusion due to the Mexican revolution against Spain damaged the missions. Secularization in 1832 ended most of their work prematurely, for few of the Indians were yet sufficiently civilized to withstand first Mexican and then American pressures.

The location of the capital of the Spanish province of California at Monterey was influenced by erroneous reports of the original explorations, which described a fine harbor there near the area where the Russians, moving south from Alaska, were threatening Spain's territorial claims.

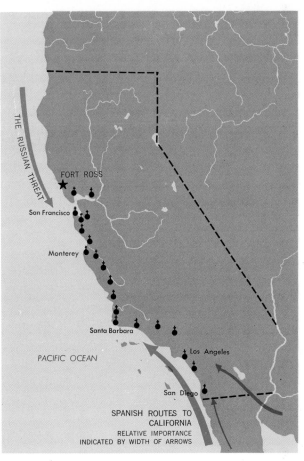

THE RUSSIAN THREAT

FORT ROSS

San Francisco

Monterey

Santa Barbara

PACIFIC OCEAN

Los Angeles

San Diego

SPANISH ROUTES TO CALIFORNIA
RELATIVE IMPORTANCE INDICATED BY WIDTH OF ARROWS

Stockton Harbor. Although the Spanish overlooked the natural waterways of the San Francisco bays and the advantages of the immensely rich delta region of the San Joaquin–Sacramento rivers, modern California has capitalized on them. (*Upper*) Ocean-going ships penetrate to the heart of the Great Valley at the port of Stockton, 88 miles from the sea at the Golden Gate. (*Lower*) En route, the ships pass through America's Holland, the diked and drained peat lands of the delta that are said to contain 1000 miles of waterways. These immensely rich lands are below sea level, and ships passing through the channels loom over the land just as they do in Holland (see page 307). *Stockton Chamber of Commerce.*

system that could be the basis for development of the country. However, given the basis of a royal order as to the placement of the capital and the prior establishment of the capital at Monterey, the San Francisco Bay region was not so used.

A mission was placed at the present site of San Francisco, but the capital, in spite of all its environmental disadvantages (location on an exposed coast and in the fog belt, outside the main lines of movement in the region and lacking any easy communication with the interior) remained at Monterey. The glowing accounts of 1540 had described a fine harbor and this had determined the location of a capital two centuries later, a location that was to remain fixed there as long as the Spanish retained control of California.

There exists a romantic notion of Spanish California as a land of riches, but it was really a poor mission-frontier settlement. True, horses could be had for the asking; travelers (virtually none) could find open hospitality; and guests probably would not have touched a pot of gold left in the guest room, but what would gold have bought in such a region?

The missions themselves were productive centers, where fields were cleared, orchards and vineyards planted, and irrigation begun. The Spanish knew the Mediterranean climate, and they successfully introduced into this similar land wheat, barley, oats, olives, citrus, grapes, cattle, sheep, and horses. It was too dry for much farming at San Diego, but northward, with increasing rainfall, the crops were more productive and the missions the richer. Although grapes and citrus and other fruits did well and grain production was excellent, there was no market for their produce. Shipment to Spain was out of the question, citrus and other fruits would spoil, wine was bulky, and even grain was not profitable enough to send overland in a country that had no roads to ports where ships rarely called. And no Spanish colony, of course, in this age of mercantilism, could trade with any nation except Spain; any more than an English colony could trade with any country but England. The result was a meager handful of Spaniards in an undeveloped land,

though the streams in the foothills of the Sierra Nevada were full of gold and one of the world's greatest silver lodes lay just to the east at what was later to become Silver City, Nevada. Spanish California was almost as poor and backward and isolated as Indian California.

When Mexico won its independence from Spain in 1821, the missions were secularized and their vast holdings distributed to Spanish Mexicans. A trickle of trade opened up with the United States, whose vessels collected hides along the coast (an episode preserved for posterity in Richard Dana's lively book, *Two Years Before the Mast*). A few Americans looking for beaver wandered over the mountains and were promptly thrown in jail. A few settlers, such as Sutter, a Swiss, managed to obtain land and settle down, but again too few men in an immense rich land, peopled by a gentle, simple, illiterate people, were unable in the brief period between 1769, when the first mission was founded, and 1848, when the United States took over the territory, to do more than scratch the surface.

AMERICAN CALIFORNIA

When California became United States territory in 1848 there had been little change. Climate, soil, vegetation, all were nearly as the Spanish had received them from the Indians. There were now horses and sheep on the land, but only in the southern and western part. The only significant change was in the make-up of the grasslands, where there had been a major shift from native grasses to introduced grasses that had come in as weeds in the Spanish packing materials. But this changed little; the grasslands had been there before, only the kinds of grass had changed.

The United States acquisition of the lands of the Far West was not looked upon with favor by all. George Perkins Marsh, one of the greatest scholars of his time in America, was then in Congress, and he viewed the action with alarm. Why take in those vast arid lands of the West? Most of it was useless by all accounts. It was rumored that there was better land along the coast, but Marsh considered it to be of no use to the United States. He spoke of it as being so far to the West and so separated from the rest of the nation that it was virtually lost in the Orient. And he was not alone in his view: if it was of so little use to the Indians, the Russians, and the Spanish, how could it be different for America?

Gold Populates the State: From Mining to Farming

After the cession of this territory by Mexico in the Treaty of Guadalupe Hidalgo, the unexpected happened. Gold was accidentally discovered in the foothills of the Sierra just east of Sacramento. The excitement of the time is difficult to recapture. Thousands of men stampeded for California. Distance suddenly became a minor problem in proportion to the overwhelming drive for gold. Hordes set out by all possible means of travel to cross the continent. Indians, heat, drought, disease, cold, mountains, and rivers all took their toll. The Donner party made headlines by perishing in the deep snows of the Sierra Nevadas, and one group ran into serious difficulties in trying to cut through the Death Valley country. Thousands died in more prosaic ways: disease, accident, and drowning.

Another flood of mankind took to the seaways. Some went around Cape Horn: counting the tacking of the ships, they probably traveled the equivalent of the circumference of the world at the equator. Another impatient group tried to shorten the trip by taking a ship to Panama, crossing the isthmus overland, and then taking a ship again on the Pacific side. Men dropped dead in 24 hours time from the pernicious fevers or were robbed and murdered in the crossing. If they reached the Pacific side, there usually were no ships. If distance, difficulties, and death could stop men, no one would have gone to California, yet thousands of men from all over the world poured in through the Golden Gate.

The gold fever was of almost unimaginable intensity. The ships dropped anchor in the harbor, and there most of them stayed for a year or so. The sailors jumped ship and took off for the gold fields. Soon the bay was a vast forest of masts rising above idle ships while the world cried for transportation to California.

There was gold, but not as described in the rumors going around the world. It could not be scooped up by the bucketful, but had to be won by hard work. This often meant standing in icy water all day, digging down through sands and gravels to reach the bedrock where the gold would be found, if any. It was bone chilling, back breaking, hard, wet, and dirty work. At the end of the day there were no comfortable quarters, and food cost unbelievable prices. Gold dust and nuggets melted away about as fast as the average man could dig them. A few lucky ones struck it rich, and some of them even got home with their gold. More lost it in gambling or were cold-bloodedly murdered for it.

Some men looked about them and decided that plowing, planting, pitching hay, feeding hogs, and all the other chores of farming looked less irksome than digging for gold. It was a work that they knew, and with prices what they were, they knew that they had a chance to make more profit from the land by cultivating it rather than just digging in it. They might miss a bonanza, but they might never hit one anyway. So many men turned to the rich earth. The great Central Valley of California contains thousands of square miles of gently sloping alluvial lands. The Sacramento River Valley has good rainfalls; the winters are mild and, though the summers are blazing hot, there are many streams coming down from the mountains on either side. It was found to be an ideal land for barley and wheat. When the disillusioned sailors began to return to their ships, there was a whole fleet available and looking for some cargo to carry back to the East. Grain began to move, and the barley won prizes as the finest malting barley in the world. Grain was indeed profitable, even in this distant land. Some men became wealthy, and great farms came into existence. Near Sacramento one such large-scale effort totaled 50,000 acres. Sheep became inportant in the 1870s and 1880s and wool was exported.

The mining, too, gradually became big business. The easily accessible placer gold soon was worked

Erosion in California. The rounded, earth-covered, vegetated hills of California have started on the road to becoming bare, angular, rocky hills such as characterize many of the anciently cultivated, similar climatic regions in the Mediterranean. (*Upper*) A gully 75-feet deep in a valley floor in California. (*Middle*) Gullying in denuded hill slopes in the foothills of the Sierra Nevadas. (*Lower*) Sheet wash in sandy loam in the coastal area; in one area like this, twenty years of bean farming led to total soil loss over an extensive region, leaving a bare sandstone surface. *USDA Photos.*

out, and the large gravel deposits were attacked by hydraulic operations. This consisted of using a super fire hose to wash down the gravel banks, sluicing the material through a flume with traps in the bottom to catch the heavy gold. This led to water management: the building of dams and flumes and the accumulation of a great deal of engineering know-how. The transfer of this kind of knowledge to the supplying of the water to the land was an easy step; all the required parts were there. The idea of agriculture, what plants were suited to the climate, even the idea of irrigation, were all present in the land; they already had been introduced, tried out on a small scale, and found to be successful by the Spanish. The Americans with their characteristic vigor made a much bigger production of it.

Orchards and vineyards were set out; the yield was huge; the quality, fine—but where was the market? Fresh fruit could not last the trip via Cape Horn, and overland transportation in wagons was equally out of the question. The answer was drying: in the hot, desertic dry summers of this region, the fruit could be dried with speed and with practically no risk of rain spoilage. Dried peaches, apricots, pears, and prunes became specialty crops of different areas. At one time a large proportion of all the dried prunes of the world came from the Santa Clara Valley at the southern end of the San Francisco Bay. Dried fruit is no longer as important today because now swift means of transport and refrigeration make fresh fruit useful, but it was an important solution for its day.

Mechanization of Agriculture, California. This vineyard is laid out on flat land, thereby allowing the use of heavy cultivating equipment. Rich but steep hill lands of the type intensely cultivated in lands such as Italy are left untilled in California. *Caterpillar Tractor Co.*

This land that the Spanish had found so little to do with was now growing rapidly in population and in productivity and in wealth. San Francisco had become a great city and Sacramento a large town, while southern California lagged. For a time it was to harbor the sleepy, sunny, relaxed heritage of Mexican California, and some wish that it still was that way. Change is not always progress. Change, however, was in the wind. The nation was determined to bind the two coasts together. The railroad had been invented, and steam engines harnessed to

the cars were revolutionizing transportation. The government sponsored military surveys to find routes to the West and soon lines were reaching across the Great Plains, through the mountains, and down to the Pacific coast. The land so far to the West that it was lost in the Orient was now linked to the rest of the nation, but the land through which the new railroads ran was still largely empty, and the land that they reached was still thinly populated, only beginning to be developed.

Railroads, Oranges, and Cooperatives

But the railroad entrepreneurs of the day plunged optimistically ahead, subsidized by government grants of enormous tracts of land along their right of way. The amount of land thus given to the railways has often been grossly exaggerated. The land was of little value unless it had transportation brought to it, and the land was not a totally free gift, for the railroads promised free transportation to the government, including its armed forces, and subsequent costs of this have been worthwhile to the federal budget. Great profits were made by speculators of the day but the railroads were built, and they made possible a new era for California.

Now produce need not be dried, it could be shipped fresh. Now manufactured goods bought in California need not stand the extra cost of shipment more than half the way around the world. Now people could get to California swiftly, cheaply, and safely. The "geographic location" of California had suddenly changed. The railroads pressed for development, for they needed people at the far end of their line: they sold one-way tickets to California at unbelievably low prices.

A classic example of the economic development that followed the railroads was the citrus industry. Americans had not eaten much citrus. Johns Hopkins' famed E. V. McCollum, however, discovered that one could eat all the calorie-producing food needed by the body to survive and still fall sick. Tiny amounts of certain other things were needed; these he named vitamins. Oranges were found to contain large amounts of one of these vitamins, C. The Californians had oranges and plenty of land to produce a great many more. More and more people could afford to buy oranges as the level of productivity, in the Northeast in particular, raised the average standard of living–higher than the world had ever experienced before. Even though that area was at the opposite corner of this continent-sized nation, the railroads made possible the moving of even perishable materials that far. The potential market was there, the means to reach it had been built, the product had been supplied by the Spanish, the key to motivation had been supplied by medical research, and all that was needed was to take advantage of these factors. But it is misleading to say "all," for we have already reviewed large areas of the earth that in vast expanses of time have had innumerable opportunities on which they have not capitalized. California was to do otherwise.

The shipping of oranges began on a small scale; it was profitable but filled with difficulties. It was still difficult to preserve the fruit for long periods of time, and the conditions in the distant market were hard to anticipate. Market fluctuations could do great damage to the individuals who had large investments in land and improvements and a relatively high overhead. Orchards had to be irrigated, sprayed, pruned, protected from frost, whether the price was up or down. Solution to these problems was found in cooperatives and in individual inventiveness. Oranges were picked without tearing the skin at the stem end—that is, they were cut off the tree; they were washed and waxed to prevent decay; and they were packed in specially designed boxes. Heaters were invented to ward off the occasional cold waves that threatened the orchards, while specialists were called in to develop sprays, fertilizers, and irrigation techniques. What individuals could not do, large organizations could do.

Orange-growing cooperatives built large packing houses, bought their own box factories, and finally even bought the forests and saw mills to produce their own lumber for the boxes. They spent money on full-page advertisements in the leading home magazines to convince the whole country to buy Cali-

fornia oranges, not only because they tasted and looked good, but because they were essential to good health. The orange industry of California became a spectacular case of organization and salesmanship that seized on an opportunity that had been latent in the physical environment and made a paying proposition out of it.

There are many sides to this, of course. The California Indians could have grown oranges, if they had known of them and how to irrigate the land, but their opportunities for marketing them were limited. The Spanish had the oranges and the irrigation, but their potential market was Mexico and the other Spanish colonies, all of which had their own oranges. It was the special circumstance that American California was a part of the United States and had the rapid transportation that made possible this development. In passing, one should not forget that the orange is not a native to the Mediterranean climate. It is not Spanish, for the Arabs brought it to Spain. It is not Arabian either; the Arabs had probably gotten this delicious fruit through their trade with India. The home of the citrus fruits is in Southeast Asia. It is grown in Mediterranean lands more in spite of the climate than because of it. If there were not tariff and quarantine restrictions, our oranges could best be supplied by tropical areas such as the Caribbean or tropical Latin America, where there is no frost risk and irrigation cost. Orange growing is not a simple response to the subtropical climate of southern California. It is a very complex response in which the physical environment of a California located within the political boundaries of a very productive nation, with a highly developed communications network was offered an opportunity that was seized and developed at a particular time in a particular way by a particular group of men.

Other agricultural opportunities of this kind followed much the same pattern. Off-season crops grown in California are sent to the winter-bound markets of the north and east. Lettuce, celery, carrots, canteloups, watermelons, and tomatoes are a few of the crops that move out of specialty areas in trainload lots. The specialty areas are of interest. When one sees an area that grows lettuce in large amounts, almost to the exclusion of other crops, it is the usual thing to conclude that there must be some special thing in the physical environment at this spot that makes this so. This is seldom true. Most berry, lettuce, peach, or potato specialty areas have been developed because of the economies due to mass production, shipping, and marketing rather than because of special soil and water and climate factors. A single lettuce grower can seldom assemble a carload lot of lettuce, but carloads move more cheaply. Insecticides are expensive in small lots, but the local supply house can cut the price if it can buy by the carload. Most specialty produce centers could be in any one of dozens, if not hundreds, of spots. They are grouped for economic reasons.

Manpower and Industry

California has now passed through its agricultural stage. The dominant role of agriculture ended with the vast flood of people that came in after World War II. There had been floods of immigrants before; in terms of original numbers, the days of the forty-niners brought the greatest number. The railroads brought a boom in the 1890s that was followed by a colossal "bust." World War II brought floods of soldiers who were either stationed in California or at least spent some time there on their way to the Pacific. It sometimes seems now as if they all came back and brought all of their relatives with them. A steady growth of population had long been underway, and it burgeoned when industries began to move west.

California is in many ways a have-not area. It has no coal; it has used up most of its oil and gas; and it has little iron ore. Light industry came first. The movie industry came because of the daylight and sunshine. The early movie capital was in the east, but film could be exposed only between 10 A.M. and 2 P.M. in good weather: California had more bright sun through more of the year and also had a greater variety of scenery in a small area. Does the change reflect physical environment? Well, yes, but only

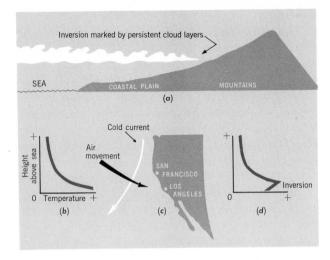

Figure 4-1 The Atmospheric Basis for the Smog Problem in Southern California. The general atmospheric situation at Los Angeles is shown here. Due to an inversion layer marked by a persistent cloud cover a few hundred feet above the ground, the mixing of large amounts of air is prevented (a). Only the air below the inversion layer is available for human and industrial use.

The physical basis for this situation is as follows: The offshore current is cold due to upwelling of cold waters; the vast expanse of the Pacific to the west of California is warm. Air from over the warm Pacific has a normal decrease of temperature with increasing altitude, as shown at (b). Such air masses are easily mixed in depth. However, when such an air mass moves over a cool zone, such as a cold ocean current (c), it is chilled in its lower layer and develops the temperature-elevation distribution shown at (d). Under these conditions the air becomes extremely stable, and the line of change of temperature increase to temperature decrease acts as a barrier to vertical air circulation. In effect this puts a lid over the Los Angeles plain.

for a short time, because today film is not so limited, most movies are made on sets, and in fact the film industry is more and more using other locations.

The airplane industry is a light industry that moved west, partly because of better weather for testing planes. In part, too, it was taking advantage of the growing pool of available manpower there. Originally, a growing population attracted industry;

now, growing industries are advertising for people—special people such as engineers, it is true, but people nonetheless, who will also need doctors, tailors, plumbers, and electricians. Just when the population of California will level off is anyone's guess.

Problems in Paradise

Problems have appeared in this paradise. At Los Angeles, a particular feature of the physical environment has suddenly taken on a malignant aspect. The water off the coast of California is cold because the ocean current along this coast moves south along the continental border. The force due to the rotation of the earth drives the moving surface water to the right, away from the continent. To replace this water, deep ocean water moves toward the surface. This is cold water. The warm air masses coming toward the continent from off the Pacific must cross this cold belt and are cooled in their lower layers, creating an inversion: a very stable air situation, much fog, and a persistent, high-stratum cloud layer, without which southern coastal California would be blazing hot and very much more desert than it is (see Figure 4–1).

All was well until too many people, too much industry, and too many automobiles were put into this situation. Then it was found that the inversion over the Los Angeles area acted like a great lid beneath which there was only so much air. A limited amount of air will support just so many people and industry and absorb just so much waste gas material; the Los Angeles area used up all of its quota of air twenty years ago. Now the citizens of that area are breathing second- and third-hand air, air that has been run through someone's automobile and through some factory furnace and through many other lungs. The air has become loaded with industrial waste products, especially with partially burned automobile fuels, which react with the oxygen in the air to form a variety of irritating compounds. The beautiful, sparkling clear air of the Los Angeles basin ceased to exist twenty years ago, and a yellowish brown acrid substance that irritates the eyes, nose, and throat and damages the vegetation has taken its place. Once more man has changed the environment. Great effort and immense expense is now going into attempts to solve this problem. Industry has enormously reduced its pollution of the air; backyard trash burners have been eliminated; and now the automobile with its polluting exhaust is being controlled. Southern California, however, simply has a limit on its air supply, and no one has yet found a way to increase it.

Mediterranean California has also a limit on its water supply. Northern California has the water; southern California has developed almost all of its local supplies, reached across the state to tap the Colorado River, and is now reaching up the state to take water from northern California. Arizona has fought California in the courts for the right to Colorado River water and won much that California has claimed for herself. Northern California is a bit cool to southern California's plan to tax the whole state to supply the billions of dollars needed to transfer water to the south. The vastness of the projected transfers of water are difficult to grasp. For Los Angeles to bring water from the Boulder Dam to its area is the equivalent of Baltimore getting its water from Lake Erie, or Boston and New York City getting water from Lake Ontario, or Minneapolis getting its water from Lake Michigan. In a sense, it is a case of the physical environment offering a natural limitation to the number that can live in southern California; but southern Californians are willing to pay the cost to live there by extending those natural limitations.

The water problem is complex. The use of pumps on underground supplies has lowered the water level, and areas that had shallow wells now must lift water 100 feet or more while some areas have exhausted their underground supplies. Others near the sea have found that they were drawing salt water in through their underground wells and thus ruining their land by irrigating with sea water. The Colorado River water is loaded with dissolved salts and when used as irrigation water, evaporation leaves these salts to accumulate in the soil eventually to deadly levels. In the midst of all this, Californians continue

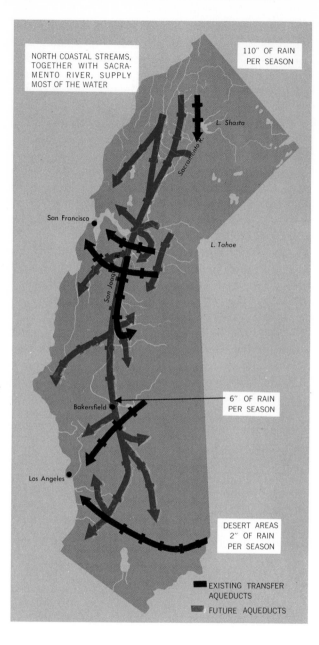

NORTH COASTAL STREAMS, TOGETHER WITH SACRAMENTO RIVER, SUPPLY MOST OF THE WATER

110" OF RAIN PER SEASON

L. Shasta

Sacramento R.

San Francisco

L. Tahoe

San Joaquin

Bakersfield

6" OF RAIN PER SEASON

Los Angeles

DESERT AREAS 2" OF RAIN PER SEASON

■ EXISTING TRANSFER AQUEDUCTS

■ FUTURE AQUEDUCTS

Map 4-8   Proposed Water Distribution in California

California's water problem is due to the concentration of rainfall in the north while more than half of the population is in the arid south. California is 900 miles long, and the overall length of the proposed major canal is 700 miles. A parallel situation would exist on the east coast if, for example, New York City proposed to get its water from Lake Michigan near Chicago. In California man is determined to overcome the water deficiency of the southern part of the state even though the effort will cost billions of dollars.

to dump millions of gallons of slightly used sewage water into the sea and with it goes enormous loads of nutrient material that might better be returned to the land. Meanwhile millions of dollars are being spent in trying to find some economical way to desalt sea water. This now hovers on the brink of achievement. If accomplished, the human geography, not just of this region, but of most of the arid parts of the world, would be changed overnight.

CHILE: CALIFORNIA'S PHYSICAL TWIN

Chile is the physical twin to California, but not an identical twin. As we have already noted, the Mediterranean climatic sections in both countries fall in about the same latitudes, Chile's being somewhat closer to the equator than California's, and in both areas there is a coastal mountain range, then a central valley, and then very high mountains. A minor difference is that the Andes are much higher than the Sierra Nevadas, for the highest peaks in the Andes are over 20,000 feet, while the highest peak in the Sierra Nevadas is only 14,400. In both cases the ranges are excellent precipitation catchers, but they are also formidable barriers to wheeled travel. As might be expected, the passes through the Andes are higher than those in the Sierra Nevadas: around 10,000 feet versus 7000 feet.

The coast ranges are about the same width and height in both cases: about 50 miles wide and 2000 to 7000 feet high. However, the California ranges are composed of series of steep ridges, while the Chilean coast range is a plateau. Both coasts are straight and often precipitous, with few good harbors. California with San Diego and San Francisco is far better off than is Chile, whose best harbors are more like the open bay at Monterey. That this is no absolute handicap is illustrated in California where Los Angeles, lacking a natural harbor, built one. The coast ranges in California are broken at only one point: where the rivers from the interior valley pour out to the sea at San Francisco. In Chile, on the other hand, each major river crosses the coast ranges at right angles, reaching the sea through steep gorges, which are, of course, potential sites for reservoirs, water storage, and hydroelectric developments that California would be delighted to have, but lacks.

The central valleys of the two regions are strikingly alike in general. They are both about 50 miles wide, and the Mediterranean climate sections of each extends for about 300 miles. In Chile, the northern, dry, end of the valley is cut off from the rest by a spur of mountains so that Valparaiso on the Aconcagua River is separated from the rest of the central valley and a 2600-foot high pass must be crossed in going from one section to the other. This is matched in California by the separation of the Los Angeles basin, the dry end of California's Mediterranean climate, from the Central Valley there by the transverse ranges whose Tehachapi pass reaches an elevation of 4000 feet. Perhaps the most significant difference between the two great valleys is that of elevation. Santiago in Chile's central valley has an elevation of 1700 feet above sea level, while representative cities in California's Central Valley have much lower elevations: Sacramento, 30 feet; Fresno and Red Bluff, 300 feet. Since temperature decreases about 3 degrees for each 1000-foot increase in elevation, this has important effects on the climatic comparisons.

The climate of such lands must be greatly varied because of coast, mountain, and interior-valley conditions. In both countries the presence of an off-shore current with a marked upwelling of cold water cools the coast and creates a strong inversion, with the potential smog problem that has already developed in California. The situation also creates the setting for an immensely rich off-shore fishery, which is extensively used in California and little used in Chile. Sharp change of temperatures accompanies the change to the interior in both areas, but with lower summer and winter temperatures in Chile's interior valley due to the increasing elevation. Chile, then, has moderate summer temperatures compared to the blazing heat of California's Central Valley. Santiago in Chile's interior valley has winter average temperatures about 46° F. and summer averages of about 69° F., which is closer to San Diego's equable winter 52° F. and summer 63° F. than it is to such interior California stations as Fresno. Finally, the north-south rainfall gradient in Chile is much steeper than in California. Coquimbo has 4.5 inches, Valparaiso 13 inches, and Conception 30 inches; the comparable sequence in California would be San Diego 10 inches, Los Angeles 16 inches, and San Francisco 22 inches.

In both areas the great snow fields on the high mountains melt during the summer periods and supply vast amounts of runoff at just the time that it is most needed in the hot interior lowlands. The same geomorphic processes in Chile and California have built alluvial fans sloping westward from the foot of the high ranges, with natural slopes ideal for distribution of this water by gravity flow over the great alluvial-filled valleys. In California, as we have seen, the Indian people did nothing with this agricultural invitation, and even the Spanish left the interior valley untouched. The Americans have swept through a grain-raising development that makes their Central Valley one of the most productive areas in the United States. Given the same physical-environmental opportunities, what has happened in Chile?

Despite the primitive conditions under which many of the Chilean people live, the population is growing, doubling between 1885 and 1940. At present the population of the country is about 7.5 million, and 90 per cent of these people are in the central valley—this is about the population of Los Angeles county. Two cities, Santiago and Valpariso, have been growing and developing some manufacturing, and population is tending to move to these centers. People are also emigrating from this relatively empty land to adjacent Argentina, suggesting that it is not the number of people that determines whether a land is overpopulated or underpopulated, it is the state of development that determines it. Chile has the familiar problems of development. Increasing mechanization of her agriculture should free many hands for industrial and service work, and education and industrial development must parallel such changes in agriculture or economic and social chaos will result. Already the flooding of illiterate landless poor into urban areas not equipped to employ, house, and educate them is creating severe social problems. But these are not Mediterranean climate problems, and they are only accidentally and not uniquely Chilean problems.

Why is this land that had so much better a start on the Indian level and so much earlier a start with Spanish development—and which physically is so much like California—still so poor? Why has it not, even now, matched California's achievements?

Chilean Cultural Growth

Mediterranean Chile came within the area of influence of the Peruvian-Bolivian civilizations. The Inca empire even reached to the Aconcagua River valley in the northern end of the Mediterranean climate region, and the ideas of irrigation agriculture were introduced into the central valley of Chile, while simple agriculture of the forest clearing type extended to the island of Chiloe. This was a remarkable spreading outward. If the center of Andean civilization is considered to be between 10 and 15 degrees south of the equator, then irrigation agriculture was spread to 32 degrees south and simple agriculture to 42 degrees south. The comparable

thing in North America would have been for Mexican agriculture, with irrigation, to have reached into the Central Valley of California, and for simpler agriculture to have reached Vancouver Island on the coast of Washington. Had this been true, the history of post-Columbian American surely would have been greatly different.

In 1540 when the Spanish looked at California, they found it a beautiful land, but one lacking in settled people. As we have seen, they then ignored it for over 200 years. In Chile they came looking for gold and empires, and though they found none of these, they found people settled on the land, irrigating the rich central valley. This moderately advanced and modestly dense settlement of people was attractive to some of the Spaniards, and they took over this land even though it was as distant from the center of their interests in South America as California was from their principal area of interest in North America. It is clear that the difference was developed land versus undeveloped land, and once again we see that it is men and ideas that make land valuable.

Santiago was established in 1541 and Concepción in 1550; and despite vigorous warfare on the part of the Araucanian Indians, the Spanish maintained their hold. Since the area lacked gold, the Spanish made the land the source of wealth and prestige, which in reality was only a continuation of an ancient Mediterranean pattern easily traceable back to Roman times and further. The land was soon divided among the few Spaniards to form great landed estates that often have been held intact to this day. Since there were few Spaniards and since in common with most Mediterranean peoples they were relatively free of race prejudice, they intermarried freely with the Indian population and created a mixed race. The Araucanians and the Spaniards were both proud, independent people, and this spirit has endured in the land.

The Spanish development centered in the Mediterranean climate area of the central valley. Here was a land with a climate that they knew well, that was easily and abundantly irrigated, and that had a settled and agriculturally skilled labor force. To the north lay the great desert of Atacama, one of the most barren lands on earth. To the south lay forested lands held by warlike, less settled Araucanians. Major military force exerted against them would eventually find the task so difficult that a peace treaty rather than conquest would be the fate of these efforts. On this early Spanish colonial frontier there was no such force available, so the Spanish settled down to the development of a land that they understood. The result has been such a concentration of development that 90 percent of the country's population is still to be found in this small area.

Of Chile's 6 million people, 30 percent are in the single province of Santiago, and more than half of the entire country is uninhabited. California has a seemingly comparable situation in that one third of the population there is in the Los Angeles area. However, very little of California is really uninhabited and there is no agricultural population in the Sacramento-Stockton area in any way comparable to Chile's. The Los Angeles population concentration is industrial, and in all of California the agricultural areas are thinly, not densely populated. In Chile the central valley has population densities of 125 per square mile, and near Santiago the rural population densities approach 500 per square mile. These extremely high figures reflect the ancient agricultural system that characterizes much of Chile—and most of the rest of the world where the scientific, chemical, mechanical, and industrial revolution has not yet penetrated.

Landownership in Mediterranean Chile is enormously concentrated. Small farms, and a 500-acre farm in Chile is considered small, are rare. In the central valley large properties, called haciendas, are only 7 percent of the total number of properties, but they occupy 90 percent of the land. In the Aconcagua Valley 98 percent of the land is owned by 3 percent of the property owners: 375 properties cover over 20 square miles in size, occupying

52 percent of the privately owned land in this region. The largest of these estates is about 600 square miles, an area 40 by 15 miles, roughly one half the size of the state of Rhode Island. This is not quite as bad as it seems, for these vast estates often have relatively small amounts of irrigable land and large amounts of dry and mountainous land. On the other hand, studies suggest that some of the large properties in Chile grossly underestimate their acreages in order to decrease tax payments, and air surveys now being carried out are designed to check this. It is a notable step, however, for this could only be done if the large landholders themselves agreed to such remedial measures.

The great estates and the small farms are almost uniformly run on an agricultural system that is similar to the colonial one, which means that the mechanization is at a minimum and the use of labor is at a maximum. It is this prodigal use of manpower on the land that accounts for the dense rural populations. It is estimated that only one quarter of the cultivated land is worked by mechanized units. The bulk of the farms rely on ox-drawn carts and grain is hand sown, reaped with scythes, threshed by trampling horses, and winnowed by men pitching the straw into the air so that it will be blown away by the wind while the heavier grain falls to the threshing floor. Only one quarter of the land, therefore, can be said to be in the twentieth century, with machinery replacing manpower on the land. This cannot be changed easily, for if men are displaced from the land, they must find employment somewhere.

The principal crops are cereals, with wheat predominant. This is the stage that California was in just after the Gold Rush a century ago. It is probably not far from the truth to say that Chile today is about what California would have been today had it remained subject to Latin American social, economic, and political traditions and economic and political ties. Although cereals predominate in Chile, only about one tenth of the productive land is in grain in any one year; the rest is fallow, or in pasture. This emphasis on livestock is again a Spanish heritage, and it will be seen affecting the land use of Argentina and Uruguay in much the same way. In Chile animals are driven from winter lowland pastures to upland summer pastures, as has been done in Spain and Switzerland for long ages.

The great bulk of the people on the land are tenants on the haciendas, and their condition long was approximately that of serfs. As in medieval Europe, the men belonged to the estate and had both duties and rights. A meager living was man's lot, but it was an assured one. So long as a man stayed on the estate, he would never starve and his sons could continue to work there after him; he might be legally free to move, but he is by custom firmly bound to the land. It is not easy to leave, for the tenant knows no other life, has no education that would equip him for doing a skilled work, and usually he is emotionally attached to the land where he and his forefathers have lived and served one great landowning family for 500 years. For cradle-to-grave security he has paid in freedom and the acceptance of poverty. The oddity of it all is this: most of mankind since the spread of the Neolithic revolution has lived this way, and today much of the world is again in danger of bartering freedom for security under some form of paternalism.

The actual working of the Chilean agricultural system is a productive one. The proof is the number of men who live from the soil, the bulk of them very poorly by our standards, it is true, but relatively well by much of the world's standards. Each tenant has his own house, though unheated, with no running water, no separate kitchen, and no bath. Two acres or so about the house are his to raise domestic animals and to garden; in addition, he is assigned fields where he can grow his own grain. A Chinese peasant would consider that he had wealth indeed if this were his. On the other hand, a Californian would be hailed into court if he put migrant laborers in dirt-floored, thatch-roofed, unlighted houses and told them to use the polluted irrigation ditch for their water supply. Although the large estates are considered an evil and there is a strong emotional drive to break them up and to distribute the land to the people, such a move would be counter to the present land-management trend. We need less and less men on the land; the use of more and more machinery calls for large farm operations. The problem is less the size of Chile's estates than the low productivity of their system built as it is around the use of large quantities of unskilled, cheap labor.

SOUTH AFRICA AND AUSTRALIA

SOUTH AFRICA'S REGION OF MEDITERRANEAN CLIMATE

The part of Africa marked by concentration of rainfall in winter and by summer drought is a triangular area on the southwest tip of the continent. The dimensions are roughly 200 by 200 by 300 miles, an area somewhat comparable to the similar climate in California south of San Francisco. Just as the Mediterranean climate of California is only a part of the state, so too in South Africa this summer dry climate is only a part of the Republic of South Africa, which includes large arid and humid areas as well.

In South Africa there is a coastal plain backed by ranges of folded mountains, and behind them looms the high plateau edge of the continental mass of Africa. Aridity increases to the northwest; while rainfall increases to the northeast and soon becomes well distributed through the year. It is only the Cape region, then, that is Mediterranean in climate. Here the mountains parallel the coast and their seaward flanks intercept moisture, but the in-

Cape Town, South Africa. The landscape is typically Mediterranean: sea, narrow coastal plain, steep mountain slopes. The mountains behind the town are smooth sloped because of the intact vegetation and cover. Compare this photo with that of the Greek shoreline, where destruction of the vegetation has allowed loss of soil and reduced the land to bare rock (p. 190). *Information Service of South Africa.*

Landscape at Worcester, near Cape Town, South Africa. This location is in an interior valley and the landscape would be completely interchangeable with locations in California or Chile. Here Frisian cattle are grazing on lucerne (clover). *Information Service of South Africa.*

terior valleys are made that much drier, and this rainfall can be over 200 inches on the mountain tops, but under five inches in the valleys. As in all Mediterranean climates, the greatest problem is water, especially during the long, dry summer months, and the high mountain ranges with their abundant rainfalls are therefore invaluable. So far all is familiar. There is gold to be found, a desert "to discover," and a scenic, pleasant land to attract people: it could be California all over again. There are differences of course.

The folded mountains create many valleys, but there is no great central valley as in Chile or California. The higher of these valleys are well watered, but the lower ones are dry. For example, east of Cape Town lies the 100-mile long, 10-to-12-miles wide, Worcester-Robinson Valley where rainfall in the lower end is only 5 to 10 inches, on the flanks 20 to 30 inches, and at the head of the valley 30 to 40 inches. Permanent streams flow through many of these valleys and the irrigation potential is large. There is a broad coastal plain, but here the rainfall is generally low: 10 to 20 inches—and the area is like the drier end of the Palestinian or Californian comparable climates. All in all, however, the region is the now familiar land of sunshine, mild winters, and opportunity for crops grown on the winter rains and for summer crops dependent on irrigation supplied by the rain-catching mountains. As we have seen, these can be areas of great opportunity.

Man was as slow to see that opportunity in South Africa as he was in California. The earliest inhabitants of this part of Africa seem to have been the people known as the Bushmen—a small, yellow-skinned, slant-eyed, triangular-faced race of mankind. Quite clearly they once occupied much more of Africa, and have only recently been driven from the well-watered parts into the arid environment that no one else wants, which has led to the curious and erroneous conclusion that some of their unusual bodily characteristics were developed for life in the desert. On the contrary, their history is that of long development in the high, cool, well-watered lands of East Africa, and of slow retreat before the onslaught of physically larger and culturally better-equipped people, until today they find themselves thrust into their ultimate refuge, the Kalahari steppe and the Namib Desert. As in all such cases, men had the possibility of changing their ways to meet the thrust of new ideas or of clinging to their old ways. In an extraordinary number of cases, men of all races have chosen not to change. This is much like the story of the Indians in California, except that until the coming of the Europeans they were left undisturbed.

Early Cultural Lag

Like California, South Africa was far from the centers of growth and development of ideas and long lagged in the hunting and gathering stage of development. However, ideas had reached the area before the Europeans arrived and the ancient way of life of the seed gatherers and the collectors of animals was ending under the onslaught of another way of life.

The idea of cattle-keeping, a form of pastoral nomadism complete with milking, had reached South Africa some time before the Europeans arrived there. The Hottentot people, who had taken up this way of life, had moved into the Cape region and were competing for space with the Bushmen. Racially, the Hottentot seem to be intermediate between the Negro people and the Bushmen, and in all likelihood they do represent the result of an incoming people mixing with the indigenous people. The use of a Mediterranean climate by simple hunters and gatherers was the original California land use, succeeded by ranching, a settled way of cattle-raising. In South Africa a pastoral nomadism of the type usually associated with the steppe or desert areas developed, which suggests that pastoralism is less limited to the semiarid regions than relegated to them as wheat growing is displaced from the more humid regions where it would actually do better than other more demanding crops.

European Occupation

Into this scene of an already changing cultural landscape, two streams of people converged by the seventeenth century. The Portuguese early discovered the Cape region, but in 1510 a sizable group of Portuguese were slaughtered by the Hottentots, and the Portuguese thereafter centered their interest in the more settled and prosperous trading towns on the coast of East Africa. The lovely lands of the Cape region, with a climate like their homeland, was forsaken in favor of the steamy, more civilized areas offering greater and more immediate profits. It was 140 years later, in 1652, that the Dutch decided that the Cape area made an excellent stop-over point on the long voyage from the Netherlands to the East Indies. The amenities of a Mediterranean climate had almost nothing to do with the choice: the initial settlement was purely strategic. Thereafter the desirability of having provisions always available led to colonization, and by 1662 there were 60 free burghers (farmers, fisherman, and craftsmen) established there. Not only Dutch but German and other northern European people came to the colony. The scarcity of labor and the availability of land suggested extensive rather than intensive land use and led to a shift toward cattle culture. Expansion into the interior was slow, for the population was small and away from the coast the valleys within the folded mountain ranges were increasingly arid. After 1750, however, ways into the interior and up onto the East African highlands with their immense areas of rich grasslands were found and the Dutch-German settlers (Boers) eagerly spread into them. Here, however, they met another stream of settlers, equally spreading, but southward, not northward, and African, not European. These were the Bantu, a Negro people from the Sudan area north of the equator, who late in African history began an explosive spread into East Africa and southward. They were a tribal people, with no sense of unity, and with an economy based on cattle-keeping combined with agriculture. In some ways, such as their warlike nature, their rapid overrunning of vast territories, and their combination of farming and cattle-keeping, they are reminiscent of the Germanic tribes of Caesar's day. The Bantu and the Europeans were soon engaged in border wars for control of the territory, wars that were to continue into the twentieth century.

When the British took over the Cape region in 1795, they found a population of 16,000 Europeans (Dutch 50 percent, German 27 percent, French 17 percent, others 5.5 percent). In addition, there were 17,000 Malays and Negro slaves and no one knows how many Hottentots and Bushmen. An occupation of 225 years had not seen much European population growth, but it had seen the beginnings of the racial mixture that was to become the dominant characteristic in the life of the region. In 1806 the European population was 26,000, Hottentots 17,000, slaves 29,000; and the Bantu were the enemy being held at bay along a borderland to the northeast. The frontiersmen were the Boers who lived as cattlemen moving over the land renting vast tracts at minimal rates. The British were anxious to establish a more permanent and productive settlement and brought in settlers; 5000 in 1820, 4300 in 1850, 12,000 in the 1860s. Yet after 350 years the number of people on the land was few, and the tempo and mode of life like that of Spanish California.

The pre-British settlers, largely Dutch and German, had developed their own way of life and were none too pleased to be under British rule. In the early nineteenth century their cattle frontier had penetrated the headwaters of the Orange River in Natal, and they had discovered the vast, rich, tropical-highland grasslands there. In 1836 some 10,000 Boers moved out of British controlled territory northward into the Natal area in the "Great Trek." Head-on conflict with the Bantu won the country for the Boers. Land was distributed in huge amounts, each settler getting not less than 6000 acres. This led to much use of native labor, to a landed gentry, to a scarcity of land for new settlers, and to an extremely extensive use of the land. In some

Johannesburg, South Africa. Immense mine dumps dominate the middle distance, accurately portraying the role of mining in this modern city. *Information Service of South Africa.*

Great Vats of Fine Wines for Export from South Africa. The scene could be duplicated in California, Spain, or Chile. The grape and the Mediterranean climate and fine wines are strongly associated. However, the association did not exist outside the Old World Mediterranean before A.D. 1500. *Information Service of South Africa.*

ways, the pattern repeated the Chilean situation, and is what probably would have developed in California had that land remained in Spanish-Mexican control. However, the African situation was developed by northwestern Europeans, basing themselves on a Negroid population, and, in Natal, establishing themselves in a tropical highland climate rather than in a Mediterranean climate. It was not the climate that mattered: it was the political institutions, and these had taken on their characteristics in the Mediterranean climate of the Cape region and were then carried en masse into the adjacent area.

South Africa might have lingered in a modestly developed agricultural stage had it not been for the discovery of great mineral wealth. The discovery of diamonds at Hopetown in 1867, and later at Kimberley, brought a flood of immigrants from all over the world. Later came the great gold discoveries on the Witwatersrand near Johannesburg in 1887, and again the immigrants numbered in the tens of thousands. What government planning and encouragement had not accomplished in centuries was quickly accomplished when economic opportunity beckoned, and a large European population became established in the land. Another by-product of these discoveries was the Boer War, through which Great Britain took over these mineral-rich territories, adding them to her Cape area, and once again the Boers were back in the British Empire. The mineral discoveries were not, however, in the Mediterranean climate region, and the great growth of population therefore centered in the northern part of the Republic of South Africa, of which the Cape area with its desirable Mediterranean climate was a less-valued appendage. The great modern city of Johannesburg marks the center of the mining community, while Cape Town marks the center of the development in the Mediterranean climate region.

In the Cape area, the real Mediterranean climate zone, the present development is strongly centered on agriculture. Wheat is the dominant crop on the inland part of the coastal plain, and the commercial production of deciduous fruits and grapes and the export of wines is a very important part of the economy. The deciduous fruits require irrigation in the summer, but the mountains with their perennial streams flowing down the alluvial fans along the mountain flanks make irrigation feasible here just as in California and Chile. The area runs the curious risk of too warm a winter for the deciduous fruits: when there is not sufficient cold to make the trees shed their leaves and go into their normal dormant period, their seasonal rhythm is so disturbed that they may yield no crop the following years. Apples, pears, plums, peaches, and apricots are grown in large quantities for export. These are, of course, just the fruits with which California began her horticultural period. Vine cultivation is also important: grapes, raisins, and wines make a multimillion-dollar export industry. Productivity of the land expressed in yield of wine per acre in the Cape region shows 440 gallons per acre, as compared with Europe's average of 176 gallons per acre. Cape wines, grown under a stronger sun, have more sugar and less acid than European wines; but Europeans prefer their thinner and more sour wines. This is cultural determinism at work again: Why should thin sour wines be preferred to full-bodied sweet wines?

Table grapes bring high prices and are shipped under refrigeration to the European market. Some of this development was early dependent on the empire-preference system that gave members of the British Commonwealth preferred status in the British market. Difficulties focused on the race problem have caused South Africa to withdraw from the Commonwealth, but a market for her products still seems assured because the increasing productivity of Europe is greatly increasing the number of people able to afford imported fruit and wine. Increasing prosperity in South Africa should eventually create local markets, too. Liquor is withheld from the tribal peoples just as it was withheld from the American Indians during the past 100 years. Freedom for the Negro Africans could create a large market, though whether the Negroes as a

Meadowlands, a Bantu Township South of Johannesburg. Some of the 130,000 family-size brick and concrete houses planned as a total project to be built in 8 years to accommodate more than 700,000 Bantu. The total cost is expected to run $100,000,000. Rentals are to vary from the equivalent of $3 to $12 per month. *Information Service of South Africa.*

mass are more ready for this dubious gift than the American Indians were 100 years ago remains to be seen.

The Race Problem

South Africa's problem is not a physical-geographical one, but a racial one. It is an old and complex problem for which there is no easy solution. The Bushmen are no longer troublesome today, largely because there are so few of them, almost none in the Cape area. The Hottentot are a lesser problem than the Bantu who have come to outnumber them. It would be simpler if this were the end of the race problem, but there are also the large numbers of Malays and Indians who were imported as a labor supply in the early days of the colony. In addition, each group has intermarried with each other group until there is as well a complex series of "coloreds."

Within the European group, there is considerable division concerning the proper treatment of this problem. In general, the Boers favor complete separation of the races, while the people of British origin favor some form of programmed integration.

Great stress has been placed by critics on the segregation program, apartheid, and too little stress on the difficulty of the problem and the strenuous effort that has been made to help the nonwhite populations. Populations is used in the plural for there is no unity among the nonwhites; even the Bantu are separated into tribal units with divergent languages and aspirations to separate national status. The difficulties are formidable. Nowhere in the world has a quick and easy way been found to bring people from the hunting-and-gathering stage into the twentieth century. The problem is only a little less formidable when one begins with pastoralists such as the Hottentot, or tribal agriculturists such as the Bantu.

In each case there is massive illiteracy, complete ignorance of and consequent disregard of the simplest hygienic practices, and totally different cultural views on sex, business, and politics. One need not make value judgments concerning which system is best, although there is no reason that such judgments might not validly be made, to see that such discrepancies create enormous difficulties in a society. Those in favor of apartheid favor complete separation of the races, with each race having its own national-racial territory. Since the apartheid group is in the majority among the whites, and they are the race in control, it is their program that is being enacted.

The white sector of the population is not ignoring the needs of the other races, but is carrying on a massive educational, housing, and development program. This includes a housing program designed to produce tens of thousands of modern dwellings for the native people and the destruction of the slums surrounding the major cities. For vast numbers of the natives, it is their first experience with running water, electric power, and such advanced devices as outhouses (such as characterized America in the eighteenth century, but persist as a sanitary arrangement only in our most remote rural areas today). The magnitude of the effort and the amount achieved is indicated by the following summary:

Economic Growth

South Africa leads the world in gold, gem diamonds, platinum, and antimony

1946–1962: gross industrial production increased five-fold, and per capita income improved by 35 percent

Foreign investment, two thirds British, exceeds 4 billion dollars

Steel production is 6 times and electrical production 2 times that of all the rest of Africa combined

Native Development in South Africa

50 years ago the Bantu were still principally illiterate tribal people many of whom lived in mud huts and wore animal skins. In 1962, 30 newspapers and 8 periodicals were produced for the Bantu market and carried 30 million dollars worth of advertising.

The Xhosa, a Bantu group, have the highest percentage of literacy, skilled manpower, professional personnel (doctors, teachers, attorneys) of all black African nations.

Four out of five Bantu children attend school and illiteracy should end in 25 years.

Vaal Dam near Vereeniging, south of Johannesburg. *Information Service of South Africa.*

Steel Plant near Pretoria. Production in 1961 was over two million tons. *Information Service of South Africa.*

There are 28,000 Bantu school teachers, and 47 teachers' colleges add 2000 more per year.

The per capita expenditure on education is 4 times that of the next African state.

Taxes pay for this and the Bantu pay the lesser share, for example, 28 percent of the educational cost comes from the numerically dominant Bantu. Bantu development on the average costs each white family 280 dollars per year.

Contribution of the various population groups to the national income: Whites, 71 percent; Bantu, 23 percent; Coloreds, 4 percent; Asiatics, 2 percent.

There is a developing Bantu middle class and the Bantu already have a higher per capita ownership of cars than the Russians.

If the experience of the rest of mankind is a guide, the future of South Africa will not be a happy one. The oppressive acts of the Europeans in the past will be magnified and the constructive acts of the present will be minimized. Bushman, Hottentot, Bantu, Indian, and Malay may join together in ousting the minority group of Europeans, and they probably will, even though this will be detrimental to the community. Equally surely they will then attack and oppress each other. Apartheid simply can not be expected to work, for the more education and opportunity the Negro and colored population gets, the more it most naturally will want.

It would be fine if, in a golden haze of humanitarian sentiment, it could be predicted that at some future time, when educational and economic and political opportunities have been realized, this area's population would settle down to completely equal treatment of each group. The immediate future is predictably one of increasing strife, increasing pressures by each group that is striving to gain its rights, and with the probability that whichever group emerges victorious, it will then proceed to oppress the others. It is worth recalling that the Hottentot were expelling the Bushmen and exterminating another Negroid group when the

Europeans arrived. The Bantu are as recent intruders and were more ruthless than the Europeans in their treatment of their predecessors in the area. Man's inhumanity to his fellow men is not just a matter of race, of colored versus white here. There is only one solution, and that is the universal recognition of the brotherhood of man, a goal that must be kept in view even while the realities of the present situation oppress us. Sadly, then, this beautiful piece of potentially productive and climatically most attractive geography must be said to have a poor prospect for growth and development, but not because of its physical geography.

AUSTRALIA'S MEDITERRANEAN LANDS

Australia has two areas of Mediterranean climate: one in the southwest corner around Perth and the other around the series of gulfs and peninsulas west of the southeastern corner of the continent, with Adelaide as the principal city. These regions differ from the other Mediterranean lands so far described in the lesser importance of mountains in the landscape. Western Australia has none, and the area around the gulfs has only the modest-sized Flinders Range, with general elevations of 2000 feet and with peaks to 4000 feet. Although the two areas have had similar development, they can best be discussed separately, except for the aboriginal situation.

All of Australia, whatever its climate, remained in the stone age until the British settlement. For people with a hunting-and-gathering economy, all environments are useful; hence there is nothing significantly different about the way of life of the Australian aborigines whether one is discussing the tropical north, the seasonal south, or the arid interior. On so simple and unspecialized a level, there is something to gather and something to hunt wherever you are, and the increasing fitting of economy to the land that marks the growth and development of economic life, hardly appears at this level of human activity. This tends to undermine the com-

Well-developed Mediterranean Landscape, State of Victoria, Australia. As in California, gold attracted people who then stayed to build the state. The capital city, Melbourne, is second only to Sydney. *Australian News and Information Bureau.*

mon saying that man has increasingly won freedom from his environment, for in a very real sense the simpler people were less environmentally bound than we are.

The Coming of the Europeans

Australia was first reached by Europeans crossing the Indian Ocean on a southerly route that brought them to the west coast of the continent. The discovery areas then focused on the southwest corner of the continent, an area much like California in climate, soil, and vegetation, and also in being occupied by a people of extremely simple culture. The reaction of these early seventeenth-century discoverers was much like that of the Spanish in California and the Portuguese in South Africa. They saw little value in such land and went on to the attractive hot and steamy tropics to the north of Australia where there were plenty of settled people who were producing spices of great value.

Belatedly the British began the settlement of Australia, but from the east coast, in 1787, beginning in climatic zones similar to the southeastern United States. This effort occurred nearly 200 years after the first discovery of the continent, and then was undertaken somewhat reluctantly and primarily for use as a penal colony. Only later did the British colonize the Mediterranean lands. Truly, as one reviews the reluctance of the Europeans to settle the lands with Mediterranean climates considered so attractive that all of America seems to be trying to move to California, one begins to wonder whether their judgment or ours is correct.

West Australia

Western Australia as a political unit is a huge slice of the continent. Its southwest corner, known as Swanland, is characterized by winter rainfall that is abundant (40 inches) at the southwestern corner of the continent and decreases inland until with the 10-inch line the boundary of the humid land is reached. The adequately watered and thus Mediterranean-climate area amounts to 150,000 square miles. Most of West Australia's 746,169 people are in this humid corner. Compare Great Britain's 52,675,000 people in an area of 94,500 square miles of less productive land for a measure of the emptiness of even the good parts of Australia. It is a low-lying, largely level land, for heights are only hills of some 1000-feet elevation. Settlement began at Perth in 1828 and the first ten years saw the arrival of only 2000 settlers. As in California and South Africa, wheat was the important crop, and in typical Australian fashion, sheep became the other important use of the land in the early period. Settlement has been aided by the attraction of gold, for in the 1880s gold was found at Kalgoorlie in the adjacent dry region. This brought the usual gold rush, and the flood of miners included men who then elected to settle on the land.

Development of the land has followed the rainfall belts. The rainier southwest has an apple-growing region, and along the coast of Perth there is a zone of orange-growing and an area of concentration of vineyards. Inland, toward the drier regions, there is a wheat belt, stretching 450 miles north and south and extending 30 to 100 miles east and west, where farms run to 1000 acres. Rainfall here is from 10 to 20 inches per year. On the arid side of this belt the land is dry farmed, that is, part of the land is rested and allowed to accumulate moisture for a year or two before a crop is planted again. Beyond that, sheep are grazed out to areas having only 7 inches of rain per year, and beyond that lies the desert.

The area has no great advantage in Australia. Australians have plenty of sunshine and warmth over most of their country all year round, and they can grow oranges or grapes or tropical fruits or vegetables in the winter almost anywhere. There is, then, no tourist trade for Western Australia in winter, nor any possibility for the development of specialty crop areas to supply a winter-bound adjacent area. It is not surprising therefore that growth

in this region has been modest and that the area is to be thought of as about in the stage of California 50 years ago, or of South Africa today. This is not to say that this is a backward area, for none of Australia is that. Perth is a modern city with some manufacturing, and its population of 358,000 equals more than half the total population of the state. The strong urban concentration of the population is a mark of efficient, modern agricultural production to feed the urban population and the growth of manufacturing and service industries associated with high standards of living. Lightly populated Western Australia is simply a California attached to a tropical and subtropical country, and this places it in an entirely different situation from a similar piece of geography attached to a mid-latitude country.

South Australia

The Mediterranean climate area centered on Adelaide is the smaller of Australia's two such climates. The 100,000 square miles of land with winter rain, year-round sun, and moderate temperatures would be a most welcome addition to most countries. In Australia it has attracted less than a million people and more than half of them live in the principal city. Settlement here began with 500 settlers shortly after Western Australia: 1836 compared with 1828. With few men and immense areas of available land, the development was toward extensive use of the land and the choice in terms of the Australian viewpoint was wheat and sheep.

Australia's history is oddly intertwined with that of the United States. It was the breaking away of the American colonies that precipitated the settlement of Australia. It was the Gold Rush in California that set off a comparable rush in Australia, for it was an Australian who had gone to the California gold rush and then returned to Australia still infected with gold fever who discovered gold there. By 1850 nearly 100 years after the beginning of settlement, Australia's total population was only 400,000 people, and development seemed to have slowed to a walk. But gold soon had it galloping,

Racks for Drying Currants, Sultanas, and Raisins in Red Cliffs, Northern Victoria. The important fruit industry prepares much of its production for export by drying the fruit in the hot rainless summers. This exactly parallels California's pre-industrial stage. The scene shown here is in an area irrigated by the Murray River. A similar California area would be the Fresno grape and raisin district. *Australian News and Information Bureau.*

for in the four years after 1851 the population doubled and redoubled, and the land began to fill up. The biggest gold strikes were in Victoria, adjacent to South Australia and the flow of settlers that followed the gold rush added to the men on the land around Adelaide.

It was a fine land that they settled. Peninsulas and gulfs provide pleasant land-and-sea contrasts, and the Flinders Range, even with its modest heights, add to the scenery and catch much-needed moisture. Rainfall declines rapidly from an abundant 40 inches at the southern end of the Fleurieu Peninsula south of Adelaide going northward, to 30 inches, then 20 inches, and then more slowly to 10 inches; and to the north thereafter lies the, in Australia, ever-present desert. The heaviest rainfall in the area, 47 inches, is on Mounty Lofty, behind Adelaide, but this is a modest amount compared to the immense rain and snow falls on the lofty ranges of California and Peru and the 200 inches on the ranges of South Africa.

As in West Australia, the land use is adjusted to the rainfall belts. Apples are grown in the rainy area; oranges and vine crops are raised south of Adelaide in the 20 to 30 inch rainfall zone; and wheat is grown on the dry side of the 20-inch isohyet. Beyond that lies the sparse grazing areas of the desert and semidesert. As with Western Australia, there is no great advantage in South Australia's favor. Oranges and grapes can be grown in much of Australia; deciduous fruits can be grown as well or better in adjacent areas. North Australia is warmer in winter than is South Australia, and when anyone wants sun there is always the desert handily adjacent in all of Australia. Again, the Mediterranean climate when so situated has relatively little advantage, and when its summer drought is considered, it actually comes to be at a disadvantage to the adjacent subtropical regions.

Summary

Australia's two areas of Mediterranean climate therefore remain lands relatively thinly occupied not for any fault in the land, but because in the present stage of Australia's development—with the whole land thinly settled—these sunny, mild-winter and warm-summered lands, with their high year round sunshine, must compete with adjacent lands that also have mild climates and high percentages of sunshine, and are often better watered throughout the year. Nonetheless, these are attractive areas and are bound to develop along with the rest of humid Australia, which continues to attract a strong flow of European immigration and to develop its industry. The future clearly seems to be one of steady growth on a high standard of living based on balanced industrial and agricultural growths.

MEDITERRANEAN: FINAL DISCUSSION

We have, then, five areas of land that share a common climate, sea-border positions, and, in four cases, rugged topography as well. Two of the areas, Chile and California, are alike to a quite striking degree. The question now arises: In these similar environments, just how much similarity of human activity has there been? Is there a Mediterranean way of life whose primary conditions have been determined by the similarities of these environments? The answer is No.

In the Mediterranean proper, cultural accomplishment was generally high, and in spots it was at times the highest that man has attained. The other two Old World Mediterranean climates were cultural low spots, and this is true also of the New World Mediterranean climates. If the physical environment did not cause cultural uniformity, or similarity, or stimulate much of anything in the way of human accomplishment in four out of five cases, we may well expect that crude physical environment (soils, climate, topography, position in relation to the sea) simply was not a major causative factor. What then?

We might well suspect race. Accomplishment in the European Mediterranean was primarily in the hands of the swarthy, graceful, Mediterranean race with an assist from the closely related large blondish neighbors from northern Europe, and here ac-

complishment was followed by a long decline. It does not seem to matter what the race, for neither Australians nor Negroids in South Africa nor varied types of men lumped under the poorly fitting name of American Indian accomplished anything in this finest of all physical settings, if one were to judge by what the Greeks were able to accomplish. Race is a shifty argument. While it is true that the native Australians accomplished little and the primitive people of South Africa about as little, the American Indians in other settings proved themselves to be most able people. Race must, at least for now, be left in the limbo of unanswerable questions. We do not know enough to tell just what, if anything, this factor has played. We can do much more with the cultural factor.

In the European Mediterranean it is clear from a survey of history that the initial cultural impetus came not in the Mediterranean, but in the adjacent Near East. It was the spread of Neolithic and Bronze Age cultures around 4000 B.C., reaching out into the islands of the eastern Mediterranean, that brought that land into the realm of high culture. The island of Crete was an early center of civilization; here the Minoan culture flourished about 2500 B.C. and came, by 1700 B.C., to dominate the Aegean Sea. Minoan culture was clearly built in large part on trade between the Aegean and Egypt, and the main source of cultural stimulus lay in the much more ancient and advanced culture of Egypt. The major basis for advances in knowledge then, lay outside the area of Mediterranean climate.

If we concentrate on Greece as the earliest seat of cultural growth in the Mediterranean (outside of Crete) and the center of some of the greatest of human advances, we find that at all times she was receiving ideas from adjacent areas. The beginnings of Greek cultural growth appear in such cities as Mycenae and Tiryns. Characteristically such growths were based in large part on local populations and imported ideas, apparently with sufficient supply of immigrant skilled people to organize, to teach, and eventually to get a local development going. It is difficult to see either a physical-environmental argument or a racial argument in this. It looks like a simple case of cultural diffusion. As we have seen, increasing distance from this center of influence is accompanied by a steady falling off of early great accomplishment.

This story changes little for the other lands with this climate. Those near centers of ideas stood higher on the cultural ladder than those far from such centers. Since only one of the Mediterranean lands was really close to a great center of advancement, only one of them enters the list of early cultural innovators and centers of accomplishment. When the wheel of history turns, the positions of these countries shift. The Old World Mediterranean has been in an eclipse despite its proximity to the Euopean mental powerhouse. That this may be only a temporary situation, if already centuries long, we have indicated by reviewing developments in Italy today. Spain and Greece have similar potentials. That changes in these lands are likely to continue have been indicated by an analysis of coming decline for South Africa and growth for Mediterranean Australia. All of this, of course, is going on in the unchanging physical environment of the present world. The causative factors must then be nonphysical.

In the New World, the story is the same but with the addition of the abrupt changes due to European impact. California and Chile, as alike as two peas in a pod, have opposite histories. California starts low and after a slow start goes up the ladder of civilization. Chile starts well, but then goes nowhere. The changing world and the differing political associations and cultural heritages are clearly the causes of the differences. The future of each of these lands is predictable over a short time in terms of the people, their attitudes, and their situation in the world. California, with its association with the other 49 states, its large, highly educated population, and its full access to the technology and capital sources of the world—combined with a passionate drive to be the best—has an unlimited future. Chile's similar area with a small, poorly educated population, an underdeveloped small nation with little access to technology and capital—but even more importantly, lacking either the drive to achieve or the social mechanisms to please such drives—seems destined to stagnate a while longer. South Africa's future, as we have noted, can only be said to be nearly hopeless for as far as one can see into the future—that is, for a century or so. The future of Australia's Mediterranean lands is uncertain only in that just what future that part of Australia will play in the total Australian development is uncertain. In general, prospects there are good because of the people and their educational and technological development—and one must add for Australia, because of their indominitable spirit. The future of the Mediterranean lands turns on the same type of analyses. On this basis Italy, the more advanced in education and industry, should hold her lead. Spain and Portugal and Greece could press her in a matter of some decades if they continue their educational and industrial growth. North Africa, in particular, seems to be second only to South Africa in the bleakness of its forseeable future because of its socio-political situation. Expulsion of all Christian and Jewish minorities and withdrawal into the Arab world is not the kind of program that is likely to make northwesternmost Africa bloom. This potentially rich land, blessed with a start toward civilization as early as 4000 B.C., is seemingly doomed to stagnate still longer. Perhaps it is race; if so, here it is the Caucasians at fault.

5-East Coast Mid-latitude Forest Lands

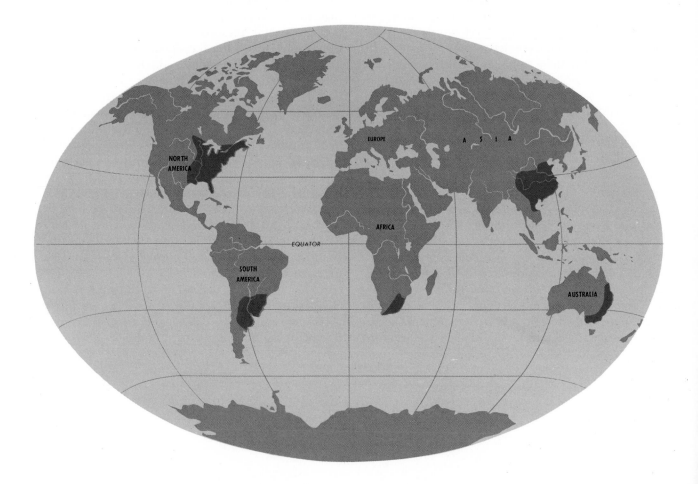

THE MIDDLE LATITUDES, roughly from 30 to 60 degrees away from the equator, are moderately to extremely moist lands. On the west coasts of continents in these latitudes the westerly wind belt with its cyclonic storms is present through the year. The flow of the wind and the structure of the storms brings precipitation. On the east side of continents in these latitudes the cyclonic storms bring rains, especially during the winter season, and are reinforced during the summer by monsoon tendencies, the inflow of air onto the continents from over the warm tropical seas. The result is precipitation well distributed throughout the year, generally ranging between 20 and 60 inches annually, with 40 inches the usual amount. In the cooler parts of these lands, even 20 inches is enough for forest growth; therefore, wherever there is sufficient rainfall, and as long as at least one month of the year is above 50° F., a forest cover is found over these mid-latitude lands—with rare exceptions.

Under cool, moist, forest-covered conditions, weathering goes forward at varying rates. In the cooler north, where there are long cold winters, the rate is slower than it is in the warmer, short-wintered southern parts. This tendency is reinforced by the former presence of glaciers in the north, for where these rested on the land, they left either bare rock or fresh debris. Since the great retreat of the glaciers dates to about 10,000 years ago, that is the maximum amount of time that weathering can have occurred in formerly glaciated regions. The difference is easily seen in the eastern United States. Weathering penetrates tens of feet deep into the solid rocks in the South, and the rich coloring of the soil materials, often a bright red, expresses the degree of chemical action. In the North, the soils are not deeply weathered, the colors are never bright red, and the rocks are only weathered to slight depths. The rounded forms that the glaciers gave to the bedrock masses that they overrode can be seen in the rocks in the Hudson River Palisades, and the smooth polish that the glaciers gave to the granite rocks can still be seen and felt in many places in New England.

All other things being equal, younger soils are richer in humid climates because of the tendency of the weathering process to remove the soluable nutrients. The longer this weathering process goes on, the poorer the remaining mass of material becomes in the chemicals that plants need for growth—a phenomenon discussed in the section on the soils of the tropical rain forest (see Chapter 3). It applies to *all* forest climates. Within the mid-latitude forest climates, then, the older soils will be poorer than the younger ones. Those weathered under the wetter and warmer climates will have more of their soluable nutrients leached out than those weathered for less time in the cool, formerly glaciated regions.

There are two quite different mid-latitude forest climates on the two sides of the continents. Those on the eastern sides of continents have continental-type climates marked by hot summers and cold winters. Those on the western sides of continents have mild, oceanically modified winters and summers. The physical similarities between the areas of mid-latitude forest climate is greatly increased if we discuss these two kinds of mid-latitude lands separately.

The eastern United States is an excellent example of an east coast mid-latitude forested country. Rainfall ranges from a 60 to 80 inch high along the Gulf coast, through a 40 to 60 inch belt that covers most of the South and East, declining to a 20 to 40 inch belt that extends west to the 100th meridian and takes in the Great Lakes region. Most of this area was once forest covered. Except for the hill country of the Appalachians it is a low-lying area dominated by great riverine plains.

The region has considerable variation in weather and climate. The South has long, hot, humid sum-

Lake-filled Maine. The gift of the glaciers was innumerable lakes that regulate water runoff and add enormously to the recreational attraction of the whole region. *Maine Department of Economic Development.*

mers, and as noted in the discussion of the tropical climates, such cities as New Orleans, St. Louis, Charleston, Baltimore, and even New York have spells of hotter humid weather than any equatorial location can expect. The winters are of varying intensity, too. In the South, winters are mild, snow is rare, and it seldom stays on the ground longer than a day or so. In the southern Great Lakes region, the winters are subarctic, daylight becomes short, temperatures fall below freezing and stay there for considerable periods, and snow may cover the land for periods of weeks.

This description of weather and climate applies to a number of other areas of the world as well. South America has a block of land that is very much like our East, both in physiography and in climate. From southern Brazil, through Uruguay, including southern Paraguay, and extending south to nearly 40 degrees in Argentina, there is a great Atlantic-facing lowland that has much the same type of rainfall and seasonal change as we have just de-

scribed. China is another major area of this mid-latitude forest climate. Again, the rainfalls are greatest in the south and near the sea and drop off toward the north and the interior. The south of China is like our South and the northwest of China and adjacent Manchuria is like the Dakotas in our country. Climatically, then, it is closely comparable to our East. This surprises some people, for China seems to have acquired the label tropical in many peoples' minds. China differs from the United States and South American counterparts in its physiography: the south of China is hilly and mountainous; and the plains are in the northeast of the country.

Australia's east coast is similar. Its climatic range is much like that of the east coast of the United States, but the extent of this type of climate is very limited. It forms a strip along the coast and ends to the west of the mountains that parallel the coast. There is also a small region of this type of climate on the southeast side of Africa.

All of these areas share similar physical settings to some degree, and some of them are comparable to a high degree. Rainfall, seasonal regimes, and variation in climates both north and south and from the coast inland are similar. With rare exceptions the land is, or was, covered with forest. Under similar rainfalls, climates, and vegetations, similar soils can be expected. Again, we have a laboratory for examining what man has done, and is likely to do, in these similar areas.

The population map of the world shows that these lands differ greatly in density of population: China is among the most densely populated areas of the world; The United States and the South American area have moderate population densities; while the Australian environment is thinly populated. If the population map were looked at for the year 1500, the Chinese density of population would still stand out, while the United States and South American densities would fall to low levels, and the Australian density would fall still lower. Another 500 years is likely to see still further changes in these patterns of density, both in relative positions and in absolute numbers.

THE EASTERN UNITED STATES

The Indian Scene: Population and Culture

The eastern United States in the pre-Columbian period had a modest Indian culture varying in intensity, tending to decline from a cultural focus in the south toward a less developed north. Corn, beans, and squash were the staple crops, raised on lands cleared of forests. As elsewhere in the world, the forest was used as a long-term rotation crop to clear the land of weeds and to renew the soil fertility. The level of development had reached the stage of town dwelling, pottery making, and broad field cultivation that approached the early stages of civilization. Little was lacking except political organization into larger, more stable units. Towns of considerable size existed; populations were dense enough and had enough organized productivity to free much labor for monumental works; and men

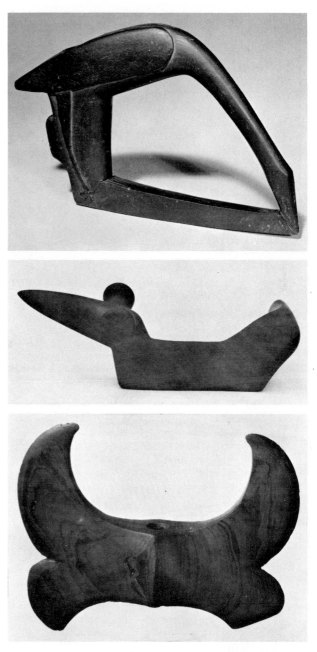

Art of the Eastern United States Indians. (*Upper*) Pipe of red stone representing a crane, found in Ohio. (*Middle*) Bird stone, Union County, Illinois. (*Lower*) Banner stone, Kankakee County, Illinois. *Museum of the American Indian, Heye Foundation.*

Evidences of Influences from Mexico in Eastern United States Art. Found in Sumner County, Tennessee, this scene of a warrior holding the head of an enemy in one hand and a weapon in the other is strongly suggestive of similar Mexican scenes. The details of the headdress, the design of the eye, the ear spool, and the total art form are all found in art of Middle America. *Museum of the American Indian, Heye Foundation.*

Cahokia Mound (drawing). The structure is 1100 feet across the base and 100 feet high. Such immense structures suggest large populations and an advanced political status. *G. F. Carter, Jr.*

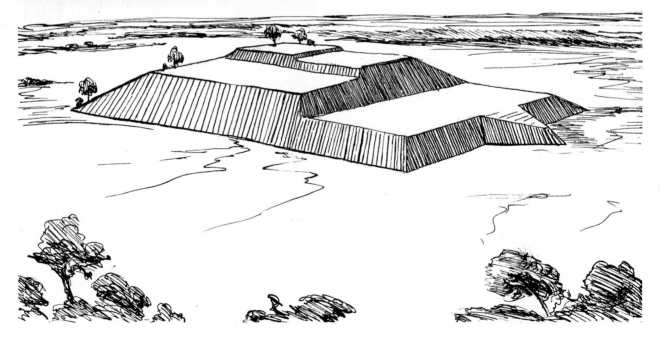

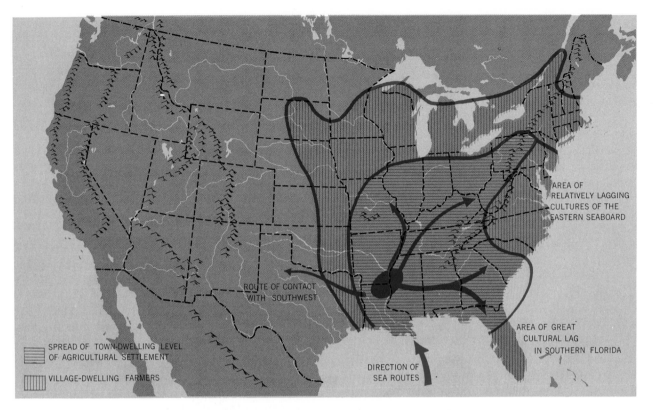

Map 5-1   Cultural Level in Pre-Columbian United States

Within the central area outlined, agriculture was the pre-Columbian way of life, and villages grew to the size of small towns or larger. The peak of cultural achievement lay in the lower Mississippi valley. Art, pottery styles, truncated pyramid mounds, and agricultural minutiae all indicate that the lower Mississippi was the focal area into which ideas were pouring. Continuing work has failed to find a route for this inpouring through the west Texas area. It seems increasingly probable, therefore, that the major contacts were by sea. That the routes were not primarily from the Caribbean via Cuba, however, is suggested by the low level of culture in pre-Columbian southern Florida, as well as by the focusing of cultural change patterns on the lower Mississippi.

with sufficient political and architectural skills had appeared to direct this labor force in large-scale works. Some of the earth mounds built by the southern Indians rivaled the pyramids of Egypt in their bulk. The great mound at Cahokia, Illinois, was shaped like a truncated pyramid 1000 feet on its base and 100 feet high. The level of development

was approximately that of predynastic Egypt. As always, one can only speculate on what would have developed if the cultural process had been left to go on undisturbed by the European contact.

The degree of development and number of people in the eastern United States in pre-Columbian time has usually been greatly underestimated, the figures being some 350,000 Indians cultivating less than 1 percent of the land available for maize growing. The simple gatherers of California are credited with twice the population density of the farmers of the eastern United States. Both in terms of ecology and of culture this is contrary to what might be expected. The anthropologists have tried to explain what seems to be an unexpectedly low population in the East as the result of warfare. While there undoubtedly was warfare, it did not hold down the populations in great areas elsewhere in the world, so why should it have done so here? It seems much more likely that the populations of the East were much greater than they have been formerly estimated. There is some support for this view in a 1568 traveler's account of a trip from Mexico to upper New England. Towns en route of up to one and one-half miles across were noted; such urban centers would make vast pyramids like Cahokia more understandable than a picture of a relatively empty land.

Analysis of the distribution of buffalo in the eastern United States reveals a similar story. Prior to the time of European contact, buffalo were seemingly absent east of the Mississippi River. Shortly thereafter they flooded into the wooded East, and the colonial landscape was dotted with areas called Buffalo Spring, Buffalo Falls, and Buffalo Creek. Buffalo are grazing animals and require grassy pastures; their presence therefore indicates extensive pasture. Why were they not present before the Europeans came? Why did they appear in the interlude between the disappearance of the Indians and the taking up of the land by the white men?

The answers may be something like this. The Indian population had been so large that it had cleared large areas of the land. When the Indian population was greatly reduced by Old World diseases to which they were totally nonimmune, the population fell so drastically that vast areas of cleared field were abandoned to go back first to grass and eventually to woods. This man-made grassy environment was suitable to the buffalo, and since the land was virtually empty, it could move in.

The pre-existing agricultural fields would also have suited the buffalo, who would have found succulent maize and beans to his liking. But since there was a relatively dense Indian population on the land that considered buffalo a succulent dish for man, there was no opportunity for the buffalo to invade the humid East. The buffalo's opportunity turned on man's inadvertently preparing a suitable environment and equally inadvertently removing man from that environment. The buffalo's opportunity was short lived. In a state of nature, the forest would have reclaimed the grassland in due time, or the Indian population would have re-established itself with immune people. In this particular case, however, the culturally advantaged, disease-immunized European population moved in to take permanent occupancy. They removed the rapidly expanding forest and slaughtered the bands of buffalo. For a time the land reverted to the agricultural state it had experienced in the hands of the Indians; but with the coming of the industrial revolution to America, the growth of population and the development of the land were both intensified.

Mention was made earlier of the devastating effect of the introduction of European diseases among the Indians. It may be that contacts with traders and fishermen let loose a deadly flood of disease among the Indians of the East, and that the populations seen by the first colonists may have been only the fractional remnants that survived these epidemics. At Plymouth the Indians told the colonists that there had formerly been very many more people, but that a few years before a great epidemic had nearly emptied the land. There is corroborating evidence too. The colonists mention that they were able to take up the already cleared, unoccupied land of old Indian fields. This would bear out the buffalo diagnosis.

The impact of man on the environment should be expanded to include the impact of new diseases. It is quite clear that after A.D. 1500 the expansion of men over the world often brought isolated peoples suddenly into contact with virulent diseases to which whole populations were not immune and for which no resistance had been built up. The effect of the lack of immunity to such a disease as small pox has been documented. The reduction of the Mandan from 2000 to 200 in one winter is an example (see p. 111). The reduction of the Easter Island population from something in the neighborhood of 3000 to 111 is another. Before the days of vaccination, populations were composed of individuals who had had the local diseases and survived: they were then immune. Only children or the rare adult who had not yet been exposed came down in the recurrent epidemics. But since the children made up only a small part of the population, such a reduction as the Mandan or the Easter Islanders experienced could not occur. That is, if children not yet exposed to small pox make up only 10 percent of the populations, then even if 90 percent of them die in an epidemic only a 9 percent reduction of the total population occurs. Small pox introduced into a population never before exposed might well kill 90 percent of its total population. Small pox, of course, was only one of a great many such diseases that the Europeans inadvertently set to clearing the land of its native population, in America and elsewhere. In America the effects of such diseases were immense and our judgment of the occupancy of the land before 1500 often has been greatly influenced by our not recognizing them.

Agricultural Evidence of Cultural Origins

It is easy to trace the origin of the cultural impulses that created the semicivilization of the pre-Columbian eastern United States. Man had lived in the Americas for a very long time; he was well established as a skilled hunter of horse, camel, ground sloth, mammoth, and mastodon long before the last glacial retreat. About 10,000 years ago, his way of life began to change: the big game animals were becoming scarce or were extinct. Thereafter, the beginnings of agriculture appear. Some local plants are taken in hand; the sunflower was developed for its seeds and tuberous roots and soon the Middle American plants appear, first corn and squash, later beans. Immediately, one knows some-

thing of the direction from which ideas were reaching the eastern United States. These tropical plants could only have been introduced from the south. They probably came from Mexico, though the exact route has never been demonstrated. This leads to the suspicion that it may well have been by water—where no evidence would survive.

By using botanical data we can make a tentative map of the time, place, and sequence of influences from the south. In passing, it is clear that other influences were coming in from the north, but they were relatively minor in comparison with the current of ideas that flowed in from the south bringing temple mounds, religious cults, pottery forms, and agricultural plants. The most revealing data are found in the corn plant. We know that maize accidentally crossed with a wild-grass relative in Mexico, providing great variability, as the result of which the Indian was able to bring about the many varieties of corn that we now have. We know that in this process the tiny original corn ear was gradually increased in size and in the number of rows of kernels. We know that the original corn had a hard flinty kernel and that later other types of corn with soft kernels and mixed hard and soft starch in their kernels came into being. When we plot the distribution of these traits on a map of the eastern United States, we find that the early types of corn are found on the periphery of the area, and that the closer we come to the Lower Mississippi area the more evidence there is of the later types.

This kind of evidence can be expanded. When the original primitive corn crossed with the wild grass, certain markers were transferred. In the nucleus of each living cell are chromosomes, threadlike bodies along which the units that determine the heredity of the plant are arranged. Each plant has its own characteristic number of these chromosomes: those of the original corn were plain; those of the wild grass with which the corn was crossed had knobby lumps on the chromosomes. In the plant crossing, some of this knobbiness of chromosome was transferred to the maize plant, and as time went on, more and more of this material was transferred

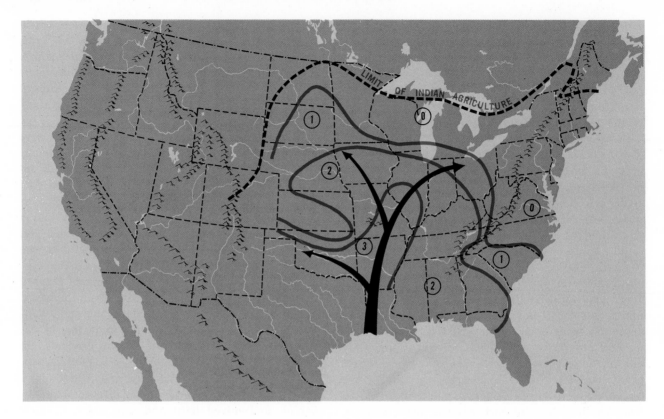

Map 5-2   Knobbiness of Maize Chromosomes as Evidence of Cultural Movements

The numbers refer to knobs on the sixth chromosome of maize, which can have either no knobs or knobs in one, two, or three positions. The earliest condition is presumed to be that of no knobs, with increasing knobbiness measuring additions of new genetic material later in time.

The data, then, suggest that the first maize to enter the eastern United States was knobless. Further, the direction of introduction is from the south, centering on the lower Mississippi valley. This is also the location of the peak of native culture in the eastern United States. The building of great mounds and many other evidences of town-dwelling ways of life in pre-Columbian eastern United States fit this pattern. The maize picture is therefore simply a reflection of a complex flow of ideas.

The routes of movement of culture that the chromosomes of maize suggest are natural ones. The flow seems to have been up the Mississippi River to the Ohio and the Missouri. A further flow seems to have crossed the Great Plains via the Red River and via the Arkansas-Canadian river system to the Southwest. It is notable that the later types of corn failed to reach New England, the Middle Atlantic states, or southern Florida.

While at first glance this seems to be a simple case of agriculture following the path determined by the physical geography, note the failure of this type of agriculture to spread northward through the piedmont and coastal-plain provinces of the Middle Atlantic states, an environment richly suited to it.

to the maize plant. Knobbiness, then, is to some extent a measure of the degree of mixture and of time.

This knobbiness pattern works out interestingly on a map. The original corn began spreading northward before there was much, if any, of this mixture; later, forms with a little mixture started north; still later, increasingly mixed forms started the trip. Those that started earlier had more time to be adapted to increasingly short seasons and cold springs. If the frequency of knobs on the chromosomes of maize in the eastern United States is plotted on a map, the result is what is seen in Map 5–2. A map of cultural advancement follows much the same pattern (see Map 5–1). The details of distribution suggest that the influences from the south were entering somewhere in the Lower Mississippi area and spreading up the Mississippi Valley, across the coastal plain, and northward. This pattern is very much like that made by the distribution of some of the archeological remains such as the great mounds and therefore is a further illustration of the importance of location in relation to the major center of cultural growth and development. For the pre-Columbian eastern United States, it was the Gulf region that was nearest the center of growth and development, and the degree of influence from this center diminished to the northeast, leaving New England a relatively backward area.

The European Scene: A Reversal of Cultural Sources

This was completely reversed in the period of European settlement (see Map 5–3). The area of greatest proximity to the center of cultural and economic growth and development was along the northeastern seaboard. The first colonies were along this coast, and it was here that American cultural growth and development got its start, and it spread almost concentrically from this area for the next 300 years. Irregularities in this early period reflect a mixture of physical and cultural forces. Colonization followed lowland water routes for the first 250 years, but the Spanish to the south, the French to the north, and

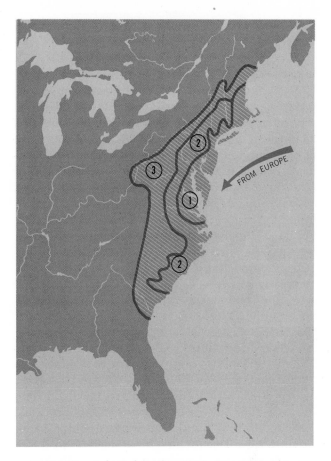

Map 5-3   Colonial Settlement in North America

The focusing of European settlement on the north and central Atlantic coast of the United States is shown here by the location of settled areas in the early decades. Area 1 was being settled by 1700. Area 2 represents the reach of settlement by 1750. Area 3 marks the expansion to 1775. Proximity clearly played a large role. It was not the only factor, however. The presence of Spain in Florida and of France in Canada also played a part, as did physical geography. Lord Baltimore's colonial effort in New Foundland was shifted to Maryland because the New Foundland climate was found to be too severe for English tastes.

the Iroquois Confederation in New York were even more influential forces than land forms.

The general conclusion to be drawn is that the importance of the physical environment was here also very modest. New England's dominance in the realm of American thought and culture has been greatly overstated. The Middle Colonies and the South made greater contributions than it has been fashionable to acknowledge. For instance, Maryland's contribution to the concepts of religious tolerance and freedom probably exceeds any similar contribution by any other colony. The South still leads in the number of Presidents it has supplied, despite its smaller numbers and the handicap of the Civil War and its aftermath.

The dependence of Colonial America on Europe eventually came to an end. Settlement expanded across the continent, the center of population shifting steadily southwestward, until it is now beyond Chicago. Centers of industry, education, and political power have shifted with it, though with a lag determined by such cultural factors as resistance to change and the cost of change. Moving or abandoning a factory is a costly business; moving a university is also, but the biggest resistance is probably cultural. Harvard is still acknowledged as our greatest university. It is in the New England area formerly dominant in America, but now rapidly losing in its relative importance. But who would think of moving Harvard from its "yard"?

The momentum of the early start of the Northeast has kept it going for a full century beyond its time of vitality. While much of northernmost New England has now reverted to wilderness, southern New England is still maintaining momentum from its past. In this progression from a backward area in pre-Columbian times to an area of great growth and development during the eighteenth and nineteenth centuries, to a modern period of decline the physical environment of New England has remained constant. It is the same land, with the same climate, occupying the same place in the physical world. But the cultural world has pivoted around and around, and it has been this change that has been decisive. New England developed *in spite of* its physical environment; it continues *in spite of* both detrimental locational and physical factors.

American Greatness: Environment or Culture?

This development and decline of New England leads us to the next environmental consideration, How much did the physical environment of the United States have to do with the greatness achieved? It is commonly held that the United States became great because of its extremely fortunate physical geography. Since the West only belatedly became a part of the United States, and is only now being fully developed, that greatness must have been founded in the East.

The United States has the world's greatest coal resources; unlimited iron ore in the Mesabi Range; vast interior plains of unbroken expanses of good soil; vast, enormously valuable forests of fine hardwoods and excellent soft woods; fisheries that are among the world's best; and precious metals as well as immense reserves of oil. It has also been alleged that New England has one of the most stimulating climates in the world. Statements reciting these advantages often suggest that any country with the United States resources could have achieved similar success. The land would have made a great nation, runs the argument, under almost anyone's management. Therefore let us review what did happen.

Settlement began at various points along the east coast of America early in the seventeenth century. This is an oddity. America had been discovered in 1492. Why did the British wait a century before beginning settlement? We do know that they did not particularly want North America. In Hakluyt's *Voyages*, published in the sixteenth century, there is a discussion of where colonies should be sought. Not in latitudes similar to Britain's, ran the argument. Instead, tropical colonies will produce what England can not, and England can supply them with what they can not well produce. What use is it to have colonies that produce wool and wheat? England produces those items. How can one build a trade that way? However, the tropical areas were largely in the hands of such powerful nations as Spain, Portugal, and the Netherlands. The British had to take what they could get, and there was a section of the North American coast, handily adjacent to Britain, that was open to settlement.

Settlement took several directions. The Virginia colony was one of gentlemen adventurers. They might have been splendidly successful if there had been an empire to conquer; instead, they found themselves set down in a fever-ridden swamp among village-dwelling Indians. There was only a moderate opportunity for trade, and no treasure of gold to be had for the looting as in Mexico, nor even any rich mines to be discovered as in California. The colony faced hardship, starvation, dreadful loss of life from disease, and Indian attacks. It was a most difficult situation. Reading the accounts, one wonders why the colonists and their British backers persevered. New England was no better. There may have been less fever there, but the winters were much harder.

In both colonies the wheat did poorly, for it was not adapted to such a climate. After all, the climate of the eastern United States is not at all like that of Britain, as the colonists always remarked. They spoke of the violence of the seasons. Winter was hard, and in New England very long. Summer was hot and humid and marked by violent thunder storms. Plants used to the gentle rainy summers of Britain were far from at home in this land of sudden, violent weather changes, with a supertropical summer to the south and a subarctic winter to the north.

An example of the geographic ignorance of the times is illustrated by Lord Baltimore's attempts to found a colony. He first sought and obtained a grant for a colony in New Foundland. Since this land lay in the same latitude as England, it was expected that it would also have the climate of England. A very well-planned party was sent out in the early summer so as to have time to erect buildings before winter. By winter they were snugly housed, but that season proved so long and so severe that the colony was given up. Thereafter a petition was filed, and finally granted, for a colony near the Virginia colony, and hence the state of Maryland.

The New England colonists worked hard at making a living out of their land. Fisheries helped the food supply, but the bulk of the people worked the land, clearing it of woods and rocks. A trip through New England today still reveals the fruit of these labors, the stone walls that were the result of laboriously picking up the stones in the fields and hauling them to the field borders and stacking them. It was stupendously hard work. The land was far from "free." It had to be won from the forest, defended from the Indians, and freed from the burden of rock that the glaciers had left. Even then the growing season was short and the risks from early and late frosts were very high. Yet New England was at one time largely cleared and farmed. Today it has largely gone back to forest. Even after the immense effort at improving the land, it was simply marginal land climatically, and soon left behind by the developing centers of population in America. The greatness of New England was *in spite of,* rather than *because of,* the physical environment. Perhaps it was the challenge of a difficult environment that shaped the New England character, but more likely their stern Puritan consciences had even more to do with it.

The other colonies had little better beginnings. In the Middle Colonies and down the coastal plain, the early settlements were on the sandy coastal soils. We think so little of many of these poor soils today that much of this coastal plain is abandoned and has reverted to timber. Sands are poor for agriculture. They had the advantage for the early colonists that they could be cultivated with light and simple tools, but labor shortage and abundant land led the Middle Colonies into bad agricultural habits. The poorness of the soils and the early dependence on tobacco made a system of forest slash and burn and the early abandonment of the land seem an economic way of land use. The land was never cleared; stumps were left standing; and cultivation was by hoe. This labor was early done by indentured servants, and soon thereafter by slaves.

Old Stone Walls Marking the Boundaries of Abandoned Fields. Such scenes are typical of much of New England and mark the decline of agriculture in this region and its southward and westward movement in the United States. *Maine Department of Economic Development.*

Eastern Shore of Virginia. This scene indicates widespread agricultural abandonment of the coastal plain. The settlement in the foreground is Wachapreague, a fishing village on the Atlantic side of the peninsula. *Virginia State Chamber of Commerce.*

Factory at Lisbon Center, Maine. New England industry began at relatively small and manageable power sites. Despite summer droughts and winter freezes, they were advantageous sites in their day. *Maine Department of Economic Development.*

Visitors from Europe were shocked at the miserable, weedy state of the agriculture. People moved so frequently that it hardly paid to build a good house. In one of the Middle Colonies, a law had to be passed against burning down houses just to get the nails out of them to use at the next plantation. Tobacco did not prove extremely profitable. Although some people made money on it early, when more and more land was put into production, the price dropped. After a relatively brief period of good returns, therefore, a long period of very small profits followed. Meanwhile, the poor soils were further impoverished by the tobacco and the accompanying poor agricultural practices. Nor in all of this were the forests of any great value. Trees were weeds; they had to be felled and burned to clear the land. Timber was not profitable enough to ship to so distant a market as Europe, except for specialized uses like timbers for masts, but there were not even many of these—the millennia-long Indian custom of annually burning the forest had left few tall, straight trees. Mast trees were found largely in swampy, fire protected areas. Man, again, had modified his environment.

New England found a way out of some of this difficulty when the industrial revolution began. Close contacts with Britain paid off when the know-how of making spinning machinery was brought to New England. Here there were a number of favorable factors. The natural increase of the population had created a labor force, and the land was so poor that it was easy to get some of the people to come to work in the factories. The small streams coming down out of the glaciated uplands often went over falls and rapids and could readily be harnessed as waterpower to support mills. Mills at this stage were small, and streams now not considered worth harnessing to light a house ran a mill. The South was producing cotton, and New England spun and wove it. The young nation had little industry. New England plunged into supplying the need.

As always, the physical environment was playing its role as the backdrop for the culturally determined action. Even as stated here, the physical environment's role is overplayed. The initial utilization of machinery in New England was a historical accident; it could as well, or better, have begun in the Middle

Atlantic or Southern states that had as good or better waterpower opportunities, and better raw material supplies.

After the Revolutionary War, the population expanded over the Appalachians, posing transportation problems. The interior rivers flowed to the Mississippi and so led to the Gulf, but Americans did not control this vast inland area. The Ohio River ran to the Mississippi, and the Mississippi was alternately in French or Spanish possession. The British and French held some of the adjacent land and the Spanish held the rest. There were no roads, and in the days of wagon transportation, only materials of immense value in proportion to their bulk could stand the cost of overland transportation. This situation was the basis of the Whisky Rebellion in the 1790s. The only way people of the interior of the country could get their bulky, low value corn to a market was to concentrate it to high-value whisky. When this was taxed, they rebelled.

Strenuous efforts were made to overcome the problem. Canals were dug, or at least projected. Attempts were made to put canals across the Appalachians, and a canal linking the Chesapeake and Delaware bays was discussed in George Washington's day. The first railroad built in America was laid across this narrow neck. But all such efforts are costly; a better endowed land would have supplied the necessary waterways at much less cost than the Americans had to bear.

The early colonists had no major iron ore resources. The bog irons of Maryland so important in colonial times are so poor that no one touches them today. Coal was no resource until later, and oil was not even dreamed of. Yet the bumptious colonists freed themselves at the end of the eighteenth century and 150 years later were the world's great power. They had of course fought Great Britain in a second war, fought Mexico and annexed the West, bought the whole Mississippi Valley from France and Alaska from Russia. But these are evidences of the strength that had already been engendered in the colonial East, which was no great natural gift.

The land that they eventually came to control, extending from sea to sea, was none too good. A full third of it is dry land. Only 40 percent of it is considered agriculturally useful land. As we saw in the section on the Mediterranean lands, it was the driving of the railroads west and the vigorous capitalizing on the advantages of being linked to the East that made California what it is, instead of another Chile. America *is* what Americans have *made* it.

The Role of Freedom

The Europeans early in colonial times remarked on the air of freedom that permeated America. Fewer men seemed to accept the role of someone else's inferior: everyone believed he could become whatever he wanted. As one European traveler commented with astonishment, anybody seemed to feel free to have a coat of arms painted on his carriage.

The drive was to own land and to produce. Land-ownership for various reasons never went into the hands of a few. In New England the settlement was from the beginning one of small holdings. In the other colonies this was true, though to a lesser extent. In Maryland large grants were made. However, large estates often were accumulated from the buying and selling of various properties, and at the end of each generation, inheritance tended to break the estate up into a number of smaller estates. After 1862, the distribution of the western land by the government in 160-acre lots assured a very broad ownership of the land. It created the possibility that anyone with the strength and the will to go out and make a start in life as an independent, self-employed worker could do so. This set free what is probably an unprecedented amount of human energy. It also tended to distribute the population over the land, for the free land was always on the frontier.

In most of the world for most of civilized time, conditions have been the opposite. The structure of human society after the Neolithic revolution has been characterized by a tiny percentage of the people in a privileged position, with the rest of the people in a menial position. One of the miracles of

America is that we broke away from this pattern. In part, the great disparity between nobles and commoners in the past was a matter of productivity. It took many men producing only slightly more than they needed for bare existence to support one man in a way of life that did not produce food, clothing, or tools. It is difficult to be a learned man if one's time is taken up with growing potatoes and hunting game for the table. Yet until the productivity of the workman went up, a hundred men had to toil so that one man could have leisure.

But the American accomplishment was based even more on the idea of individual freedom. Other nations by this time, in fact for a long time earlier, had had the opportunity to strike out on such a new line. They were sufficiently productive. However, the inertia of a going social system inherited from the past prevented change. The abrupt transplantation of groups of Englishmen into America placed them for a time in considerable isolation from each other. The various colonies worked out somewhat different ways of government, but each based their ideas on the liberties guaranteed by the Magna Carta and such ideas as popular representation and self-determination. The businesslike New Englanders drew up a contract, the Mayflower Compact, explicitly stating the purposes of their group and the rights and duties of each member. This was America's first written constitution.

The Marylanders, escaping from religious persecution, instituted religious freedom. This has been curiously misrepresented in the American history texts of the past. The religious dissenters who fled to New England fiercely demanded that in their colony everyone believe as they did, yet New England is often spoken of as if religious toleration began there. Among the early colonies, religious toleration was in fact the innovation of the Marylanders. But the point here is that each colony was experimenting in some isolation with a set of ideas that they had brought from Europe. Among the most important of these ideas were the rights of individuals, the right to have a say in government, the right to own land or to go into business, and the right to limit what the government could do.

In most of history, a man could be hard working and intelligent as a genius, but if born a share tenant or a serf or a peasant, his chances were slim of ever having a chance to be more than an ordinary farmer. Education was for the very few at the very top, and position, honor, and opportunity were similarly limited. If a society elects to allow only the ability that appears in 10 percent of its population to develop, it will get a much smaller return than a society that attempts to give all its people a chance. It is impossible, of course, to give everyone exactly equal opportunities, but one of the things that has made America great has been the idea, firmly fixed very early, that the way was open to all—and to a remarkable degree it was.

Much of this has also been said many times. We therefore have two opposing themes: one, that the physical geography of America made it great; the other, that it was a set of ideas that made America great. Some people have put them together: a set of favorable ideas placed in the most favorable imaginable environment made America great—but the physical environment does not deserve even this much credit. It seems probable that just such a development as America has had could have occurred in any one of a number of environments. Conversely, a settlement of this country by some other mixture of people would surely have led to a different kind of development of the country, and most probably would not have led to the enormous productivity that underlies our high standard of living, vast educational system, and relatively leisurely life.

We can explore this idea, much as we did the idea of the growth of culturally different "worlds" beginning with a uniform world. In this case, we will imagine that the British settled Brazil instead of the United States. To complete the story, we will also imagine that the Portuguese settled the United States instead of Brazil.

WHAT HAPPENED IN BRAZIL

The Portuguese discovered and exploited Brazil. Unlike the Spanish, they did not find great native empires laden with gold and silver. They found, instead, a tropical country occupied by native people with a simple way of life. They found an immense river up which they could sail three quarters of the way across the continent. Along the Atlantic coast, low ranges faced the sea, with only a narrow coastal plain, and many small streams descended these hills to the sea. To the south the climate was temperate, not unlike the American South. Along the western highlands, the climate was temperate because of altitude. The vast interior was principally plain and gently rolling land. Almost the whole of this land was well watered, but like the United States it was an undeveloped resource to which the energetic Portuguese had to apply themselves to make a productive land.

The Portuguese had long been producing sugar on tropical islands under large-scale production methods using Negro slave labor. They used what we now call the plantation system. A tropical setting such as Brazil gave them a chance to expand this type of industry, and they transferred it entire. The Portuguese were the managers and the armed force. At first they used Indian labor, but as the local supply diminished, they sent armies deeper and deeper into the interior for more. When rounding up Indians for a labor force became more expensive than importing Africans, they did the latter.

Sugar was a booming crop, commanding a staggering world price. Its value at this time can be measured in part by remembering that when settling one of her squabbles with England, France elected to give up all of Canada rather than surrender one tiny sugar-producing island in the Caribbean.

Exploration inland soon uncovered gold, and during the eighteenth century Brazil produced 44 percent of all the gold in the world. Thereafter came the rubber boom; then coffee. Early Brazilian history has aptly been described as one bonanza after another.

Why has Brazil failed to develop, to fill her land with people, to produce sufficiently to give her people a high standard of living? It had, and has, everything: It is a larger territorial unit than the United States, without Alaska; and it is one of the best watered lands of the world.

Arable land and production in Brazil and in the United States are as follows:

Brazil 80 percent is potentially productive
      2 percent is used, therefore food must be imported
    90 percent of the inhabitants live on or near the Atlantic coast
United States
    60 percent is waste land
    40 percent is potentially productive—we feed ourselves and export food
    The population is well distributed
World 25 percent is arable (average)

Brazil uses only 2 percent of her land and does not even feed herself, yet 80 percent of her land is potentially productive as compared with 40 percent of the United States, and a world average of 25 percent. She has abundant iron ore, has had a near monopoly on industrial diamonds, known, but little exploited ferroalloy minerals, some coal, and immense hydroelectric potential. Perhaps most characteristically, although high-grade petroleum was found in the upper Amazon years ago (and the Andean piedmont is still a rich prospect), Brazil imports petroleum products at great cost.

Brazil by all measures is potentially one of the richest nations on earth. But under a boom and bust, plantation-slave agriculture, with broad ownership of the land concentrated in the hands of a few, it has done the minimum with these goods. If the United States might be said to have succeeded in spite of its physical resources, Brazil might be said to have failed in spite of its physical riches. Perhaps it would be fairer to say that too much easy money has delayed the development of Brazil.

These statements so often provoke outright dis-belief that it may be well to quote as an authority one of the American geographers who has made a life time study of Brazil, and who, in turn, quotes the Brazilians themselves. The Portuguese

. . . were attracted less by the prospects of earning a living by persistent toil than by the opportunities for speculative profit. As one Brazilian writer puts it, the ideal was "to collect the fruit without planting the tree." Whereas some of the peoples of America have been led by force of circum-stances to be content with less spectacular returns from more intensive forms of economy, the Brazilians, with their huge land area, and their small numbers, are still seeking new ways for the speculative exploitation of the treasures stored up in nature.*

Could it have been otherwise?

British Brazil

Suppose the British had colonized Brazil. Not having a tradition of sugar plantations, let us sup-pose they began a settlement of the land just as they did in North America. From study of the British colonial efforts in the Caribbean at this time we can conclude that the climate would not have deterred them. Given the politico-economic climate of the American colonies, and an equally good human material, they should have faired well. They could have produced sugar on small farms under a freeman's husbandry, as indeed they did successfully in the Caribbean whenever they had the opportunity. Tobacco, rice, indigo, cotton, and maize are all at home in Brazil. There seems to be no reason that a healthy growing British population should not have developed along the Atlantic sea-board of Brazil at least as easily and probably more prosperously than it did in America.

A British assessment of Brazil would probably have emphasized the cooler south. As the popula-tion expanded, it could have spread into the vast,

* Reprinted from *Latin America* by Preston E. James (3rd ed.; New York: The Odyssey Press, 1959), p. 399, by permission of the author and publisher.

rich interior. Given the rapid send-off from sugar, capital would have been available to develop the machine textile industry which their home con-tacts would have brought to them. The small streams coming down the flanks of the coastal mountains would be far better than the streams in New England. There would be no winter freeze and the rainfall would be large in amount and well distributed through the year. Cotton grow-ing could well have been linked with spinning and weaving, just as in the United States. Just as in the United States this could have been the founda-tion for a broad industrial and commercial devel-opment.

As the population spread inland, gold, diamonds, iron, coal, and oil would all be found. There would be no deserts and mountains for the railroads to cross, and the river system would be more exten-sive and more useful than that in the United States. There would be temperate highlands, a seasonal south, a wet tropical north, and no dry-and-nearly useless desert dividing one-third of the land. There would be no reason why, under an American constitution and with the growth of American free enterprise, population should not have spread evenly over the land, and agriculture, industry, and commerce should not have flourished. There is probably nothing done in the United States that the same people could not have done more easily in Brazil, and there are as well nu-merous opportunities in tropical agriculture in Brazil that do not exist in the United States. In-deed, a sobering thought is this: Life might have become too easy, wealth too easily accumulated by a few, and a pattern established more like that which did actually develop in Brazil. The theme would not be changed greatly. Rich resources do not necessarily make great nations, but ideas may.

A Portuguese United States

What might the Portuguese have done with the United States? The Portuguese assessment of this country would probably start with coastwise exploratory trips. They would note the near-tropical South and Gulf Coast. To tropical plantation experts these low wet coasts would look attractive. To the north they would note that the low coastal plain narrowed, that winters increased in intensity, and that north of Long Island soils were thin, sandy, and increasingly stony.

In the Gulf Coast they would discover the mouth of a great river. Occupation of its mouth would give control of the interior. Similarly, occupation of Florida's east coast would provide control of the sailing route to the homeland. Given their background of tropical agriculture, they could be expected to place their major settlements from Georgia, around Florida, into the Gulf coastal plain. They would establish plantation agriculture, rapidly use up the Indian labor supply, and begin importing African slaves.

Their Indian-hunting would take them into the interior. Up the Mississippi they would find rich plains. To the north would be cold lands of little attraction. New England would have been left as a fur-producing wilderness. To the west the increasing aridity and the vast mountains would make that area seem useless. In all probability they would, like the Spanish, consider the Pacific coast of the United States too far and too poor even to occupy, except possibly as a mission frontier. Hence, like the Spanish, they would probably find no gold. Nor would they have any world monopoly in anything like rubber or coffee, for the land would not provide these resources. Their plantations would lack even so rich a product as sugar, for the United States is distinctly marginal for sugar cane. They probably would have specialized in suitable crops such as indigo. Nor would the Portuguese United States have access to the new ideas of the industrial revolution. These were not developing in the Iberian world.

So, the Portuguese United States would expectably be an agricultural nation, perhaps far poorer than modern Brazil. Viewers of the twentieth century might assess the situation as follows:

What could you expect? The land is one-third arid. There *may* be some resources there. We hear of possible iron deposits up on their northern border. But of course that is too far away from the center of things to be useful, and besides it is impossible to work in that area during half the year because of the intense cold. Geologists tell us that there should be oil, and one test well indicates that there are really high-grade resources there. But, unfortunately, they have never been developed. There is some coal. But what can you do with a country that has a partly frozen north, whose good land in the West is separated by mountains and deserts from the good land in the East? They only have one good navigable river and it is full of shoals. It is just a mediocre lot of land, poorly arranged, and *that* is why the Portuguese United States is a second rate land!

And what might the explanation of British Brazil be?

Why, how could such a land be *other* than populous and productive? Look at the magnificent, gently rolling terrain! Consider the well-distributed rainfall. No other large land even approaches it in potential arable land. Then consider the great inpourings of capital from sugar, gold, rubber, coffee, and industry. Of course, they have been ingenious in making their meagre coal match their rich iron. But with a near monopoly on industrial diamonds, with quantities of the necessary ferroalloy minerals, with vast forest, immense hydro-electric power, and the world's greatest, most navigable river, how could they fail to be a great nation? What's that? Something about freedom, rights of individuals, capitalistic free enterprise? Don't be ridiculous! Those British Brazilians simply fell into a vast natural resource. Any system would have succeeded!

There is a danger that this presentation be twisted into an attack on the Portuguese. However, the Portuguese have an admirable record of peace and stability and a great record of exploration and colonization indicating organizing and creative ability of high order extending far back in time. Consider that their homeland is only about the size of Tennessee. They have proved themselves able people, but by nineteenth-century American standards, they have been handicapped by a very restrictive socio-governmental system. This system is not strictly Portuguese; it is quite simply preindustrial European. It has survived in Portugal, Spain, Italy, and Eastern Europe. The slow tide of change is just reaching some of these lands. Note, for example, the recent developments in Italy (Chapter 4).

Comparative Forecasts

Today Brazil is in a ferment that includes railroad building, hydroelectric development, industrial development, expansion into the interior, and a general dynamic drive that reminds one of the United States in the nineteenth century. Should Brazil finally turn its attention to "planting the trees" and to releasing human energies on a broad front, rather than drawing primarily from a few families, then in the twenty-first century it could be the home of a numerous, prosperous, educated people on a standard of living at least equal to that of the United States. At present, however, Brazil is faltering. Inflation rages, expropriation of foreign-owned properties discourages foreign investment, and internal political strife tears the country apart. The future depends on the solution of these problems, not on limitations in the physical environment. Brazil can be populous or relatively empty, rich or poor, with education and opportunity widely dispersed or restricted to a few, a first-rank or a third-class world power, all depending on the social solutions that are adopted. The geographical potential is large, as it has always been.

The forecast for the United States is only slightly different. Since our physical base is no better than Brazil's—it may actually be argued that it is poorer —the enormous discrepancy between what we have done in our physical environment, compared with what the Brazilians have done, must be due to some cause other than physical environment. In the United States it clearly was the release of human energy from a very wide slice of the total population which, coupled with widespread settlement of the land, a broadly based educational system, and a

rapid population growth, led to a steady increase in productivity in both material and immaterial things and thereby to the world's highest standard of living.

The gist of this is that the United States is not the only place where people could have achieved great things, and that we should take care not to change the fundamentals, for if this imaginative comparison is correct, then the American physical environment will support us in the style to which we have become accustomed only as long as we maintain the cultural outlook on man and land that made the American development possible. Should we adopt some set of institutions that would suppress the burst of individualistic achievement that has marked America, then it is conceivable that we could lose our position of world leadership in productivity in both material and cultural fields. A shift in cultural values such that Brazil would come to surpass the United States in standards of living and educational and cultural achievements is not unimaginable, and all of this could occur without any change in physical environment.

Discussions of this sort are most difficult to hedge about with all possible disclaimers. It is not contended that everyone in the world should copy the people of the United States, nor that being a great world power is the most desirable aim in the world, nor even that the materially rich life of the United States is the ultimate goal in life. Neither is any slight on the Portuguese or the Brazilians or the Latin Americans in general intended. Insistence on a proper distinction between what is physically environmentally determined and what is socially determined is the aim of these comparisons.

On the other hand there is no intention to underplay the American achievement, nor to portray the United States as a barren haven of material goals. While it is true that our productivity has made possible better houses with more indoor plumbing and television sets than in any other country, the same productivity is the basis for more doctors and public health measures, which give our

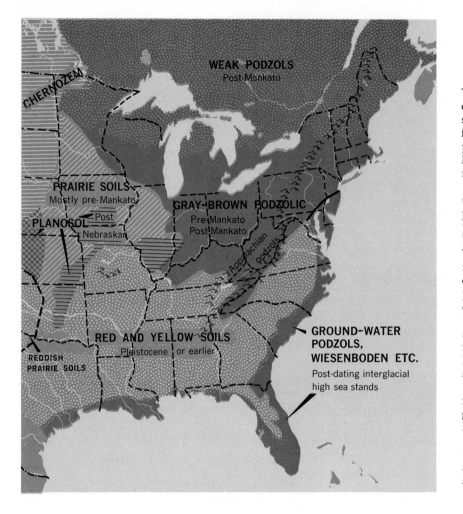

Map 5-4 Soils of the Eastern United States

These soils fall into four age groups depending upon their relationship to the glaciers and the glacially fluctuating sea levels. (1) The weak podzols are very young, for they have developed in the areas freed from an ice cover within the past 10,000 years. There has been little time for weathering processes to impoverish them. (2) The gray-brown podzolic soils are somewhat older, but not yet greatly weathered. (3) The red and yellow soils are in the nonglaciated regions and are quite old, strongly weathered, and often poor. (4) Along the coast are series of soils usually developed in relatively poor, sandy materials. Their age and degree of weathering are related to sea levels of past times. In general, the higher soils are older and poorer. On the western margin, the approach to the arid lands is marked by the appearance of the grassland soils: prairie and chernozem types. The red prairie soils are the older and more weathered of the grassland soils. The planosols are moderately old soils with strongly developed subsoils.

people about double a primitive man's span of life—a period of years that can be spent in obtaining and profiting from a lengthy education made possible by a productive society, whose educational products in turn make the society still more productive. Further, the American society is rich in artists, musicians, writers, and spiritual leaders, and these also are the result of a productive society that both supports and produces such people.

The point here is that the productivity that has made all of this possible is not due to our land's being the world's best, but to our cultural heritage, which led to the world's broadest-based re-

lease of human energies. The product of this release of energy has now pervaded all fields of human activity—spiritual, cultural, and economic. The opportunities for others to do likewise is virtually unlimited, and becomes more so as technology advances. This is the gist of the Brazilian-American contrast.

THE EASTERN UNITED STATES TODAY: NORTH VERSUS SOUTH

If now we return to the eastern United States to look at it in more detail, we find considerable difference between the North and the South. The eastern, humid, originally forested United States is not physically uniform. The soils to the north are young and relatively rich. In some areas they are richer than others because the glaciers brought to them ground-up limestone rock. In Iowa, it is possible to plot the limits of particular glaciations by the fertility of the soils and by the need for drainage. The greater fertility is found in the younger glacial soils, and the greatest drainage is needed on the same areas because of the irregularity of the land that is a heritage from these same glaciers. In other areas, as in New England, the irregular topography is not accompanied by so large a blessing of lime-rich soil, and the product is poorer. These northern areas are also short seasoned. This is a handicap for crops because of the risk of early and late frosts. It is a handicap for forestry, for the amount of tree growth is related in part to the length of the growing season. It takes nearly a century to produce a saw log, one capable of yielding boards, in our Northeast.

The South has no broad area of recently renewed soil fertility; many of its soils are old and leached. But the growing season is long, and the winters mild: crops that cannot be grown in New England flourish in the South. Trees that need a century to reach saw-log size in New England need only 50 years in the South. Cattle that have to be carefully housed all winter in New England, with feed expensively harvested and stored, can live outdoors all year round in the South; and in the deep South they can graze on green pasture throughout the year. Carefully managed pasture in the South can carry one cow per acre per year. New England probably needs 4 times this amount, and in the arid West it may take 40 times as much land to carry one cow for a year. The physical environment is really there, and given a particular choice of way of life, it has its real influences.

That the role of the physical environment can change with changing cultural outlooks, however, is well illustrated by the use made of the hill lands in the humid eastern United States in the past

Forest Land in Virginia. The extent of forest land in the well-settled eastern United States is illustrated by this view of the piedmont. *Virginia State Chamber of Commerce.*

The Everglades, Florida. Much of this landscape is thought to be the result of fires set annually by the Indians for millenia. Ecologists think that if the fires are stopped for long, the land will become a closed forest. *Florida State News Bureau.*

Slash Pine in Florida. The rate of tree growth in the South is illustrated by this stand of slash pine. At 3 years, the trees were 5½ feet high. Thereafter, the rate of growth was 4 feet per year. *Florida State News Bureau.*

A Red Pine Plantation in Upper Michigan. These trees have grown about 15 feet in 14 years, or roughly 1 foot per year. Rate of growth in the South may be four times as great, or in a tropical location such as Hawaii, ten times as great. *U.S. Forest Service.*

Second-growth Forest at Stowe, Vermont. This type of forest represents more than half a century of growth in New England. *Maine Department of Economic Development.*

Lumber Mill, Bucksport, Maine. By 1900 New England had been cut over. Bangor, Maine, once the greatest lumber port in the world, rapidly declined. In the succeeding half century, the regrowth of timber has been such that a large pulp industry now flourishes. *Maine Department of Economic Development.*

Cattle at Cornish, Maine. Abandonment of agricultural land in New England has left extensive areas of potential pasture land. However, the cattle must be fed through the long winter. *Maine Department of Economic Development.*

and in the present. In the pioneer stage the hilly lands of the Appalachians were viewed as good land. In New England the hills were cleared of rock, and small homesteads covered the land. When men were aiming at a subsistence from the land and little more, when the land was worked largely by hand and even plows were little used, these steep lands were adequate. Small pieces of good land sufficed for crop lands, the surrounding rough lands supplied wood for fuel, timber, and were a source of game.

As farming shifted from subsistence to commercial and as mechanization crept into agricultural production, this situation changed completely. Now land is worked in large plots, and the large machinery requires large, flat expanses. The high yields and low costs achieved through heavy capital input for fertilizers and machinery sent the small hand producer right out of business. We can produce rice by machine cultivation cheaper than the oriental labor can produce it. We can produce chickens and eggs under mass production methods cheaper and of higher quality than can the farm wife who counts her labor at zero. At the same time, the wants of the hill farmer have increased; he is no longer satisfied with mere subsistence. He wants a radio, and television, and running water in the house, and store-bought shoes and clothes, and a car or truck and the requisite gasoline. The little patch of land in the hills cannot supply these

things. Hence the hill lands are being abandoned: all over the hill country of the Appalachians and throughout the Ozarks, the land that once supplied a subsistence living is being abandoned. Yet it is the way of life, not the land that has changed.

The textile industry has moved out of New England to the South. Was it for reasons of climate? In the South, factories could be built more cheaply and they needed less heating in the winter. On the other hand, they need air conditioning in the torrid southern summers—or at least many people are coming to think so. Closer examination of the forces leading to movement shows that much of it was due to the attraction of a large, stable, relatively low-cost labor force in the South. This existed because of the shifts in agriculture that were being brought about. As the southern hill farmers are drawn into the commercial life of our day, they move down out of the hills into the factory towns. This ready-made labor supply is an enormous asset. It is the same kind of asset that built the New England textile towns 100 years before. The abandonment of the New England hill farms started earlier. Today it has progressed so far that many areas of New England no longer have a large pool of labor. With industry moving out, unemployment is created. Some of the labor also moves. The remaining labor pool is small, and often older, for it is the young people that move. The result is an unattractive labor situation. New England, described 50 years ago as the epitome of all that was good in America, is distinctly losing its place. But it will not sink to the level that it might have remained in if the accidents of discovery and settlement had not made it an important area in early America. There is too much invested there now. Boston is not likely to wither away. Yet, had America been settled from the West, or from the mouth of the Mississippi, New England would probably never have emerged from its forests.

This is not to say that New England is now a land without a future. Its harsh winters are less of a handicap than they once were. Central heating, paved roads, and the automobile have changed our reaction to the winter very greatly. Indeed, with the growth of interest in winter sports, the area has suddenly gained in attraction. Even its loss of population has increased its value as a vacation area. For those who long to escape the social pressures and confusions, and the crowded and fume-laden population centers that grow bigger and more artificial year by year, areas such as the cool green-in-summer, snow-mantled-in-winter hills of New England are a place of blessed relief. But again, the values of the natural landscape are being assessed not only in terms of themselves, but in terms of the man-made setting to which they find themselves now peripherally located, instead of centrally located as they were in the past.

Meanwhile the South has belatedly begun to forge ahead. One of the best things that has happened to the South has been the boll weevil. This highly destructive pest entered the South from Mexico in 1888. By 1920 it had spread throughout the cotton-growing area of the South, and the cotton industry began moving out of the South to the arid West. This was the straw that broke the back of the cotton monocrop system in the South. The South was forced to do what agriculturists had long been urging: to diversify, to grow crops less destructive to the soil, less corroding to the social structure, and more productive economically. This, combined with the growing industrialization of the South, has started a revolution. In a very real sense,

the South in the mid-twentieth century has finally entered the industrial revolution.

It is a far-reaching revolution. Agriculturally, the land is highly productive because of its long growing season, and its extensive areas of plains suited to mechanized agriculture. It is now one of the most important cattle regions, for the reasons mentioned earlier. Its forestry can be put on a sustained yield basis for the rate of growth is high enough to allow harvesting before so great an elapse of time that any reasonable counting of interest charges on investment has eaten up all the possible gains. The labor supply, freed by the mechanization of agriculture and the collapse of the subsistence farming way of life, has become an asset. It is too often unskilled and uneducated labor, but it has some value in industries not requiring technical knowledge. Even here the South is being aided by the mass migration of Negroes to the big cities of the North and West. This transfers the enormous burden of a mass of uneducated and unskilled people over more of the country. The South is in the midst of social and economic revolution, and by many measures of economic growth, it is one of the most rapidly developing parts of the nation. Why was it ever otherwise?

Causes of Southern Lag

Explanations for the backwardness of the South have often stressed the physical geography. Common statements are: the area is better suited to agriculture than to industry, or the depressing effect of heat and humidity and the absence of the stimulus of seasonal change doom the area to low mental effort. It is certainly true that the South has enormous advantages in agriculture, over the North's short season and over the West's aridity. It is strange to argue that any area possessed of the abundance of hydroelectric power found in the South, and possessing some of the major minerals such as sulphur and petroleum, is ill-equipped to do well in industry. Especially is it hard to dismiss such a situation as Birmingham, Alabama, where coking coal, iron ore, and limestone are found al-

Cattle at Greenwood, Florida. Cattle in the Southeast have year-round pasture, so there is no need for barns or expensive hay storage. *Florida State News Bureau.*

Florida Citrus Groves. This is an example of man's changing the natural mixed forest cover to a single species of economically desirable tree. *Florida Development Commission.*

Harvesting Tomatoes in the Florida Everglades. The concentration of American agriculture on the extensive flat lands and the mechanization of agricultural production to the fullest possible extent is illustrated in these two pictures. *Florida State News Bureau.*

most side by side. This gives Birmingham the lowest assembly cost of raw materials for iron and steel making of any industrial site in America. Nevertheless, the South has lagged. Perhaps there is something to this climatic argument after all. Or perhaps there are other factors at work, and this is just another of the numerous examples of a potentially good region standing relatively still. We certainly have seen enough examples of this.

In some areas we have studied the question of race was present. That is not the problem in the South. Two races are present, but the white race has been in charge. If there was a racial failure, then it must have been due to the inferiority of southern whites. But this is ridiculous. The southern whites are the same racial stock as the northern whites. An obvious correlation strikes one. Northwest European whites placed in the cold, strongly seasonal North were energetic developers of trade and industry. The same racial stock placed in the warm, weakly seasonal South became planters, and decayed into nonintellectually-inclined agrarians. This is one of the classic cases where a fine correlation may indicate virtually no causal correlation between the two phenomena so closely correlated. It is particularly interesting to twist and turn this a bit.

First, our survey of the success of white settlers in much more tropical situations than the South indicated that there is nothing in the physical environment that stops white settlers from doing well for a period of centuries. Second, if we look at the situation in the pre-Columbian period, we find a reversal of the cultural argument. The peak of Indian achievement was in the South, and culture declined toward the north with New England being toward the lower end of the scale of human achievement among the eastern Indians. There is no biological basis for an argument that the differences between the American Indians and the Europeans are such that the climate that stimulates one is deadening to the other. A much simpler explanation is found if one looks at proximity to ideas. The stimulus of Indian America was coming primarily from the south. For Colonial America, the stimulus

was coming from the northeast. In each case the area closer to the center of ideas led in cultural accomplishment.

This can be overdone, however. In Colonial America the South was a progressive region that produced more than its share of national leaders and cultural advances. The retardation of the South follows the Civil War. This is worth considering, for again and again the situation is found where a country or area was far in the lead of the rest of the world, and thereafter fell far behind. Often the period of loss of leadership followed devastation and war. The story of the South illustrates how such an event can affect a region, how long the effects may last, and how our judgments about an area are warped if we look at the momentary situation without considering the events that have conditioned the present use of the land. For the South, one could well substitute Italy, Spain, Greece, India, or any one of dozens of other cases.

It is now 100 years since the Civil War. The South is still a distinctive part of our nation, marked by greater emphasis on agriculture than most of the country, with a single-party system, and with segregation still firmly entrenched. Yet recently the first breaks in this structure have appeared. The South had emphasized agriculture before the Civil War, and it was the industrial might of the North that was decisive in the war. The South was a devastated and defeated nation in 1865. Major cities were destroyed, manpower was at a low ebb, and the mass of illiterate slaves were freed. If nothing worse had happened, the South would still have had a difficult period of rebuilding. The worst was yet to come, however.

The North occupied various southern states for 3 to 10 years after the fighting stopped. In contrast to our treatment of defeated European nations in later wars, we did virtually nothing to help the starving South. In addition to a loss of $4 billion through the freeing of the slaves, the South had $2.5 billion in worthless bonds and currency, and on top of this, United States Treasury agents seized $30 million worth of cotton, land, and other property that they alleged had belonged to the Confederacy. The Negroes were organized by the Northern carpetbaggers and made to vote the straight Republican ticket. Under the leadership of the worst elements from the North, the South was robbed and beaten and left in debt. A debt of more than $100 million was accumulated by the southern states between 1866 and 1874. In one southern state, the carpetbaggers organized the Negroes and elected a northerner for governor. On an $8000 a year salary this governor accumulated $1 million in four years. The southerners were not in charge, and there was almost nothing to show for the squandering of this vast sum of money.

The problem of Negro voting in the South must be seen against such a background. They did vote for 25 years after the Civil War. Their votes were straight Republican while the Northern armies were there. Thereafter they voted straight Democrat, with the particular candidate getting the most votes being the one who could buy the most. The problem was that of an illiterate mass that could not be expected to take up the heavy responsibility of wise action in so difficult a field as government.

The obvious answer to this problem was to educate the Negroes. The Freedman's Bureau created 4000 schools for Negroes in the South. This Bureau was supported by taxes on cotton. Out of each $4 that it collected, it spent $1 on such projects as relief and schools. Incidentally, no aid was given to the South for building schools for the whites. Our public-school system is a relatively recent growth, and during the time that it was expanding most rapidly in the North, the South was struggling merely to live. At that the South did what it could to create a dual school system and to give some education to both races. The low status of Southern education even today is a measure of the problem that they faced. As late as 1936, the South, with one sixth of the nation's income, had one third of the nation's school children, in a dual school system. The result was that a white teacher received only one third what she might expect in a state like California. Primary and secondary education were limited and poor, and graduate schools and medical and dental schools almost nonexistent. Schools are expensive, and advanced schooling is immensely expensive, but the South was our poorest area.

The South had its economic base virtually destroyed by the war and the freeing of the slaves without compensation. After the war, cotton was heavily taxed and given no protection in the world market. Northern manufacturing enterprises, meanwhile, were heavily protected. The resources of the South were bought up at distress prices by Northerners. Pine land, more than 5 million acres of it, sold for as little as 25 cents per acre. The southern railroads were bought up and freight rates were so fixed that southern industry could not compete with the North. So vicious was the rate setting on freight charges and steel prices that it was cheaper for a business man in New Orleans to buy his steel from Pittsburgh than to buy it from nearby Birmingham. These discriminatory rates were finally ended in 1945.

Seventy-five years after the Civil War, more than half of the South's farm families were tenant farmers with an average yearly income of less than $75 per person. Only 3 percent of the farms had indoor plumbing. More than 2 million families had malaria, and child labor was common. Wages in industry were about two-thirds those outside the area. Cotton had impoverished the people, and led to the greatest soil erosion problem in the country. The South was a rural slum.

Revolutionary changes in the South came with World War II. The textile industry had been shifting toward the South to take advantages of the large pool of labor there. Abundant timber, hydro-electric power, oil and gas, sulphur, and water made the area one of attraction for light industries such as the synthetic textiles, plastics, and chemicals. Meanwhile, farming was changing. Cotton was being displaced by diversified agriculture, and mechanization of agriculture was coming in. This was displacing the tenant farmer, creating a continuing flow of manpower off the land and into the towns available for industry: the same situation that had existed in New England 100 years earlier and had supplied one of the impulses for the industrialization of New England.

By the 1950s the South was booming. Factory employment was growing four times as fast as in other states. Increase in numbers of cars and trucks was at a rate 50 percent higher than in the rest of the United States. Between 1950 and 1960, personal income rose from about $1000 per person to $1700 per person. White population grew one-third faster than in the rest of the states, but Negro population grew at only one-fifth the rate of the Negro increase in the rest of the states. This figure represents the migration of Negroes from the South and into the big northern and western cities where they found a better opportunity than they had in the South as tenant farmers. The tremendous burden of educating and employing these people has in considerable measure been transferred to the other parts of the nation. This has come at the very time when the growth of income in the South has made possible the building of a good school system, and when the industrialization of the South has offered an opportunity for these people to be employed productively. Belatedly the rest of the nation is picking up the burden of giving the Negroes the educational and economic opportunity that mere freeing them in a devastated, impoverished, and economically hobbled South could not give them.

The opportunity for the industrial growth, the diversification of agriculture, and the accompanying rise in health, welfare, and education were inherent in this geographical region at all times. Notice how the race and climate argument has changed. The same white race, in large part the same families, are still dominant in the South. The monotonous heat has had even longer to work on them. Now, however, they are vigorous entrepreneurs, busily developing their country at a much more rapid rate than the rest of the country. At this very time New England, the land of stimulating climate, has gone into a period of very slow growth, and in upper New England, of absolute loss of population and loss of productivity. The physical geography and especially the climate has changed little. Within the past 50 years the temperature of mid-latitudes has risen somewhat. This means that the South is somewhat hotter in summer and New England a little less frigid in winter, and still New England declines in relation to the rising South.

The ills of the South cannot all be attributed to the Civil War and the unjust treatment the region received thereafter. The southerners were plantation minded and far too interested in cotton for their own good. Like most men through most of time, they tended to keep alive the system that they knew. They faced an enormous task of rehabilitating their land, readjusting their society from slave to free, and working out a new economic and social order. It would have been difficult enough under the best conditions, but the war and the attendant crises made the situation worse.

In a wider view of the history of land use, consider now the effect of the Civil War. The South is a part of the United States, and the Confederates were our own people. Despite this, we treated that area in such a way as to retard its development for 75 years. Only after a full century do we see it making a recovery that promises to make it a leading part of the nation within 25 more years. Consider what the situation might have been had the area not been a part of our nation, with people speaking our own language and having our own religions and sharing our outlook on life. The North might well have oppressed them worse and longer. If this had been the case would we be explaining the backwardness of the South in terms of physical geography? Or would it be in terms of race? Or perhaps religion? If the South were not a part of the United States, would it be as successful as it now is? Its sources of capital, its markets, and many of the key people in its recent spurt of growth have been drawn from the West and the North. They could operate freely within the boundaries of the United States. Had the South been successful in the Civil War it might have made a more rapid initial recovery, but its enormous potential as a part of a continent-sized republic would have been lost.

Thus within the mid-latitude forest environment of our East, a series of dramatic cultural growth and land-use changes has occurred in a relatively brief time. Indian America had its greatest cultural centers along the Mississippi River and in the South. Population density and cultural achievement declined steadily northward and eastward reflecting the importance of Middle America as a source of stimulation.

The Colonial period saw the reversal of this: the eastern seaboard became dominant. Although differing economic and social systems marked the various colonies, both North and South prospered and produced notable men in all fields of endeavor. Then came the Civil War and the South was reduced to poverty. The geographical explanation offered in the twentieth century was that the climate caused this. At mid-century, the South, without benefit of climatic change, has sprung into a race for leadership in the nation. If the pattern of the eastern United States of the future looks more like that of Indian America, will we now conclude that the South is an environment that is superior? A review of what man has done in similar climates elsewhere in the world may help answer that question.

SOUTH AMERICAN MID-LATITUDE FOREST

The South American area with a climate like the eastern United States centers on Uruguay and includes adjacent parts of Brazil, Paraguay, and Argentina. Equivalent latitudes are Saint Augustine, Florida, and Porto Alegre, Brazil; Buenos Aires and Cape Hatteras or Memphis; Bahia Blanca, Argentina, and Philadelphia. The Brazilian highlands decline into plains in southern Brazil, the rest of this climatic zone in South America is characterized by extensive plains. Most of the area is drained by the La Plata–Paraná river system, which can be thought of as somewhat like the Mississippi

in its location and potential function. As in the United States, aridity increases to the west and seasonality increases poleward. Within one climatic area, largely on one land-form type, under the domination of Mediterranean peoples, remarkably unlike nations developed. A brief review of southernmost Brazil and adjacent Uruguay, Paraguay, and Argentina will bring out these differences.

Southern Brazil, Uruguay, and Paraguay

The south of Brazil has varied cultural settlement areas. In order to settle the extreme south of Brazil, especially the state of Rio Grande do Sul, German immigration was encouraged in the nineteenth century. The settlement was made in an otherwise sparsely settled country, and the settlers brought their European patterns of crops, fields, houses, and animals. Consequently this area looks different from the rest of Brazil. Note the sequence of causes and results. The area was a thinly held frontier to which the Brazilians wished to establish their claim. A convenient source of desirable settlers was found in Germany. Southern Brazil is the least tropical part of Brazil. Its development has been in a mid-latitude pattern. It would be extremely easy to turn this into an environmental-deterministic argument: "The mid-latitude of Rio Grande do Sul was the only area suited to northern European people. Here it was that the German settlers found a stimulating seasonal climate. Naturally then, it was here that they settled. And quite naturally this has become one of the dynamic centers of Brazilian development." However, the causes for settlement here were political rather than climatic.

Later other Europeans emigrated into this area. For instance, there is an Italian area. Here the houses and crops and field patterns are more like Italy. Where the Germans raise hogs, the Italians are more noted for their vineyards. Note again the importance of cultural tradition. These settlements are set down in the midst of Portuguese settlements. Each has its own distinctive type. The environment has not demanded that there be one use of the land. Southeastern Brazil, even though it is cli-

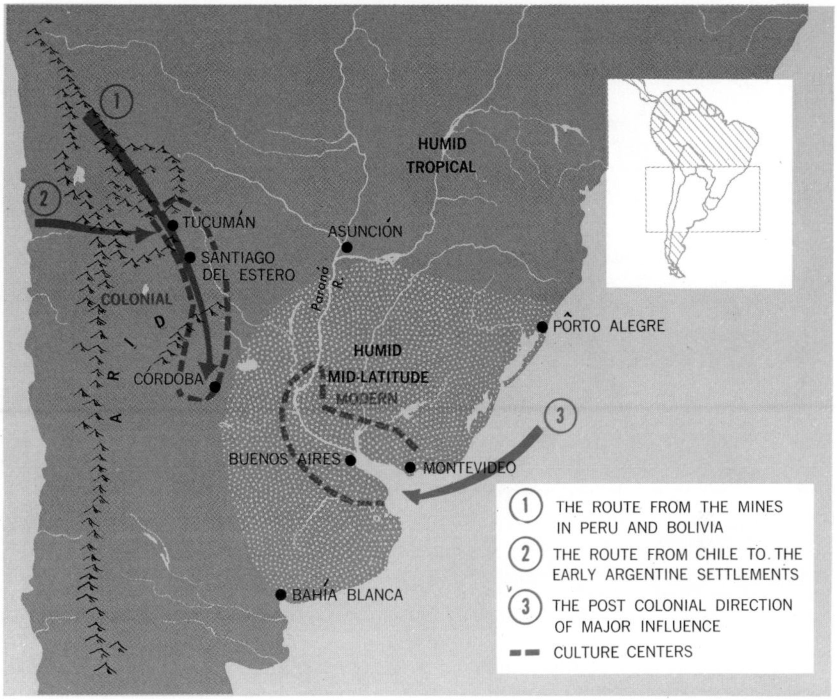

Map 5-5 South American Mid-latitude Forest Lands

The South American mid-latitude forest lands center on the La Plata estuary and the Paraná River. They include most of Paraguay, the southernmost part of Brazil, Uruguay, and part of Argentina. In Argentina, much of the land was in grassland at the time of discovery and it is thought that much of this humid grassland was the result of fire driving the trees out of their natural habitat.

The colonial approach to the area was from the west, via Chile, and from the highland areas of Bolivia. The early centers of growth and development were consequently on the dry margin of the area. With the breakdown of Spanish controls, the focus of the area came to be the La Plata estuary and the two great cities of the region, Buenos Aires and Montevideo, developed there.

matically like our South, has not developed like our South, nor even like adjacent Uruguay.

Uruguay is approximately half the size of California. It has a population of 2,700,000, about one sixth that of California. Since our country is more urbanized than is Uruguay, the density of rural population is to be thought of as much like that found in rural areas in the eastern United States. The settlement of this country was by Spanish people in the colonial period, and the population today is nearly 90 percent European race. Interest was in live stock; thus grain, cotton, fruit, and many other potential crops are relatively little developed. Only about 7 percent of the land is cultivated, nearly 60 percent being in pasture. As with most of the Latin American countries, a high percentage of the population is in one large city. Montevideo, with about three quarters of a million people, has nearly one third of the population of the nation.

Uruguay offers free education to its citizens and has a high literacy rate (65 percent). Also there are pension plans, child care, free medical care, and other social programs. As elsewhere, the costs and abuses of these systems have proved prohibitive, and the country is experiencing financial difficulty. As a geographic unit, Uruguay is small but extremely well endowed in topography and climate. Mineral resources are known but little explored or developed. It is in a stage of economic development similar to our South in the period of cotton dominance; only in Uruguay, cattle ranching is king.

Paraguay is a land of a mixed Indian and European race, with more than 90 percent of the population either Indian or part Indian. It has a tropical to subtropical, humid climate, similar to lower Florida. Much of the land is flat, and the amount of potentially useful land is high. Citrus grows virtually as a wild plant. Yet the land is little developed and population density is only about 10 per

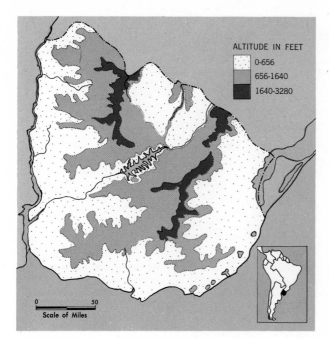

Land Form

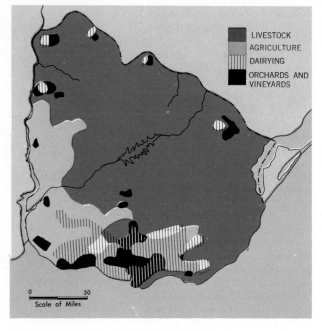

Land Use

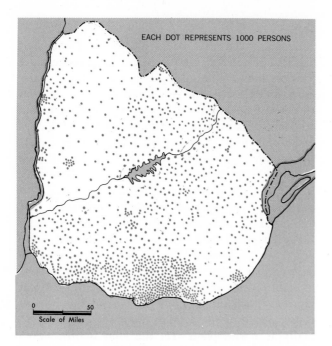

Population Density

Map 5-6   Uruguay: Land Form, Land Use, and Population

Uruguay is a land of little relief, as shown on the land-form map. It has abundant rainfall well distributed through the year. With such a physical base the whole country could be developed for intensive agriculture. Instead, cattle raising dominates the area, and a modest population is fairly evenly spread over the country. *Adapted from* Focus—*The American Geographical Society.*

square mile. Paraguay, the same size as California, has only one and a half million people. Interior location, poor transportation, and absence of coal, iron, and any developed oil resource (although oil is thought to be present) are the usual reasons advanced for the lack of development of such a nation. Comparison with Switzerland or Belgium shows that these are not sufficient causes. The Paraná River is navigable and leads to the Atlantic. Undeveloped transportation and idle resources, illiterate people, and restrictive government are not parts of the physical environment. A nation need not have coal, iron, or oil to be a prosperous and productive nation. Paraguay is a classic case of low level use of a potentially rich piece of geography.

Argentina

Argentina has long been the most advanced nation in this area. The Spanish development of this land, so like the eastern United States in its physical setting, was to reach down into the Argentine grassland and develop it as a reservoir for the beef and mules needed in the mines in Bolivia and Peru. Argentina was approached from Spain via the Caribbean, through Peru, and across the Andes. Entry to the grasslands was from Tucumán and Córdoba. The sea lane that led so easily from Spain down the Atlantic to the La Plata estuary was unimportant until the time of the American revolution. Here again men worked in defiance of what the natural setting demanded.

In 1776 the restrictions against direct sea trade were removed. At that time a vice-royalty including what is now Bolivia, Paraguay, Uruguay, and Argentina was created. If this political unit had survived to become a state at the time of the breakup of the Spanish empire in America, it would have been a nation of the size of the United States east of the Mississippi, with a comparable climate and with comparable amounts of navigable rivers and well-watered plains. The possibilities that have gone unfulfilled are forever influencing the development of the present. Too often the results of such his-

torical accidents are then read as geographical determinations. It was the human decisions made at the time of the collapse of the Spanish empire that isolated Paraguay. It was the orientation of the colonial period that made Uruguay a tiny ranching nation rather than a farming nation. Argentina was similarly molded by the Spanish interests and has only slowly reoriented herself. The political fragmentation of this part of the Spanish empire has hindered, and will continue to hinder, its economic growth and development. Note how important are the cultural versus the physical causes.

In Argentina, as on the American plains, the introduction of cattle soon led to a large wild population in the grasslands. As in America, the Indians learned riding from the Spanish and soon were mounted horsemen. As in the United States, these fierce horsemen of the plains became a military problem. It took major armed force to put them down and make the plains useful to the Europeans.

As an aside, it is the role of ideas that is again important here. There had been wild horses in the grasslands both in North and South America. The Indians had eaten them all up. There were wild camels present, and the idea of using them as domestic animals was present in adjacent Bolivia. But they were not so used in the plains of Argentina. When the North American Indians took up the trait of hunting from horseback, they used the bow and arrow for killing their prey and developed very short, powerful bows for use on horseback. Not so in South America. There the Indians used the bola, a set of stone weights attached to the end of strings to be whirled around the head and thrown to entangle the prey. We know the bola to be a very ancient implement, and we know the bow and arrow to be relatively recent in its appearance in the Americas. It seems probable that the bola was still the major implement, not yet fully replaced by the bow when the Spanish arrived. In Argentina, custom, not need or efficiency, decreed that the bola rather than the bow should be used on horseback when pursuing game, while in the United States the bow was used.

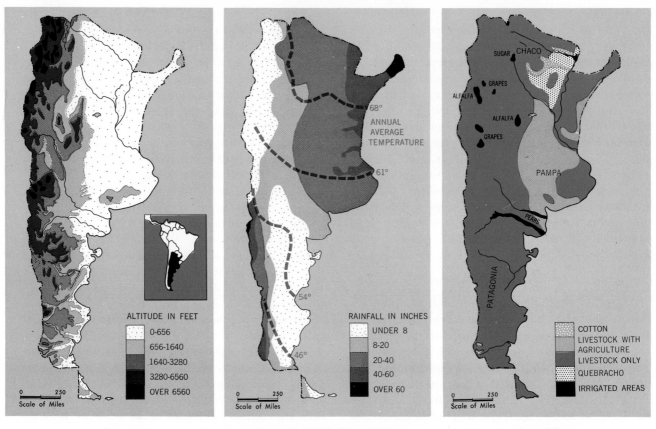

Land Form   Average Annual Rainfall and Temperatures   Land Use

Map 5-7   Argentina: Land Form, Rainfall, Temperature, and Land Use

Argentina has a plain facing the Atlantic, and the spine of the Andes forms its western boundary. Rainfall is abundant in the northeast and declines toward the south and west, except that the southern Andes get heavy rainfall because they are in the westerly wind belt. The dry area to the east of the Andes is due to their intercepting the rain-bearing winds. The steady decline of temperature toward the south parallels the type of temperature decline northward along the east coast of the United States. Land use reflects physical geography, history, and economic development. The irrigated oases in the northwest of Argentina owe much of their development to colonial times. The great emphasis on cattle also reflects the colonial and Spanish background. The general zoning of land use within this cultural-economic orientation is fitted to the rainfall pattern. *Adapted from* Focus— *The American Geographical Society.*

After 1776, Buenos Aires, which had languished as long as trade largely came from the Pacific, became the active center of the country. The development of modern Argentina has centered on this city that has grown up in the La Plata estuary with access to this great inland waterway, on the sea with access thereby to the lanes to the entire world, and on the edge of the vast rich grasslands of Argentina, the pampas. In 1776 its population was only 20,000. By 1800 it had a population of 40,000 people. Today it is a city of 4,500,000.

The settlements of Argentina, then, were a bit as if the settlement of the United States had started on the West coast and had become centered on a mining economy—a thing that could easily have happened had history been slightly different. The East then would have been developed from some points such as Sante Fe and Denver. The first use of the East would have been to supply livestock raised on the Great Plains. Later, the port of New Orleans would have gained importance. With this sequence of events, New England probably never would have been developed to important levels. The development of the United States would center rather on New Orleans. This is roughly comparable to what did happen in Argentina. The early cities were at the foot of the mountains in the dry interior, at oasis locations. Tucumán, Córdoba, Santiago. Only after the Spanish grip began to slip and the colonies began to go their own ways did Argentina reorient herself to the Atlantic. The major city has become Buenos Aires, at the mouth of the Rio de la Plata, the great bay at the mouth of the Paraná River. The La Plata is as long as the Mississippi River, has nearly four times as great an amount of water, and is potentially an enormously useful freight artery.

Argentina remained a nearly self-sufficient cattle-raising country until the mid-nineteenth century. By then, the growth of industry in Europe had created a market for food stuffs to feed the population now drawn into manufacturing and gaining a higher standard of living, and thus able to import food stuffs including such costly materials as beef and mutton. Under European stimulus, and largely with European financing, railroads were built to bring the produce of the interior to the ports, and great slaughtering and refrigeration plants were built to process the cattle for export overseas in refrigerator ships. Grain production also became important, and corn, wheat, wool, and meat became the major exports.

The Latin tradition was for ranching, and the land was in the hands of a few families that held large blocks of land. Immigrants supplied the farming labor—a steady inflow from Europe, especially from Italy. The country evolved a mixed farming-ranching system geared to the world markets. The strong European basis of the nation was reinforced by the steady inflow of immigrants. As the wealth of the nation grew, industry began to grow. Urban growth became phenomenal. Nearly one third of the population has come to be located in the four major urban centers of Buenos Aires, Rosario, Córdoba, and La Plata. Partially this is due to the concentration of the land in large states, and partially it is a measure of the world-wide shift of man from the land to the cities as the efficiency of the world's agriculture improves so as to free the mass of mankind from the task of producing food stuffs. It is parallel to the shift in the United States.

Argentina has recently passed through a politico-economic upheaval under a dictator, Perón, that has set it back severely. Currently the country is struggling to stabilize its economy, re-establish its world-wide trade, and resume its program of internal development of manufacturing. The physical potential is good, the population has been drawn from nations of great accomplishments. Argentina's future is as great as its people have the will to make it.

The South American equivalent of our eastern United States, southern Brazil, Paraguay, Uruguay, and northern Argentina, is physically well endowed. It is politically divided, and the degree and kind of development is clearly related to the political present and the historic past. The differing cul-

Chinese Pictographic Writing. China's unique development is symbolized by its writing. Although early Chinese pictographic writing resembles Near Eastern writing, the Chinese followed an independent course, avoiding the alphabetical revolution and never going beyond a highly developed ideographic system. This writing was done by Sung Kao Tsung (A.D. 1107–1187), an emperor of the Sung Dynasty. *Chinese News Service, N. Y.*

tural landscapes developed in similar climatic and physiographic settings again express the dominance of the role of culture.

CHINA

China, firmly fixed in most minds as a tropical country, is actually very much like the United States. It has a warm subtropical south, a strongly seasonal north, and an arid west. Its slightly more southerly latitude is compensated for by its edge-of-a-great-continent position. The cold air of inner Asia brings very cold weather to north China when it pours out in the winter. This area, including such outer territories as Tibet, Mongolia, Sinkiang, and Manchuria, is a vast country nearly one and one half times the size of the United States. However, just what the political fate of these outer territories is to be remains in question. The heart of China is east of the 100th meridian, and south of the 40th parallel. This area is about half the size of the United States, and climatically it is much like the humid forested eastern United States, although the shape of the land is different. The plains are to the north, in the latitude of northern Florida to Maine. To the south lies a rugged hill land with much of the land between 2000 and 5000 feet in elevation.

Racial and Cultural Origins

There are two Chinas, north versus south, which differ in race, language, culture, climate, and land form. They are nonetheless bound together in a national history and share a unique writing system. The east-west trend of the Chin Ling Shan Range divides China and makes the north-south contrasts more marked than they are in the United States.

The Chin Ling Shan mountain range is long and high enough to deflect the outpouring of cold air from inner Asia from a southerly course, giving southern China mild winters. Northern China is subject to invasion by masses of cold dry air. Thus, in winter the north becomes cold and dry, and the south remains mild and rainy. In summer both are hot and wet. Some of the differences between north and south China are summarized in Table 5–1.

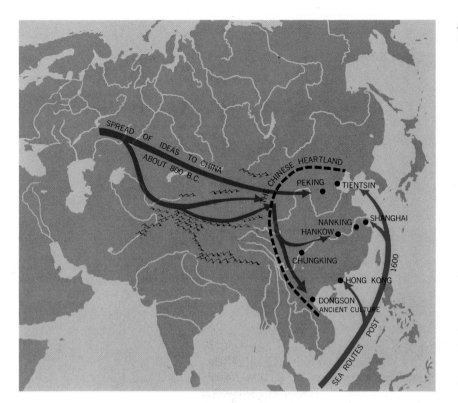

Map 5-8 Cultural Contacts with China and the Location of Cities

Two major routes of contact with China are indicated. The path shown by the arrows is based upon Heine-Geldern's map of the spread of ideas to China about 800 B.C. and eventually to a major capital city at Dongson on the Tonkin delta. This ancient contact route through the continental interior served not only for the flow of the cultural ideas that stimulated the growth of China, but also later as an important trade route. The inland location of cities such as Peking, Chunking, and Nanking illustrates the dominance of this continental orientation. The vast growth of sea trade after A.D. 1600 shifted the orientation of China toward the sea. Tientsin, Shanghai, and Hong Kong illustrate this outward-looking interest. Currently Chinese orientation is again toward the continental interior. It is probable that such shifts of emphasis were known to ancient China, too, and that there was more orientation toward the sea-trade lanes in early times than has usually been estimated.

Table 5-1 North and South China Compared

	North China	South China
Major rivers	Hwang Ho	Yangtze
Land	Great delta plains	Few small plains
Rainfall	Under 40 inches	Over 40 inches
Crops	Wheat, millet, soy-bean	Rice, tea, mulberry, bamboo, tung tree
Animals	Ox and camel	Water buffalo
Racial features	Taller, lighter color	Smaller, darker
Cultural characteristics	Slower in mental action. quicker to take physical action.	Quick in mental reaction, subtle in action, shrewd in business.

What is the reason for these differences? The predominance of rice in the warm, humid south and of wheat in the dryer, colder north seems a reasonable physical-environmental response. But does the warm, humid south versus the cold, dry north also account for the difference in physical make-up of the people?

Further, most descriptions of the Chinese distinguish between the northerners and southerners in mental characteristics. We have seen that there are reasons for some bodily changes from hot to cold climates. We are familiar in our own country with the clichés about the slow, easy-going southerner and the quick, driving northerner. However, in China it is the southerner who is the quick-witted, shrewd businessman. Can it be that climate has opposite effects on different races? Or is this a case of culture-history rather than geography being the cause?

Just as there are two Chinas in terms of physical geography, there are also two Chinas in terms of cultural history. It is the joint effects of the two sets of facts that have made two Chinas. The beginnings of this division go back almost to the beginning of the human occupation of Asia, for as earlier discussion brought out, man reached China very early by a southern coastal route and was living near Peking about 400,000 years ago (see Map 9–2).

Other people spread from the Near East after the third glacial period. They followed a route through Turkestan that led via the Selenga River toward Lake Baikal. During the last part of the glacial period, Europeanlike people—with most of the cultural equipment well-known to us from cave excavations in France—arrived in force in the area from Lake Baikal to the northwest of China; this was about 20,000 to 30,000 years ago. We see, then, an early tendency for two lines of expansion toward China. People from Southeast Asia moved up from the south, swinging eastward around the Tibetan highland. People from the European side of the Eurasian continent persistently flowed eastward along a route that led from the Caspian area toward the Baikal area. It is quite possible that the physical differences in the Chinese, tall, lighter-skinned northerners versus the smaller, darker southerners, stems in part from these ancient differences.

The differentiated lines of influence have continued. North China begins in the great bend of the Hwang Ho about 2000 B.C. This is a cold, dry, interior location near Mongolia. One could well expect Near Eastern rather than Southeastern cultural influences here. The basic grain is wheat, the domestic animal is the ox; these are Near Eastern, not Southeast Asian traits. Metallurgical arts and design elements, among other things, suggest that during the late bronze age, cultural influences from the Caspian–Black Sea area were extremely important in China. The existence of an empire, called Dongson, that spanned the zone from the Black Sea to the coast of south China has been reconstructed from archeological remains. The Mongol invasions of Genghis Khan are only a late example of such move-

ments from west to east. The Great Wall of China is the physical embodiment of the Chinese attempt to block off such repeated invasions.

From the northwestern corner of China came political and population expansion down the Hwang Ho onto the immense delta plain lying north and south of the Shantung peninsula. Soon, men and ideas spread over the Chin Ling Shan mountains into the Szechwan basin. This sheltered, warm interior, moderately high basin became a major population center. Chinese political domination spread, and with it went the development of a distinctive Chinese culture, marked by a sense of the importance of the family, the strong development of ethical systems, and a respect for learning—and all of this based on an intensive agricultural system that made possible one of the densest populations the world had yet seen.

The original people of south China were seemingly very different. On Formosa, the aborigines are small, dark people; if intermixed with north

A Bronze Tripod of the Chou Dynasty (1122–255 B.C.) (*opposite*), a Painting of a Shepherd and His Horse from the Tang Dynasty (A.D. 618–907) (*right*), and Pagodas at Modern Taipei (*below*). China created some of the world's greatest art. These examples illustrate the continuity of creativity in the Chinese culture. *Chinese News Service, N.Y.*

A Bumper Crop on Taiwan (Formosa). The lag in agricultural modernization in China—and Asia—is shown in this picture. Hand work requires large manpower input per bushel of rice. Here the rice is cut by hand, and the bundles of rice are then threshed by banging them against wooden tubs. The screens are to cut down on loss of rice by scattering. Compare the Australian and American production. *Chinese News Service, N.Y.*

Chinese, the result would be much like the present south Chinese. In the mountainous parts of southwest China there remains today 20 million tribal people sometimes described as primitive Caucasoids, of which the Lolos and the Miaos are examples. Quite possibly they are remnants of some ancient racial variant of man that has been there for tens of thousands of years. They probably intermixed with the expanding northern people to enter into the formation of the typical southern Chinese. The use of rice and water buffalo is characteristic of these people, just as the use of wheat and oxen characterize the northerner.

These hill people were not all primitives; some of them used pictographic writing and had domestic elephants. Domestication of elephants is distinctly an Indo-Burman idea. These elements are evidences of another stream of ideas coming from the south into China. It seems possible that the orientation toward business in south China may be related to such influences.

Population and Land Use

China's population is a double problem. No one really knows how many Chinese there are, for no modern census has been taken. The UN estimate is 660,000,000, but famines, wars, and revolutions change the figure by some millions in brief intervals. The rate of population growth is said to be 5,000,000 per year. Those who would advocate emigration as the solution for population growth such as this should consider the fact that all of the shipping in the world could not carry Chinese out of China fast enough to overcome that rate of production. It is also well to remember the story of Italy, once the classic case of overpopulation in Europe and now on the brink of needing more people to do the work in a developing industrial society.

China's problem is the primitive state of her agriculture and the near absence of industrialization. China is overpopulated in the sense that her people are not productively employed. The Communist regime by upsetting the intensive peasant agriculture has thrown the country into chaotically lessened production and increased the population problem to catastrophic levels.

Even with all of this population, parts of China are still only thinly to moderately populated. Conversely, the heavily occupied parts have very high population densities. Taking the area of China to be 3.8 million square miles, an estimate that some 260 million acres are under cultivation indicates that only slightly more than 10 percent of the land is cultivated, or less than one-half acre of cultivated land per person—one of the lowest figures in the world. Part of this is due to the land and part is due to the Chinese pattern of land use. The Chinese have developed an intensive agriculture. They can well be said to be gardeners rather than farmers for the land they farm is cultivated with hand tools. The labor input is high: it takes 26 man days of labor to produce an acre of wheat, Chinese fashion—in the mechanized agriculture of the United States it only takes one. Only a small piece of land can be cultivated by one family in the Chinese way. Therefore the yield must be high if the family is to be supported by the land, and only the best land can do this. Hence, the type of land used in our extensive, power-rich, agricultural system would be useless to the Chinese—useless, that is, unless he changes his way of farming. Again, it is the Chinese methods, not the Chinese land that dictates this land-use pattern.

Thus China is a land climatically much like the United States or southeast South America; physically it is more rugged; and its densest population is very spottily distributed in the county because of the requirements of its unmechanized, hand-labor, intensive, self-sufficient agricultural base. There have been two great lines of racial and cultural influence that have persisted since the beginning of human history, and it is generally thought that it was the northern stream of ideas that initiated the population and political development that gave rise to the dominant pattern of Chinese culture.

Modern China

China in our day has been reduced to a near-colonial status. It has not shared in the industrial revolution, and its accomplishments in recent centuries have been minor. Is this due to the land, the people, or to some other cause?

It surely is not due to any racial failure. The Chinese have a most distinguished list of inventions to their credit despite a relatively late start. After all, dynastic China only begins about 2000 B.C. while the Near East is well underway by 4000 B.C. However, gunpowder, compass, paper, porcelain, printing, paper money, and a well-developed civil service are only a few of the important achievements that flourished in China before they were developed elsewhere in the world. Their art is acknowledged as extremely fine, and their literature is equally developed. To what do they owe their present relative backwardness in comparison with the West?

It is not the "land." China is rich in basic resources: it has the world's largest reserves of tungsten, antimony, and tin; and its coal, iron, copper, lead, and aluminum reserves are among the world's largest. In this sense China is not a "have-not" nation. China is one of the many nations in the world that were not prepared to share early in the industrial revolution. The expansion of Western Europe came during a period when the Chinese were stagnating in a withdrawn state, sure of their superiority and contemptuous of those they considered relatively barbaric white devils. If one considers that Marco Polo was regarded as a liar for his reports on what was to Europeans the unbelievably advanced state of China in his day, the Chinese may be thought to have had much on their side to bolster their point of view.

However, the Western world was then entering the ferment of the industrial revolution, and those nations in a position to share in the ideas then current, and disposed to use them, were about to forge into a commanding lead in world affairs. The humid,

mid-latitude United States at this time had a fluid new society that contained few fixed traditional barriers to such new developments. Humid, mid-latitude China was just the opposite: It was at a peak of development of a socially fixed structure, and just past a peak of cultural-political achievement. Change was resisted at the moment it could have very advantageously been embraced. China had abundant cheap labor and abundant waterpower. These resources could readily have been combined with the ancient Chinese silk industry and the new spinning and weaving machinery to establish the basis of an industrial-commercial society. Everything was available in the physical environment.

As need for more power arose, and coal became important, they would have had ample supplies: iron for heavy industry is abundant. When hydroelectric power became significant, they had available such immense resources as the Yangtze River gorges. In the great gorge of that river, the Yangtze drops 300 feet in 20 miles. At one point the gorge is only 600 feet wide and the variation between high and low water is 200 feet. A miniature Boulder Dam would make this one of the greatest power sites in the world and would level out the fluctuations between high and low stages, thus changing a dangerous and costly river passage into a placid lake ideal for water transportation.

If industry had developed, manpower would have been attracted into the cities, and machinery would have replaced manpower on the land. Extensive land use would have made more land useful. The need to feed the growing cities would have required development of a vast transportation system. Had the start been made, nothing in the physical environment would have seriously impeded development, and many items favorable to that development would have been found. China could be a land of great productivity and a high standard of living.

However, the course of events was otherwise. When its problem was to maintain the fertility of the land at such a level that it would support a sizable population with a surplus to support some effort beyond mere subsistence, China made a great advance. A pattern of life that allowed very dense, continuous settlement on the very best lands was worked out. A surplus of food was produced sufficient to support a tiny aristocracy of government, learned people, and a small merchant class. China then became set in this pattern. Most countries and most people, throughout history have become "set in their ways." The progressive nations of today are in danger of becoming the has-beens of tomorrow. China's solution of her land-use problem was a brilliant one for its day, and it gave China a leading position in the world for millennia. Then Europe entered its period of exploration, mercantile expansion, colonialism, and industrialization, and China became a semicolony of Europe.

The colonial period in China created a situation somewhat like that of Brazil. Since contact with the European powers was by sea, there was a strong development of the port cities. This is opposite to the older order in China. Peking, Nanking, Hankow, and Chunking are all interior cities; they represent the former internal focus of the country, and the importance of contacts to the west via the old caravan routes across Asia. With the shift to dominance of sea-borne trade, especially in the nineteenth century, sea ports replaced the interior cities in importance. Shanghai (6,000,000), Tientsin, Nanking, and Hongkong are all cities over 1,000,000 in population: all of these have had large population growth in the past 100 years.

Industry has barely started. China's principal exports before the Communist takeover were such items as cotton textiles, tungsten, and pig bristles. With a renewed importance given to contacts across Siberia, and lessening of contacts overseas, the trends of the past century now may well be reversed. China's coal is in the interior; its great metallurgical wealth is in the mountainous south. Mountains and abundant rainfall give that area an enormous hydroelectric potential. If these factors have any influence, and if China is to develop industrially, it is to be expected that the south may be the land with the greatest future. However, as we have seen, political and cultural orientation persistently outweighs mere

Map 5-9   China: Land Form, Railroads, Water Power, and Minerals

The very weak rail network shown here is a measure of China's slight industrial development. Her actual situation is in sharp contrast to her potential, as expressed on this map by the widespread major coal deposits. Note also the wide distribution of known major deposits of other minerals important to industrial growth and development. The strong rail and industrial installations of Manchuria are due to Japanese influences prior to World War II. *Adapted from* Focus—*The American Geographical Society*.

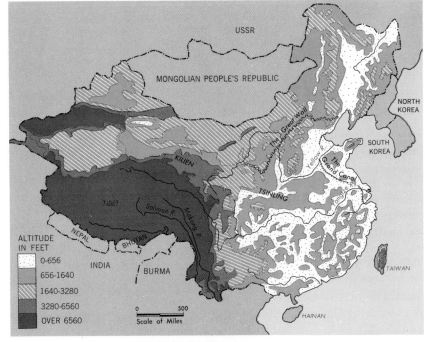

Land Form

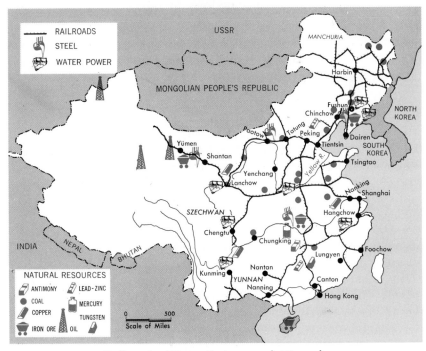

Railroads, Water Power, and Minerals

physical geography. At present China is tied to Communist Russia. While this lasts, the orientation will be toward the continental interior. When this changes, China's orientation will again turn to the Pacific ports.

The present Communist experiment seems unlikely to achieve a high standard of living even if it turns to the development of China's enormous potential resources. The Communist experiment in Russia has failed to match the growth of the free enterprise system in the United States or Europe. Yet in Russia it had a much better developed economic system to start with than it has in China. Withdrawal of individual incentives, breaking up of families, driving out foreign professors, businessmen, and missionaries, and creating a climate unfavorable to investment capital marks a semireturn to the earlier time when China elected to withdraw from the world and lost its position as one of the leaders in world civilization. The present economy of the early 1960s is so disrupted that famine is being avoided only by immense purchases of Australian and Canadian wheat. Further declines in production are probable and an enormous loss of life seems predictable in this potentially rich land.

AUSTRALIAN MID-LATITUDE FOREST

Another land with an area of east-coast mid-latitude forest is Australia. Australia is the size of the United States without Alaska. However, the population is less than 10 million. Forty percent of the continent is desert and another 40 percent is semiarid. Aridity alone is not enough to account for one sixth as many people in the United States. Time is perhaps more of a factor. (See Map 2–10.)

Australian settlement by Europeans was immensely delayed. The Portuguese and Dutch discovered the continent and explored its margins. They found the land to be occupied by a primitive people who had curly hair, dark skins, flat noses, beetle brows, and beards. They were not Negroes, for Negroes are not bearded. They were not white in color, nor were they Mongoloid. They are therefore usually placed in a separate category termed Australoids.

For the development of Australia their racial classification was unimportant; it was their cultural status that was decisive. They were simple hunters and gatherers. They had no fixed residence, and virtually no houses. They produced nothing that the Europeans wanted. To the north lay the spice islands where goods of low bulk and high value could be obtained in trade; or, if settlement were made, where settled agricultural people supplied the labor for a profitable colony. Native Australia offered no inducement, and so European settlement came even later than it did in the United States— where, as we have seen, there was a 100-year delay after the discovery of the New World. Australia saw a nearly 300-year delay.

Captain Cook surveyed the coast in 1788 for the British. The well-watered coastal areas were charted, and colonization began shortly thereafter. The American colonies were 150 years old and had won their independence before even a penal colony was established in Australia. Australia was to get a poor start as a penal colony, and not until the discovery of gold in 1851 brought a flood of people, did the country begin to develop. Australia's development is therefore to be compared with California's: no early advantage despite much good land; a gold rush bringing population in the mid-nineteenth century; rapid growth and development thereafter. (See Table 5–2.)

A country that developed in the second half of the nineteenth century started in the railroad era: Australia began with the building of railroads. However, Australia's development was from several centers, each of which was independent of the others, much as the North American colonies were originally independent of each other. The rail lines were not integrated and were of differing gauges, hence rolling stock could not go from one line to the other. All goods had to be reloaded at transfer points, and this put a heavy cost on transportation within the country. Movement of goods focused on the major ports emphasized the dominance of urban centers,

Table 5-2   Settlement and Population Growth in Australia

Settlement

1788	Penal Colony, Sydney
1824	Brisbane
1828	Perth
1835	Melbourne
1836	Adelaide
1851	Gold Rush to Victoria

Total Population

1788	1500
1800	5000
1820	33,000
1840	200,000
1850	400,000
1860	1,100,000
1890	3,000,000
1920	5,000,000
1950	8,500,000
1960	10,400,000

(By 1960, 1,000,000 immigrants, half of them British, had entered Australia since World War II.)

a phenomenon generally of the nineteenth and twentieth centuries: in Australia, there is only the nineteenth and twentieth centuries. Urbanization so characterizes this land that half of the total population lives in four cities: Sydney, Melbourne, Adelaide, and Perth. One fourth of the total labor force is in factory employment. Most of Australia, including even the humid lands, is virtually empty.

The British settled the humid east coast. They avoided the tropical north, found the interior to be forbiddingly dry, and the southwest to be good, but far from the rest of the developing part of the continent. The east coast is to be thought of as like the eastern seaboard of the United States, but lacking our southern coastal plain. One end of the coast is as tropical as the Caribbean, the other end is mid-latitude forest land comparable to Virginia. It was the seasonal, mid-latitude areas that the British settled first, and they have developed the most since. One could easily argue that the physical environ-

ment determined this; however, note that a tropical people might well have selected the north coast, a Mediterranean people the south coast, and an oasis agricultural people the Central Basin as their focal areas.

From Brisbane, Sydney, and Melbourne, settlement pushed across the dividing range. This situation is the equivalent of the American expansion across the Appalachians, but instead of a broad area of well-watered plains, the Australians found a narrow belt of lightly forested land, then park landscape (trees scattered through grasslands), and then the brushy-grassy lands of the desert. Exploration soon showed that the heart of the continent was desert.

The eastern side of the interior is called the Central Basin. Here there is an artesian water supply that makes the area more useful than the 10- to 20-inch rainfall in a subtropical position would lead one to expect. The southern part of this area has a river system capable of extensive development for irrigation. The Murray River rises from the Snowy Mountains in the southeast corner of Australia where high annual precipitation, heavy snow falls, and summer melt-off supply a steady runoff. The Darling River is the northern part of this system and also carries a useful amount of water. The drainage toward Lake Eyre is too erratic to be useful: Lake Eyre is normally dry, though in exceptional years it becomes an inland sea. The mid-latitude forest-land environment, then, is from Brisbane south to Adelaide, and reaches only a short distance over the dividing range (see Map 2–10).

Modern Australia

Sheep, cattle, and wheat have been Australia's principal exports. Cattle production is concentrated along the humid coast, while sheep and wheat are centered on the edge of the arid land and reach into the desert—until it takes 15 acres of land to support one sheep. The dominance of agriculture is measured by the fact that the major exports are wool, wheat, and meat, while imports are machinery, cotton goods, and petroleum products. Wool

Views of Sydney (*right*) and Melbourne (*opposite*). Between them, these cities house 40 percent of Australia's population, illustrating that country's twentieth-century urbanization. *Australian News and Information Bureau.*

alone accounted for 44 percent of the value of all exports in 1956, and this wool made up a third of the world's wool production. Neither the concentration on sheep nor the lack of industry is due to the country's physical environment.

Australia is well supplied with coal and iron. While the petroleum prospects seem slim, extensive exploratory drilling has not yet been carried out. Australia does have important deposits of coal, iron, copper, lead, zinc, silver, and gold; all that is needed is development. Two world wars have had much the same effect on Australia as they had on the United States. In 1918 the United States was still dependent on European machinery, dyes, chemicals, and similar goods. The war cut off the German sources and greatly reduced the amount that could be obtained from Great Britain and France. This forced local development; Australia's experience in war time has been similar, and it is following the same course, again with a time lag. Iron and steel, automobile, and other heavy industries are now developing. In some ways, Australia today is much like the United States in the early 1900s, but with the super cities of the mid-twentieth century.

Australia faces serious problems. Wool is in a position of declining importance; competition from synthetic fibers is cutting steadily into the market formerly dominated by wool. Sheep are losing their advantage as a dual purpose animal. Their fate illustrates man's use of his environment. Goats were once the preferred food animal. When wooly sheep came into existence, the advantage shifted to this dual-purpose animal, and mutton came to be preferred to goat meat. If wool ceases to be a valued product, we might shift back to goats as a major meat source, and we could then use larger areas of dry land to raise goats than we ever could for sheep. We may also try to breed a woolless meat-sheep. Thus we see that custom, not the animal best suited to the environmental requirements, is likely to decide the issue.

Technological changes, such as the displacing of wool by synthetics, are common in our day. Rubber and quinine are also examples of how drastically technological changes affect the production pattern of the world. Australia is fortunate that this change in textiles is coming at the very time when she is changing to a more industrialized society in which there will be less need for an export crop to supply the foreign exchange to pay for refrigerators, stoves, and automobiles.

Australia's east coast, with a humid and forested climate, is settled by a people of the same race and with the same cultural background as moved into the similar climatic zone in the United States, and it has considerable similarities today to the eastern United States. There are the same huge modern industrial cities, supported by a thinly occupied countryside and linked together by rail, highway, and air. The developments show variation in detail.

Australia's rural areas are more thinly settled than those of the United States, though we are rapidly approaching the Australian condition. Simultaneously, Australia is industrializing and urbanizing in a way parallel to the United States pattern. Before the conclusion that race and environment must naturally create such a landscape, however, one must review other factors and other lands, for these peoples share a British cultural heritage as well as similar climates.

In the comparable climates elsewhere in the world, cultural developments were more or less like the American and Australian developments depending on the extent that the countries were more or less influenced by Europe and the industrial revolution. Thus Argentina, strongly influenced by British enterprise, is Australian in its well-developed agricultural base, to which there is now being added a growing industrial base. Adjacent Uruguay has hardly begun its industrialization, and Paraguay has not done much even with its agricultural potential; the differences become even more marked when China is considered. While most of the areas of the world with this type of climate are currently moving ahead, the Chinese mainland is falling into chaotic conditions. Thus, within this one type of climate in the past 500 years, China has fallen from a position of world leadership into a state of continuing decline; Australia has emerged from a stage of life that disappeared from most of the world 50,000 years ago and become a modern, increasingly industrialized nation; while the United States and South America have undergone large-scale changes between these two extremes in extent.

SUMMARY

Racially these four parts of the world with similar climates, soil, and vegetation were occupied before 1500 by American Indians, Australoids, and Mongoloids. Their cultural status varied from extremely primitive through town- and village-dwelling agriculturists to sophisticatedly civilized. After 1500, race changed almost completely in the United States and in Australia, changed variably in South America, and hardly at all in China. In the United States, cultural change went from Neolithic town dwellers to advanced civilization. In South America change followed political rather than natural boundaries: from little or no advance in Paraguay to great advance in Argentina. China has stood still while the rest of the world has advanced. Australia is off to a late but strong start. Such enormous variability in similar physical environments underlines the relative unimportance of simple environmental factors such as climate, vegetation, and soil, and the overwhelming importance of the cultural-historical factors. Race seems to supply no basis for causal explanations. This continuing failure to find a racial answer suggests that race is no answer.

6-West Coast Mid-latitude Forest Lands

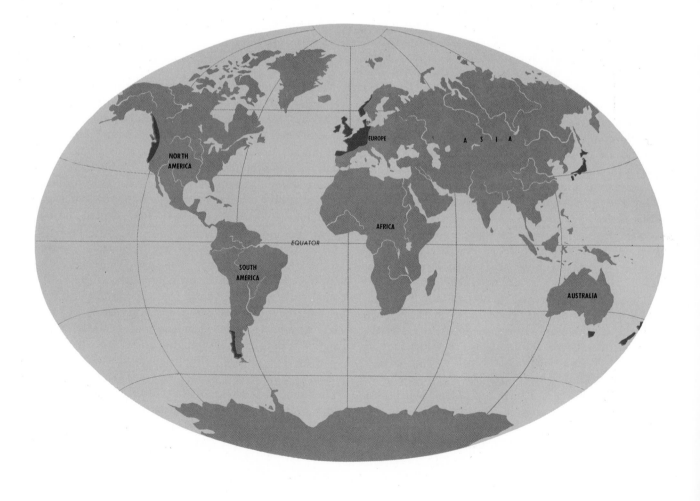

THE WEST SIDES of continents between 40 and 60 degrees of latitude are in the westerly wind-belt throughout the year. Winds blow from the ocean onto the land, bringing with them oceanic, tempered weather conditions. Since the oceans are relatively cool in summer and warm in winter, the lands so influenced have winters mild for their latitude and cool summers. A measure of the oceanic effect on climate can be seen by comparing the mild climate of Great Britain with frigid, barren Labrador. The January temperatures are, respectively, 40° and 0° F.; yet they are in the same latitude. But winds from the oceans flow over Britain while winds from the continent flow over Labrador. The westerlies are characterized by cyclonic storms. The winds are fresh from the oceans, the great reservoirs from which the air gains water to moisten the land. These western coasts are therefore very well watered: precipitation is 40 to 60 inches or more. Where highlands near these coasts force the moisture-laden air masses to rise over them, the precipitation may go up to 200 inches per year. The continuous moisture supply and the long growing season allows for immense forest growth. In some places there are rain forests in these latitudes that rival the great tropical rain forests.

Very high rainfall and no dry season lead to active leaching of the soil. The great forests supply masses of dead vegetation, and the low temperatures through the year prevent rapid decay. A thick mass of acid, partially decayed vegetable material then comes to cover the area. In boggy places, partially decayed plant material accumulates in thick masses and forms peat. It is notable that slightly decayed plant material does not accumulate under conditions of warmth and moisture nearly so much as it does under these cooler, moist conditions. This suggests that our coal deposits accumulated under cool wet, rather than tropical, wet conditions.

The four major areas of this climate in the world are: northwest Europe, the northwest coast of North America, the southwest coast of South America, and in the South Pacific, Tasmania and New Zealand. All these lands have mountains on their coasts, and only northwest Europe has extensive areas of plain. For convenience Japan is included here. Japan is an island world off an east coast. Air masses reaching these islands come from the west across the sea. Their temperatures are modified so that they arrive warmed in winter and cooled in summer. Japan is also mountainous, as are the rest of these maritime-dominated areas. Therefore, despite the colder winters of Hokkaido and the warmer summers of Japan's southern islands, Japan will be included with the mid-latitude areas dominated by oceanic air masses.

Mountains in latitudes of 40 to 60 degrees, in a position to get much precipitation, are bound to have a great deal of snow in winter. All mountains in these latitudes get some snow; west coastal ones get much snow; and higher mountains in these latitudes have perpetual snows. There are permanent ice caps, and glaciers reach the sea in southern Alaska, and there are glaciers in the mountains of southern Chile, southern New Zealand, Tasmania, and Norway.

In the past, all of these lands were heavily glaciated. The ice scoured the soil off the uplands, carved deep gorges whose bottoms extend below present sea level, and let the sea enter these mountainous coastlands for long distances. Such glaciated, mountainous, coastal lands characterize Norway, Scotland, the panhandle of Alaska, British Columbia, southern Chile, Tasmania, and the west coast of the South Island of New Zealand. Once again, then, we have a set of lands widely distributed over the world with many physical environmental features in common. Once again the questions are: What

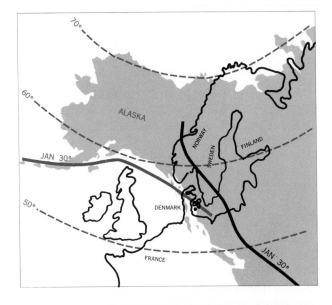

Map 6-1 The West Coasts of North America and Europe

The west coast mid-latitude forest lands of North America and Europe are shown here at similar latitudes to stress the high-latitude position of this type of climate. The isotherm for 30° F. for January is added to show the average winter temperature of the two areas.

Jostedal Glacier, Norway. This glacier descends from a highland ice cap into a valley that was filled by the glacier at the peak of the glacial period. Except for the cattle, this scene could be in Alaska, southern Chile, or southwestern New Zealand. *Norwegian Information Service.*

Skaters on a Canal in the Netherlands. The high mid-latitude location of northwest Europe brings long, cold winters. Despite their low, poor land and at a time when modern machinery and power were not yet developed, the Dutch created one of the world's most advanced nations in a land that lies just south of the southern end of the Panhandle of Alaska. The American counterparts, such as Vancouver Island, remain undeveloped. *Netherlands Information Service.*

were they like and what are they now like in human occupation? How much of their similarity or disparity is due to physical environment, and how much to the play of cultural forces?

Human geography has been greatly concerned with the idea that there are ideal climates for man. On the basis of the present accomplishment of man, the climates in which these achievements predominate have been assumed to be the best for man. Correlations have been made indicating which climates were best for physical work and which for mental work, and they have indicated that the greatest center of human mental activity for the past three centuries has been around the North Sea. In this cool climate, lacking great summer heat or extreme winter cold and having a great number of cyclonic storms throughout the year, are to be found the

dynamic English, Germans, and French with their immense accomplishments in science, art, industry, and commerce. They print and read more books than anyone else in the world, and their literacy rates are the highest in the world. There is no question that there is a perfect correlation here between a specific climate and very high achievement, but is it a causal connection? Or is it an accident? Could it perhaps be said to have come into being almost in spite of a most disagreeably dull, gray, overcast climate? If this is the world's most stimulating climate, and the best for mental effort, should we not expect similar achievements wherever this climate is found? And if that is too much to expect, should not areas of similar climate at least be outstanding for their part of the world? This kind of question can be tested by comparative study of these regions.

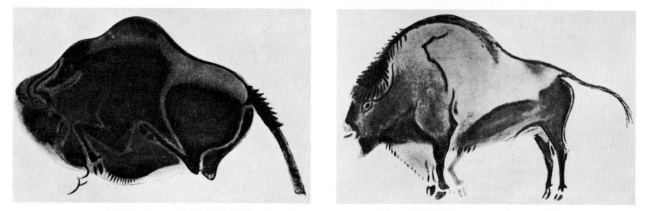

Paintings from the Cave of Altamira near Santander, Spain. These Paleolithic paintings were made about 20,000 years ago, during a period of great creativity in art. *Embassy of Spain.*

NORTHWEST EUROPE

PREHISTORY

Northwest Europe has a long, well-known history. When the ice last lay over Scandinavia and extended south of the Baltic Sea, man had already learned to use fire, he had dug snug houses into the ground for protection from the cold, and he was unquestionably wearing clothing made from the skins of the animals he was hunting. The Neanderthal men lived in western Europe about 60,000 years ago at the height of the last ice age. Then the ancestors of some of the modern Europeans appeared on the scene. The Cromagnon, Brünn, and Boreby people, still represented in modern populations of northwest Europe, appeared about 20,000 to 30,000 years ago. This was the time of the wonderful cave paintings and the engravings on bone of spirited scenes of their days. We know from such evidence that these people were skilled hunters of mammoth, reindeer, horse, deer, and bison.

As the ice retreated, the reindeer hunters had to follow the reindeer northward out of France into Denmark and Scandinavia if they were to continue to be reindeer specialists. Some of these men elected to stay at home. They shifted to eating new animals appearing with the increasing forest cover of the land: horse, bison, and deer.

Europe was a changing world at the end of the ice age. The melting ice fed the seas; the seas rose; the melting ice took an immense weight off the land; and the land rose. Depending on the rate of such movements, land was rising above or being overwhelmed by shallow seas. At the height of the ice age there was no English Channel, and much of the floor of the North Sea was land. The Rhine, Seine, and Thames rivers were the headwater streams of a large river flowing northward to the sea. Modern Europe took on its present shape when the Baltic ceased to be a fresh water lake and became an arm of the sea, the North Sea ceased to be land, and the English Channel came into existence to make England an island. All of this has happened within the last 10,000 years, and much of it within the last 5000 years.

The modern European climate was established by 10,000 years ago and has fluctuated since only to a minor degree. By then the influences that were to change Europe from the realm of hunters and fishermen had made a start on their way to this distant land—distant, that is, from the center of growing civilization in the Near East, and hence a retarded, backward area. Agriculture, the basis of the Neolithic revolution, was spreading along the axis of the Mediterranean and from various points there, beginning to spread northward into northern Europe. By 2000 B.C. it had reached the English Channel (see Map 2–2).

When agriculture reached toward the cold wet lands to the north and west, it met serious problems. Wheat and barley belong in the warm lands and need hot weather for good growth and dry weather for harvest. Marine west-coast areas are wet and cool, and there is no dry season. Even today it is only southeastern England that is wheat country. Ireland, Scotland, northern Germany, and Scandinavia are lands of oats and rye. Imaginative reconstructions of how oats and rye came to be important domestic plants have portrayed them as weeds that in time came to supplant the crop. Oats flourished where the climate was cool and very moist, hence in Scotland and Ireland. Rye dominated where summers were short and winters long and severe, hence in Scandinavia and northern Germany.

When man introduced agriculture into northern Europe, he sometimes changed the environment drastically. At other times, technological changes even more drastically changed his assessment of the environment.

In England, for example, the early farmers stayed on the thin light soils of the uplands. Their simple plows could manage them, but they could not work the heavier clay-rich soils of the lowlands. The early agricultural settlement pattern of Britain, then, was culturally determined. The concentration on one kind of land form and one soil type was determined primarily by the tool, not by the physical environment. Later, when the modern type of plow was introduced, the richer soils of the lowlands could be used. The forests that had been a haven for wolves and outlaws were cleared, and population centers grew up in their stead that dwarfed the old upland centers. Today, the ancient roads and towns on the uplands have declined to such an extent that many of them have to be reconstructed from archeological studies. Aerial photographs sometimes reveal the old field patterns, town plans, and roadways on the uplands. Many of these date to Neolithic and Roman times and were abandoned after the Germanic invasions brought in the heavy, earth-turning plow that made the heavy richer clay soils useful.

Another agricultural revolution in Europe occurred when a new plant was introduced from America in the seventeenth century. The cold, wet ground and cool, short seasons of northwestern Europe are not the best grain lands. When the so-called Irish potato was introduced from South America, land of marginal utility suddenly became productive. The potato not only grows in cool, moist, short-season conditions, but it gives a heavy yield per acre. This revolutionized the agriculture of the north German plain and was so important in Ireland that many people came to think of the Irish potato as truly Irish. The potato that made modern Ireland possible is an artifact, a domestic plant, that changed the potential of the landscape as much as the idea of the heavy Germanic mold-board plow.

Northwest Europe early was influenced by ideas coming from distant centers of cultural growth. There was placer gold in Ireland and tin in Cornwall, and there is a half-hidden history of extensive exploration and prospecting of these regions by early bronze age people of the eastern Mediterranean who sought copper, tin, and gold. Somehow they found their way to the British sources by 2500 B.C. and developed them. This would seem less remarkable if we knew all the steps. Trade is ancient. In Neolithic times Baltic amber was traded to the Mediterranean, and the rich metal deposits of Spain were discovered early. Fishing probably has supported the people of Europe for more thousands of years than is commonly thought, and fishermen move about to a considerable degree. Quite probably the

Stonehenge, Southwest England. A memorial to the Mediterranean influences that were reaching England and Ireland by sea routes around Spain in the period just after 2000 B.C. *British Travel Association.*

Hadrian's Wall, Northumberland. A remnant of Roman influence in England, this 70-mile long wall was built across Northumberland and Cumberland counties in the second century A.D. as a line of defense against the unconquered Scots to the north. *British Travel Association.*

metal-seeking people of the Mediterranean simply followed well-established land and sea routes to the North Sea region where they found the minerals that they valued. The Irish gold and Cornish tin led to long-sustained influences.

Ireland and adjacent southern England became a cultural center in the north. Stonehenge and similar monuments are some of the tangible evidences of these early contacts. Much of the doubts as to the age of the monuments has been dispelled by carbon-14 dating, which places them about 2000 B.C. Most recently, outlines of bronze implements typical of the eastern Mediterranean bronze age have been found carved into the great stones.

This is an example of how we get to know things, for the paths to knowledge are often indirect. Dating by radioactive carbon, for example, depended on developments in atomic physics. Knowledge is often belatedly gained from overlooked obvious sources. The carvings of bronze age implements persisted for nearly four millennia, but were not noted as such until the mid-twentieth century. From such dating we learn of the extremely long-continued influence from distant centers in the eastern Mediterranean; and we learn that distance dilutes effect. Thus, despite millennia-long influences that gave this northwestern corner of Europe a distinct opportunity, relatively little happened.

More probably happened than is commonly thought, however, for the Norse destruction in the area erased much of the evidence of bronze age progress. When the Romans reached the English Channel, they were reaching better-known territory than had been the case in France. The ports of southern England and adjacent Ireland, they said, were well known to them because of the ancient and extensive commerce carried on from those places. Northwesternmost Europe, then, has had a very long maritime history and through that activity has maintained contact with the center of civilizational ferment at the east end of the Mediterranean Sea for at least 4000 years. In that case, why was western Europe so long delayed in its ascendency?

Glencoe, Scotland. The Scottish highlands are losing population in a way similar to New England. Vast areas of uplands are reverting to pasture land, being reforested, or being held for recreational purposes. *British Travel Association.*

CULTURAL LAG IN NORTHWEST EUROPE

It has been argued that the climate of northwest Europe is the optimum one for human mental efficiency, but it has been that for approximately 10,000 years. In addition, for the past 4000 years, people with advanced ideas and skills have been reaching it in important numbers, enough to stimulate the building of Stonehenge about 2000 B.C., and enough Roman influence in the 400 years between A.D. 43 and 443 to build cities, roads, and baths for Roman England and walls to contain the unconquerable Scotch and Welsh. Where was the climatic stimulus when for 400 years the Romans made potentially, and to a large extent really, available the advanced knowledge of the Mediterranean?

The northwest European states are often described as having become maritime powers because of their advantageous position on the Atlantic at the time that world commerce broke out of the Mediterranean Sea. It is a fact that 90 percent of the earth's land surface is in the half of the earth centered on France. This land includes 94 percent of the world's population and 98 percent of the world's industry. It is said that for these reasons no other area of the world has so advantageous a position as Europe, but how much of this is determined by physical geography and how much by culture? The land-sea distribution has not changed greatly in the past million years, or even slightly in the last 5000 years. The industrial concentration centering on Europe has come about in the last 200 years, and its dominant position, quite possibly, will have ceased to exist in another 200 years.

The notion that world commerce burst out of the Mediterranean about the time the northwest European powers began their rise is untrue. World commerce never had been contained within, or restricted to, the Mediterranean. World commerce plied the Indian, Pacific, and Atlantic oceans long before A.D. 1500. As we have seen, even the Mediterranean people were reaching outside the Pillars of Hercules as early as 2000 B.C. to reach to England. How much farther they may have reached we have yet to learn, but that they reached America is by no means impossible, and the recent finding of a Roman artifact in America and the appearance of American domestic plants in the Mediterranean area in pre-Columbian time now makes it seem probable. In every way, the climatic stimulus and Atlantic ocean-edge type of explanation for the rise of northwest Europe fails to prove its case.

In a way, the people of northwest Europe are to be placed in parallel with the long-retarded Africans, or with the Yuman Indians: they were not oriented to civilization; they were too far away for massive impacts of civilized knowledge to reach them and force a rapid change. Change therefore came enormously slowly and was subject to costly setbacks such as the Germanic outpourings in the post-Roman period.

The parallels with the American Southwest are interesting. Heavy civilizational influence reached southern Arizona. Canal irrigation began; monumental structures were built, and the Casa Grande near Phoenix is in a sense a Stonehenge, for not only is it a multistoried building but slits in its walls oriented for celestial observations suggest cultural influences from distant centers of civilization. However, the ideas did not spread far and fast. The Yumas were, like the Scotch and Welsh, adjacent, but resistant, to change. Finally the civilizational impulse was greatly set back by the incursion of a raiding people: Germanic tribes in Europe; Athabascan tribes in America. The parallel can be carried even further: the Spanish influence on the Southwest was like the Roman influence on Britain; London was a distant colonial outpost comparable to Santa Fe. The Roman influence lasted for 400 years; the Spanish for 300. The effects were astonishingly small in both cases. It does not seem to have mattered whether the climate was arid or humid, warm or cold. Distance to an outpost among barbaric peoples seems to have been the controlling force. Later, new conditions led to rapid cultural advance. In both Europe and North America the physical environment was the passive stage on which the culturally determined events were played out.

In Europe the Germanic outbreaks and the collapse of the Roman Empire initiated a cultural setback equivalent to the collapse of the Hohokam culture and the retreat of the Pueblo culture in the Southwest (see Chapter 2). This initiated the European Dark Ages, usually portrayed as far blacker than they were. The interesting socio-economic system called "feudalism" came to dominate the scene. Crop yields were low, but they probably always had been. Even under the three-field system in which some of the land rested and the cattle pasturing tended to aid the renewal of fertility, the return was low. Wheat only gave 6 to 10 bushels an acre, as compared with modern yields of 30 to 40. Population had to be in proportion to the ability of the land to produce. Further, this was a time of many small, warring political divisions, and much good land was kept out of production for political reasons.

However, trade never stopped. Old knowledge was kept alive in the monasteries, and new knowledge was brought by the traders. A great burst of new knowledge accompanied the increased contacts outside Europe that came with the Crusades. In the seventeenth century, the middle class was rising with the growth of commerce, and the nation-state was developing in Europe. The little feudal units were forged into large units, until even Germany, the last of the major units, was hammered together. Around 1750, the industrial revolution was underway, and one of the crucial periods of human geography was initiated. Notice that all of these changes—from pre-Roman barbarism through Roman colonialism into the political fragmentation of the Dark Ages, into the nation-state of the eighteenth century, and into the industrial revolution that has shaped the present—all took place on a single geographic scene. The physical geography did not change one meaningful bit.

ANTECEDENTS OF THE INDUSTRIAL REVOLUTION

The industrial revolution is usually placed as beginning in England about 1760. It is marked by a shift from cottage to factory work, and is clearly related to shifts in the use of power and machinery, for prior to this time the use of power was very limited. For nearly 2000 years, men had very slowly been moving toward the application of nonhuman energy to the heavy daily work that mankind had always had to do. The moving of loads across the land was eased by a machine composed of wheels and a frame, a wagon. But this required costly roads, and for a very long time no one thought of any way to apply anything except animal power to this device. Movement of goods over the water was more efficient, for not only did we have an excellent load-carrying machine in the ship, but man rather early learned to harness wind power by means of the quite clumsy square sail. He then was astonishingly slow to learn to use the fore and aft sail that allows a ship to tack into the wind.

The greatest power need of early man was for the grinding of his daily bread, and it was in the solving of this problem that the major advances were made that finally led to the broad application of power to all kinds of industrial needs. Grain can either be pounded or ground into flour, and mankind very early divided on this. Neither motion is easily converted into the circular motion that is characteristic of our wheel-based machinery. It was the grinding motion that finally did come to be converted into a circular grinding, long to be done by hand, but potentially ready to be power driven. This change from grinding with a back and forth motion came in Graeco-Roman times. Thereafter there is a very long and little-known history of solving the problems of applying power to wheels to grind grain.

It is these long, slow, halting periods of solution of such problems that are the critical ones. All too often they are hidden in the historical addiction to telling of kings and empires. Then, when the fruit of these hidden periods of discovery bursts forth in something like the industrial revolution, we are mystified at their "suddenness." Beginning with Roman times, water was harnessed by wheels, often to grind grain. There were innumerable problems to be solved. The water had to be controlled: the wheels were at first directly driven by the current; later, the wheels were set on edge and at first undershot and then overshot. This required gears, to change the plane of rotation from the vertical water wheel to the horizontal milling stone. Gears could not be very satisfactory until metal was commonly in use. Steady, though microscopically slow, progress was made along these lines for centuries. Among other inventions that came along was the windmill, which was first made in Persia in the eighth century A.D. The windmill too required gears. In sum, these inventions and adaptations, being made over a wide area in Europe and the Near East, laid the base for the industrial revolution.

Notice that by the application of the principle of antecedents we can eliminate large parts of the world as possible centers of origin for the industrial revolution. All of South America, North America, tropical Africa, Australia, New Zealand, Polynesia, and Siberia are out of consideration because these areas lacked the necessary ingredients. Some areas such as the Americas had agriculture and consequently the necessary economic base. In parts of Indian America the complex loom—with all the parts found in the European looms—was present; however, the development of the idea of the wheel was lacking. There were no potters' wheels, rotary grindstones, or even wheeled vehicles, though it must be noted that some of the Indians most certainly had the principle of the wheel, for wheeled toys have been found in their graves. Nonetheless, the rotary principle was not elaborated and without it the harnessing of power and its application to do the work that man had always done by hand was blocked. If it was blocked for agricultural, civilized, mechanically skilled Indian America, how much less chance there was for the other areas listed above. It is worth stating these distributions in reverse: only in the belt from Europe to China and India were the necessary ingredients for the industrial revolution present before A.D. 1500.

Theoretically, the shift to a much broader application of machinery to production could have come at any point in this vast area. In fact, it appeared first in Great Britain, giving that country such a head start that 200 years later it is still one of the leading industrial nations of the world while large areas of the globe have yet to begin to enter the industrial era. The cultural lag remains even in these times of enormously speeded-up communication.

But why Great Britain? Was it a stimulating climate and a channel-protected position; or was it a combination of poor climate and soil with proximity to the sea that led to the taking up of trade and the consequent contact with ideas? None of these factors has changed significantly in the past 4000 years. Yet after 1750 a change began in Great Britain that was to change the world.

We meet here the role of the superior individual operating within his cultural setting. The scene was set; the requisite preliminary steps had been made; all the parts were at hand. It was only a matter of time until the parts were put together and the first spinning machines were made and harnessed by means of the already existing methods. As the repeated case of simultaneous inventions of such things as the telephone, calculus, and anesthesia show, when such a state is reached, the invention follows. But such simultaneous inventions are always made within one cultural-geographical area and spring out of a similar background of ideas. The idea of natural selection as the basis of the changing of life forms occurred to two Englishmen, Charles Darwin and A. R. Wallace, who were well acquainted with the line of thought in biology that had been developing among the northwest European scientists for 100 years. It was one of the accidents of history that it was two Englishmen rather than some continental scientists that are credited with the idea. This in no way detracts from the role of the individual. Darwin and Wallace were notable men, but the nature of their accomplishment was culturally shaped. This is the way in which the broad-scale application of power to industry must be viewed.

The beginning came in the spinning and weaving industry. In the consumption of manpower the preparing of cloth came second only to the never-ending task of grinding the grain. This was a most tedious and time-consuming task. Few today realize what was involved. Wool had to be clipped from the sheep, washed to remove the oily lanolin, carded to get all of the fibers lying in parallel then spun into thread, then the threads had to be woven into cloth. All of these were originally hand processes, which gradually have been mechanized. Spinning wheels were an early, moderately complex machine. They pointed the way toward the possibility of mechanization, and the rotary spinning motion was a relatively simple one to harness. Looms had long been in existence and had been growing more and more complex for at least 2000 years. From simple hanging warps and all finger work, man had progressed to warps fixed in a frame, with shuttles to carry the thread, and with systems of attached strings that alternately raised one set of warps and then another. These were difficult motions to harness.

BRITISH LEADERSHIP

After 1750 in England, men began to give major attention to these problems. A whole series of solutions was reached. It then became possible to apply power to machines and to increase the rate of production of cloth many times over. This could not be done in each cottage, for power was at first water power, and later steam power, and these installations were too cumbersome and too costly to make at every worker's home. The workers therefore had to come together at specific points, instead of working at home. This was the beginning of the factory system, which led to the growth of the factory town, and eventually to the large-scale movement of people off of the land into the towns. Since the increase in productivity of these mills allowed the British to undersell the world in cloth, their trade and commerce prospered and their industrial cities grew. Britain's lead in manufacturing became so great, that it paid her to use her manpower in manufacturing and commerce and to import her food. Grain importation became important for Britain as early as 1750 and increased thereafter.

This is doubly interesting, for the means to make large-scale grain movements had marked Roman and even earlier civilizations. In Britain about 1750, however, the need to import grain was probably less than it had been. New ideas about crop rotation and manuring had come into being, and ideas about chemical fertilization were being promoted. The ability of the British to feed themselves was rising to higher levels than it had ever been. However, the choice was to use the land to produce wool, and to put the labor force to work in factories. The comparative advantage of machine-woven goods was so great that the British could make more by exporting cloth and importing grain.

It is a common thing that once an advantageous start has been made in a new line of endeavor momentum quickly builds up. More and more effort and brains are poured into the new type of work, and further innovations are made. The present burst of discovery and invention in atomic energy and rocketry and its associated fields are an excellent example. In Britain, the success of the application of power to the first simple spinning machines led to greater and greater inputs of human inventiveness. These led to further successes, that led to still further efforts. Yet these inventions were limited to one area—the applications of power and machinery to familiar tasks—and limitations on human inventiveness are apparent even then.

The spinning jenny dates to 1764, and the power loom to 1785. Water power was proving inadequate to supply the necessary power. The steam engine was invented in 1769 and was in factory use by 1785. At first these engines were fired by wood, but between the use of charcoal in smelting and the demands of the steam engines, England was rapidly being deforested. Coal had been used in pre-Roman days in Britain, but for a long interval it was used very slightly. About 1650, it began to be used as home fuel. Its use for smelting was long hampered because unprocessed coal is not ideal for use in smelters, but it wasn't until 1859 that coal was roasted to produce coke. This seems like an inordinate delay, especially when it is remembered that wood was customarily heated to produce charcoal for furnace use. The transfer of this idea to treating coal in similar fashion to improve its qualities in the same way for the same industry illustrates the difficulty with which men produce ideas, and this is the more notable since it occurred at a time when men were invention minded.

Each of these ideas changed ways of living and thus changed the cultural landscape of Great Britain, and each of these changes gave that country an added advantage over the remainder of the world. This advantage enabled it to pour still more time, money, and manpower into further improvements of history. The cloth industry required power, this led to machines; machines required metal, and this speeded up mining. Machinery was applied to mining both of iron and of coal, and this lead. to still further demands for more kinds of machines and more metal to make machines and machinists both to make and to run the machines. Meanwhile, shipping had to be expanded to bring in grain and raw materials and to carry out the manufactured products. The process, once started, expanded like a chain reaction that reached far and wide through the whole way of life of the people. Once Great Britain had the start, all of the cultural forces thrust it forward. The factors of distance, cultural resistance, and, to some extent, deliberate effort on the part of the British, kept other nations from getting an equally early start.

It is clear that the beginning of the industrial revolution could have been in any number of places in the European world. Within that area it seems to have been in the nature of a historical accident that the beginning was in Britain. Once the process was started, the momentum of the movement toward industrial development swept it into an increasing lead, while the forces of distance and cultural disconnection held other nations from making a similar start. That the forces of cultural relationship could be greater than mere distance is well illustrated in this case by the fact that it was not the most adjacent countries that most quickly became industrialized. It was the culturally close, but geographically distant, country of the United States that led off, with adjacent Germany a close second.

Great Britain by virtue of her start in industrialization, rapidly became *the* leading nation of the world, a role that it was to hold until the middle of the twentieth century, when with the loss of its colonial empire it would recede to the place of *one* of the leading nations of the world. This is an amazing performance when it is considered that England, Ireland, Scotland, and Wales put together only equal in size the state of New Mexico.

Britain is now an urbanized, manufacturing nation that produces only a fraction of the food necessary to feed itself, even though annual food production is greater today than it was a hundred years ago. On their little bit of land, the British sustain a population of 50 million people. This is a population density of 540 per square mile. The land is in the hands of relatively few people. In Scotland 600 people own 80 percent of the land. In England and Wales, about 2500 people own one half of the cultivated land. These are interesting facts. In Latin America such ownership of land is called "latifundia" and is severely attacked by social critics. It is considered one of the causes of Latin American lack of progress. It would appear that such landownership has in some way failed to hold Britain back from progress. The lesson seems clear. It is not the landownership pattern, but the economic pattern that determines whether or not such landownership is good or bad. In Great Britain the major employment of the people is not on the land but in the factories, while in Latin America there are not yet enough factories to employ the people. Latin America may find that it is easier to add factories than to distribute land. Further, the movement in the whole industrialized world is away from the small landholding that has characterized man's use of the land for thousands of years to large mechanized farms of very high productivity per man on the land. This is distinctly the American pattern, and is to some extent, the British pattern.

The British development can be seen, then, as being little related to the "stimulating climate," its position near the center of the land hemisphere of the world, or at the center of the manufacturing part of the world. The climatic stimulation took a belated effect on men in Great Britain, and seemingly has lost some of its effectiveness in this century. Nor did the central position near the center of the land hemisphere have any effect until the arrival of the industrial revolution. The industrial revolution was the creation of the British and it put them at the center of the industrial world. The urbanized, capitalized, industrialized England of today is what the British have made of their land. Its rainy, overcast, foggy climate, with its long, dark winters, may be stimulating to some, but it would be very depressing to anyone used to the sun. The factors that made Britain great were the human forces released within that country by the developments in the fields of government, economics, and science. British greatness is little dependent on the land; it is enormously dependent on such human factors.

Since Britain is now in a period of decline, or at least of failure to grow at the same rate as much of the rest of the world, it must be concluded that a change has occurred, not in the physical geography, but in the cultural geography. Several things have been taking place simultaneously, and are often mentioned by those who try to explain the decline. Great Britain has been through two great wars, has lost her colonial empire, and has shifted her governmental structure from a predominantly capitalistic free enterprise system toward a predominantly socialistic system within which the tax burden is so distributed as to virtually destroy extreme private wealth. British failure to keep up with economic growth rates elsewhere is measured by the fact that the average per capita income of the United States Negro in 1960 equaled that of the average Briton.*

Something in Great Britain has changed, and it is not the climate or the country's position at the center of the land hemisphere. Wars can hardly be the answer, for Great Britain has survived numerous wars as severe and of greater duration than those of this century, and countries more devastated by the wars of this century, such as Germany,

* "Just How Well Off Is the American Negro?" *U.S. News & World Report*, July 22, 1963.

Belgium, and Italy, have all recovered, while it has not. Although the loss of its colonial empire was a blow, this was probably not enough to account for the matter. Colonies can be costly, and Great Britain has borne large costs both directly and indirectly. Giving Dominions such as New Zealand preferential treatment amounts to paying more for dairy products than they cost in the open market. Devotees of the capitalistic free enterprise system will of course be impressed by the parallel between the growing socialization of Great Britain and the destructive taxation levied on the capitalist class, with the attendant decline in Great Britain's fortunes.

IRELAND

Ireland's lack of development despite being a part of Great Britain for so long deserves notice. There is little that England has that Ireland lacks. Its climate is equally stimulating, if cool, cyclonic storm-dominated climates are stimulating. It has some water power, sufficient surely to have made a start on industrializing. Thereafter local coal would have been useful, and still later, coal could have been imported. Why did the industrial revolution leap to the United States, but not to Ireland? Surely it is an oddity that the Irish have had to emigrate to find industrial employment.

The Irish beginnings as civilized people go far back. They were one of the centers of the Mediterranean influences that reached northwest Europe as early as 2000 B.C. In Julius Caesar's time, the Irish were still an important, sea-faring, advanced people. The Irish setback came during the Norse outbreaks, for Ireland's location in the sea left it subject to pillage by rampaging Norsemen. The great monasteries with their ancient libraries—early centers of learning—were sacked and burned. Thereafter came the period of English conquest and colonialism. Only someone who has read of the 1000 years (roughly A.D. 900–1900) of English conquest and rule of Ireland with its endless revolutions and reprisals can understand the almost pathological

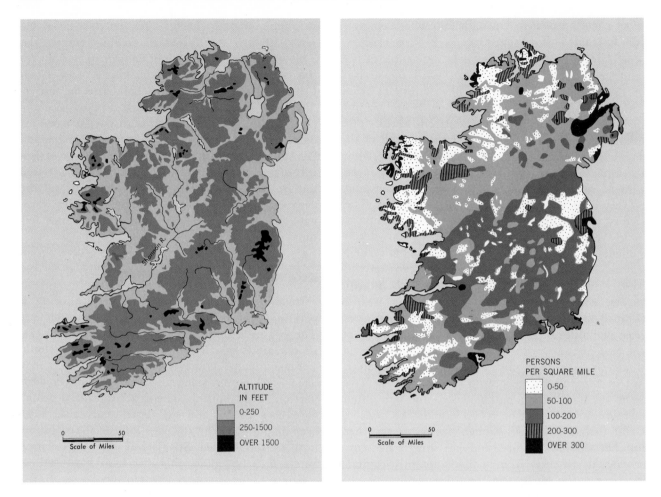

Land Form   Population Density

Map 6-2   Ireland: Land Form, Population, and Farm Size

A low land with high rainfall, surprisingly few people, and many totally empty areas characterizes Ireland. There is a striking correlation between larger than average farms on the uplands of the southeast and lower than average population density. *Adapted from* Focus—*The American Geographical Society.*

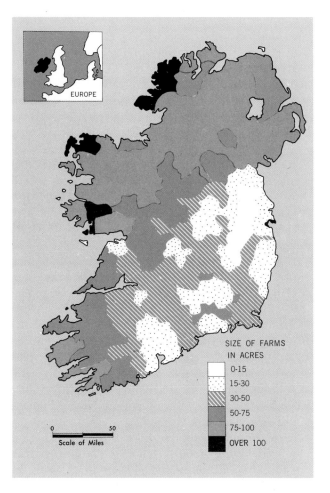

Average Size of Farms

SIZE OF FARMS
IN ACRES

- 0-15
- 15-30
- 30-50
- 50-75
- 75-100
- OVER 100

EUROPE

0   50
Scale of Miles

causes, but one of the important ones was the arrival of the Peruvian potato. This plant does well in cool climate and short seasons and produces an enormous yield of carbohydrate food per acre. It replaced the oat and rye cereals to a large degree and with a greatly increased food base, the population began to grow. By 1846, there were 8,5000,000 people in Ireland, and the potato crop was the dominant crop in the land. Then disaster struck: disease attacked the potatoes. So great was the crop loss, and so great was the dependence of the people on this one plant, that millions died in the ensuing famine. Millions of others emigrated, 90 percent of them to the United States. By 1850, the population had fallen to 4,000,000; in 1960, it was 2,800,000. Emigration has remained high, and the population has never recovered. In this time, when most lands have greatly increased their population densities, Ireland has dropped to less than half the population that it had in the mid-nineteenth century.

Since 1922, southern Ireland, five sixths of the land, has been allowed to move away from union with Great Britain, to an independent status as the Republic of Ireland. In this time, industrial growth has been marked and it is clear that Ireland is in process of becoming an industrialized nation. Ireland, then, becomes a clear example of the failure of mere proximity. The complex interplay of nationalism, religious wars, and the disaster of the potato famine combined to prevent either industrialization, such as Belgium achieved, or commercialized agriculture on the Danish pattern.

Irish ways of doing things seems always to come out the reverse of the expected. The greatest emigration in the past century did not come out of the poorest lands but out of the better lands. The greatest density of settlement is not now on the best lands, but on the poorer lands to the northwest. The size of landholding is in direct inverse proportion to the density of population. Today the major emigration is from these small farms on the poor lands. Irishmen now migrate to England in search of work, but the Irish hope Eire will soon

hatred that the Irish have for the English. Ireland was not industrialized because it was a rebellious colony that was held by force. So great was the problem that the English at times tried what today would be genocide. It was a bitter, black history of fighting without quarter that went on intermittently for seemingly endless time. Learning, science, industry, do not thrive on this sort of fare.

Toward the end of the seventeenth century, there were about a million people in Ireland. Population thereafter grew rapidly. There were a number of have its own industry. Labor is an important commodity. As we have seen, industry flourished in New England when a ready labor supply was pouring into the cities from the rocky hill farms, and is now flourishing in the South where the mechanization of agriculture is displacing small farmers from the land. Eire seems to have the same labor-surplus situation that could become an industrial asset. The current figures on industrial growth in Ireland suggest that industry is moving in to take advantage of this labor resource that long has been sitting on the doorstep of the European industrial center.

In the original industrial revolution, power requirements brought people to the power site, enforcing urban growth and centering industry on the coal fields. Transportation was so rudimentary that masses of people had to be jammed into a very small space in order to keep a large population within traveling distance of the factory centers. Today, many of these conditions have changed. Electric power can be distributed readily over wide areas. Coal and oil are moved with relative ease. Factories can now spread over the countryside. Transportation is such that workers, too, may live dispersed over large areas. Ireland could develop industries spread throughout her countryside in a pattern quite different from the nineteenth-century industrial cities. It will be interesting to see if this possibility is grasped, or if the pattern established when conditions were quite different from what they are now will rule the form that is adopted in the mid-twentieth century.

FRANCE

The other countries of western Europe have followed separate courses in the history of their developments. France is only partially in the marine west-coast climate. Its south coast is Mediterranean in climate, and inland, summers are rather hot and winters rather cold for a typical marine climate. Yet, its northwest European location places it in this zone of alleged climatic stimulation. France,

a nation with a land area the size of Texas, has a good agricultural base; wheat, cattle, and wines suggest some of the variety of its products. France feeds itself.

French contacts with the civilizations of the Mediterranean began very early. Marseilles is a Mediterranean port, and was a port of call as early as Phoenician times. The Roman contact with France was much longer and stronger than it was with Britain. One of the measures of this contact is that while the British retained their Germanic speech through 400 years of Roman occupation, France lost its Celtic speech and changed to a Romance language, with the exception of the people of relatively remote Brittany.

With this longer, stronger influence, France took an early lead in northwest Europe. In the preindustrial period, its population was relatively large and it was one of the centers of learning. However, when the industrial revolution arrived, France lagged. By 1870, Germany exceeded it in population, and in 1900 even tiny England surpassed it. After 1900 France's population was not only stable, but actually began to decline. In 1930 even lightly industrialized Italy passed it in poplation. Today France's population is rising.

It is true that France is short of coal and that oil has been found in only limited amounts. Its iron ore supplies, on the other hand, are good as are its water power resources. Its location near the center of the land hemisphere, at the center of the industrial world, and on the edge of the Atlantic is fully as good as that of Great Britain, and France has the advantage of greater size, more diversity of climate and soils, and an all around better agricultural base. In the eighteenth and nineteenth centuries it had the advantages of greater population. Despite all these advantages, France fell behind in the period of European economic growth and development in the nineteenth century.

It would be easy to claim that lack of coal, or later of oil, or some other set of physical factors was the cause of this relative decline of France; but that this can scarcely be true is shown by noting that its neighbor, Belgium, with virtually no oil, little coal, and no iron, has nonetheless made a prospering manufacturing nation of itself. Adjacent Germany, with less access to the sea, equally devastated by wars, and with a colder and wetter climate and less useful agricultural land, has used its considerably better coal and iron resources to do an immensely better job of industrializing, providing for its people, and expanding its population and prosperity. The causes cannot be said to be simple physical environmental.

It could be argued that they are indirectly environmental. France's better land with its good agriculture may have diverted attention to food, cattle, and the vine. The incentive to try to do something to break out of the limits set by adverse climate and soil may have been lacking. Or, it could be argued that the French, as has so often happened in history, became complacent during their time of cultural pre-eminence and were unconvinced that the upstart manufacturers and merchants across the channel had set off on a line of development that was to change the world. Such an attitude would give the British a head start that the French would then have a difficult time overcoming.

The role of a spirit of a nation has seldom been so drastically illustrated as the French change after World War II. The postwar period was one of chaotic government with almost constant changes of premiers and governments. The French finally came to a state of weary confusion. The return of De Gaulle to power, with his firm belief in France, gave them a rallying point. The industrial growth that had been coming along in spite of all the handicaps of uncertain governments then accelerated. The growth of the economic unification of Europe is giving France an enlarged opportunity at the very time that it may be disposed to use it. Already France is rated as more prosperous than at any time in its previous history. With the physical-geographical factor held constant, France is now likely to change the whole course of its development, and with a rebirth of French accomplishment, it has already reversed its population trend from downward to upward.

GERMANY

Germany, for centuries France's principal enemy on the continent, is a classic example of a late starter and a strong finisher. Germany was the last of the north European peoples to be organized into a national unit. German expansion had long been eastward into Slavic territory, and this had added the low, wet plains east of the Oder River to Germany. Germany then came to have two distinct parts: northern Germany, a land of plains draining to the North and Baltic seas; and southern Germany, a hill and mountain country.

South Germany was the closer to the centers of ideas in the Mediterranean. Trade routes from the north Italian area crossed through the Alpine passes and kept the South German area in contact with the advances in the Mediterranean world, while northern Germany, through its merchant and fishing contacts, maintained wide contacts around the Baltic and North seas. The industrial revolution began in England in 1750, but it is not until about 1850 that industrial growth began in Germany. Significantly, it began in northwest Germany. The delay is of great interest: the distance was small, and the contacts between the peoples were direct and frequent.

It seems difficult to account for this technological delay in any way except in terms of the lack of interest of the Germans at this time in a factory-type system of industry. They had many highly skilled enterprises. For example, German map making is centuries old and has long been one of the world's finest, but this is typical small-scale industry, using artisans to produce a low bulk, high value product. Further, it was centered in southern Germany, the area in close contact with the north Italian industrial centers with similar outlooks. As with everyone else, the Germans had to grind their grains and spin and weave their fibers. Once England had shown the way, they could have made the same start and followed much the same line of development. Nevertheless, there was a lag of about one century.

German industrial development gained a great impulse through the unification of Germany and the successful war against France in 1870, which gave them control of the iron of the Alsace-Lorraine— a district which could be combined with the great coal resource of the Ruhr. This was also the time when the coking of coal to improve its value for smelting was invented. Yet all of these things can be overstated. The political boundary drawn to give Germany Alsace and Lorraine was drawn with strategic defense in mind, not to gain the iron. Further, the iron ore was of little use because of its phosphorous content, and the solution of the problem of making it useful lay ahead in time.

The good coal had been there for a long time; its usefulness had been potential for thousands of years. Coal for household heating had become important in England by 1650, and was in use in France by 1715. The very high-grade coal of the Ruhr, with iron ores nearby, located in a country with contacts reaching southward into the Mediterranean and northwestward around all of northwest Europe, and in the world's most stimulating climate (according to the Elsworth Huntington thesis, see Chapter 1), should have been the center of the industrial revolution, instead of a hundred-year laggard. The story is again that resources, and other physical factors, are secondary in importance in relation to cultural factors.

Once Germany began her industrialization, her development went at a phenomenal pace. The cultural elements on which to build were there. The educational base was broad; there was a widespread, diversified, small industry; and trade and commerce were ancient callings. Well-developed routes up the Rhine, over the Alpine passes, and down the Danube had long been in existence. When national unity, with purposeful direction of

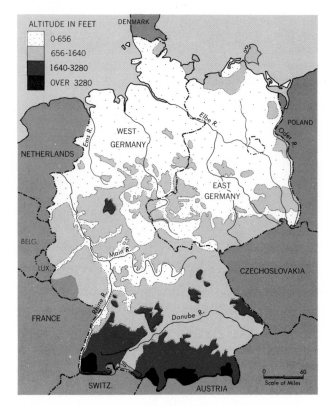

ALTITUDE IN FEET
0-656
656-1640
1640-3280
OVER 3280

Land Form

the nation's growth into industrial lines and away from the dominance of agriculture, began in the 1860s, Germany sprang from a minor position to a first rank industrial nation within 50 years. The change was as dramatic as the emergence of Japan from its long isolation into the modern world.

Germany had an advantage in its late start, because the latest improvements could be incorporated in its new industry. England in contrast had an investment in going plants that were on their way to obsolescence but which it was reluctant to scrap, and this reluctance to make necessary improvements, along with the punitive tax structure of the post-1900 era, cost it its world position. After each of the wars in this century, Germany has made a phenomenal come back. In each case, energetic

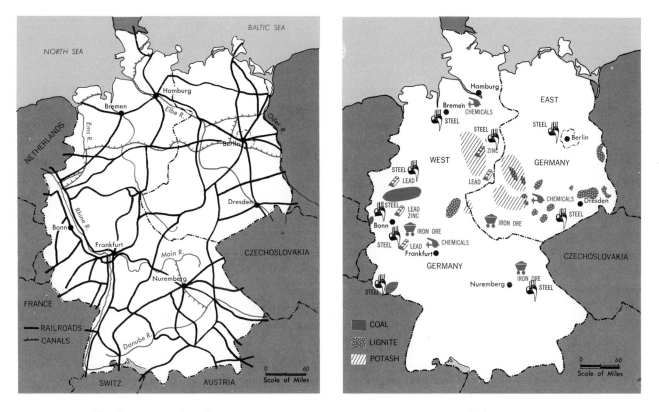

The Transportation System

Industry

Map 6-3 Germany: Land Form, Transportation, and Industry

Germany is a land of low elevation with a great coastal plain to the north and modest highlands to the south. The relatively flat land has allowed Germany great freedom in laying out its railroad network, and the fact that Germany developed industrially in the railroad era has led to a dense network. The major rivers of Germany are navigable and carry a great deal of freight. In addition, the glacial edge ran east and west, creating east-west lowlands, which the Germans have utilized as connecting links between such rivers as the Ems, the Elbe, and the Oder.

Germany has important coal, lignite, and potash deposits, and before World War II had developed industries based on these deposits in what are now East and West Germany. In the postwar period, under an enterprise system, West Germany has rebuilt its industries and become one of the world's most prosperous areas. East Germany, despite its good resource base, has stagnated under the restrictive planned programming of the Communist regime. Note also on the map the location of major industries at port locations such as Bremen and Hamburg where there are no notable natural resources. *Adapted from* Focus— *The American Geographical Society.*

application of human skills and rebuilding with the most advanced and newest equipment has allowed them to jump back into an advantageous competitive position.

It is too often said that Germany's advantages are enormous. It has the greatest coal reserves in Europe, vast areas of lignite, and the valuable Stassfurt salt deposits (see Map 6–3). This omits the fact that Germany is short of oil, iron, copper, and a long list of essential materials. The scale and intensity of Europe is well exemplified by the Ruhr. This industrial zone is 45 miles long and 15 miles wide and has 5 million people in its nearly continuous urban development. Several individual United States centers exceed this in size, equal it in population, and approach it in production. German soil is poor in the north and limited by the rough nature of the land to the south. Less than one fourth of the country is suitable for agriculture. The prewar area was only equal to that of the state of Texas. Crippled by partition between the western powers and the Russians, with its capital city divided between these powers and isolated in the Communist Zone, with the eastern provinces given to Poland including the industrialized Silesia areas, Western Germany today has nevertheless come back as an industrial power. It is a classic case of man over environment.

The role of economic and social systems has seldom been more clearly demonstrated than in the different courses of East Germany and West Germany. The division of the country, meant originally only as a matter of convenience while a peace treaty was worked out, has turned into a protracted division of the country, due to the Soviet seizure of every pretext to make of East Germany a colonial area subject to its exploitation. East Germany was the more agricultural part of the country, yet it contained important industrialized areas in Saxony and Silesia. Under Russian domination there has been a continous flight of people from East Germany. This has drained off particularly the educated and skilled part of the population. Recovery is slow and production is low. While Rus-

sian need of German productivity should supply an endless market, the fixed prices and controlled production in a socialist planned society have stifled productivity instead of stimulating it.

West Germany adopted an aggressively free enterprise system after the war. Despite the loss of nearly half of its territory, occupation by the Western Allies, immense destruction during the war, and the loss of many of its leading scientists to both the East and West, under an enterprise system cities have been rebuilt and industries re-established, and now the general situation can only be described as prosperous.

Among other problems, West Germany had to absorb over 10 million refugees. Although this was an enormous immediate problem, industry, in its explosive growth, has absorbed this nearly one fourth increase in population and even run into labor shortages at times of peak employment. With expanding unification of the European Common Market, this industrial and commercial growth seems assured of widening markets and further prosperity.

BELGIUM

The manner in which modern transportation and industrial developments make the land and resources secondary in importance even in heavy industry is shown by Belgium's development. This tiny country, about 12,000 square miles—less than the size of Connecticut plus Vermont—has a population of nearly 9 million. The population density is a high 733 per square mile. Coal is its only major industrial resource, yet it is a major steel, pig iron, and railroad equipment producer and has an important textile industry. Belgium has been called the workshop of Europe. It is, of course, true that its position in the midst of industrialized countries gives Belgium an immense locational advantage, but it is equally true that most of the development is due to input of human energy and skill on a very meagre physical base. Equally interesting is the fact that heavy destruction in two wars

in this century has not stopped growth and development.

NETHERLANDS

The story of the Netherlands is equally important as an example of how man makes his environment. Density of population in this tiny country, about the same size as Belgium, is even higher than in Belgium. Farming land long ago was used to its limits, and reclamation of land from the sea was then undertaken. As the growth of technology has made it possible, more and more land has been reclaimed. Now more than one fourth of the nation's area is below sea level, and another one fourth is only three feet above it. On this reclaimed sea bottom and coastal marsh, and on the adjacent firm ground, the Dutch carry on intensive agriculture.

Is this the only area in the world where such a reclamation is possible? Certainly not. Consider the Chesapeake Bay. This vast bay, about twice the size of Zuyder Zee, has immense areas of shallow water; its entrance is narrow and relatively shallow; and it is entirely within our means to close this entrance, lower the bay level 50 feet, and gain an area equal to the land reclaimed by the Dutch. San Francisco Bay is another example. Relatively simple construction could close off most of the San

The Triumph of Man over Physical Environment in the Netherlands. (*Upper left*) Rich farms on land reclaimed from the Zuider Zee. (*Upper right*) Cows grazing below sea level. (*Above*) Tulips in bloom. Beautiful productive land has been created by diking the Zuider Zee and reclaiming over half a million acres, an area two thirds the size of Rhode Island. Intensive agriculture produces high-value export crops and helps support one of the densest populations in the world—over 950 persons per square mile. *Netherlands Information Service.*

(*Upper*) Muiderslot Castle near Amsterdam, built in the thirteenth century to control and dominate the Rhine. (*Lower*) Barge traffic on the Waal, a branch of the Rhine. (*Opposite*) The harbor at Rotterdam. The importance of the Rhine River in Europe, despite its minor size, is evident from these photographs of the Netherlands. The harbor of Rotterdam is first in Europe in extent of tonnage, and in the world it is second only to New York. This indicates the focus of world trade on the Netherlands and, via the Rhine, on northwest Europe. *Netherlands Information Service.*

Francisco Bay's south end and all of the San Pablo and Suisun bays. The rich alluvium of the bay bottoms could be highly productive.

The Dutch use of fertilizers and intensity of cultivation give them some of the highest yields per acre in the world on the kind of land and in a latitude that is equivalent to southernmost Alaska. There is a large dairy industry, with a sizable export of milk and cheese. There is also a large machinery and chemical industry, and such specialty crafts as diamond cutting. It would seem that anyone looking at the Dutch accomplishment would be moved to give them the prize for accomplishing the most with the least. Again, as with Belgium, their location in the center of the world's most industrialized area is a factor of immense value. This factor, however, is man-made, for it is an accident of history that the industrial revolution started in Britain rather than in China. Had the industrial revolution not started in northwestern Europe, it is doubtful that Europe would now be more than a colonial appendage of some set of Oriental powers, and the Netherlands a vast area

of shallow seas, lakes, and marshes utilized for little more than fishing and pasturage.

DENMARK

Denmark is another of the remarkable cases of an industrious people making much out of little. Its country is low, flat, and sandy, the result of the dumping of sands, gravels, and silts at the terminus of the glaciers that swept down from the heights of the Scandinavian peninsula. This process suplied a relatively poor soil, for sands are poor sources of nutrient minerals. The youthfulness of the soils is one of their only advantages; what nutrient materials they do possess have not been leached out of them to any great extent. Their age can only be in the neighborhood of 12,000 years, for the ice stood over Denmark until that late in time. Although this may seem very long in terms of human history, as indeed it is, it is a short time in terms of soil weathering.

In times past, the Danes have utilized their position at the entrance of the Baltic Sea to control the

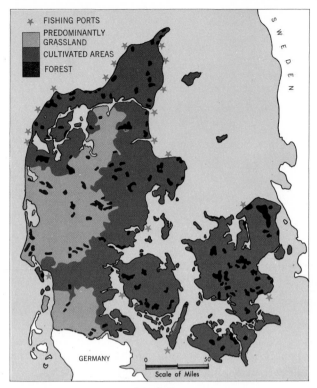

FISHING PORTS
PREDOMINANTLY GRASSLAND
CULTIVATED AREAS
FOREST

Land Use

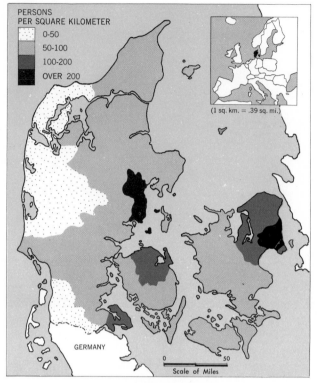

PERSONS PER SQUARE KILOMETER
0-50
50-100
100-200
OVER 200

(1 sq. km. = .39 sq. mi.)

Population Density

Map 6-4   Denmark: Land Use and Population

Denmark, located in the latitude of southern Alaska, is a major agricultural nation with a high standard of living. Note the low amount of land left in forest and the dominance of cultivated areas and grasslands that support cattle raising and dairying. The large number of important fishing ports expresses Denmark's dependence on the sea. *Adapted from* Focus—*The American Geographical Society.*

Rune Stone, Enköping, Sweden. Runes are the characters of the alphabet used in early Scandinavia. Their history is obscure, but they are related to the early alphabet systems of the eastern Mediterranean and are evidence of the important flow of cultural stimuli from that region to northwestern Europe which continued for millennia. Stonehenge and Hadrian's Wall are other monuments to this cultural path. *Swedish National Travel Office.*

trade in and out of that area. They have, for as long as we have records, turned to the sea for a good deal of their livelihood. The growth of large productive populations in the neighboring countries to the south that either were unable to feed themselves or, as we have seen, chose to use their manpower in industry instead of in agriculture provided an opportunity for the Danes. They have specialized in supplying high-value eggs, milk, cream, bacon, and the like to this market.

Note the Dane's location for this type of production. They are geographically close to a market that can pay for such produce because of the high productivity of the industrial workers. The Danes have a good, flat, well-watered land. But it should not be overlooked that this land is in a climatic position that in North America is most nearly duplicated by the panhandle of Alaska, or in South America by Tierra del Fuego. It is generally argued that these American lands are limited by their physical setting, especially by their climate. Physically, they are perhaps limited by their rugged topography, but primarily they seem in comparison to Denmark to be limited by their isolated location and the absence of an energetic, educated, productive people. That geographical position alone is insufficient reason will be shown below by the example of New Zealand.

The measure of the Danish achievement in making their land a major agriculturally productive area can be further grasped once it is realized that their location, in terms of latitude—which determines the distribution of length of day and the length of the seasons—is equivalent to the coast of Labrador. This is far to the north of Maine, and Maine is close to our center of most productive industrial population, yet we are letting it go out of agricultural production. The usual reasons advanced for this in Maine are: the winters are too long, the soils are too poor, the markets are too far away, and so forth. By Danish standards, winters in much of Maine are little colder than theirs, summers are as warm, and the periods of short, dark days in winter are much less. The

soils are no worse and often better than those of Denmark. The immense markets of the northeastern United States look attractive and are close, and there are no national boundaries to cross. The difficulty for Maine is that it is part of a vast area with highly developed means of transportation that make it easy for everyone from Florida to California to sell advantageously in the industrial heartland of America. Still, one wonders what a group of produce-minded Danes might do with some of the good areas of Maine that are being allowed today to revert to woodland.

NORWAY

North of Denmark lies Norway, almost the classic case of a far northern marine west-coast land. Norway lies in the latitude of mainland Alaska: the parallel of 60 degrees latitude passes through southernmost Norway, near Oslo, and through Alaska at the base of the Aleutian island chain and the Kenai Peninsula (see Map 6–1). There is no land in South America so far from the equator. Tasmania and the South Island of New Zealand are far nearer the equator than these lands. The human assessment elsewhere in the world is that lands so far poleward are virtually worthless. Enormous Alaska has less than 250,000 people, and most of them live in the southward extending coastal section, the Panhandle, that lies in the latitude of Denmark. Norway, on the other hand, has a population of over 3,000,000. While this population is mostly in the south, there are settlements all along the coast to beyond the arctic circle.

The Norse have a poor physical environment in many ways. Minerals are scarce; coal and oil virtually nonexistent; and areas of good soils are best described as rare. The uplands are granite from which most of the soil was stripped by the glaciers, and the lowlands are few and limited in size. The growing season is short, and the summers are wet; and because of the persistent cloud cover, relatively little of the potential sun can get through to the land. Few crops can be grown: principally potatoes,

Fishing Fleet at Svolvaer, Lofoten Islands. Norway's economy is dependent upon fishing. The location here is similar to a position north of the Bering Strait in North America. *Norwegian Information Service.*

Norwegian Farms. The farmsteads are placed on the lower slopes, as a change of elevation of a few hundred feet brings temperatures below the critical limit for crops. Compare this with tropical stations, where a change in elevation of a few thousand feet may cause only a shift from one crop to another. *Norwegian Information Service.*

Drying Hay on Poles, Norway. The season is too short and sunless for curing hay on the ground. *Norwegian Information Service.*

Gokstad Viking Ship. This type of ship was used by the Norse in their conquest of the North Sea areas and in the discovery of Iceland, Greenland, and America. Note the construction. No other marine west coast climate produced a similar boat. *Norwegian Information Service.*

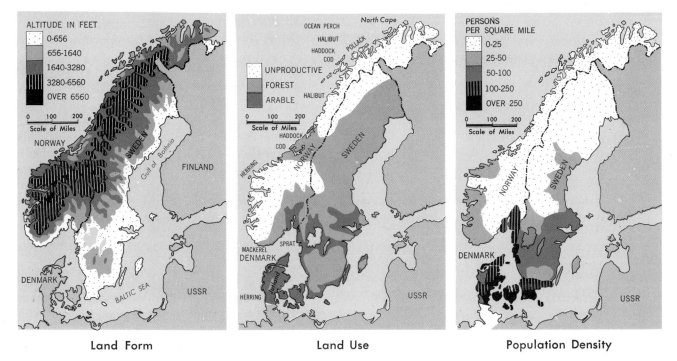

Map 6-5   Scandinavia: Land Form, Land Use, and Population

The heavy concentration of population in certain areas reflects not only climate but also relief and soil material. The uplands are in many places stripped by glacial action. The large unproductive areas are mainly bare, rocky highlands. The lowlands are mantled with glacially deposited sands, gravels, and clays. The small percentage of arable land in Norway and Sweden, as compared with Denmark, and the large amount of forest in Sweden, as compared with Norway, are equally striking. *Adapted from* Focus—*The American Geographical Society*.

oats, and cabbage. The Norse have turned to the sea for fish and to shipping as a means of obtaining foreign exchange. The forests supply them with wood and pulp, for export either in pulp form or in paper. In an environment that mankind has, in recent time, largely avoided, the Norse have built a good life and maintained a national existence. It could well be said that they have done so in spite of the environment. It is about equally true to say that they owe their advance to their proximity to the advanced developments in northwest Europe!

SUMMARY

We may summarize the developments in the marine west coast climate of Europe as follows. Unquestionably, the development would have been utterly different had the course of human history been other than what it was. The beginning of civilization lay in the Near East. The Mediterranean provided a seaway leading west. This opened up the southern side of the peninsula of Europe to the penetration of ideas, setting the stage in northwestern Europe for the beginning of the industrial revolution. This technological change could just as well have come about almost anywhere in the whole European area, and in the Mediterranean, the Near East, India, or China as well. That it began in Great Britain is a bit like a home run being hit by one man rather than another in a world series game. The stage was set; many men were prepared; they were at the plate, ready and waiting, and someone was due to hit sooner or later.

Once the start was made, whole series of events were set in motion. Many of these had momentum; many had what has come to be called "feed back." Machines required metal; this promoted metallurgy. This in turn increased the efficiency of machines which required more metals, and so on. This long sequence of unique events, from early beginnings in the Near East, with the radiation outward of these ideas, set the stage for a unique growth in human history. Its almost accidental correlation with one climate has led to the grossest hypothesizing about stimulating climates and the role of favorable natural resources. Comparisons with what occurred in other marine west-coast lands can serve to give a better perspective.

THE AMERICAS

The Americas have two areas of marine west coast climate. The northwest coast of North America, from 60 degrees north to northern California at 40 degrees north, is cool in summer and wet throughout the year. It is a narrow strip because the mountains parallel the coast and are close to the sea. Beyond the mountains, the rainfall drops rapidly due to the rain shadow effect and the seasonal temperatures increase due to the blocking of the oceanic influences. The identical situation prevails in southern Chile from the tip of South America at 55 degrees south, to just north of 40 degrees south. This climatic physiographic resemblance extends into the common past glacial history of these two lands, the presence of sizable glacial remnants in both, and the inheritance of ice-scoured valleys—over deepened valleys now drowned by the sea (fjords)—small amounts of flat areas with good soils, and a dense cover of rain forests. In both areas, the flatter land with better soils is at the equatorward end: the Puget Sound and Willamette Valley in North America, and the southern end of the central valley of Chile in South America. Poleward of these flatter, soil-mantled regions in both areas, the mountains rise out of the sea. This gives an island-filled sea with innumerable channels, inlets, passages, and potential harbors. This fjorded, island-guarded coastal effect is much like the Scottish and Norwegian coasts.

THE NORTHWEST COAST OF NORTH AMERICA

The Pre-Columbian Period

In northwest America in pre-Columbian time, the coastal lands from 60 to 40 degrees north were used by a sea-faring people, and the center of their development was approximately the Puget Sound area. Their culture area was bordered by the Eskimo to the north and trailed off in height of development toward the simple tribes of California to the south. Tribes with the most advanced form of this culture were such people as the Tlinkit, Kwakiutl, and Haida.

These tribes were skilled, wood-working people. The vast forests supplied them with immense straight logs of soft woods, such as spruce and cedar. From these they made large sea-going canoes. They also split planks off the standing trees for making houses. House frames of huge posts and girders and ridge poles were often maintained at several sites, and when the people moved seasonally, they took the planks for roofs and walls with them. These are the people who made the totem poles, so well-known to everyone. It is less well-

Old Indian Settlement at Tanu, Queen Charlotte Islands, British Columbia. Notice the totem poles, the use of planks, the huge logs used as frames, the beach location, and the heavily timbered landscape. *American Museum of Natural History*.

Totem Poles in Southern Alaska. This gigantic form developed from smaller forms after the Indians obtained steel tools. Compare these totem poles with the Maori door posts (p. 317). *Division of Economic and Tourist Development, Alaska*.

known that the totem poles as we know them were a post-European development. Steel axes and adzes made it possible to produce in gigantic size a type of carving that up till then had been made in small scale. Ceremonial staffs grew up to super telephone-pole size. Their wood working also extended into house furniture. Spoons, boxes, and combs were made of wood, beautifully carved according to a rich art tradition. Did the abundance of a suitable wood determine all of this?

The sea supplied a rich fishery: not only is this the area of immense salmon runs, there are also rich halibut fisheries, great shellfish resources, and seasonal abundance of other fish such as the sardine-sized oulachon. With a seashore deeply indented by the sea, with innumerable islands forming endless sheltered passages, inlets, and harbors, what could be more natural than taking to the sea? Under these circumstances the northwest Europeans also went to sea. For Europe we have traced much of what they did back to ideas coming from the Mediterranean, and often ultimately from the Near East. Where did the marine west-coast people of Northwest America get their ideas? Or did they develop their own in response to the environment in which they lived?

It was noticed long ago that many of the things that the people of the Puget Sound area did were repeated in New Zealand. The fish hooks of the Americans, for example, resembled those of the Maori of New Zealand. Both groups built great seagoing dugout canoes; both built great community houses with post-girder-and-ridge-pole frames with plank covering; both groups were great wood carvers; and both carved the posts of their houses in similar grotesque art forms. Well, why not? The environments were both marine coastal climates, with all the similarities of forest cover and availability of large logs, and both people were oriented to the sea. But why should their compound fish hooks be identical, and oddest of all, why should their art forms be so alike? The similarities can be expanded greatly: for instance, both people built similar fortified villages and indulged in great give-away contests to create personal prestige.

The list of similarities becomes so great that the question must be asked: Are we looking at environmentally conditioned results that have led to such similarities? Or are we looking at transmission of ideas? Geographers have paid relatively little attention to these two peoples, for most geographers concentrate on the present-day scene. Although the anthropologists have been interested in the cultural similarities, they have used a geographic reason to deny any probability of exchange of ideas between these two people. They point out that the two areas are almost at the opposite ends of the earth; a distance much too vast for men equipped with mere dugouts to travel.

This is a curious bit of reasoning. First, these two peoples are on the same ocean; they are seafarers; and the seas are better highways for long distance travel than the land. Second, their "mere dugouts" were often 50 feet long and some of the New Zealand canoes approached 100 feet long. These are not mere dugouts: they are ships. The *Niña,* of Columbus's fleet, is thought to have been only about 40-ton capacity and not to have been entirely decked over. Further, once men take to the sea, the inevitable storms are bound to create castaways, and the ability of man to survive at sea is so great that he will reach virtually all the adjacent shores of the seas. As an extreme case, the Eskimos have repeatedly reached the British Isles from some point in the American arctic, probably Greenland, in their tiny kayaks. Japanese junks, some of them bearing living crewmen, reached the northwest coast of America repeatedly in the nineteenth century. From inscriptions on South Pacific islands we know that mariners from Java sometimes reached them, or were drifted far out into the Pacific. Beyond that, Thor Heyerdahl and others have demonstrated that purposeful long-distance voyages were easily within the means of the people of the Pacific.

Perhaps the resemblances between the New Zealand and American northwest-coast way of life, art, architecture, and tools, is due not to either group having voyaged the length of the Pacific, but to their both having common origins in Asia. Studies of New Zealand art indicate that it is relatable to Asiatic art, specifically to early Chinese art forms. Studies of the American northwest-coast culture show that it is filled with Asiatic traits, and their art has the same foundation. Among the Asiatic traits are specific types of raincoast, special kinds of armor, and mythological accounts of the coming to them of people from the west. Perhaps the clearest case is the parallel between the whaling techniques of the American northwest-coast people and those of the Asiatic coast. In both areas, whales are hunted with poisoned harpoons, and the poison used is identical. Both during preparation for and during the hunt itself, identical taboos are practiced by both peoples. While it may or may not be thought natural to hunt whales, it is very unusual to kill them with poison. That the same poison should be used is suspicious, but when the same nonfunctional magical practices are used by both people, a clear case of spread of ideas is before us.

Once the door is opened to the spread of ideas, the American northwest-coast people, with their highly developed sea culture, with their fine art and peculiar customs, turn out to be a transfer to this part of America of a way of life that was anciently highly developed along the coast of Asia from Japan to the Kamchatka Peninsula. The transfer was from one climate and one physical environment to another. The common factor was the sea and the rich fishery. A similar area lay in New Zealand. People coming from the Asiatic coast eventually reached this area too. Since both groups started with a similar stock of ideas, including how to achieve their art work, the results turned out much alike.

This cultural contact or spread of ideas also answers the question of why, when in America there is a general decline in cultural level as one goes farther and farther away from Middle America, there appears in the marine west-coast area, a sudden heightening of cultural level. This area is much farther from Middle America than California or the Great Basin. Could it be argued that it is due to the

Maori House-post Carvings, New Zealand. These are strikingly like the northwest coast Indian totem poles, which were also originally house-post carvings. The likenesses are in part obscured by such stylistic details as the elaborate use of decorative scrolls on the Maori carvings as compared with the simpler forms used by the northwest coast Indians. Certain details suggest the close relationship between these art forms. The protruding tongue, shown on the second post from the left, is continued today in the Maori haka dance (see p. 328). Protruding tongues are also a regular feature of the totem-pole art. *American Museum of Natural History.*

stimulating climate of the marine west coast? The evidence seems much more clearly to indicate that it is due to increasing proximity to the Asiatic centers of cultural growth. It seems very probable that the northeast-coast culture area is the result of introductions of ideas by fishing people who crossed the Pacific and settled in this area. Perhaps the first

Kemano Hydroelectric Project, Aluminum Company of Canada. The magnitude of the hydroelectric development in the Pacific Northwest is seen in this powerhouse being built 1600 feet inside a mountain. It will have an initial installed generating power of 420,000 horsepower, capable of being extended to an installed capacity of 2,240,000 horsepower. This is almost twice the Niagara's output.

A Farm in Mantanuska Valley, Southern Alaska. The soil is very fertile loess recently deposited by winds from the outwash of the glacier visible in the right-hand corner. The conditions that exist here—exceptionally fertile well-drained soils in a sheltered valley near a sea that is warm for its latitude—are found also in southern Sweden and Norway. *Division of Economic and Tourist Development, Alaska.*

Spruce and Hemlock Being Shipped from Juneau, Alaska. Lumber is a major export of the marine west coast lands of the northern hemisphere, but not of the equally heavily forested, similar climatic areas of the southern hemisphere. *Division of Economic and Tourist Development, Alaska.*

contacts were made by storm-driven fishermen, some of whom returned to their homeland to report a good area for settlement. Probably they found this rugged, wet, coastal area very lightly held by relatively simple, shellfish-gathering people who were easily displaced. Thereafter, they developed their own culture, probably with minor additions from time to time from renewed contacts with Asia.

The Modern Age

This rich area, this strip of coast, is the climatic analogue to Norway, Denmark, Great Britain, Brittany, and most of coastal France. It has an immensely rich fishery, great timber resources, known mineral resources, stupendous hydroelectric potential, sheltered coastal waters, and vast natural harbors. According to one theory, it has the most stimulating climate that man can live in, especially modern Western man with his knowledge of good housing and central heating. Yet it is one of the empty parts of North America.

The coastal strip of Washington and Oregon today is thinly populated; the population of these states centers in the interior valley paralleling the coast. British Columbia's population centers on the south end of the Puget Sound at Victoria and drops off very rapidly to extremely low levels both along the coast and inland. The American settlement along the coast of Alaska amounts to little more than a few villages located at fishing and mining centers, yet this Alaskan area has coal, copper, gold, water power, timber, and fisheries that vastly exceed the Norwegian resources. Today Norway is a thriving nation with 3,500,000 people, while Alaska is an undeveloped area with less than 200,000 people. The causes are not difficult to find. Alaska in American hands has been treated, to use the Alaskans' words, as a colony. Perhaps things will change greatly now that Alaska has been granted statehood. However, up till now there has been so much greater opportunity in the 48 states that there has been little incentive for Americans to develop Alaska, or for large

Cattle Ranch on Kodiak Island, the Innermost Island of the Aleutian Chain. Nearly treeless and lying in the latitude of Denmark, this large island has only recently attracted settlers. The ranch shown here has built up a herd of 200 Angus cattle in a few years. Angus cattle are a Scottish breed widely used for beef. A winter scene such as this could be found also in Montana or Wyoming, but those continental interior states have lower temperature extremes. *Division of Economic and Tourist Development, Alaska.*

numbers of people to go there. Indeed, the course of our development has featured progressive abandonment of good land in equally good climates and much closer to consuming centers. For instance, a tier of states from North Dakota down through the center of the Middle West has, in recent decades, either stood still in population or, in extreme cases, even lost population. Nor is this by any means the whole picture. Within states such as Maine, large areas have never been effectively settled, and large areas of New England that were once settled and cleared at great cost have been abandoned.

The story is the familiar one of differing histories, differing population pressures, and differing assessments of the best use of the land. Given the cultural setting of the Americans of the pre-Columbian level, this area became one of the cultural high points in America north of Mexico. With the shift to European development of the continent, beginning in the East and belatedly reaching the West, the West has seen a delayed development. The American Northwest (Oregon and Washington) is now beginning to grow at an accelerating rate. Perhaps Alaska, now that it has emerged from territorial status, can take advantage of the sizable population centers that are developing on the Pacific coast and transportation services that are ever increasing. But notice again in all of this that the physical environment has remained passive. The wealth of the area has always been there. Man's assessment and decision about how and when to use it have been the variables.

CHILE

At the opposite end of the Americas is southern Chile, a land much like the northwest coast of America. Here there is extensive good land from 40 degrees south, including the island of Chiloe. These latitudes are the equivalent of Oregon and northern California. As in Oregon and Washington, there is an interior valley parallel to the coast with much good flatland. South of the island of Chiloe, the land is mountainous, with islands rising out of the sea; creating a landscape like that of the coast of British Columbia and the panhandle of Alaska. The southernmost extent of this area reaches to the tip of South America, about 55 degrees south. This is closer to the equator than Sitka, Alaska, but the climates are much the same; and Sitka is considered to have a mild climate. Fifty-five degrees is close to the latitude of Glasgow in Scotland, Copenhagen in Denmark, Belfast in Ireland, Newcastle in England, and Hamburg and Königsberg in Germany. It

Waterfalls on the Pilmaiquén River, the Andes in the Background. The wealth of water supplied to the coastal areas by the snow-covered Andes is well illustrated. *Consulate General of Chile.*

is not a land of impossible climate, but judged by what the Europeans have been able to do with it, it is a most useful one—or as the physical environmental determinists would have it, the most stimulating climate on earth. What then has man done with this land in Chile?

Pre-Columbian Chile

In pre-Columbian time this was an undeveloped land. It had received some influence from the Inca empire and there was a beginning of agricultural village settlement at the extreme northern end of this woodland area.

South of the island of Chiloe, the land was occupied by groups of the simplest peoples in the world. The way of life was dependent on the sea. Shellfish were a major source of food. They were gathered from the intertidal zones, fished up from deeper waters by means of a split stick, or sometimes the women dove for them. Sea birds and their eggs were used; sea lions were clubbed if caught on shore. Inland hunting and gathering of plant foods was minimal. For travel on the water, a bark canoe was used, not like the birch bark canoe of the North American Indians but one made of a single sheet of bark, bound together at the ends, and

propped open with sticks. It was so fragile that it could not be beached; the occupants had to get out in shallow water, and the canoe was tied offshore so that it would not be injured by contact with the land. Yet whole families traveled in them. Along this coast, composed of mountains rising out of the sea, the sheltered passageways let so weak a vessel function and made other types of travel difficult. The same environment contained trees whose bark could be removed in huge sheets and thus could have been used to make far larger and stronger bark canoes. Such large trees could have supplied logs for dugouts similar to those that the people on the american northwest coast used, or finely-made plank boats such as the Norsemen used. When it is said that this is an area favoring water travel, it still leaves open what kind of water travel man is to use, if any.

The climate of this coast is a cold and wet one. As we have noted, the climatic analogue of Tierra del Fuego is Sitka, Alaska, and the northwest-coast Indians with their good clothing and snug houses were the occupants of the Sitka area. The southern Scandinavians built warm houses and dressed to withstand the cold of this type of climate. Yet the people of Tierra del Fuego had virtually no clothing and next to no housing.

Darwin was astounded in his trip through Tierra del Fuego to see a boat come out to his ship carrying a family. The boat was leaky; the day was stormy; and sleet was falling. Yet the occupants of the boat did not have shirts or trousers or shoes or robes: they were practically naked. A woman was along, and she had a tiny naked infant in her arms; and ice water dripped on it from the sleet that caught in its mother's hair and melted. By our standards, the whole boatload of them should have died of exposure, especially the infant. If the environment could urge, compel, encourage, or suggest anything, it should have shouted at these people to get some clothes on. Somehow or other, they seem to have been deaf to the obvious.

Is it possible that there was no material for clothing in their environment? This cannot be true. Bird skins can make a robe; feathers engaged in the strands of string can be made into puffy ropes and these can be woven to make a soft warm blanket, as was done in the Great Basin area by a people on almost as simple a level of living as these Tierra del Fuegians. Further, these people killed seals and thus had hides that could have been used to make capes, pants, moccasins, and leggings. The limitation was not in the physical environment, therefore, but in the cultural environment. Despite what is to us a seemingly imperative need for clothing for mere survival, and an absolute need for clothing for any comfort, these people simply did without anything but an occasional skin worn loosely as a cloak.

Their ability to withstand cold was phenomenal. They were often wet, for rain was frequent, and if it was not raining, the grass and brush were wet, and there were streams to cross. In these circumstances, clothing loses some of its advantage. Wet clothing is long in drying, while skin dries quickly. Wet clothing is cold and, if body heat is used to dry it, there is some question as to whether it is worth the drain on body temperature. One explanation for the Scotch addiction to kilts is that since the heather is almost always wet, anyone walking through it is going to be wet to mid thigh. Trousers would then be soaking wet, and would be wet for hours after.

Kilts would be above the wet heather, and within minutes after entering a house, legs would be warm and dry. Nevertheless, the Scotch herdsmen who live in this Tierra del Fuegian climate felt a need for warm wool clothing, long cloaks, and snug houses.

The Tierra del Fuegians did not bother with much of a house. They built shelters of pole frames, thatched with grass, over which they might also throw a seal skin or two. This slowed the breeze down to a draft, and delayed most of the rain. A smoldering fire in the middle of the hut supplied some heat and a lot of smoke. It was noticed that the large fire that we find so comfortable caused the natives to retreat a long way off. They could not stand that much heat.

This has led to the suspicion that these people may have been somewhat different physiologically than the rest of mankind. Belatedly, for these people are on the verge of extinction, an expedition has gone out to study them, and has found them to have some adaptation to cold. Their rate of heat production when at rest is found to be half again as high as ours, that is, their basal metabolism is 150 percent of ours. This allows them to withstand exposure that would be fatal to us. Again note that as with the natives of Australia, this phenomena of physiologic change to meet environmental stress is found among the least culturally equipped people. Culturally equipped mankind interposes such artifacts as clothing, housing, and heating between himself and direct environmental impacts.

Among the Tierra del Fuegians the women were the ones who could withstand the most cold. In obtaining shellfish in winter, it was the women who dove for them. At Tierra del Fuego in winter, the sea water is just above freezing. Because of its salt content, sea water freezes at 28° F. instead of 32° F. At times it is so cold that rainwater (which is fresh water) resting on the broad leaves of the seaweeds freezes, forming a glaze, as we sometime see in higher mid-latitudes in winter. The women nonetheless swim through the kelp and dive for mussels. They can stand only about 20 minutes of this, and then must be taken ashore and warmed at a fire. That the men can not do this at all, is of considerable interest. In our own society it is noticable that women dress less warmly than men. Women are thicker bodied than men and tend to distribute their fat accumulation in a layer under the skin. Men tend to accumulate their fat in the visceral area. The thicker, fat-insulated body of the woman is much better suited to withstand cold than is the lean, high surface area, uninsulated body of the man. It is a good measure of how close to the limits of human tolerance the Tierra del Fuego climate is that this relatively small difference plays so decisive a role.

The introduction of better boats, clothing, improved housing, and better weapons for hunting and fishing did not cause a great increase in population among these people. Instead, a wave of disease that accompanied these things reduced these people to the vanishing point. From a few thousand people scattered along a thousand miles of the coast of Chile, they are now reduced to a few hundred people, and most of them are now of mixed parentage. This is another of the grim stories of the impact of the whole gamut of mankind's diseases that we carry around the world so easily today on a people who have lived for vast periods of time almost completely out of touch with the rest of mankind—out of contact with most of mankind's diseases—and hence without any immunity to even the commonest mild diseases.

Just how long these people have lived in this area is not known. Excavations in caves in Tierra del Fuego show a long period of occupation, with carbon-14 dates going back to 6000 B.C. It seems probable that men were living in this area far longer than that, for the type of spear points, dated about 6000 B.C., are known to be later in time of appearance in the Bolivia-Paraguay-Argentina area than very simple stone work. Man was surely in southern South America for far longer than 10,000 years. He may have been living in the marine west coast type of climate of that area even during the last glacial period. This would fit the simplicity of his culture and the physiological adaptation that he has undergone.

Modern Chile

As we have seen, when the Spanish conquered the Inca Empire, they quickly explored the adjacent regions also. The beautiful, rich central valley of Chile with its favorable water supply and equable, homelike (Mediterranean) climate, attracted only a thin settlement. What is mere land, when gold and silver and great cities and masses of people can be seized and put to work and taxed? Besides, Spain is a small nation: there simply was not enough manpower to settle all these new lands.

The Spanish penetration southward down the coast of South America was rapidly played out. The rich, well-watered and forested country of the southern end of the central valley of Chile was left to the Araucanian Indians until the end of the nineteenth century. The southern end of the central valley was finally pacified when armies were systematically used. Thereafter, German settlers were brought into this wet, forested land. They have introduced northwestern European ways of life including important dairying development. In this rainy area, Valdivia is a modern city, flourishing despite an annual rainfall of 100 inches per year.

The densely forested, very wet, mountainous seashore of southernmost Chile was left untouched. Even in this century the Chileans do almost nothing with this land. There are some sheep ranches at Tierra del Fuego; otherwise, this land now has less men that it had before 1500, for the native people who used it have now virtually disappeared. This is a land much like our northwest coast, where we have done almost as little. Both these lands are richer in minerals, forests, and water power potential than their European counterparts. The disparities are the result of different histories, different present positions in relation to the great productive and consuming centers of the world, and differing viewpoints of peoples with separate economic traditions. Today, when the principal movement of man is out of marginal lands and into urban agglommerations, the probable course of development for such lands as this of southern Chile is one of slow and very slight development of the potentially rich resources. Over-population is a meaningless phrase in southern Chile. A nearly empty land awaits the coming of modern man, but modern man's view of his "over-populated" earth is not one easily to tempt him to move into such empty lands as these.

LANDS IN THE SOUTHWEST PACIFIC

TASMANIA

Among the other areas of marine west-coast climate is the island of Tasmania. It lies in the latitude of northern California or northern Portugal. It is a mountainous land, covered with forest, with rainfall well distributed throughout the year—not as excessive in amount as that found along the marine west coasts of America, but more like that of northwestern Europe. From this description, one would be led to think of this island as a favorable land, but its geographical position has been against its development. From Tasmania, it is about 7000 miles to South America, 8000 miles to San Francisco, 5000 miles to Tokyo, 4000 miles to Singapore, and 6000 miles to Bombay.

Yet man reached Tasmania fairly early. The original inhabitants were a small, dark-skinned people, probably of Negrito origin. They had a level of cultural development somewhat like that of Tierra del Fuegians. As with the Tierra del Fuegians, in addition, contact with the European diseases proved fatal. Further, when the British introduced sheep, the Tasmanians considered this new animal as an added food source. The British thereupon hunted down the Tasmanians to put a stop to the destruction of the new economy, and the last native was soon gone. The British were then free to expand their sheep industry.

Tasmania has an area of 26,304 square miles, the size of Ireland. The population is under 360,000 people, one eighth of Ireland's population. There are two towns, Hobart with 87,000 people, and Launceston with 47,000. The bulk of the island remains in forest, and lumbering is one of the principal industries. There is some stock raising, mining, and farming. Copper, tin, silver, lead, gold, and zinc are mined; and wheat, oats, peas, hay, potatoes, and fruit are the chief crops. When it is noted that this is a land as large as Ireland, lying in the latitude of northern Portugal; blessed with dependable, well-distributed rainfall, with mountains creating possibilities of good hydroelectric potential, and with immense forests; and possessing a whole list of valuable minerals including coal, the lack of development and population is striking. Without population there will be no development in this remote land, and here distance seems to have outweighed all other factors. But distance is coming to mean less and less in this world of increasingly rapid transportation. The shrinking world in these terms is familiar to most, and as we will see, adjacent New Zealand has not been deterred by mere distance.

However, Tasmania is not developing parallel to transportation growth. Instead, the dispersed population of a century ago is ending, and people are moving down out of the interior hilly country. This is of course parallel to what we have seen for most of the industrializing world. In Tasmania it is removing the few people who once lived in the interior. The exodus is selective, and those remaining show up on intelligence tests as distinctly inferior. As always, it is difficult to separate cultural, physical, and biological factors. Since we are dealing with one race in one limited physical environment, those factors can be considered constant. This leaves cultural and biological variation within one uniform group. Are the lower intelligence test results due to biological selection? Or is it due to the increasing isolation of the hill people, with decreasing educational and cultural advantages? It is a typical problem. To the unknown extent that the intelligent are the more

Beautiful Tasmania, a Well-watered Land in the Latitude of Oregon. (*Upper*) Derwent River, New Norfolk district, 21 miles from the capital of Hobart. (*Lower*) Cradle Mountain, 5069 feet high. The size of Ireland, and with a similar climate, Tasmania has only one eighth the population of that relatively empty land. The hydroelectric power potential is large and is beginning to attract industry, but the major product is newsprint from the abundant forest cover. *Australian News and Information Bureau.*

enterprising, it is to be expected that the more intelligent would move out as conditions worsened.
However, decreasing population below certain limits
creates a differing social order. Value systems tend
to shift from bookish skills to frontier skills. Most
mental tests measure bookish skills.

Tasmania is one more example of the extreme
unevenness of the human occupation of the world.
Its extreme isolation in the past allowed the survival of a people there who preserved a Lower
Paleolithic way of life; a way of life that disappeared
in most of the world 50 to 100 thousand years ago.
British occupation of the island came at the same
time of their occupation of Australia. The course of
development has paralleled that of Australia, but
Tasmania has been peripheral to Australia in the
same way that the Alaskan panhandle has been
peripheral to America. Modern land-use tendencies
are leading to concentration of its population in a
few urban centers and the extensive rather than intensive use of the land. Tasmania's future is tied to
that of Australia. As population and industry in
Australia grow, Tasmania should also develop. However, despite its having the "stimulating" climate of
northwestern Europe, it seems much more likely that
the Mediterranean and east coast mid-latitude forest climates are likely to remain the dominant areas
in the Australian-Tasmanian world. Tasmania must
be viewed as a potentially rich land, undeveloped
in spite of, rather than because of, its environment.

NEW ZEALAND

New Zealand is more isolated than Tasmania, yet
it is prosperous, growing, and has one of the world's
highest standards of living. New Zealand has a
marine west-coast climate. The North Island, lying
between 35 and 40 degrees, is to be compared with
the coast of northern California. The South Island,
between 40 and 47 degrees, is to be compared with
the coastal strip from northern California to British
Columbia. The European counterparts are from
northern coastal Portugal and Spain to Brittany in

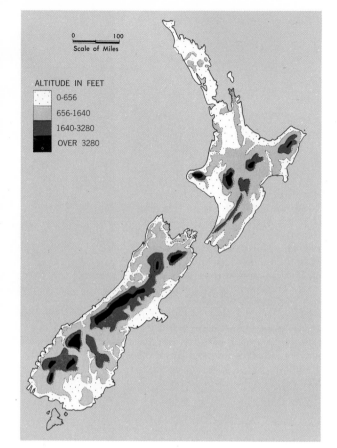

ALTITUDE IN FEET

0-656

656-1640

1640-3280

OVER 3280

Scale of Miles

0   100

Land Form

France. The total area of the two islands is slightly
smaller than Great Britain plus Ireland, or about
equal to the state of Colorado.

The Maori

The Maori in New Zealand is an interesting chapter in the impact of man on the environment. When
the Polynesian people reached New Zealand perhaps
two thousand years ago, they found a land untouched by man. It was well covered with vegetation,
and populated almost exclusively by birds. This was
the result of the great isolation in the sea for only
forms that could fly could reach this land. With no
ground dwelling predators, the birds evolved to fill

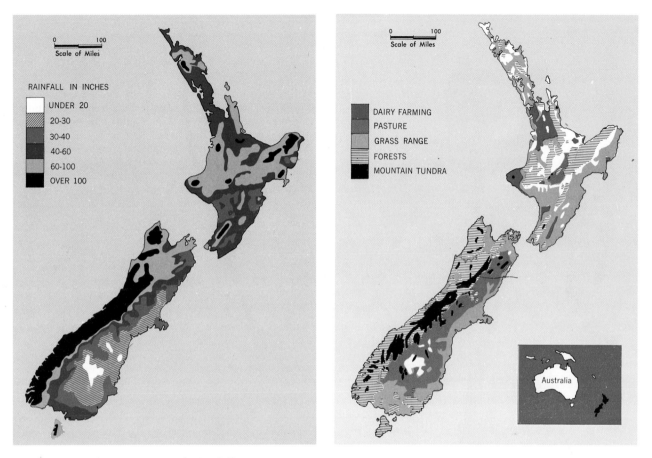

Average Annual Rainfall   Land Use

Map 6-6   New Zealand: Land Form, Rainfall, and Land Use

The very large extent of New Zealand's dairy pasture and grassland is shown on the land-use map, and the land-form map shows that much of this land is in steep hill country. The immensely rainy southern alps stand out in the rainfall map; there is an absence of railroads in this region, indicating the absence of development there. *Adapted from* Focus—*The American Geographical Society.*

The Maori in Transition. (*Left*) Two men in traditional costume, but with wrist watch and war medals, in a ceremonial dance, the haka. (*Below*) Meeting of the school council, Native School, Whakarewarewa, North Island. This group runs the social activities of the school. Both Polynesian and European race types are represented. *Embassy of New Zealand.*

the ecological niches open. Some became small, flightless feeders on worms—the kiwi. Others—the giant moa—became immense grazers of the grasslands, the largest ground dwelling bird that existed, larger than the ostrich.

The Maori entered this land from the warm central Pacific with equipment suited to life on tropical islands. He was entering a subtropical land mass of far larger size than he had been accustomed to. Many of his familiar plants would not grow there. The coconut, breadfruit, and mulberry, the source of his tapa cloth for clothing, could not stand the seasonal climate. The sweet potato succeeded only if handled with care. For a time this made relatively little difference, for the supply of flightless birds, especially the huge moas, supplied an abundance of meat. The Maori became strongly specialized on hunting, and their settlements were often inland, and well distributed over both and North and the South Island. However, the eruption of a fierce predator such as man into an animal population that had a reproduction rate unadjusted to heavy predation had a familiar result. The moa became extinct. Man had again decisively altered his environment.

The Maori then shifted back toward the coasts and again became fishermen and farmers with an agriculture based on the sweet potato. Since the sweet potato is a tropical plant, it did best on the subtropical North Island, and the Maori center of population came to be located there.

The decision, of course, was only partially determined by the physical geography. Primarily it was based on choice of retention of an agriculural way of life, and the lack of plants suited to the strongly seasonal climate of the South Island. Had their basic crop been wheat, their primary area of settlement would probably have been on the drier, grassy plains of the east side of the South Island.

These are the people who are strikingly similar in many cultural details to the Indians of the northwest coast of America. Their art, house types, canoes, and many other items suggest some common origin. The two fundamentally similar peoples ended in different corners of the world, each of which offered varied physical environments. In North America the people settled on the wet, west-facing coast, ignored the drier interior valleys, and did not spread equatorward to occupy the subtropical coast. In New Zealand, they occupied the subtropical north, used the drier plains to the south only slightly, and ignored the wet, west-coast region almost entirely. The contrast is heightened here by the common race and culture in similar environmental settings.

To the Maori, New Zealand was first a vast hunting ground, then a poor farming area, with good fishing grounds; to the Europeans, the assessment of useful land is utterly different.

New Zealand Today

How can it be that this bit of land, nearly in the center of the water hemisphere of the world, is one of the most prosperous spots in the world? As we have seen, climate alone cannot account for this. Location which seems to have worked so great a hardship on our own northwest coast, the Chilean south coast, and Tasmania, seems somehow not to have damaged New Zealand—despite its even greater isolation. Is the land that much better? Even the very practical consideration of situation within the British Empire is common to Tasmania and New Zealand, but Tasmania languishes while New Zealand flourishes.

New Zealand is mountainous. Plains are limited in extent and, except for the northern part of the North Island, are strictly marginal to the mountainous interior. The population is strongly concentrated on these plains. However, away from the four major cities of Aukland, Wellington, Christchurch, and Dunedin, the density of occupation, even on the best lands, is only about 50 per square mile. The mountainous interiors have less than 5 people per square mile. On the South Island, there is little population on the very wet, western side, and a concentration of population on the drier, sunnier plains of the east side of the island. Rainfall on the islands is heavy; large areas in the North Island and virtually the whole west side of the South Island

Snow Fields in the New Zealand Alps, South Island. The peaks are Tasman and Cook, the source of Fox glacier. *Embassy of New Zealand.*

receive 80 inches of rain per year. Such heavy rainfall on mountains produces an enormous hydroelectric power potential.

New Zealand is rated as having 2 percent arable, 47 percent meadow and pasture, 27 percent forest and woodland, and 24 percent waste land, mostly high mountain land. Such figures are deceptive because they contain the human decision as to how the land is to be used. The nearly one fourth of the country that is useless because it is rugged mountain land, is about the only purely phyical measure. What is meadow and what is forest depends in large part on which man chooses to emphasize. In New Zealand, the emphasis is on livestock. Much land that elsewhere would be left in forest has been converted into pasture, and much land that would be used by other people for field crops has been used for very high yielding pasture lands. If the western half of the states of Washington and Oregon were used in comparable fashion, it is probable that more than half of their land would be in meadow and pasture, instead of the very high percentage that is left in forest.

New Zealand has only 2,500,000 people. Of these, the Maori, the original inhabitants, make up 160,000, a figure that might be compared with Great Britain's population of 50,000,000 on a comparably sized set of islands in a similar climate—with the climatic advantage definitely being with the warmer land of New Zealand. New Zealand has managed her native population well and the 160,000 Maori are rapidly being assimilated into the political and economic life of the country. The immigrant population was largely British, and they brought with them high levels of education and technology. Immigration is controlled to continue this type of population, and the educational policy within the country maintains these high levels.

The economy is based on modern, mechanized farming: 90 percent of the country's exports are products of the livestock industry. This has gone so far that the economy has been said to be based on grass. New Zealand is the world's largest producer of mutton, and most of it goes to London. Wool is a natural associate product and this, too, largely goes to the United Kingdom. There is a large dairy in-

(*Upper*) The western mountains of South Island, New Zealand, from the east. (*Lower*) The relatively dry grassland country in the rain shadow of the mountains. *Embassy of New Zealand.*

Milton, South Island, New Zealand. A neat, clean, prosperous and tidy landscape. *Embassy of New Zealand.*

dustry, and butter and cheese are exported in such large amounts that milk products make up one third of the exports.

The expansion of the grasslands has been pushed at the expense of the forests, until this land could as well have been discussed in the grassland section as here. The choice was made on the basis that this is a naturally forested land that in most respects is more like Chile, Great Britain, and the rest of the marine west-coast lands, hence best discussed with them. Grass has the great advantage that rolling land can be put into pasture, and if properly managed, there is very little erosion. However, the New Zealanders have at times pushed their clearing of forest onto such steep slopes that they have set off accelerated erosion. In the main, however, they have made a vast, rich grassland out of much of their islands. They have imported grasses chosen from the world's available plants for their nutritive value and suitability to the soils and climates of New Zealand. These grasslands are carefully managed, and heavily fertilized. In areas where cattle for a long time did not do well, they have now discovered that the difficulty was caused by the absence of a minute amount of a necessary nutrient: cobalt. Additions of

this mineral to the soil have changed a large area in the volcanic plateau of the North Island from a virtually sterile area into a highly productive cattle-producing region. This is typical of what an educated and vigorous people can do with a land.

New Zealanders have a welfare state with a curious background. The original plan, as set forth by Grey, one of the early governors, was to create in New Zealand another England, with the land held in large estates by a landed gentry. The price of land was kept high artificially in order to keep the land in the hands of the wealthy. This could only be done by government planning and strong central government control, which among other things deliberately held immigration down. A struggle developed between those aiming at an aristocracy on the land and the people who wanted land of their own. The people won and got the land but they continued the planned economy and strong governmental controls, which then became a system of governmentally supplied social benefits and governmentally controlled production. Today agricultural production is controlled through marketing boards. Most produce is sold to a governmental board at a fixed price, and the board in turn sells, largely to Great Britain, also at a fixed price. A considerable amount of New Zealand's governmental costs are paid from the profits that these government marketing boards realize from the difference between the price that they pay and the price that they receive. Through these boards, the government controls the land, its produce, and the return that the individual gets from his land. With the assured British markets the system has worked well, and the people are quite content with the large return for their labor—a return sufficient to give New Zealanders one of the highest standards of living in the world.

The largest industry in the land is the fertilizer business, and the second is meat packing. Due to the early policy of holding immigration down, the population is now too small and labor shortages appear on all fronts. In much of the world the mechanization of agriculture is releasing labor, and countries are struggling to absorb this manpower in industry. In New Zealand the already highly mechanized agriculture is itself labor short, and there is no surplus of labor to feed potential industrial growth. Within the country the struggle is between the urban population and the rural population, each wanting the controlled economy to favor their sector of the economy.

Two thirds of the New Zealand population now lives in cities, a situation typical of the advanced nations of today, and it would appear that in time more industry will develop. Industrial development is handicapped, however, by the shortage of labor, the small internal market, and by high production costs, in part related to the heavy burden of social benefits for workers. The largest city is Auckland with a third of a million people. This city is unusual in that it does not tower over the other cities of the country in the way that Paris dominates France, London dominates England, and New York dominates the United States. New Zealand has only moderate power resources. The hydroelectric potential is large, but the building of dams and transmission lines is expensive and characteristically will increase in cost since the best sites are always developed first. The ingenious New Zealanders have tapped volcanic steam in North Island, and in 1961 found a natural gas field on the east side of the island. Conservative estimates place the productive capacity of this field at 100 million cubic feet per day. This is sufficient to generate as much electricity as Auckland now uses. New Zealand's immediate future does not seem to be industrial, however.

Currently there is some worry over the possible entry of England into the European Common Market with the possible loss of preferential marketing in Great Britain. In view of the increasing standards of living in much of the world and the concentration of much of the economic growth in such highly urbanized areas as northwest Europe, there should be a permanent and growing market for New Zealand's meat, butter, and eggs. Nevertheless, New Zealand works against the greatest distance handicap of any land, and the other lands of like climate that we have discussed would with equal input of human skill and enterprise do at least as well as it has done. Even with the advantage of a preferred position in the British market, New Zealand's success is a triumph of man over distance. If New Zealand were to lose its preferred position in the British market, this might place a severe strain on its economy, but the changing economic world may compensate for this. Japan's industrial population is unable to feed itself and is increasingly prosperous. New Zealand is a logical source of supply, and Japanese manufactured goods could replace British goods in New Zealand's international exchange.

JAPAN

Climatic comparisons can never be absolute. Japan is included here with the west coast-marine climates because her total setting is more like the kinds of lands that we have been discussing than it is like any of the others. Like Great Britain, Japan lies just off the coast of a continent from which the impulses of civilization came to her. Like the island dominion of New Zealand, most of Japan lies between latitudes of 32 and 44 degrees. As in New Zealand, this creates sharp climatic differences from north to south. Hokkaido, the large northern island, has a climate with summer–winter contrasts about like Newfoundland and the coast of Maine. The southern islands have summer–winter contrasts like those of our deep South. Climatically then, these lands are more like our east coast, but the island setting, with its limited size, mountainous structure, and limited amounts of plain, makes this land much like New Zealand and Great Britain. In size, Japan is about equal to California; about one third larger than Great Britain or New Zealand.

Prehistory

Japan was settled early by people with a Southeast Asian Lower Paleolithic culture. Just as a long sequence of invasions from the continent brought ideas to Great Britain, later people brought the cultural advances that were developing on the Asiatic mainland to Japan. These included Upper

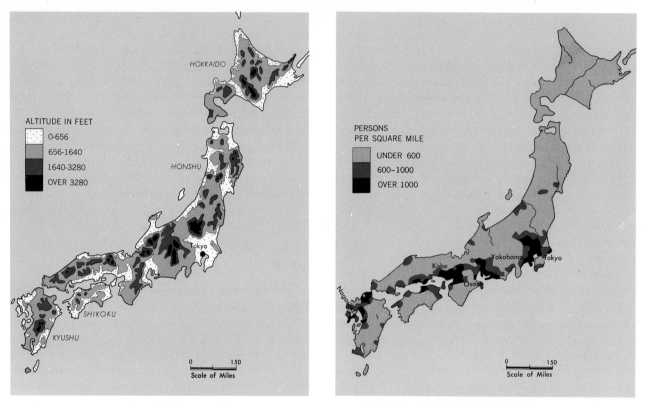

Land Form

Population Density

Map 6-7   Japan: Land Form and Population

The concentration of population on the small coastal plains of the south is clearly shown here. The mountainous interior and the colder north are much less densely occupied. Hokkaido, the northern island, is climatically like northern Vermont. The climate of Tokyo resembles that of North Carolina; and the climate of Kyushu, the southernmost island, that of Alabama. With the population concentrated in the lowlands, more than half the land is left in forest. *Adapted from* Focus—*The American Geographical Society.*

Paleolithic types of stone flaking, followed by pottery making and finally agriculture. The Japanese taking over from the Koreans of Chinese style of writing, and govenmental forms is then simply a continuation of a millennia-old sequence of movements of ideas. Among these ideas was orientalintensive, garden-farming techniques that make possible the development of dense, agriculturally based populations. This was apparently introduced by the people that we see dominating Japan today. They were preceded in the islands by another race, the Ainu. These interesting people are a swarthy, bearded dark white race, whose origin and history remain obscure. They have been gradually displaced by the modern Japanese over the past 2000 years, and today the Ainu hold about the same status in Japan as the American Indians do in the United States. They are now limited to the north, principally on the island of Hokkaido. If the racist argument is followed, should we conclude that since the white race never has done anything here, it never will do anything here or elsewhere?

Snow-covered Countryside in Northern Japan. Japan is too often thought of as a tropical land, disregarding its strongly seasonal, midlatitude position. A snow scene reveals its winter aspect. *Consulate General of Japan, N.Y.*

Horyuji Temple, Nara. Japanese temple forms closely resemble those of Korea, China, and even Indochina, 3000 miles away. This spread of similar art forms neatly records the flow of ideas that started Japan on its earlier road to development. *Consulate General of Japan, N.Y.*

Western-style Development in Japan. (*Left*) A subway in Tokyo. (*Right*) An elevated highway in downtown Tokyo. Japan has achieved a near miracle since 1868 when after a long period of seclusion the country was opened to such Western influences as the industrial revolution. *Consulate General of Japan, N.Y.*

Fishing for Yellowtails, Kumano Sea, Japan. Japan's limited agricultural production has long been supplemented by extensive fishing. Not only are coastal waters fished, as shown here, but sea-going fleets operate throughout the Pacific Ocean. *Consulate General of Japan, N.Y.*

The Japanese population growth was limited by its agricultural outlook to the relatively flat and fertile plains where rice could be advantageously grown. Since Japan is extremely mountainous, this means that relatively little of the total land surface could be used. It is estimated that only 20 percent of Japan is potentially useful agricultural land, and that only 16 percent is actually so used. More than half of the cultivated land is in rice. While the overall population density of the country is high, the density of people per arable acre of land is enormous: 3000 people per square mile. Population densities in much of Japan are 500 people per square mile, and even in Hokkaido there are areas of this density, though most of the populated part of that cold northern island is about 250 to 500 people per square mile. Japan's population is now 93,600,000, nearly 6 times that of California, or more than 30 times that of New Zealand.

The present population cannot be fed from the land despite an intensive agriculture with immense input of labor and fertilizer with the resulting highest yields per acre in the world. It remains an inefficient agriculture, however, for the amount of labor per acre applied to the tiny fields is costly by our Western standards. Even with extreme application, Japan can only raise about 80 percent of her agricultural needs.

The Emergence of Modern Japan

When Japan decided 100 years ago to emerge from her self-enforced withdrawal from the world, there already was a moderately dense agricultural population on the land. Japan possessed a developed fishery, an educated upper class, a system of writing, and had behind it a considerable tradition of trade and commerce. The strongly structured society was adapted to modern production; the agricultural society was left little changed. Through the upper social level was added those parts of the industrial and commercial development of the Western commercial and industrial world that fitted into the land and society. Labor was abundant and cheap, and water power was available due to the high precipitation on the mountainous lands. One of the important early industries was built on the putting of these resources to work on the traditional silk industry of the Orient. Western mechanization made Japanese silk fabrics available in quantity and at attractive prices. This is like the British and American beginnings; and as in these countries, the growth of industry and commerce stimulated a whole series of industries.

Japan has some coal, copper, and sulphur, though the coal supply has proven insufficient. Nevertheless, Japan has developed such heavy industries as iron and steel production, shipbuilding, the manufacture of machinery, and now even an automotive industry. However, the principal development was in textiles, cotton, silk, and rayon, and continues to stress light industry such as chemicals, ceramics, optics and toys.

The growth from a deliberately isolated and retarded nation, to a major world power in 100 years by copying what others had done has often been treated as a joke, as if it indicated some inability to do more than imitate. It indicates, on the contrary, an extraordinary ability to assimilate useful ideas. Japan is the classic example of the fact that what determines whether or not ideas will spread to a given area is the human attitude. Japan deliberately chose not to change, and then to change, and once decided, it accomplished in decades what often has taken people millennia. In Japan's case, the highly structured society with effective control in the hands of a small group, helped to make this possible. It was the fact that Japan was already civilized, literate, and politically organized that was decisive. In contrast, the Yumas were illiterate, economically undeveloped, and had virtually no political organization. Under these circumstances, as we have seen, opportunity can beat on the door interminably and change will come interminably slowly.

Japan's population growth has been from about 50 million in 1910, to 65 million in 1930, 85 million in 1950, 93.6 million in 1960, and is estimated to reach 175 million by 1975. The land is now producing at its maximum. The Japanese have always fished to supplement their diet, and in this century, power applied to fishing boats has extended the range of fishing over all of the Pacific. They have been among the world's leaders in developing refrigerator ships, floating cannery ships, and deep-sea fishing methods. At the end of World War II, they lost some of their northwest Pacific fishing grounds to the Soviet Union, largely through the usual Soviet maneuver of extending any temporary agreement in their favor into a permanent arrangement. How much protein food can the sea be made to yield? There is probably little danger that we have yet begun to harvest the total yield that the sea can supply. But we also do not know how such a harvest can be gathered economically. The Japanese are among the world's leaders in exploring this question.

Japan is now supporting a large part of its population through industry, seemingly has little opportunity to expand its agricultural base, and already is doing an immense job of harvesting the sea. Where then is Japan going to return for the resources to support her growing population? An attempt at building a colonial empire has been repulsed. Emigration is never a solution for expanding populations, hence Japan must take care of its population growth primarily at home. In the main they must be supported through further industrialization, and further expansion of world trade.

It it worth noting, however, that there are probably some untouched agricultural resources at home. While it is true that Japan cannot be developed in the New Zealand pattern, would it not be possible to use some of the 65 percent of Japan that is in forest to develop intensive pasturage of the New Zealand type? While the native grasses may be poor for cattle feed, grasses can be introduced and rich pastures created. Or what would the Swiss assessment of the high mountain slopes of Japan be? Is it not likely that they might think of them as little utilized? The combination of population pressure and increasing knowledge is already moving the Japanese mountain people toward stronger development of forestry and dairying.

However, Japan's population has already outrun any likely land development program for feeding them from their land alone. What then of the future with its predicted immense population? Quite possibly it will never come to be. In the rapid rebuilding of Japan since the war, industrial and commercial power has spread more broadly through the nation than it ever has before, and there is an increasing middle class. The probable course of events is going to be the gradual decrease of the peasants on the land, the increasing growth of the urban industrial population, and, with this, a declining rate of increase of population growth. Already the Japanese birth rate, through conscious national effort, has been cut in half. In an expanding world economy,. with more and more people demanding more and more goods, and with increasing ability to pay for them, there seems to be ample opportunity for an energetic people to utilize almost any base to build an industrial and commercial ecenomy that can supply these goods in return for the industrial raw materials and food stuffs that are needed. As we have seen, there are today potential butter and egg areas lying almost totally unused in various parts of the world. Already developed areas such as New Zealand may find Japan a major customer, for industrialized Japan needs foodstuffs and unindustrialized New Zealand needs manufactured goods.

Japan is another Britain with a population dependent on skills exported in the world market. Growth is now well beyond any possibility of making the land yield the food stuffs and raw materials that could supply the people or the industries. This is by no means unique. Japan's uniqueness lies more in this development occurring in Asia, an area that has not otherwise entered into the industrial revolution to any appreciable extent. Japan is an example of the potential free movement of ideas, and the ability of men with ideas to make much from little.

SUMMARY

A survey of these lands of similar environments and physical opportunities reveals the usual disparities between what could be and what is. The northwest European peoples, with opportunity beating on their Mediterranean and Atlantic doors for something between 5000 and 6000 years, developed industrially in the middle of the nineteenth century and for a time seemed on their way to world domination. Hidden behind the apparent suddenness of this eruption lay the millennia-long seepage to the north and west of the ideas of agriculture, of writing, of machinery. Through all of this time, northwest Europe occupied the land center of the world, England held her channel-protected island position, and the climate changed in no meaningful amount.

In the Americas, proximity to Asia made it possible for fishing people to reach the northwest coast of America and start up a minor culture center there on the pre-Columbian level, but when the Europeans took over, this was an offside location. Our exploitation of the region has set back the aboriginal development, and we have only belatedly begun to develop the potential resources of the area. In South America, the comparable area was so far from the centers of ideas, and especially out of the effective reach of any tradition of use of this type of sea and land, that virtually nothing happened there. Neither was this sort of land of any interest to the Spanish; hence the Chileans have no tradition for the use of such land. The usual explanation given for its lack of development is that its position is against it. That this is inadequate is shown by comparison with the development in New Zealand, the most out of the way land in the world.

Similarly, Tasmania's slow development cannot be attributed to poor location, nor does its record enhance the argument that these cool marine cyclonic climates are enormously stimulating for mental work. And, finally, the Japanese accomplishment, in a short time period on a relatively poor island in the mid-latitudes, is to be seen as similar to that of Great Britain. Back of the spectacular burst of Japanese accomplishment since the middle of the nineteenth century lie centuries of growth of traditions, learning, and political structures that formed the real basis for the events that so impress us. In this, too, Japan, is like Great Britain.

In these mountainous, coastal, rainy lands, representatives of all the races of mankind have lived for millenia. Despite the myth that these are the world's best climates for mental effort, in no case were they centers of early cultural growth. Every case of cultural growth can be shown to have been due to the arrival of cultural stimuli, relatively late in time. Those areas that received such influences flourished; the others did not. Western Europe, starting late, gained world dominance. Japan, starting later, has jumped to Asiatic pre-eminence, and has provided us the interesting case of an early white race failing to progress in this "stimulating" climate. The explanation, of course, is to be found in the sociopolitical climate. This should counteract any tendency to judge the Negrito failure to progress in the Tasmanian climate where the European is lagging a bit even in the mid-twentieth century. Location, opportunity, and receptivity—not raw physical environment or race—emerge as answers.

7-The Grasslands

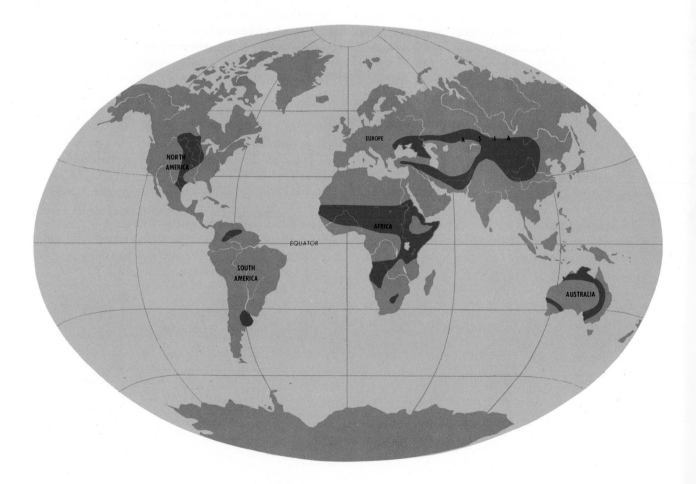

THE RICH, FLAT LANDS of Iowa, Kansas, and Nebraska were originally in grass. Today we use them for grain and cattle production and proudly count them as among our richer agricultural areas. How could it be otherwise? Grasslands are endowed with rich soil. Wheat and corn are grasses. Where could grasses grow better than in a grassland? Cattle are certainly dependent on grass. So again, what could be more natural than for man to seize the grasslands as a superior resource, ideally suited to grazing animals and to growing grain? However, such a judgment is based on our present view and our Western culture. A survey of the use of grasslands through time and space will show that man has found other uses and had differing views of the grasslands. Our own outlook is perhaps the most interesting because of the changes that it has undergone, for we once called the great grassy center of the United States the "American Desert."

LOCATION

The grasslands of the world characteristically are found in the transition areas between the more arid climates and the fully humid climates. Thus the North American grasslands are in the center of the continent extending north and south. This is a zone into which the moisture-bearing winds from the Atlantic and the Pacific penetrate with difficulty. The winds from the west are blocked by the mountains, and the winds from the east and south are deflected by the westerly drift of the air in these latitudes and by the distance that they have to go to penetrate the continental interior. Primarily it is the rain-shadow effect of the mountains that creates the strong north-south orientation of the grasslands.

The pampas of Argentina are similar mid-latitude grasslands. They lie in the rain shadow of the Andes, and between the more tropical and rainier areas to the north and the more arid land to the south. The other major area of grass in mid-latitudes is in Eurasia. These grasslands start in Hungary and extend through south Russia, through Siberia south of Lake Baikal, and terminate in the grasslands of Manchuria. This location along the 50th parallel is a transition zone between forest to the north and steppe and desert to the south.

The tropics also have extensive grasslands, quite contrary to the expectation of those that think of tropical lands as tree covered. The typical location again is in the transition between the zones of equatorial, high, year-round rainfall and the belt of great aridity between 20 and 30 degrees of latitude. The New World has less tropical grassland than the Old World. The llanos in Venezuela are a minor area. The southeastern quarter of Brazil, and the Gran Chaco of Paraguay are other major areas of tropical grassland. Africa has truly huge areas of grasslands forming a great horseshoe around the relatively small equatorial rain forest. The other major grasslands of the world are found in Australia in the transitional areas from the humid margins to the arid interior.

ORIGINS: BOTANY, ZOOLOGY, OR MAN?

The close association of the grasslands with specific climatic situations suggests that they are a direct vegetative response to a specific climate, but the causes are probably more complex. Grasses are relatively late to appear in the long span of geological time. It is not until the opening of the Tertiary period about 70 million years ago, that grasslands came into existence.

The preservation of such delicate plant materials as grasses is relatively rare. Further, it is difficult to know from a few rare specimens much about the distribution of a grass or to learn such things as whether it was a scarce plant, growing along the edge of streams and in forest openings, or a plant

Farm land, Saskatchewan, Canada. The vast extent of flat land suitable for mechanized grain harvesting is evident in this aerial view. *National Film Board, Ottawa.*

Indian Head, Saskatchewan, Canada. Wheat fields and grain elevators present a standard sight in the North American wheat belt. *National Film Board, Ottawa.*

found dominating vast areas of the earth's surface. It is from fossil animals that we learn when the grasses have come to be dominant plants over large areas. When animals appear with their teeth specialized for the grinding of grasses and their legs specialized for rapid fleeing over open territory, we know that the grasslands are present.

It has frequently been said that man has had much to do with making the grasslands. Properly stated and properly understood, this is certainly true. The grasslands only partially fit the climatic boundaries. In the United States grasslands extended east of the 100th meridian, which approximately marks the border between arid and humid in our continent. Along the 40th parallel, the grassland reached east of the 90th meridian, as far east as Chicago. This is land with adequate rainfall to support a dense forest. The Argentine grasslands lie in a climate that is like our southeastern United States climate where a forest cover is expectable. The adjacent Uruguayan and Paraguayan grasslands, even though they contain a sprinkling of trees, are climatically such that a complete forest cover is to be expected. In Africa the great bulk of the tropical grassland is in the savanna climate. In India and Southeast Asia and in Central America, such climates have forest covers. In Africa most of this climate has only scattered trees and much grass.

Tropical Grassland Scenes in the State of Rio Grande do Sul, Brazil. Rolling grasslands are used for cattle production (*above*) or, near Guaiba, for rice production (*below*). The odd combination of bullock carts and tractors in the rice field is a neat expression of the transitional nature of the Brazilian economy. *Brazilian Government Trade Bureau.*

Such observations suggest that something besides climate is at work in creating grasslands. There are several possibilities: plants, animals, and man.

If the plants available are greatly different, there may be considerable difference in response to the similar climates. In one part of the world there may be grasses better suited to taking over wetter areas. A wet grassland, a prairie, may then be found, and would therefore be botanically caused. This aspect of the grassland problem has been relatively little explored. The possible effect of the animals of the different parts of the world in creating or expanding grasslands has also had little discussion. Perhaps it is the least important cause, even though animals do have effects on vegetation. However, most of the data that we have of great vegetative changes caused by animals is based on observations of the effect of domestic animals. Much of mountainous northwest Africa would be forested if it were not for the activities of man herding goats and camels. In the discussion of the American Southwest the effect of the Navaho sheepherders was described as turning grassland into desert. Quite probably the effect of wild grazing and browsing animals is similar, though less drastic. Man, by herding and holding his animals in restricted areas, increases the effect beyond that of wild animals—who are freer to move when the grass or the browse is depleted and would usually move on before the damage became severe.

Is it significant that Africa, where the greatest number, both in kind and quantity, of grazing and browsing animals have survived into the present time; is the continent with the greatest amount of tropical grassland? An equally great number of varieties and, perhaps, equally great numbers of similar animals were once found in the Americas. American camels, horses, elephants, many forms of antelope, and a lengthy list of other grazing animals became extinct within relatively recent times. We suspect that man has had a great deal to do with this extermination. What effect would this relatively sudden removal of grazing and browsing animals have on the vegetation?

It must have had some effects. Grass that was not grazed down would grow higher. Fires that started in the grass would then burn more fiercely; this in turn would tend to destroy woody perennials that were adapted to withstanding the lesser fires of shorter stands of grass. The grassland would then tend to spread. Or, trees that had been severely pruned by browsing animals would be released from this burden; they would grow bushier and would have more limbs left near the ground and could better shade out the competing grasses. This suggests that in some areas removal of the animals might shift the balance in favor of the trees, and in others, in favor of the grasses. We do not know just what did happen. We can be sure, however, that the removal of a long list of grazing and browsing animals must have had an effect.

What about man? The effect of man on the grasslands has been argued vehemently. Unquestionably, man changes the vegetation of the earth. He may clear the forests and plant grasses such as wheat and corn; he may remove the native animals and introduce his own. These may be fenced and kept on limited pastures, or they may be herded widely over the landscape. We have abundant evidence that all of these activities change the land that is so used. We have been altering significant amounts of our humid East to make of this naturally forest area a grassland for the grazing of cattle. This is a radical change indeed. Earlier it was noted that in the East Indies some cattle-raising tribes, by the frequent setting of fires, have converted considerable areas of tropical rain forest into tropical grassland. This is certainly an extreme example of man's ability to change the landscape and to create grasslands. However, from the field of zoology we can demonstrate that extensive grasslands existed long before man. Clearly, man did not create the grasslands; at most, he may have expanded them, and the extent to which he actually did so is the real question. The answer in areas where we see grasses reaching far into lands where humid forests are climatically expectable must be: quite a bit, and as will be

Chernozem Soil, South Dakota. This extremely fertile soil has formed under grass on glacial till; hence it is younger than the last glacial retreat and has an age of approximately 10,000 years. In terms of development, it is a young and fertile soil marked by strong humus accumulation in the *A* horizon, here just over 2 feet deep, and moderate lime accumulation in the *B* horizon. An older soil would have a concrete-like lime pan for a *B* horizon. In soils terminology the *A* horizon is the zone of chemical loss by leaching, the *B* horizon the zone of addition by precipitation, and the *C* horizon the zone of little change. In this photograph the conspicuous things are the darkening of the upper layer through the addition of decayed plant material and the precipitation of lime below the depth of 2 feet, appearing in the photograph as white spots. *USDA photo.*

brought out in the discussion of the American grasslands, his major tool was probably fire.

GRASSLAND SOILS

Whatever their origins, grasslands have soils with certain characteristics. They are deeper and more humus-charged through a greater depth than are forest soils. This is due to the different growth characteristics of trees and grasses. Most trees are relatively shallow rooted. A tree overthrown by the winds usually shows a broad mat of roots that penetrated the ground a relatively short distance. The reasons for this are that the nutrients are often concentrated near the ground surface by the accumulation there of the decayed organic material, and the moisture during the summer growing season is also concentrated there. In the forest lands of the eastern United States it is strikingly clear that after spring, the ground is rapidly dried out and the trees are largely dependent on the shallow wetting of the ground by summer rains. The trees drop a load of leaves annually, and whether they are evergreen or deciduous, this load is placed on the surface. Only at long intervals, on the death of a tree, does the rotting of roots add organic material to the deeper layers of the soil. The movement of the surface organic material downward is slight. Plowing of the ground by the overturning of trees is a centuries long process, and the activity of burrowing animals is probably much more significant. The total effect, however, is to leave most of the organic material concentrated in a shallow zone, as can be seen by inspecting almost any forest soil.

On a grassland almost all of these characteristics are reversed. At the beginning of the growing season, the soil is wet to some depth and then dries out as summer comes on. The grasses are deep-rooted for their size, and have an immense net of hairlike roots, which seek moisture at considerable depth. Tall grasses may send their roots down to a depth of six feet or more, which is deeper than most tree roots. The annual grasses die down at the end of each rainy season. This adds a plant material to the surface of the soil to decay and become humus. Simultaneously, the root system that permeated the soil to a depth of six feet dies, adding a load of organic material throughout the soil mass to this depth. Perennial grasses replace their roots at relatively high frequencies, and the old roots decay and add humus at depth in the soil.

In addition, most forest soils are in wetter lands than the grasslands. There is therefore more leaching of the soluable nutrients than in the grasslands. The capacity of a soil to hold up the soluable nutrients that the plants need is in part determined by the presence of the organic compounds that can absorb and hold these materials. These organic materials are much greater in quantity and better distributed in the grassland soils. Hence, even in the grasslands, growing in humid areas where leaching tends to remove the nutrients, there is greater fertility than in the woodlands.

There are, of course, differences between the soils of mid-latitude grasslands and tropical grasslands, and between grasslands on the edge of the arid lands and those that invade the humid lands. Tropical grasses tend to be perennial, and hence to add less humus to the deep layers of the soil. Under the higher temperatures of the tropics, the decay of the surface organic materials goes on much more rapidly, making it more readily leached out of the soil. The tropical grasslands tend then to be lower in organic material than the mid-latitude grasslands.

The contrast between the soils of the arid and humid parts of the grasslands is well illustrated in the United States. The soils in the humid eastern extension of the grasslands are subject to the leaching action of 30 to 40 inches of rainfall every year. This is sufficient to maintain a permanent water table, and to maintain a movement of water down through the soil into this water table, to drain away and reappear as springs feeding streams. The soluable nutrients tend to go with this water. There is then, a steady impoverishment of the soils, with the most soluable nutrients moving out first. This includes the calcium, nitrogen, phosphorus, and potash

that are the nutrients needed in greatest quantity, and these humid grasslands then often show deficiencies in these materials. This is readily measured by their lack of basic materials, particularly calcium, whose absence leaves these soils with an acid reaction. Only the abundance of humus saves these soils from rapid depletion and reduction to the fertility of the forest soils.

Westward with declining precipitation, the degree of leaching drops. Near the 100th meridian, the boundary is met where the amount of precipitation is no longer able to move through the ground to maintain a permanent water table, which means that the ground is annually wet to some depth and thereafter dries out. The moisture moving down through the soils during the wet season will carry soluable chemicals down with it. When the water evaporates from the soil, the minerals are left behind. Water lifted back up by the plants to be transpired from their leaves brings up only a small part of the minerals that have been carried down. Consequently, soluble chemicals tend to accumulate toward the base of the zone of average wetting. This is easily seen in soils of a few thousand years age by the accumulation there of lime in visible amounts. With the passage of great amounts of time, the accumulation increases. Very old soils may have immense amounts of lime and at depth they may be cemented to a rocklike hardness.

The amount of humus accumulation must vary with these climatic conditions also, though in a different way. Under the 30 to 40 inches of rainfall in the wet grassland, the prairie, the grasses grew quite tall. In Iowa, the first men that saw the tall-grass prairie described it as so high that a man on horseback seemed to be moving along with no visible means of support. Westward, the grasses steadily shortened. It is customary to divide our grasslands into the tall-grass, short-grass, and bunch-grass regions. The short grass still forms a continuous sod, as in a lawn. The bunch grass no longer forms a continuous cover, but as the name implies, it grows in clumps with some space between the clumps. These shifts are related to the amount of moisture available. With abundant moisture, grasses of greater vegetative growth dominate and send their roots deep to tap the stored moisture. As the moisture decreases and there is less moisture stored in the soil, grasses of shorter growth, both in length of their growing season and in the height of their stems, come to dominate the scene. As the moisture falls still lower, the grasses can no longer grow close together in sharp competition with each other, but must spread out to have enough moist ground available for their moisture needs.

The climate, the vegetation, and the soil in the American grasslands came to make up the grassland environment through a complex of adjustments. The relationships are even more involved than have been described here. For instance, the geological materials in various parts of the American grasslands are different in composition and in age. To the north the land was glaciated; this brought fresh materials into the area, and these contained much more of the soluable nutrients. The time since the end of the glacial period, 10 to 20 thousand years, has been too little to leach out much of this mineral wealth. The southern grassland soils under similar climates are less rich because their material has not been renewed so recently. In Nebraska there is an extensive area of blown sand—the Sand Hills. Sand is generally poor in nutrients, in water holding capacity, and in resistance to wind erosion. Then, too, the rate of accumulation of humus varies with temperature. Much more organic material remains in the soils to the north than in the warmer soils of the south.

The high plains along the foothills of the Rockies are formed by the alluvium washed out from the mountains. Most of this vast apron of alluvium is now cut through by rivers that are flowing below the level of this plain, hence new material is not being added. The soils are therefore aging; in Texas, on the Llano Estacado, the land has been in such a condition for so long that the accumulation of lime in the subsoil has reached geological proportions. The soil is underlain at shallow depth by an immense cemented layer that now resists erosion and tends to preserve the smooth, flat, semiarid grassland landscape. While the other grasslands of the world will be described in much more sweeping terms, if they were looked at in any detail, similar differences would appear in all of them.

The grasslands are a distinctive environment. Shade is scarce; the sun shines down from a sky that is relatively cloud free. Grassland is close to the desert in the total amount of sunshine received. Like the desert, the wind velocities are relatively high and constant, for there is less vegetation to break up the flow of wind. The air is clear, and since there are few obstructions to the line of sight, it is possible to see great distances. The grass provides an immense food supply to grazing animals, and the grazing animals support the carnivores that feed on them. The grasslands are therefore a relatively rich environment in plant and animal resources, built on the rich soils.

What have these environments done to man? Or should the question be asked the other way: What has man done with these environments?

MAN IN THE GRASSLANDS OF THE UNITED STATES

America has one of the most extensive mid-latitude grasslands of the world, and it has played a large part in American thought. It has been the home of the buffalo, the buffalo-nickel type Indian, the cowboy, and other heroic American stereotypes, such as the western marshal and the cattle drive, that have provided the content for song, story, motion picture, and now television drama. The impact of the grassland has been described and debated, and at times it has been presented as almost a personified force that molded men and cultures to meet its conditions.

HUNTERS, FIRE, AND CHANGE

Man has lived in the American grasslands for a very long time. We know his history there with some certainty from a time beginning toward the end of the last ice age. At that time, the grasslands were considerably moister than they are now. The tall grasses that are now found to the east of the 100th meridian must have extended far to the west, perhaps right to the foot of the Rocky Mountains. This was the time when the Great Basin had large lakes in areas that are now desert, and the southern deserts had a grassland appearance that may have approximated that seen today in the short-grass area of the Great Plains. The animals in the grasslands then included the American elephant, giant buffalo, and horse. The men of that day were skilled hunters, and seem almost to have specialized in the killing of this large game. This is, of course, logical, for a single kill of a large animal supplies a huge amount of meat. We know too little in detail of this time to do more than mention that the animals indicate that the area was grassy, although it may, with the increased rains of that time, have had more trees, especially along the water courses, than we now see there. We know that the men hunted the biggest of the game animals, and that presently these large game animals disappeared. We therefore suspect that man played a large part in the extinction. Man may also have been modifying the flora as well as the fauna, for the driving of big game animals in grasslands often is done by setting fire to the grass to stampede the animals over a cliff or into a ravine. In this way some are killed and some are injured, and then easily finished by the hunters. Such kill-sites are known in the Great Plains.

Fire is the enemy of trees, and the friend of the grass. Grass germinates in the spring, utilizing the moisture stored in the soil during the winter as well as the rains of spring. Maturation is rapid and seed is dropped by the onset of the summer drought. If fire then burns up the grass, the seed is safely lodged in the ground.

Trees need a period of years to mature and produce seed. Too frequent fires, fed by sufficient grass to make a very hot fire, can kill the trees. The greater the frequency of fires, the less chance for the trees. Lightning-set fires would occur at a "natural" rate. They would start most easily, run the farthest, and burn any given area most frequently in the drier areas and would have diminishing opportunity to start and to run as the humid areas were approached. A balance would finally be struck toward the humid side of any arid zone, where the frequency of fire would be too low to kill out the trees; and the density of shading of the trees would be great enough to shade out the grasses so that they could not provide sufficient growth to kill the mature trees. All of this would happen without man.

Man could increase these effects. If the frequency of fire is important, then man setting fires would add to the natural frequency and the fire effect would be increased. We have a number of studies of the effect of man and his working with fire. In the south of Texas, great, grassy prairies were found by the first settlers. This is a land of 30 to 40 inches of rainfall, sufficient to support a dense forest. When the Texans put cattle on this land, they multiplied to an enormous extent. It is estimated that Texas had 100,000 head of cattle in 1830; 330,000 head in 1850; and 3,500,000 in 1860. A very large proportion of these cattle were in southern Texas. The crowding of so many cattle on the grasslands had the interesting effect that woody and brushy forms of vegetation began to appear, and the prairie began to turn into a brushland. Under the protection of the clumps of brush, trees began to grow. In the thorny brush there was less food for the cattle, and they were very much harder to round up; hence the cattlemen found the land decreasing in value to them. They found ready buyers for the land in the oncoming wave of farmers, who with an entirely different view of the land, cleared the brush and planted crops.

Analysis of these shifts suggests some causes. When the cattle population became heavy, the tall grasses were grazed down. Therefore, when fires got started—whether natural or man-made—they drew on a limited amount of fuel. They could not build up the raging inferno of heat that the lightly grazed, four- to six-feet high, natural tall grasses could create. With the lighter intensity of fire, the heavy brushy vegetation such as the mesquite could make a start; whereas in the past, the fierce fires fed by tall grasses would have burnt it out. Thus through man's introduction of cattle, the balance was shifted through overgrazing toward the lessening of the intensity of fire, and this was to the advantage of the woody vegetation. The question naturally arises: How did this humid land, naturally suited for tree growth, ever become a grassland? The answer must be that fire was the agent. Whether natural fire, or fire increased through the activity of man, is not readily answered. Surely, man increased the frequency of fire. This must have been effective, and must have further enlarged whatever grassland existed.

In the Ozark region a similar story can be found. Between St. Louis and Springfield there is a low dome of limestone, deeply eroded by stream action. This hilly upland is now largely forested. This was not its condition when we first saw it. The first accounts of the land describe much of it as parklike. Trees were scattered through a grassy cover. Trees, of course, grew thickly along the water courses and on rocky knobs, but so much of the country was open grassland with only scattered trees in it that it was possible to take a wagon and drive across country with some ease. This would not be possible today because the trees now form a closed forest over most of the area. What has happened?

We are sure of one thing: we have removed the Indians. We know further that it was the Indian custom to burn the land annually, for they had the idea that this increased the amount of game on the land. We are, or were, largely woodsmen: we have the fixed idea that fire is evil; we have everywhere taken drastic action to stop fires. In much of the West this fire prevention effort has brought on virtual states of war between the fire wardens and the range men. The range men angrily maintain that fire drives out the woody vegetation and increases the grass that their animals need. It is a fact that with the disappearance of the Indians, and the forceful prevention of fire instead of its propagation, the aspect of the Ozark country has changed from an open, grassy, parklike landscape to one of forest-covered land. For a cattleman it is a change for the worse; to a forester, for the better.

Significant shifts in the animal life have accompanied the vegetation change. The Ozarks were described in the early accounts as a sportsman's paradise. The land was thickly populated with deer, bear, turkey, quail, rabbit, and a wide range of other game animals. Today turkeys are scarce, bear and deer only a fraction of their former numbers, and the same holds true for the quail and rabbit. The reasons are closely tied to the shift in vegetation. A closed forest is poor in food for most animals except squirrels. The other animals need the browse that is found on the edge of woods, the berries and seeds that are found in the grassy meadow, and the nuts that come in greatest quantities not from trees standing in closed forest, but in open stands where the competition for light and moisture and nutrients is not so severe.

This process has been most strikingly documented for some oak trees that were grown for genetic studies at the Missouri Botanical Gardens. These oak trees, planted on the parklike grounds of Shaw's Gardens, the intown part of the institution, matured rapidly and produced huge crops of acorns at least every two years, with minor crops on the off years. The trees that grew under closed forest conditions in the woodland at Gray's Summit, where the experimental forest is, produced so few acorns that they were useless for genetic studies. Since acorns are a highly nutritious food that supports pigeons, bears, deer, and turkeys, it seems that primitive men were wise to burn the forest sufficiently to keep it open, parklike, and rich in game.

Our needs have changed. We want timber for lumber and a closed forest produces straighter trees with fewer knots, and hence better lumber. The point is that by management of the land, we can have whichever we want. The Indians wanted game, knew that frequent fires promoted more game, and managed the physical environment accordingly. The Indians even burned the forest along our eastern seaboard annually. When our European ancestors asked them why, they insisted that it was so that there would be more game for them to hunt. It is such things as this that make it probable that there is no such thing as a "natural landscape."

INDIANS IN THE GRASSLANDS

The grassy plains had only limited attraction for the Indians. They were too dry and too susceptible to being swept by raging grass fires to be useful for agriculture, except along the major river valleys. Probably the Indians would have had great difficulty cultivating the surface of most of this land anyway. The grass formed an unbroken tough sod. This is not easily turned into farmland unless you have such tools as the plow and such power as horses, oxen, or tractors. In the prewhite period, then, the Great Plains had limited value for the Indians. The tribes around the margins made seasonal trips into the area to conduct buffalo drives. Either by fire or by skilled driving ending in a stampede, they drove the buffalo into ravines, over a cliff or into a marsh. The Indians could not easily go out on the plain and approach a herd, or even a single buffalo. They are large beasts, quick as a gigantic cat and dangerous to a man on foot. No one approaches range cattle on foot either, and there are many, not very funny, stories of hunters treed by "domesticated" bulls.

The Indians got horses from the Spanish, together with the idea that they could ride these beasts, and the whole outlook of the plains changed. Instead of being an area of marginal utility, occupied by a relatively few people, they became an area of great attraction. With the horse, the buffalo could be approached with considerable safety and killed with some ease. Moreover, the problem of finding one of the herds was greatly simplified, for the horse gave man increased mobility. Suddenly, the great herds drifting slowly about over the vast sea of grass in the center of America became an endless supply of meat, hides, and sinew. The land, with no change in the physical environment, but only with the addition of the art of horseback riding, changed from one of meager opportunity to one of great opportunity.

All the other ideas needed for the utilization of the horse were at hand. The northern Plains Indians already had the tepee, the familiar pointed, conical tent, a marvelous house that was portable, easily taken down or set up, cool in summer and relatively smoke-free in winter. The Indian women set the flaps at the top according to the wind in order to make the fire draw well. The shape of the tent was chimneylike: in winter, this made the smoke rise to go out the top; and in summer, with the sides raised slightly, air flowed in around the bottom and hot air rose and went out the top. When there were only women and dogs to haul the tent, it could not be very large. Men, of course, carried little more than their weapons when camp moved, for they had to be ready to kill game or repel the enemy. When the horse was added, much longer poles could be moved from site to site; further, the horse made it possible to kill more buffalo for more skins for larger tepees.

It is worth noting that not all the Plains Indians had the tepee. Some of the southern Plains people built grass-thatched houses. The Mandan, and in the past, other Plains tribes built large houses with log frames and covered them thickly with earth. This land of scanty timber did not dictate the house type: grass was available; skins were available; and sufficient timber was available along streamways for houses for the small population.

Tepee of the Plains Cree, Saskatchewan, Canada. The tepee is the classic Indian house. This type was found in the northern Great Plains and in part of the adjacent arctic forest area, and similar dwellings existed in adjacent northern Asia. In other adjacent areas in America, however, even in such similar environments as the southern Great Plains, entirely different types of housing were used. Compare the grass lodge of the Wichita Indians. *Museum of the American Indian, Heye Foundation.*

Wichita Indian Grass Lodge under Construction. This type of dwelling could have been built in many areas of America and almost any other type of housing used elsewhere in America could have been built here. *Smithsonian Institution, Bureau of American Ethnology.*

Houses could also have been built of adobe bricks or of stone or of sod. It is too easy to look at what is or was and to conclude that it had to be, or was "natural."

It is worth considering also how useful the tepee could have been in other areas. It would have been equally good as a home in any part of America where people had a supply of animal skins: this was most of America. Hence, it becomes clear that the tepee was not made because this was the only way to meet the cultural need of a moveable home in an environment that offered little except skins for wall construction. It was a clever invention made by a people who elected to carry their home about with them instead of making a new one of grass or sod each time they moved. They had still another choice of course: to move less and to have one or several permanent houses. The choice was a cultural one. It was not, as it has too often been portrayed, a physical, environmentally determined one. Furthermore, the distribution of this type of tent in Siberia suggests that it may be an ancient invention made in some environment far from and very different from the American grasslands.

The Indians had the bow, the lance, and the shield, although they probably had had the bow and arrow for little more than a thousand years and had hunted with the throwing spear before that time. Originally, their bows may have been long, but for use on horseback they used a short bow, just as our cavalry men developed short-barrelled rifles to replace the long rifle. The Indians also evolved a special way of killing the buffalo from horseback.

The method was to train special horses to run alongside the buffalo; the hunter then leaned over and fired at point-blank range. The Indians and their mounts both knew their task. Once the herd was sighted, the Indian did not have to guide his horse. The hunter, therefore, had both hands free for his bow. Once alongside the buffalo, the expert Indian timed his shot for the instant when the buffalo was stretched out in his gallop: this spread the ribs and gave the hunter a better chance to drive his arrow through the lung cavity without touching a bone. Occasionally an Indian would drive an arrow clear through one buffalo and drop another running alongside the first buffalo.

This was a thrilling business. It had all the excitement of a football game, with the difference that all the men played and there were seldom any spectators. Great care had to be taken in the approach to the buffalo, and this was one of the few times that the extremely independent Plains Indians submitted to some discipline. Certain Indians served as police to see that no one broke ranks so as to scare the buffalo prematurely or to get a special advantage. Once the "run" was on it went for miles and a good hunter on a fine horse might kill several buffalo. The yield was tons of meat, dozens of hides, and almost more horn and bone and sinew than could be used. The Indians made good use of the material, however. The hides were stripped off, and the carcass was cut up at the kill site. In the camp, the meat would be stripped from the bones, cut into strips and dried. The dried meat might later be pounded up and have fat poured over it: this is the famous pemmican of the Indians. The bones were then often boiled in order to get the marrow out of them.

When the horse was taken up, this way of life was so attractive that many of the tribes in the areas bordering on the edge of the plains gave up farming and moved out to become hunters. This is one of the few cases in history of farming-village dwellers giving up their settled way of life for the wild nomadic life of the hunter. The whole period was a brief one, however. The Indians of the southern plains began to ride some time toward the end of the seventeenth century, and in less than a hundred years all of the Plains Indians had horses. In another hundred years this way of life had come to an end because the Americans had killed off the buffalo. In between these dates lies the history of the flourishing of the great buffalo-hunting Indian culture. The Spanish almost certainly were the source of the horses and the habit of riding them, and it needs to be emphasized that

Cheyenne Indian Women Leading Horse Travois, Lame Deer, Montana. Before 1500, dogs were hitched to such devices and made to drag loads. The horse, when introduced, was treated simply as a large dog, a classic case of cultural transfer and retention of old forms. The horses are saddled, but the women walk and use the travois for carrying burdens. *Museum of the American Indian, Heye Foundation.*

it was the trick of riding the horse that was important. The Indians had had horses before, but lacked the idea that they could be ridden and had eaten them instead.

EUROPEAN VIEWS OF THE AMERICAN GRASSLANDS

Since the Spanish were horsemen, and midlatitude men, and had wheat growing and cattle handling as a major part of their background, what was their reaction to this rich grassland?

The Spanish explored the grassland very early. Several long expeditions from the gulf area and the Southwest reached out into the plains. DeSoto entered the plains from the southeastern direction, and Coronado penetrated the plains from our Southwest. Both expeditions probably reached the vicinity of Kansas. They reported on the immense extent of level, grass-covered land, and the presence of herds of buffalo with Indian people who made their living hunting them. However, they made no move to settle these lands.

This is not surprising. As we have seen, there were very few Spaniards available and two continents to seize and to hold. There were also settled Indians possessed of great wealth of gold and silver and developed lands in Middle America. In the

North American grasslands, there were only wild Indians and undeveloped lands. Not surprisingly, the Spaniards elected to pass up this area, just as they did California. The few settlements made were along the southern border of the grasslands and at the mouth of the Mississippi, more to hold the area politically than to try to settle and develop it. It was probably from these settlements that horses and riding spread to the southern Plains Indians in the seventeenth century.

Once the Indians had the horse, the Spanish spread into this area was made infinitely more difficult. Instead of a thin population of people of limited mobility and considerable poverty, the area came to have more people, and these were a mounted, mobile, aggressively well-fed people who took to warfare as a special form of sport. For such tribes as the Apache and the Comanche and the Kiowa, the settlements in Texas and Mexico became the source of readily available horses, guns, and captives. The Spanish, and later the Mexican frontier, was actually driven back by the Plains Indians. The Spanish can be said to have made no use of the vast grassy heartland of America that was for centuries nominally, but never physically, in their possession.

Other Europeans looked at the grasslands also. The French had spread across the North, following

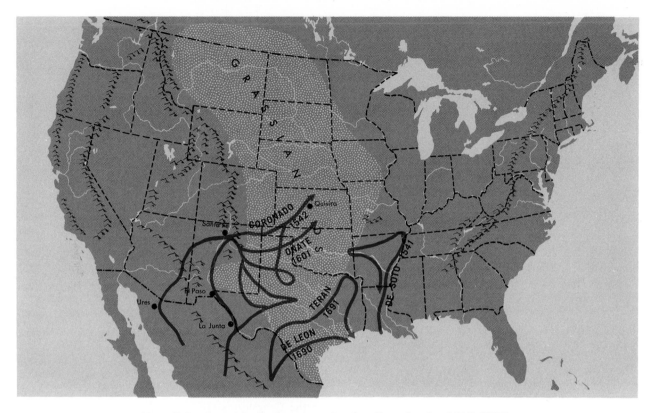

Map 7-1 Spanish Explorations in the Grasslands, 1535–1700

Except for De Soto's expedition, the Spanish approach to the grasslands was from the southwest. Expeditions left from points in northern Mexico and entered the grasslands by crossing the Rio Grande. The major trade route that developed was the one from Ures to Santa Fe. Despite explorations in the 1540s, in 1601, and in the 1690s, all of which reported on the level land, the oceans of grass, and the thousands of woolly cattle, the Spanish saw little advantage in these lands compared with the settled and mineral-rich lands they held to the south.

the great lakes waterways that led them westward. Their explorations then took them down the Mississippi and they followed the major rivers out toward the Great Plains, but their interests were concentrated in furs. These they obtained primarily from the forest Indians, hence they were deflected by their interests away from the grassy plains.

In the early nineteenth century, there was a sizable settlement of French-Indian people along what is now the boundary area of Canada and the United States, just west of Lake Superior. From here spring and fall hunting parties were organized to go into the plains for a supply of buffalo meat. They hunted in the rich agricultural area of what is now Minnesota. But the agricultural traditions of the French were a thing of their past; in this new land they approached the plains as the Indians did, as a source of buffalo, to be harvested seasonally, and they made no attempt to farm these fertile grasslands.

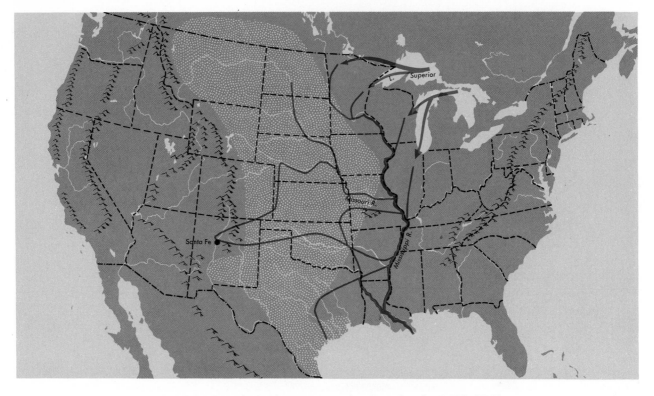

Map 7-2   French Explorations in the Grasslands, 1673–1750

For the French the Great Lakes led naturally into the grasslands and into the Mississippi. Although they traveled frequently on the Mississippi and developed a major settlement at St. Louis, they explored the grasslands relatively lightly. Their major penetrations were in the north, just to the west of Lake Superior, where they made considerable use of the area as a major source of buffalo meat. In the main, they stayed in the woodlands.

THE AMERICAN APPROACH

The American approach to this land really has to be described as plural. The first wave was that of the fur trappers. To them, beaver was the quest. The plains had few, so these men drove on west to the mountain areas where there were beaver to be had. The first settlers viewed the grassy plains as a poor land to be crossed as rapidly as possible. Their path through the plains became "the Oregon trail," traveling over the fertile prairies, our present corn belt, and the level, short grassland, our present wheat belt. They followed the Platte River to South Pass through the Rockies to reach the headwaters of the Snake River and went all the way to the Pacific Coast to find another forested area that was like the eastern United States.

These early Americans had behind them a long tradition of forest dwelling, farming, and cattle raising, for this had been their way of life in Eu-

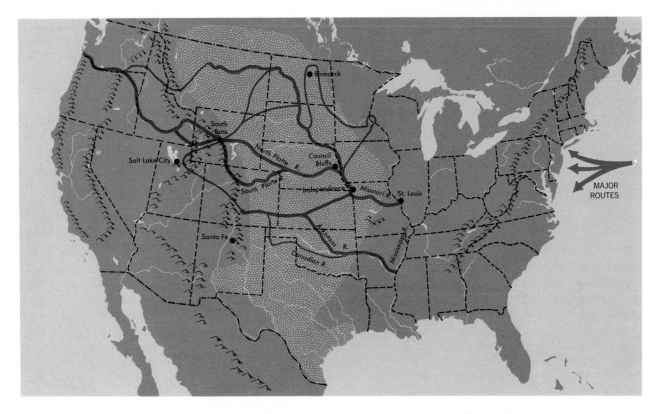

Map 7-3   American Explorations in the Grasslands, 1800–1850

The Americans came to the grasslands later and approached them on a broad front along the Mississippi. The routes of exploration and eventual travel were the rivers, with the Missouri playing the major role. The Oregon Trail started up the Missouri, then followed the Platte River to South Pass, continuing along the Snake River to the coast. The great migration to Oregon went right across the grasslands, and the settlers saw nothing there worth stopping for. Early American exploration and settlement largely avoided the Spanish-Mexican territory until that land was taken into the union.

rope. It was continued in the forested eastern United States, where their whole economy was geared to a great abundance of wood. Trees told you whether the land was rich or poor. The trees that you felled supplied the timber for your house and barn and the rails for your fences and the wood for your fires. Without wood, how could you keep stock out of your fields or keep the fire going in the fireplace for warmth in winter and for cooking the year round? A land without timber, must be a poor land

and, to one accustomed to unlimited amounts of wood, an impossible land. Better to go 3000 miles to Oregon than to try to do anything with this impossible grassland, where timber was lacking, where water was scarce, where the grass fires raged across the land faster than a man could run, and where the buffalo supported a series of Indian tribes whose avocation was horse stealing and warfare.

Eventually, changes were to come that would alter this outlook. But the good rich soils and the immense wealth of some of our richest agricultural regions were to those early Americans, even to the traditional farming people who first saw them, no resource at all. The "good" of the environment lay fallow awaiting another generation of men with new ideas and new techniques. In large part, the techniques already existed, but the applications had yet to be made. The physical environment was to continue to lie fallow until a people came who looked on it not as a repulsive desert, but as an attractive possibility.

The West was added to the nation in a series of purchases and settlements and wars: the Louisiana Purchase made in 1803; the Oregon country obtained by settlement with the British in 1846; Texas brought in by annexation in 1845; and the Southwest won by the cession from Mexico in 1848. With the Oregon settlement and the subsequent Gold Rush, America suddenly found itself with a large population separated from the rest of the country. What was called the Great American Desert (the grassy plains, the Rocky Mountains, the Great Basin and the Sierra Nevadas) separated this Pacific population from the rest of the nation. In addition, there were the mobile horsemen of the plains making settlement or occupation of that area difficult, if indeed, it were even desirable.

Opinions varied on what to do about this situation. Some thought the distance made regular contact too difficult. Others advocated bringing in camels to supply transportation across the deserts and to give to the Indians so that they would become herding people instead of hunters. It was reasoned that we could then establish beneficial relations with them, such as the peoples of the Old World had worked out with the nomadic peoples of inner Asia. They could supply us with camel hides, wool, and cheese, and we could supply them with manufactured articles. The camels were actually introduced, but they were used mostly by the army for transportation in the southern desert route to the West through Texas and Arizona. They were successful in their way, but they were rapidly displaced by the railroads. They had been introduced a few centuries too late.

The camels flourished in the arid West. Eventually stockmen shot them to keep them from multiplying and eating up the food on the range that the cattlemen desired for their stock. Were this not so, there would be wild camels in our West today—and this, like the horse, would have been only a reversal of history, for there had been plenty of camels in the past. The Indians had had a hand in their extermination; the white man reintroduced them, but with new ideas: domestication and transportation. But before the Indian could take up the idea of using them as pastoral beasts, the quickening pace of change was to sweep away the old way of life and almost to sweep away the Indian with it.

It would not have been a quick and easy thing to change the Indian to a pastoralist. The change is not a simple one, for it involves an entirely new attitude toward the land. The keeping of a domestic beast, the milking, the gathering of the wool, spinning, and weaving are all difficult new ideas that have not only to be learned, but have to be fitted into a way of life. The Indians could readily have done this, given time. They had the horses for herding, the grasslands for the feeding, and the custom of moving about. Other tribes, the Navaho, for instance, show that such people can readily take up herding, shearing, and weaving; although for the Navaho, the domestic animal was to be the sheep.

Curiously, little thought seems to have been given to the buffalo as a domestic beast. This animal is admirably suited to the plains environment: it supplies delicious meat, fine hides, and some wool. Yet it never occurred to the Indian to domesticate it. Why bother, when there were millions available for the taking? The white men all stressed the ferocity of the beast and its utter untameability. Those who have seen these animals in zoos, parks, or in Yellowstone are likely to have been more impressed with their cattlelike appearance and action. No large animal is safe; even large breeds of dogs turn on their masters at rare intervals and kill them. For quite a time, the greatest risk on our farms were the bulls, and Jersey bulls had a particular reputation for meanness. Injury and loss of life due to domestic bulls has only recently been replaced by injury and loss of life due to tractors.

We came to the Great Plains and found the buffalo a wild animal. Like the Indian before us, we continued to think of him in this way. When a thoughtful move was made to try to use these grasslands for pastoral nomadism, two patterns of thought emerged: first, that these were desert lands; second, that for desert pastoralism, the camel was the proper animal. This illustrates the dominance of men's ideas over the realities of mere physical geography. The grasslands were not desert. There were already highly suitable animals in the grassland for a pastoral way of life, but it was easier to think of an already domesticated animal and to invent reasons for not using the native animal than to see the grassland and its native animal for what they were. In passing, it should be noted that the buffalo is a Eurasian animal that entered America relatively late in time and that it is so much like the European cattle that its bones are barely distinguishable even by an expert zoologist. It is readily tamed, and does well behind barbed wire on managed pastures.

Developing the Grasslands

A series of inventions was introduced just after the Civil War that transformed the grassland and doomed the Indian buffalo-hunting way of life: the six shooter put the Indian at a military disadvantage, and the railroad provided transportation to markets. The deep-well drilling technique made water available where it could not be reached before, and the windmill lifted the water. Barbed wire supplied the fencing for fields. Transportation doomed the buffalo and moved the crops to market. The self-polishing steel plow made it possible to break the tough sod of the prairie. Since these were all needed on the plains, were they invented there in response to the environment? At best only one of them can qualify.

The six shooter was invented by a New Englander named Samuel Colt. As is often the case, he had the greatest difficulty getting acceptance for his invention. Eventually, a number of them got into the hands of the Texans, who had been having their difficulties with the Indians. With a single-shot rifle, and at most a single-shot pistol, the Americans were at a decided disadvantage to the Indians, who might easily carry 20 or 30 arrows and be able to fire them at a rate of 10 or more a minute. The Indians in fact, had perfected the art of charging the settler, drawing his fire, and then charging on in to drive their arrows home at point-blank range while the settler was reloading. And it did no good to jump on a horse and run, unless it was the fastest horse on the prairie. The Indian would chase anyone fleeing and easily pick his enemy out of the saddle with his 14-foot lance. The first encounter of men equipped with six shooters with a band of Indians proved disastrous for the Indians. The men fired their rifles and then charged. To the Indians' astonishment, they whipped out short guns that fired again and again. The Indians were routed and lost half of their men. The pistol was a needed arm and one well-suited to close-quarter fighting on horseback. However, it was still not invented in direct response to the need.

This is true of all but one of the rest of these inventions. The railroad was invented in Europe, and in America was developed along the eastern seaboard. It was to revolutionize the West, but it can in no sense be said to have been developed in response to the challenge of the great open spaces that had to be crossed. Deep-well drilling is essential in the arid lands where the water supply may be 50 or 100 or more feet below the surface of the ground, but deep-well drilling far precedes the American occupation of the West and was a European invention. The drilled well is a six-inch or wider hole bored by either a rotary or plunging type of bit and cleaned out by a long slender bucket with a valve at the bottom of it. These devices were taken up in the plains and used very extensively to get water in otherwise arid regions, but they were not invented there.

Water is readily lifted by a bucket on a rope over a pulley for distances up to 40 or 50 feet, if the water needed is only to be used about the house. If water is needed in larger quantities, for watering stock and irrigating a small garden, then lifting the water by hand-hauling on a rope is a very tedious business. For lifting the quantities of water needed, the Americans adapted the windmill. This is particularly useful in such treeless lands as the plains. There, the absence of surface roughness does not cut down greatly on the movement of the air and the wind velocities near the ground are, like those at sea, about 10 percent higher than they are over forested land. But where did the windmill come from? The usual reply is Holland; but the earliest recorded ones are in Persia. They came to be widely used all over Europe, not only for lifting water in Holland, but much more commonly for doing such work as grinding grain. It was widely used in colonial America. The idea was taken up by the men of the grassland and after considerable experimentation, an efficient, metal, fan-bladed form was developed: the familiar windmill of our West.

Fencing

The one invention that seems to have been made in the grassland in response to a real need was barbed wire. The problem was a pressing one. Stock had to be kept out of the crops. To have good stock, it was necessary to keep the scrubs and the animals of desirable qualities separated so that they would not interbreed. All of this required fencing. The American tradition had become one of rail fences. These could be of several types, but they all had in common the use of a great deal of wood. In the forested East, this presented no problem; on the contrary, it supplied a way of using some of the wood that had to be cleared from the land. In the plains, there simply was not that amount of wood available.

Fences can, of course, be made of other materials. The New England stone fences are an example of a use of a material that had to be removed from the fields. Stone fences were built in some of the rockier parts of the plains; however, much of the plains are not stony. Soil, of course, is everywhere. It can be piled up either between board forms or as sun-dried bricks to make an earth fence. This, too, was tried, and gave rise to the Americanism "as ugly as a mud fence." Earth walls were expensive in labor costs and melted down under the washing of the rains. Another means of fencing is by hedges; this is a highly developed art in England and in parts of France. A wide variety of plants can be used, and when properly planted, reinforced with stakes and branches in weak spots and carefully tended, they make excellent fences—but they have some disadvantages. They use water, and they occupy space. In the plains environment, however, hedges also cut down on the destructive action of the wind and shelter the homestead; they catch drifting snow and thus accumulate moisture.

Considerable effort was expended on hedging, and attention turned to the Osage orange. This hardy native tree is thorny and hence useful in holding cattle, but there were numerous other possible hedge-making plants. To the south and toward the arid side of the plains, the mesquite and the cactus could have been used. Hedging could quite possibly have solved the problem of fencing the grassland if the invention of barbed wire had not come along just at the time that the hedge work was in the experimental stage in the United States. There were then a number of ways in which the fencing problem could have been met. The actual solution was different.

The industrial revolution had made metal more readily available. Wire-making machinery had been invented, and wire was relatively cheap. Fencing with wire had been tried, but the animals soon learned that they could simply push their way through the wire. A number of men began experimenting with putting prickly materials on the smooth wire to stop the animals from escaping. At De Kalb, Illinois, a solution to the problem was found and our modern barbed wire was evolved. This came in the 1870s, and barbed wire rapidly became the dominant fencing material for the grassland thereafter. It is efficient, cheap to install and to maintain, and is now the dominant fencing material in America in all climates. It is unesthetic, unfriendly, uninhabitable by bird and beast (unlike hedges), and so damaging to stock that it is never used on good horse farms. It is not demanded by the physical environment, even in the grassland. It is the dominant fencing material of our day for economic reasons and not for any other.

Settlement

The grasslands of America were the last of our good lands to be settled. After the Civil War, the railroads were thrust across the Great American Desert and on across the Great Basin to link the Pacific Coast with the rest of the nation. The railroads spelled doom for the buffalo and the Indian, and salvation for the Texans. The buffalo herds were slaughtered by the hide hunters, for the buffalo was so docile an animal that a skilled hunter could locate a herd, hide in the grass at a considerable distance, and using a heavy rifle, shoot down 20 or 30 before the animals finally ran. Thus one rifleman could keep several skinners busy. The hides were moved by wagon to the railroad and thence went east to the market. Buffalo robes and buffalo coats became common items of wear in the East. But the slaughter was at a far faster rate than the reproduction rate, and within a few years, the buffalo were on the verge of extinction. Only energetic action by a few individuals saved a small number to form a nucleus for the present small herds.

With the buffalo gone, the Plains Indians had their means of livelihood cut out from under them. Weakened by unaccustomed diseases, the white man's liquor and by hunger and harassed by the army, they were soon rounded up and put on reservations. The great grassy plains were suddenly emptied of both their dominant animal and the men who had based themselves on the harvesting of this animal. This void did not last.

The Texans had returned defeated from the Civil War, depleted in manpower, to a land that had stood still or declined in productivity during the hostilities. Only one thing had increased, cattle. The semiwild, long-horned, lean and tough cattle had multiplied into millions, especially in the southeastern grasslands of Texas. But there was no market in Texas, but as the railroads reached west, the Texans hit upon the idea of driving the cattle north to reach the rail lines. This started the saga of the cattle drive, so thoroughly exploited in literature and, today, by television. It brought money to Texas, and it brought cattle to the rest of the plains, so recently vacated by the buffalo and the Indians, for when the price was not right, the Texans moved their cattle out into the grassland adjacent to the rail head and held them there for a better market. The range was then open; no one claimed its ownership. Men simply put their cattle on it and held it. For a period of a few decades, this system persisted; then ownership had to be legalized by taking up homesteads and establishing a right to the land.

The agricultural settlers moving into the grasslands were often far ahead of the railroad. They faced many difficulties. Arriving from some point of departure in the wooded East, having a team of horses, a wagon loaded with equipment, a wife, and children, the settler looked about him at this land that was his, after the Homestead Act of 1862, "for free." Except for trees along the water courses, it was treeless, and the water courses only had water in the winter and spring. The land was level and the soil was rich, but it was covered with a continuous cover of grass. Along the humid edge of the grassland it might stand four- to five-feet high. While this was fine for the stock, it posed a terrific fire hazard. Once on fire, whether by act of nature or man, it was a threat to man and beast, to field and house. The first thing to do was to plow a fire break

Pattern of Land Use in Western Kansas. The face of the earth is a checkerboard because of the application of the rectangular-grid survey pattern. Had the custom of granting land followed a different system, the land pattern would look quite different. Compare this with the land pattern of the Po Plain (p. 192). *Wenner Gren Foundation for Anthropological Research.*

around the spot on which the homestead was to be placed—this was not easy.

The sod was so thick and tough that a team of horses could not readily pull a plow through it. The old fashioned plow with a steel tip but a wooden mold board—the wide blade of the plow—did not slide through the sod, but dragged heavily. It usually took teams of oxen to pull the plow through such heavy going. An invention that soon greatly aided the farmer was the all steel plow, for the steel mold-board polished as it went through the ground and the friction was cut down and the plowing went more easily.

When the plowing was done, the sod was still there, turned up in ridges with its roots to the sky. But this was sod, not clods. Clods will break down under rain and frost or under harrowing, but sod will not. The fields plowed in the first year could not be planted in wheat. Farmers often walked along the furrows chopping a hole in the sod and planting some crop such as potatoes. It was not until the second or third year that the land could be harrowed smooth and a grain crop put in.

Meanwhile, what was to be done about a house? There were no supplies of logs for cabins. There was no mill for sawing planks. But the whole tradition of these settlers was to build a wooden house. True, brick was also known, but brick making demanded a large supply of wood for firing the brick. Further, some sort of house had to be created rapidly, for winter in the plains required some shelter. The shelter could have been an Indian house—tepee, earth lodge, or grass-thatched lodge—but that was Indian housing and not for whitemen!

The interesting solution was to take the sods, treat them like bricks, and lay them up in walls. The roof was then formed of timbers, covered either simply with the canvas off the wagon, or planked with boards from the wagon and then covered with more sods. The result was a thick-walled, weather-tight, but often damp house that was serviceable for a few years.

The psychological impact of this new flat, tree-less environment on the settlers is most interesting. They had come from the forested lands, and usually from hilly lands. This flat, treeless, windy land was strange to them, and they longed for the hills of home. The letters and diaries of the time are filled with this longing. The women felt it most, for they were confined to the sod house and its immediate neighborhood. They had no one to talk to other than the children and their husbands. The nearest farm was likely to be a few miles away, two or three hours travel by foot or by wagon. The wind blew eternally; the heat in summer was stifling; and the winter not only cold but a time of violent change—of cold waves and of blizzards. The women some-times lost their minds in the isolation, hard work, and strain.

All of that ended with the first generation, for the children raised there never knew the hills and woods. The plains with their brassy skies and their wild winters and violent summers were home, and they loved them. To them, now plainsmen, the woods would be stifling because they hemmed one in and cut off the view. A plainsman is accustomed to seeing for miles in any direction, and it is disturbing to him not to be able to see. This is a theme that runs through all of man's reaction to his environ-ment. Home is where you live, and home is right. All the rest of the world is different, and not quite as good. The desert man loves the desert, the forest man the forest, the hill man the hills, and the plainsman, the plains.

The settlers took up the grasslands. The humid section became part of our present-day corn belt; the land out to the 100th meridian became the wheat belt; and to the west of the 100th meridian the land was dominantly cattle land. The railroads increased in number, and the growing population in the East took the increasing flow of grain and meat produced in the area. Thus the land increased in value. The 160 acres that the government gave to each settler amounted to values of hundreds of dollars per acre. This has sometimes been called an unearned increment. It is too bad that those who toss this phrase around could not have been on hand to endure the grass fires, the Indian raids, the plagues of locusts, the loneliness, and the absence of all the things that most people cherish—near neighbors, a doctor within call, schools for children, and the like. True, the great rise in value benefited the second and third generation more than the first. But is it sensible to deny to the children of these pioneers the right to the product of their parents' sacrifice and work?

CLIMATIC RISK

The grasslands are lands of natural climatic risk. This risk increases as one goes farther west, toward the arid lands. Climate is an average of conditions met with over a long period of years. The humid lands are those that in almost all years have suffi-cient rainfall to keep the ground water table charged, the streams running, and the trees growing. The arid lands are those where water rarely runs, where the ground water table is nonexistent and trees grow only in exceptional spots because most years are marked by extremely meager rainfall. The grasslands of America lie in between these condi-tions. Sometimes they have a year that is truly arid, even desert, in its low amount of rainfall. At other times they may have a year that is humid, and if that is continued for many years, the grassland would turn into a forest. Wet and dry years in such lands come in spells. A series of wet years makes possible wheat growing far out into the land that is normally too dry for such crops. If the price of wheat is high, the land will be plowed. If there are a number of such years, much land may be plowed up in the hope that the streak of wet years is going to last just a little longer. Eventually the balancing sequence of very dry years comes. The wheat then fails, and the land dries out. Since the winds continue to blow, the land, lacking any protective cover of grass, begins to blow away. The Great Plains have seen at least two major such periods of blowing in the brief period of American occupation.

The first period came right at the end of the nineteenth century. The settlers had moved in during a wet spell, and plowed, planted, and harvested. Then came the dry years, and the land blew out from under them. The settlers abandoned the land and either went on west or returned to the humid, more dependable East—and the land went back to cattle. World War I brought sky-high prices for wheat together with a number of wet years in the plains. Again the land was plowed up, and the inevitable drought came in the 1930s; and the land blew away. Dust clouds darkened the skies at midday in St. Louis and Chicago, and the dust could be seen clear to the eastern seaboard. People poured out of the area like refugees from a natural disaster. It was, yet it was not. They had created the difficulty themselves; the disaster was only natural in the sense that in the environment of the plains, winds are persistent, droughts are inevitable, and land left bare will blow away in the drought years.

The environment had been there unchanging for ten thousand years. Under the buffalo and the Indian such disasters were infrequent. It is a chilling thought, however, to learn that even without plowing the plains can blow out. The sandhills of Nebraska are the remnants of a period of immense blowing at some time in the past. Archeological excavations have revealed that there have been times in the not too distant past when the Great Plains, even though not plowed, become so devegetated that there was immense wind erosion. Seemingly, this could only have been caused by droughts of greater intensity and much greater duration than any that we have seen in the 100 years for which we have good records of the area. We can expect at some time to see such a drought in the plains again.

SUMMARY

Thus the American grassland changed at the time of the retreat of the glaciers from a well-watered land inhabited by elephants to something like the grassland that our frontiersmen saw. For the Indians it was a good hunting ground, but it was not a good farming land. This meant that the density of its population was limited to some low number. The forest-hunting Chippewa had a population density of 1 person per two square miles. Quite probably the density of the hunters of the plains was somewhat less. The density of farming people, such as the Huron, was about 10 per square mile. The Plains Indian hunters, then, were in the prehorse days numerically, culturally, and militarily insignificant. With the introduction of the horse, the man-land situation changed drastically. Now man was able to harvest the buffalo with vastly increased efficiency, and the Great Plains now became an area of attraction, of growing population density, and of interesting cultural growth and military power. This development was cut short by the expansion of the Americans. With the removal of the buffalo, the Indian was reduced to a reservation existence: a miserable settled existence for men who had been as free and fierce in their occupation of the plains as the hawks in the sky.

The American assessment is notable for its early rejection of the plains. The idea of what the land was like was sufficient to prevent men from "seeing" it, even when they stood right on the rich lands of the corn and wheat belts. Then changing ideas, more men, and the use of a series of inventions, almost none of which was new, or invented in the grasslands, made possible their profitable occupation and development. In all of this the physical environment sat, little changed, while man changed and changed again in his way of using this land.

Santa Cruz in Northwest Argentina. This is typical of the dry northwest to the east of the Andes, and resembles the arid side of the grasslands in the United States. *Consulate General of Argentina.*

THE ARGENTINE AND AUSTRALIAN GRASSLANDS

THE ARGENTINE PAMPAS

In South America there is a great grassland, around the La Plata estuary. Climatically it is like the United States prairie, that is, it is humid enough to support tree growth; and like the North American grasslands, aridity increases westward toward the mountains. Also, similarly, it was the home of hunting Indians who, in times past, had known the horse, but had elected to eat this animal rather than to domesticate it. The idea of domestication simply did not become established among them, although they had a greater opportunity to get this idea in pre-Columbian time than the Indians of the North American grasslands did. The people of the Andes had domesticated the llama, a little American camel, and they used it as a beast of burden, but this idea that animals could be domesticated and controlled, and that thereby a surer food supply could be won, never took root among the Indians in the grasslands of South America.

The Spanish, when they explored southward over the Andes, discovered this great grassland. As in North America they found little use for it in terms of the few Spaniards available and the vast numbers of men and acres there to be conquered and controlled. Once the mining period in colonial New Spain was underway, however, there arose a continuous need for mules to work in the mines and for beef to feed the miners. The grasslands were then utilized as an area to produce the vast amounts of animals needed. As in North America, the contact between the Indians and the Spaniards then became close enough so that the Indians learned about riding horses and obtained horses to ride. As in North America, there rapidly arose a way of life characterized by men virtually living on horseback, extremely mobile, and making an easy living from the animals of the great grasslands. As with the Indians of the northern continent, these people became fierce fighting people, proud, able, and formidable.

The parallels are striking and it is easy to read into them the "natural responses to the environment." Given the similar cultural additions in the

Bolas. The horsemen of the Argentine grasslands used this throwing weapon instead of the bow and arrow used in the North American grassland. *Museum of the American Indian, Heye Foundation.*

similar environments, certainly there were similar responses, but there are some interesting differences also. The South American Indians lacked the buffalo. They had smaller game: the ostrichlike rhea and the camel-like guanaco. While they hunted these animals on horseback, they did not develop the short bow for this; instead, they used the bola, an arrangement of a number of stone balls attached to the end of leather thongs. When these are thrown, they entangle the legs of the prey and throw it to the ground. It is difficult to know why this difference in weapons used on horseback came about;

perhaps it was because the bola was still in use in South America at time of the change to horseback, and the habitual weapon simply became the one that was used. These differences can be multiplied. For ease of carrying burdens the Plains Indians never thought of the wheel; instead, they used two poles dragged behind a dog for the purpose of carrying burdens, and later applied this technique to the horse. Their South American counterparts never developed this type of conveyance, nor did they build housing in the style of the tepee. The similarities, then, do not go very far in detail.

Eventually the Indians of the South American plains were reduced to reservations much as the Indians of the United States were, but only after a long and costly series of campaigns. The cattle owners then occupied the land unmolested, but the pattern of land ownership was entirely different from the United States pattern. Land was granted in huge estates, in the Spanish manner—probably derived from the Romans. The result was the huge landed estates of Argentina that are still the features of the occupation of the Argentine pampas. The land is now utilized for cattle and grain, principally corn, wheat, and flax. Development has depended on the coming of railroads, which can move the produce to markets, a development that came as a result of British capital and energy, just as British capital provided early investment in the United States railroad system. It was British drive in South America that created the modern slaughter houses, built the refrigerator ships, and led to the upbreeding of cattle so that the kinds of beef produced would be salable in the European market. The development of the Argentine pampas was strongly oriented to an outside market and the ideas and the capital came from the outside. The land, however, remained in very large blocks in the hands of the original great families. Thus, though the environments were similar and in some ways the development was also similar, the details of this development show differences, despite the fact that the settlers of both areas were Europeans who faced similar problems, who came to use many of the same devices to overcome these problems, and who came also to produce many of the same products to put into the same world markets. The resemblances that do exist are hardly surprising in view of the many cultural causes that are common to the two areas and the fact that modern developments occurred at about the same time.

THE AUSTRALIAN GRASSLANDS

Other grasslands show other patterns of use and change. In Australia, the grasslands that surround the desert, forming the transition to the humid zones, were occupied by simple hunters and gatherers. European contact largely removed these people, with no period of horseback hunters intervening. Why the difference? The land is well suited to mounted hunters, and the large kangaroos can be hunted much as the American buffalo were. The Australian natives lacked the bow and arrow and used the spear thrower instead; however, this weapon could have been used from horseback fully as easily as the bola could, and as we have seen, the Indians of the pampas managed this miracle of juggling. The Australians also used the boomerang, the curved throwing stick; this would have been a powerful weapon if used at close range from horseback. The environment was suitable for horsemen; there were animals to be hunted; and the men had weapons that would have been useful on horseback. It looks, almost, like a case of human failure.

It is true that the Australian natives were among the most retarded in cultural development of all the people of the world, but as we have seen repeatedly, there are numerous possible reasons for this state. Here, isolation and initial lag had combined to leave them so far behind that later people simply swept past them. When the British finally settled in Australia, they occupied the land relatively swiftly. There was no period of a century or two of contact along a grassland frontier as there was in both the United States and in Argentina. There simply was not enough time for the Australian natives to learn the mysteries of horse domestication and riding and to adapt these new ideas to their nomadic hunting way of life. Hence, in this similar physical environmental situation, the "human response" was utterly different. Even given the presence of similar people (Europeans), introducing similar (though not identical) cultures into similar environments already occupied by nonagricultural people, the results were greatly different in the Australian case from that in the two cases in America. Time, as has been suggested for several other situations where people did not do what seems to us to have been the obvious thing, is one of the necessary ingredients for learning—and for social change.

It is an important lesson for us, at this particular time, when the whole world is in a ferment of change.

The modern Australian development of their grasslands is very much like the western United States. There is the same transition from predominance of grain growing on the humid margin to predominance of sheep and cattle raising in the more arid lands. Similarly, as the aridity increases, the ranches become larger, and the ranch houses more separated, ultimately by miles and miles of empty land. The barbed wire, the windmill, and, in times past, the six shooter played their roles similarly. Today, the railroad, the truck, and the radio play similar roles in both areas. Why should the result be different? If similar people having similar cultural backgrounds are placed in similar environments, is not a similar landscape to be expected? That such a climate need not produce such a response is best illustrated by taking lands completely outside the European sphere of influence and looking at what happened there.

PASTORAL NOMADISM: EURASIA AND AFRICA

THE IDEA OF DOMESTICATION

The use of the lands that are neither quite desert nor quite humid, and often covered with grass, for the herding of domestic animals is an invention of the people of the Old World. We know relatively little about just when and where the idea was first put into use. As with so many ideas, it seems to have begun somewhere near the Near Eastern center of growth of ideas, population, and civilization. We know that agricultural beginnings there date back to about 10,000 years ago. We know, too, that domestic animals' bones appear relatively soon after men started to settle down in agricultural villages.

The Eurasion domestic animals include the horse, cow, buffalo, pig, duck, goose, chicken, donkey, camel, goat, and sheep. Not all of these come from one area. The chicken is from Southeast Asia; the donkey may be North African; the horse and the cow probably came from southwestern Asia; and the home of the domestic camel may be Arabia. We do not know whether some of these domestications are entirely separate or if the stimulation of domestication in one area led to domestication of a similar animal in another area. In this the relationship of the donkey to the horse and of the cow to the water buffalo? Did the desert people try raising horses and find that it was a difficult and unsatisfactory business and turn to the donkey? Or did donkey-using people turn to the horse when they found that it was swifter? Did the people of the hot, wet tropics try the common cow and find that it did not do well under conditions of high heat and humidity and substitute the water buffalo?

For these thing to happen there must first be the idea that animals can be domesticated. Also, as we have seen, there must be a great deal of time for the idea to take root and spread, and still more time is required for alternatives, additions, and substitutions to be made. In America, the available animal, the buffalo, was not adopted as a domestic animal in the two centuries that the Indians had the idea of the domestic horse. The turkey, which was a domestic animal in Mexico, was not domesticated in the United States by the Indians; yet the United States Indians had considerable contact with Mexico for at least 2000 years before the discovery of America and took up art forms and ceremonies from that area.

In the Old World things took a different course. The idea that wild animals can be taken into captivity and managed, the idea of domestication, came into being very early. It had ample time to spread far and wide and to be tried out on a wide range of animals and even came to include such unlikely animals as the elephant. It is worth repeating that all of the animals domesticated in the Old World were or had been available in the New World. The Indians, who had known and eaten— and perhaps eaten up—the American camels, elephants, and horses, still had enough buffalo, ducks, geese, swan, turkey, wild pigs, sheep, and goats. Except for Middle America, where we suspect that Old World influences had been strong for more than 2000 years, these animals were never domesticated. And time was apparently too small to allow the spread of these ideas of domestication to the grasslands of America, where they could have changed the whole cultural landscape, with incalculable results on the course of history.

In the Old World these ideas did take root in the grasslands that surround the arid belt that runs from North Africa through the Near East and across the inner part of Eurasia. It is here, and particularly in inner Asia, that the use of the grassland landscape through the domestication of animals reached its highest development. Details of this distribution suggest something of the possible areas of origin of this trait of domestication. The idea never reached southernmost Africa, was relatively late to reach the East African area, and some highly adapted animals such as the camel were introduced very late to North Africa. The camel seems to have been brought into that area by the Romans. Further, with the possible exception of the donkey, there seem to be no native African animals that were domesticated.

THE EURASIAN PATTERN

The truly vast grassland of Eurasia stretches from the vicinity of the Black Sea eastward to Mongolia. This is the home of the highest development of pastoral nomadism. The people in this area had the greatest variety of domestic animals, controlled the greatest area, and dominated it and its bordering regions more frequently than did man in any other grassland area. They figure as the epitome of the picture of man moving over the grasslands with his herds. They had the horse, cow, sheep, goat, and camel as their principal animals.

These Eurasian nomads practiced milking more than any of the other herdsmen. It is only because of our European traditions that we view milking as a natural way to utilize domestic animals. Before the European expansion, milking was unknown in the Americas and much of Africa and not practiced in China or Australia. It is not unlikely that, prior to the spilling over into India in 1500 B.C., milking was restricted to the Eurasian zone north of the Mediterranean and the Himalayan barrier, and west of the Gobi. It is obviously an invention that was made once, somewhere in this area, and spread to those people who had domestic animals and were receptive to the idea (Recall our picture of invention and change in Chapter 1). The Chinese had domestic animals, but did not take up the idea of milking. This is usually thought to indicate that milking developed considerably later than the spread of domestic animals. It is a further case of the slowness of the spread of ideas, even when the necessary antecedent idea is present. The relative lateness of the idea of milking also aids in understanding its absence in much of Africa south of the Sahara.

Within inner Asia, the nomadic herders worked out a way of life in which the herds were moved about over the grasslands to harvest the natural vegetation. Man, in turn, harvested the animals. The harvest took several forms: milking is a device for extracting a part of the animal's production without destroying the animal; shearing sheep is another such device; slaughtering animals is a drastic way of harvesting that is a bit like killing the goose that lays the golden egg. Nevertheless, the carrying capacity of any range is limited, and usually the bottleneck is the winter pasturage—a greater limit in the inner Asian area than in many

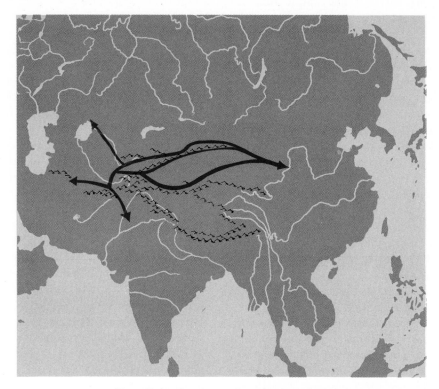

Map 7-4   Oasis Routes of Inner Asia

Routes linking the humid sides of the Eurasian continent have persistently followed the flanks of the mountains where the water supply was assured by oases fed by runoff from the highlands. Man's earliest expansions into the area followed these routes, and overland trade developed very early. Chinese dynastic beginnings in the northwest corner of China reflect the arrival of important cultural impulses from the Near Eastern hearth along these routes, and in late dynastic times, 3500 years later, the Chinese emperors were importing elephants from India via these routes rather than by sea from India. We see these routes today at a time when sea and air travel have greatly reduced their importance. In the past they were among the world's most important thoroughfares for transfers of knowledge.

of the other grasslands because of the severity of the winters. The Asian grasslands are distributed along the latitude of 50 degrees. This is more northerly than the Canadian border, and it is at this latitude in America that the maximum cold is encountered. In Asia, a much greater continental mass, still greater winter cold is met, and getting

herds through the long, cold winters poses difficult problems. The Asiatic herders in many cases had oases as operating bases; these were occupied in the winter, and the herds were pastured on areas that had been left free of grazing during the summer period. Normally some agriculture was carried on at the oasis also, and sometimes fodder was stored

Mongol Yurts. Felt tents of this type are widely used in inner Asia. Such a dwelling is a semipermanent home, resting on a base of pounded clay. *American Geographical Society.*

up to help carry the herds through the winter. However, there usually had to be some reduction of the herd because the normal increase tended to produce more animals than could be safely carried over the long winter period of reduced forage.

During the summer, various animals were milked. While most of us accept the milking of cows and perhaps, if prodded, of goats and even sheep, it still seems strange to use to milk camels and horses. Actually, once the idea of milking has been tried out and found to be an excellent one, it is difficult to find a logical stopping place. Why not milk elephants? Or horses? Horse milk is nutritious and horses are effective animals in the grasslands. Milk, unfortunately, does not keep well, but this disadvantage was overcome by the making of butter and cheese. Since butter does not keep well without refrigeration, at least in its solid form, the solution was to melt butter and strain off the solids, retaining the oily material. This clarified butter or ghee does keep well. The pastoral nomads had worked out a whole series of such solutions to the problems of harvesting the grasslands with animals and then using the products of the animals for their needs.

The horse provided transportation for speed and for war, while the camel was useful for slower transportation and for carrying heavy burdens. The horse provided milk, and the camel provided milk and even wool. In the extreme cold of inner Asia, the camel is quite at home with a heavy coat of wool grown in the fall and shed in the spring. This is a very good quality wool, and since it is shed, the animal does not have to be sheared. Goats are milk and meat animals; sheep are wool and meat animals, and the Asian pastoralists even have special varieties of sheep that store fat in their tails. This is biologically comparable to the storage of fat in the camels hump. In extreme cases, the tails become so fat that the sheep have to be supplied with little wheeled carts so that their tails will not drag on the ground. It is this type of variety and specialization that indicates the degree of concentration on this pastoral way of life and hints at its considerable antiquity.

There are many other specialties. It was in this area that felt was probably invented. This is an ingenious way to make cloth, the principle being to beat the fibers until they are interlocked to form a strong sheet of material of uniform thickness. This process bypasses the laborious steps of carding, spinning, and weaving. A simple method practiced by some of the nomadic people was to take a large sheet of felt, spread a layer of wool on it, roll the sheet up around a pole, and then drag the cylinder around behind a horse so that the continuous rolling and bumping pounded and kneaded the material until the fibers were interlocked. This clever invention seems to have been made but once. It supplied materials suitable for shoes, clothing, tents, and saddle blankets, and we still use it for slippers and for hats—and it is a measure of our reluctance to try new things that we did not make vastly wider use of this valuable technique in the days before mechanized spinning and weaving.

ENVIRONMENTAL DETERMINISM

The nomads of inner Asia have left a mark both on history and on thought. Repeatedly they have thrust out into the lands adjacent to them. The Mongol invasions of Europe reached well into central Europe. One group settled in the plains of Hungary, implanted their Asiatic languages and left just enough trace of Mongoloid ancestry that Hungarian babies have a significant frequency of a bluish spot at the base of the spine at birth. This is the so-called Mongoloid spot. The nomads also swept into China at various times and even established dynasties there. Probably this type of movement has gone on throughout the time since the addition of the horse to the pastoralists' culture shifted the advantage to them as decisively as the introduction of the camel into the western Sahara shifted it to the pastoral people there.

These movements have given rise to one of the most extreme environmental-determinist schools of geography, and this has, in turn, influenced much thinking in history, economics, and related social fields. Ellsworth Huntington, whom we mentioned in this context earlier, as a young man accompanied an expedition into inner Asia. As they traveled through the country, they repeatedly found the remains of great cities, lying in ruins, in arid country. Huntington's conclusion was that the climate had changed and that the cities had fallen be-

cause of these climatic changes. He came to think of the repeated sweeps of the Mongols out of inner Asia as resulting from alternate buildup of population in the years of good rainfall, followed by hardship and migration in the years of drought that inevitably come in these grasslands. He therefore came to speak of this pulsating movement as the "beating heart of Asia." It is a poetic and compelling thought: the Asian heartland filling with people in an expansive period of abundant moisture with its accompanying rich grass resources and then contracting during a dry period, pumping out streams of fierce nomadic mounted horsemen.

The attraction of such an explanation is that it is so simple and direct. Simple causes are preferred in science, but are seldom true in the humanities. Huntington's theory so gripped him that he vigorously assembled data to bolster his idea, instead of inspecting the data to see if they supported or denied his idea. This is too a common practice in the whole field of scholarship. Everyone is guilty of it; the only differences are in degree, and it is always easy to see this kind of flaw in the other man's work. Huntington's mass of evidence has been investigated by many scholars and in almost all cases the physical evidence of droughts as the causative factors of the great known Mongol outpourings has been found to be erroneous. The Russian studies of the evidence from lakes and streams and other climatic records simply do not support Huntington's conclusions. A cultural change such as the introduction of the horse seems to be a more likely cause for the shift from oasis-based city dominance to pastoral nomad dominance. It is not improbable. Both the camel in the Sahara and the horse in the American plains created comparably drastic changes.

Huntington went far afield at times to bolster his ideas. For instance, he went to California and measured and counted the rings on the giant redwoods. Assuming that wide rings meant wet years and that thin years meant dry years, he constructed climatic curves for a 2000 year period. He then compared the sequence of good years and bad years in California with the recorded history of Eurasia and concluded that there was a good correlation between climatic swings and historical happenings. This is an astounding conclusion for anyone to reach, for we know that the tree rings of California show almost no correlation with those in adjacent Arizona. It has been noted that in the United States, when one area is having unusual wet or cold weather, another part of the country is getting unusually dry or warm weather. If differences of these magnitudes are true within parts of one continent, how would it be possible to correlate such changes from continent to continent? This is not to deny that there are long-term changes of climate such as the glacial to interglacial shifts that have affected the world.

It is even more important to keep in mind that human changes that we can see in the full light of history are seldom necessitated by environmental changes. The Navaho and Apache invasions of the American Southwest were not linked with climatic changes. The movement of the farming folk out of the woodlands into the grasslands to take up hunting when the horse was introduced was culturally caused, not physically environmentally caused. Expansions of peoples, the establishment of kingdoms and empires, have a very large individual factor. The role of a Genghis Khan is probably more important than a swing in climate, and he is more likely to be able to muster men, equipment, and supplies for a vast military undertaking during times of good climatic conditions than in a time of poor climatic conditions. It is not necessary, however, to reverse environmental determinism here, it is simply worth noting that climatic shifts in the grasslands, lying as they do between the arid and the humid lands, are to be expected on a decade to decade basis. Great droughts of unusual extension, alternating with unusually good and long periods of moist conditions, are to be expected every century. If the outbursts of the pastoral nomads were primarily caused by physical-environmental conditions, they should have occurred at least once a century, but in fact they have been very much less than that. Other factors that may be involved would include such things as the contemporaneous occurrence of a weak period in the bordering humid lands and a period of strong leadership and unity in the grasslands, and these might or might not correlate with climatic periods of good or poor conditions. The Germanic eruptions into the Roman Empire are an example of the type of things that may occur in any area, at any time, with the causation lying in the area of culture, rather than that of the physical environment.

In the other areas where grasslands bordered on humid lands there was no comparable movement of people from the grasslands into the settled lands. Prior to the introduction of the horse, the American grasslands seem to have generated no force that struck at the settled peoples of the eastern woodlands. Neither is there any such history in the South American grasslands, or in the Australian or African grasslands. Yet in each of these areas, there were grassland-woodland contrasts, with the inevitable wet and dry sequences in the grasslands. What gave the inner Asian grasslands their peculiar ability was their possession of a way of life based on domesticated animals and particularly the immense mobility that the horse gave them. Nor can the physical-environmental determinist escape by saying that once they had the horse, the environment then operated on the given culture to produce the observed sequence of invasions. As we have seen above, the evidence when critically examined simply does not support such a conclusion.

Ghost towns can come into being for a number of reasons other than climatic change. Mining towns are classic examples: when the ore is exhausted, there is often no reason for people to remain in the area; the city is then abandoned. Another common cause is the shift of a major route, and trade routes may shift because of political changes or because of technological changes: camels to railroads, sail to steam, a route around Africa to a route through the Suez. Such shifts are the commonplaces of history and are rarely due to climatic change. The Egyptian closing of the Suez Canal to Israeli shipping is causing the establishment of a port at the head of the Gulf of Aquaba and the revival of town sites along the route leading to the Mediterranean Sea. This route was important in antiquity, and cities then stood in the desert to serve it. They were long abandoned, but they are now being rebuilt. There is no climatic change. There is only political change. Cities rise and fall also depending on stability of government. North Africa under Roman rule was a granary with rich cities. After Roman times, it declined enormously due to the collapse of authority and the incursion of the camel-using nomads who had not previously occupied the area. Under Italian- and French-imposed stability after the mid-nineteenth century, these North African areas were rebuilt and cities again prospered. Under the modern political tensions the cities may be less prosperous, and their future hangs in the precarious balance of conflicting political forces—not on the variations of the precarious climate of this borderland between humid and the arid.

The probable cause of most of the city ruins to be found in inner Asia can be thought of in this way. They are along the ancient caravan routes and are situated where there are rivers coming down from the mountain passes. Under stable political conditions, with a flourishing trade and the construction and maintenance of canals and aqueducts, they could be flourishing today. There are exceptions: in some areas, rivers have shifted widely across deltalike regions leaving the former oases miles from the present area of river discharge, but this is not climatic change. Cities in arid regions run another risk: irrigated lands in arid and semiarid regions tend to accumulate soluable salts that are brought to the land by the irrigation water and left there when the water evaporates. The land slowly accumulates these materials until the soils are poisoned with them. When all the land that can be irrigated at a given site has been poisoned, there is no recourse but to move. While this is, in a sense, a physical-environmental cause, it is primarily a cultural cause, for if the land had not been so used, it would not have lost its fertility. If properly used—an excess of water applied and drained away to some sump—the land can be used even under irrigation indefinitely. It is bad land management that destroys the soil, and management is culturally, not physically, determined.

These ideas of environmental determinism are dealt with at this length because few ideas have had so great an impact on so many fields of thought as the notion that the violent climatic changes of inner Asia were the driving force behind the great Mongol invasions that have been so important in Eurasian history.

THE AFRICAN PATTERN

African use of their grasslands has concentrated on the use of a few animals, the cow and the goat. In southern and eastern Africa, the herding is done on foot. The cattle are a mark of wealth: the more one has of them the richer one is and the more prestige one has. This leads to the keeping of great numbers of cattle without much attention to the quality of the cattle or the effect of the cattle on the land, and serious erosion results. The situation is closely parallel to that found in the American Southwest among the Navaho. The idea of cattle keeping probably spread southward from Egypt or Ethiopia; it came with a minimum number of kinds of animals and developed its own forms in East Africa. From there it spread southward, where the idea of milking is absent in some areas. The substitution of the bleeding of the cattle for milking them, while strange to our habits, is in a way more logical than the milking of the animal and blood is as good a food as milk. Milking ties man to the lactation period of the cow; bleeding an animal can be done at any time, as long as it is controlled in amount and frequency and does not harm the animal. It is a logical way to obtain a continuing return from the animal as opposed to killing the animal for its meat.

SUMMARY

The grasslands show the usual wide variety of man on the land. They have contained a wide range of cultures, from the primitive hunters and gatherers of the Paleolithic level through pastoral nomads, simple hunters, specialized hunters, farmers, and today great urban centers. The greatest contrast in the use of the grasslands was caused in the early periods by the presence of domestic animals in the Old World and their virtual absence in the New World. The dog was the only domestic animal in the New World and the Australian grasslands in pre-Columbian times. The introduction of domestic animals into the New World gave rise in both North and South America to a period of nomadic hunting cultures based on the horse. In both cases they were shortly displaced by the expansion of the European cultures. Interestingly, the grasslands we value so highly as agricultural lands were among the last lands that we have taken into cultivation. Yet these grasslands were in part, even though a minor part, caused by man's activities in the use of fire over a very long period of time. The areas least changed so far are the Old World grasslands where pastoral nomadism dominates. The African grasslands remain in the hands of the Negro cattle- and garden people, and are as yet little changed. Inner Asia is changing as the Soviet Union attempts to settle the pastoralists and to make factory workers and farmers of them. This represents a return to building cities at the oases, a completion of the cycle from cities to nomads to cities—without benefit of physical environmental causation.

8-Mountain Lands

FEW PARTS OF THE WORLD have as much real effect on man as the mountains, and yet this is more often than not overestimated. It is often said that mountains are barriers to travel and that mountaineers are backward because of their isolation, and fierce and warlike. Yet mountainous areas may actually have no population, be highly populated, have high civilization, or very low levels of cultural development. One should therefore suspect that the causes of such variety are rooted largely in the different attitudes that men have brought to the mountains. Yet mountains do have specific effects on man. The problem is to assess the effects of the physical mountains and the physical-cultural man.

Mountains are a landscape form; they are not a climatic type. There is a wide divergence in what people call mountains: all but the southern end of the Appalachian Mountains are more hill-like than mountainous; and the Black Hills of South Dakota are really mountains. It is difficult to draw a line between what is a mountain and what is a hill, but one method is to call the landscape mountainous if the differences in elevation are great enough to cause vertical zoning of vegetation. This works well in the tropics and subtropics where a few thousand feet are required to accomplish this zoning. But in the arctic and subarctic, a few hundred feet are sufficient to cause sharp differences in the distribution of the vegetation. For most people, local differences of more than 2000-feet elevation are impressive enough to warrant calling the land forms mountains. In such areas as the American West the local difference may be much greater. Denver, for instance, has an elevation of 5000 feet, and the mountains on the outskirts of the city rise abruptly to 10,000 feet. But less majestic masses than our Rockies can still be called mountains. Most of the areas to be discussed here will have at least 2000 feet of elevation change in short distances and will also exceed 5000 feet for their peaks. Such areas are truly mountainous, as contrasted with most of the Appalachians or the English Pennines, which by this definition are only hill country.

Mountains have strong temperature, pressure, and moisture relationships. The average decrease in temperature as the mountains rise through the atmosphere is 3.5° F. per thousand feet; hence at 10,000 feet on the equator the average annual temperature is no longer an equable 80° F., but a chill 45° F. Air is compressible, and the air at sea level is relatively dense. One half of the atmosphere is below 17,500 feet elevation. In high altitudes, then, it is necessary to breathe much more air to obtain the necessary oxygen, as would certainly be true on the Tibetan plateau, which averages close to 17,000 feet elevation.

The effect of mountains on the distribution of precipitation is also very strong. Mountains force moisture-bearing winds to rise in order to cross them. Rising air expands in the higher altitudes. Expanding air cools adiabatically, at a rate of 5° F. per thousand feet. Since the capacity of the air to hold moisture is related to its temperature in such a way that cool air cannot hold much moisture, the rising air mass must drop moisture, and the side of the mountain mass facing the wind will therefore have relatively high rainfall. In tropical rainy zones this rainfall can be very great; in arid zones it may be relatively small, but its effect in terms of vegetation, plant life, soils, and animals may be very large.

When winds descend the opposite slope, they reverse their effect. They are now drying winds, for in descending they are compressed, and as a result their temperature rises. They can now hold more moisture and will pick up available moisture from the land surface rather than moisten it. Since the effect of a mountain range in intercepting rain on one side and cutting off or decreasing the moisture on the other side is very much like the effect of the

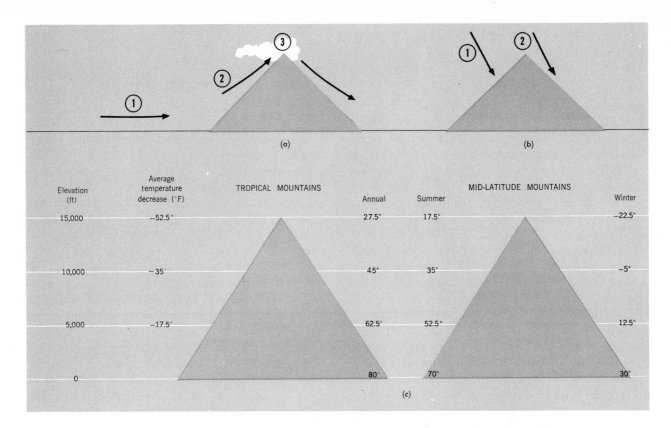

Elevation (ft)	Average temperature decrease (°F)	TROPICAL MOUNTAINS	Annual	Summer	MID-LATITUDE MOUNTAINS	Winter
15,000	−52.5°		27.5°	17.5°		−22.5°
10,000	−35°		45°	35°		−5°
5,000	−17.5°		62.5°	52.5°		12.5°
0			80°	70°		30°

(a) (b) (c)

Figure 8-1 Mountains and Climate. Climates in mountains are extremely variable over short distances due to elevation and slope exposure. At (a) the effect of wind direction is diagrammed. With the wind flowing toward the mountain mass as at 1, a forced rise will be caused as at 2. The result will be cooling of the air mass due to its rising and expanding. This process will normally lead to the formation of clouds and precipitation, concentrated on the windward slope. Over the crest the wind will descend, be heated by compression, and will not only cease to drop moisture, but will begin to pick up moisture. The two sides of the mountain will thus have strikingly different moisture conditions. This is strongly developed in the western mountains of the United States.

These conditions can be either increased or decreased as a result of the exposure of the slopes of the mountains, or of a given valley, to the sun's rays. At (b) the rays at 1 are vertical to the valley slope. This is the condition of maximum intensity of insolation. At 2 the rays are striking the opposite slope at a very low angle, and the insolation is dispersed over a greater area; hence there is less energy per unit area. Slope 1 would be warmer and slope 2 cooler. Whether this would be desirable or undesirable would depend on whether the slope were in mid-latitudes or tropical latitudes, or on the rainy side or the dry side of the divide.

Temperature distributions to be expected for tropical and mid-latitude mountains are shown at (c). Notice that only one set of figures is given for the seasonless tropical situation, but that the summer and winter temperatures are given for the mid-latitude situation. Average annual temperatures are meaningful in the tropics. In the mid-latitudes, however, it is not the average temperature, but the extremes of temperature that tell the story for crops, animals, and man.

sun flooding one side of a mountain range with light, while the opposite side is in the shade, the area deprived of rainfall by the effect of a mountain range is said to be in the rain shadow of the mountain. Where parallel ranges are arranged at right angles to the flow of rain-bearing winds, alternate wet and dry strips of land are found. In the Andes it is possible to go from desert coast up into forested heights down into an arid interior valley and back up onto a forested height again. Somewhat the same thing happens in the American West. The western coastal mountains have high rainfalls on their seaward-facing slope and dry areas to the east of their crests, and rainy conditions are met again on the west-facing slope of the next range, with another dry area to the east of that range.

The mountainous zones of the world are fairly simply arranged. The Pacific Ocean is rimmed with mountains. Since there are many volcanoes in this rim, it is sometimes called "the fiery rim of the Pacific." The other great mountain axis of the world runs from northern Spain across Eurasia to meet the Pacific mountain rim in East Asia. Where these two mountain systems meet, the greatest mountain mass of the world is formed: the Tibetan plateau with its associated mountain ranges. The only sizable mountainous areas outside these two zones are the mountains of East Africa, which include the Abyssinian plateau and the East African highlands. Mountains, then, extend from the arctic to the antarctic and are found in all the climatic zones that we have so far discussed.

VARIABILITY OF PHYSICAL ELEMENTS

On world maps of geology, soils, vegetation, or climate, mountains are normally put into a special category. This is because it is virtually impossible to make a generalized map for these features in mountains. Mountains vary in their geology: they may be largely granitic as are the Sierra Nevadas or very complex in their make-up as are the Rockies. All have much rock exposed, making them easy to prospect; and the concentration of mines in mountainous areas is as closely related to this as it is to any special localization of minerals in them. Soils vary so greatly from slope to slope that they cannot be mapped on a large scale. The unifying feature is that since all mountains are relatively young features on the face of the earth, and since on their steep slopes there cannot be much stability of weathered material, there can be old soils only in those rare areas where there are flat areas of considerable age.

Vegetation in mountains is also highly variable over short distances. It not only is zoned vertically because of the changes of temperature that come with changing altitude, but the vegetation also varies greatly depending on slope. In the northern hemisphere, in mid- and high latitudes there is a large difference in the expected temperatures on the north and south sides of any slope. The south side is exposed to the sun's rays at a much steeper angle. The most efficient angle of exposure for the receipt of solar energy is 90 degrees. A mountain slope in mid-latitudes may create a 90 degree exposure in an area where the latitude would never lead one to expect such a concentration of energy. The opposite condition (the northern slope in the northern hemisphere), however, is that much less exposed and is therefore that much colder.

This has variable effects. If low temperature is critical for plant growth, the south-facing slopes will be the more heavily vegetated. This can have striking effects on the soils. More vegetation may mean that the products of weathering of the rocks may be held more securely on the slopes. A deep soil mantle and a smoother land form may result. In a semiarid situation, the hot southern-exposed slopes may well be too dry for optimum plant growth. This is a common feature of the arid American West. The greater plant growth, soil moisture, soil depth, and smoother land forms may then be on the north-facing slope. At times the absence of heavy plant growth on south-facing slopes may lead to greater erosion on such slopes. Then an area may come to have steep north-facing

View across the Coachella Valley, California. The dark areas are irrigated lands. The barren mountains typical of desert lands stand out in contrast. *Palm Springs Chamber of Commerce.*

slopes with heavy vegetation on them, while the south-facing slopes will be marked by gentle inclinations and light vegetation. Since the soil, and soil moisture, and plant type and abundance will all vary with these changes, it is easily seen that in mountainous regions there will be vastly more complicated patterns of plant, soil, animal, and climatic variation within short distances than is to be expected in flatter terrain.

In the tropics the high mountains have important areas of vertical zonation. Near the equator there are mountains tall enough that their bases have tropical rainy climates with the characteristic soils, vegetation, rainfalls, and animal life; but with a decrease of 3.5° F. in temperature with each 1000

feet of increase of elevation—the normal amount of decrease around the world—this tropical vegetation must soon give way, for it is notably temperature sensitive. A climb of 3000 feet in a 20-mile trip in a mountain range leads to a temperature change of 10° F. This is the summertime difference between Maine and the Carolinas, or the winter time difference between northern Florida and Washington, D.C. Temperature changes within 20 or 30 miles that would require hundreds of miles of travel on the flatter parts of the earth are the striking characteristics of mountain areas.

Tropical mountains therefore have very strong, vertical plant zonation in addition to the complex pattern created by varying exposure to sun and to

Tropical Mountain Lands: Highlands (Tierra Fría) and Lowlands (Tierra Caliente). (*Upper*) In this highland situation in the Venezuelan Andes, the small farms are on the steep slopes; land of seemingly impossible steepness has been cleared and farmed. The mid-mountain and low elevations are of most value for commercial crops and are in the hands of large landowners. (*Lower*) At hacienda Santa Teresa in the state of Aragua, Venezuela, the concentration of broad, orderly fields with commercial crops in the flat alluvial valley is strikingly in contrast with the moth-eaten aspect of the surrounding mountains. The forested slopes have been cleared by shifting cultivators. *Embassy of Venezuela.*

Quito, Ecuador. This city of some 277,000 inhabitants is situated at an altitude of more than 9000 feet and is almost on the equator. The average temperature is 54° F., and the variation in average monthly temperatures is only one degree. *World Bank.*

Rogers Pass, British Columbia. This example of rugged higher mid-latitude mountain land is in about the same latitude as the mountains of southern Germany. *National Film Board, Ottawa.*

Copper River Railroad in Alaska. Trees appear here only at the lowest elevations. This multimillion-dollar rail line was built to tap rich copper ores in the area, and it was abandoned once the ore was exhausted. Compare this with the situation at Potosí in the Andes (p. 399). *Alaska Travel Division Photo.*

rain-bearing winds. Typical tropical rain forest seldom extends up more than 2000 feet. The vegetation changes steadily upward, until around 8000 feet coniferous trees often appear; and by 10,000 feet, the familiar broad-leaved trees are disappearing from the landscape. Really high tropical mountains often have shrub cover such as laurel below the snow line. The snow line on the equator is found about 15,000 feet. In a vertical distance of three miles, then, it is possible to find virtually an equatorial-to-polar range of temperature.

The word climate has been carefully avoided in the last sentence. A tropical mountain zone with a mid-latitude type of average temperature would not be like a mid-latitude area in climate, for there would be little or no seasonal change on the tropical mountain. At Quito, Ecuador, for instance, the temperature stays very nearly—delightfully—spring-like the year round.

Mountains in mid-latitudes lack the tropical and subtropical types of climate. It is as if the lower part of the tropical mountains were cut away so that one starts in the cooler climates of mid-height on the tropical mountains and proceeds quickly into the coniferous forests, then into the meadows just below the tree line, and thence into the permanent snow fields. High-latitude mountains may have their tree line at sea level and their snow line only a thousand feet above. Both of these mountain types have large seasonal changes and are different in this from the tropical mountains.

Mountains, then, offer the most varied kinds of environment for man. They vary with altitude and latitude with some degree of uniformity. High latitude mountains, except for ruggedness of terrain, are not much like tropical mountains, unless the tropical mountains reach very high altitudes. But all mountains share the characteristics of great variation not only in vertical arrangement, but in detailed differences from slope to slope depending on exposure to sun and to rain-bearing winds. In no other part of the world was man challenged by a greater variety of conditions, of plants, and animals, soils, and exposed mineral wealth in so small an area. Unlike the plainsman who might never see anything but a vast, flat grassland with a limited number of kinds of plants and animals and one type of climate, the mountaineer's environment is such that he is assured a wide range of experiences.

MOUNTAIN LANDS IN THE TROPICS: AFRICA AND ASIA

There are vast mountains in the tropics. In North America, there are high mountains in the south of Mexico and in adjacent Guatemala and Nicaragua. In South America, the immensely high Andes extending from 10 degrees north of the equator must be considered mountains-in-the-tropics at least down to the tropic of Capricorn at 23½ degrees south. In Africa, there are very high mountain lands in Abyssinia and in the East African lakes region. In Asia, the only high tropical mountains are in the Malayan area and especially in the great islands such as Sumatra, Celebes, New Guinea, and the Philippines. Note that by starting with tropical mountains, we have narrowed the amount of variation in the physical environment.

SABA

If we start in the Old World and recall that the center of origin of civilization was in the Near East and try the principle that ideas tend to spread first to the nearest areas, it becomes apparent that there are no tropical mountains areas at all near. The closest are those in southern Arabia, where the highest point approaches 10,000 feet in elevation. The highlands of Ethiopia are across the Red Sea in northeastern Africa. They are not only at a considerable distance from the Near Eastern center, but they are separated by the formidable Arabian Desert, on the Arabian side, or the Nubian Desert on the African side. Both of these highlands are in the dry belt. Their height provides for moisture catching, but only their upper slopes, and the better exposures of these, have adequate moisture for agriculture.

The high southwestern edge of Arabia has at times been a center of some cultural growth. It holds an important position near the mouth of the Red Sea, for sea trade from the Indian Ocean area coming toward the Mediterranean passes through the narrow strait there. The flow of ideas carried by traders was sufficient to lead to the development of agriculture, cities, and at times even states of some minor importance. In the past few years its history can be divided in a rough way as consisting of kingdoms of unknown extent and importance before 1000 B.C., the kingdoms of Saba and Ma'in from 1000 B.C. to the time of Muhammad; and Muhammad to the present.

It is noteworthy that the kingdoms of Saba and Ma'in were centered on the highlands of the southwest where the increased rainfall gave some opportunity for agriculture and for better grazing and hence denser populations; this area is present day Yemen and Aden. The Queen of Sheba (Saba) as recorded in the Bible, came to Jerusalem to visit Solomon about 950 B.C. Muhammad also was a native of this same area. Because of his origin there, southwest Arabia for a time became the center of the Muhammadan power. However, Mecca was too far off side to persist as the capital for a movement that was sweeping west across Africa to Spain, northward into the Balkans, and eastward toward India. The capital was first moved to Kufa in Mesopotamia, and later to Damascus in Syria. Location has worked against southwest Arabia and despite some favorable physical geographic factors and a moderately good location beside a major sea lane, it has lagged behind the rest of the world.

It is worthwhile to examine this judgment. In the time of Solomon, location did not work against this area; in the time after Muhammad it did. Yet Arabia neither moved nor had a change of climate during this time. There were vast economic and political changes in this period, however, and it was these changes that controlled the situation. When the East African trade was of major interest, adjacent Arabia was favorably located. When the shift of interest turned elsewhere, it was unfavorably located. After the opening of the Suez Canal, an important part of the world's shipping focused on the Red Sea and the location became favorable

Dam at Maarib in Yemen. Great dams such as this were built in antiquity during times of governmental stability and prosperity. In many cases they have fallen into ruin and lands once rich are now desolate. *Arab Information Center.*

Sana'a, the Capital of the South Arabian Mountain Kingdom of Yemen. Tall buildings and a crowded urban setting have been created by man in this nearly empty land. *Arab Information Center.*

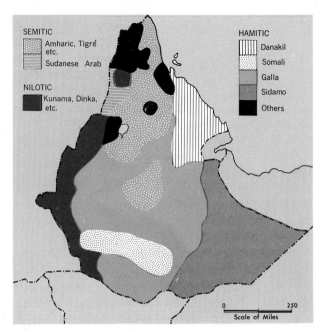

Land Form, Minerals, and Railroads

Languages

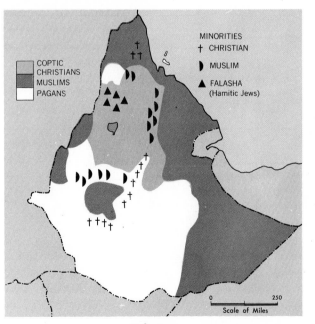

Religions

Map 8-1 Ethiopia: Land Form, Languages, and Religions

The maps present the complex physical and cultural geography of Ethiopia. The well-watered high mountains and the arid plains of the north and east and the humid lowlands of the south and west are clearly shown. The low state of economic development is measured by the scarcity of railroads and highways, in sharp contrast to the presence of major mineral resources.

The language and religion maps show the imprint of history. The Nilotic languages are associated with Negroid people. The Semitic languages reflect later influences from Arabia and Egypt, while the Hamitic languages are related to ancient Egyptian influences. Religions parallel the linguistic pattern. The Hamitic and Semitic people tend to be Muslims. The ancient Coptic Church is strongest among the Amharic and Tigré Semitic speakers. All of this linguistic, religious, and associated racial diversity is concentrated in an area the size of Texas. *Adapted from* Forus—*The American Geographical Society.*

again. Britain seized Aden in the south and held it to forestall others. Meanwhile the cultural level and dynamic drive that had once characterized the region had receded until little but ancient history and crumbling ruins of great dams remained to remind us that the potential of the land and the position were still there.

ETHIOPIA

Across the Red Sea from ancient Saba lies Ethiopia. This highland country is slightly larger than Texas plus Oklahoma. Mountains rise to 15,000 feet, with many peaks in the 5000 to 13,000 foot range. This makes this a land of moderate temperatures despite its tropical location. The lowlands are, of course, steamy tropical or hot desert depending on their location. Most of the population of Ethiopia is in the highlands. Because of its location and the range of its elevations, Ethiopia has an enormous range of vegetation and animal types; most of the African flora and fauna are represented somewhere within its varied geography.

This relatively inaccessible land has a more complex history than one might guess. Its original language was Hamitic, originally the dominant speech group of North Africa. Today the dominant language is Amharic, a Semitic language, which, of course, suggests Arabian influences in Ethiopia, for Arabia is the home of the Semitic language family. The earliest civilizational influences reaching Ethiopia came apparently from adjacent Egypt. In the eleventh century B.C. the Ethiopians regained their freedom, but now with considerable additions of knowledge. By the middle of the eighth century they conquered Egypt and dominated it for the next two centuries. This, of course, meant that even greater masses of advanced knowledge were transferred to Ethiopia. Ethiopians entered into trade with the Arabians; and according to tradition their greatest king, Menelik, was the son of Solomon and Sheba.

Christianity was introduced in the fourth century A.D., and in the sixth century persecution of the Christians led to Byzantine intervention and the

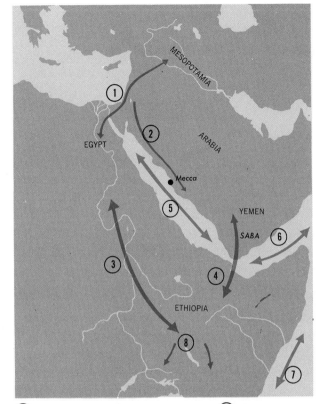

1 MESOPOTAMIAN-EGYPTIAN CULTURAL REACTION 2 MESOPOTAMIAN INFLUENCES ON YEMEN 3 EGYPTIAN-ETHIOPIAN REACTIONS 4 ETHIOPIAN-ARABIAN REACTIONS 5 6 7 MAJOR SEA LANES 8 WEAK EFFECT OF ETHIOPIA ON ADJACENT TRIBAL PEOPLES

Map 8-2 Cultural Influences and Reaction in the Tropical Mountain Lands of East Africa and Adjacent Arabia

These mountain lands are the only tropical highlands near the early cultural developments of the Near East. Mesopotamian influences reached Egypt and eventually Ethiopia; they also reached Yemen, which was on the sea routes linking the Red Sea and the Indian Ocean. Yemen profited from this favorable position and influenced Ethiopia, whose reaction was primarily toward these centers of stimulation rather than toward the undeveloped adjacent African area.

Ethiopian conquest of Yemen, the land of the ancient kingdom of Saba. This initiated a period of extensive trade and contact with such distant lands as Byzantium in one direction and with Ceylon and India in the other. Then came the rise of Muhammad, the loss of Yemen, and the isolation of the Ethiopians by the Muhammad expansion over North Africa and all of the Near East, an isolation that has now lasted for a thousand years.

The interesting points here are many. Although Ethiopia seems geographically vastly isolated, it has repeatedly been drawn into the realm of advanced civilization. Each time it has profited greatly by the inflow of ideas and has reacted vigorously. In all cases the inflow of ideas has come from the north where civilization was growing and the reaction, similarly, was primarily oriented toward these centers of growth, development, and productivity. Little effort was exerted in a southerly direction toward the undeveloped lands and peoples of tropical Africa. This is parallel to the flow of trade in the world today. The major traffic is not necessarily to adjacent lands, but is greatest between the most highly developed lands. It is one more example of the fact that it is not mere location, or distance, or even difficulties such as deserts and mountains that are the determining factors in the cultural-geographical growth and development of a land or a people.

Ethiopia has again been touched by the outside world. Italy seized and held the kingdom briefly before World War II. New ideas have again flowed in, and air and land transportation have increased efficiency so that Ethiopia is potentially less isolated than it ever has been in the past. Are we to expect that history may now repeat itself? Could it be that Ethiopia could again rise to be an important force in the world?

Ethiopia has nearly twice the land area of France. Although its present commerce features hides, skins, grain, coffee, spices, and gold, its known resources suggest other possibilities. High rainfalls on high mountains indicate great potential water power. Considerable deposits of gold, coal, rock salt, sulphur, phosphate rock, copper, lead, iron, mercury, platinum, tin, petroleum, mica, potash, and tungsten are known, although only a few of them are mined commercially. But such an array of mineral resources is possessed by very few countries of this earth. Ethiopia's lack is therefore not of the physical goods of this world. Her present status is the result of a thousand years of isolation, of virtual absence of education associated with nearly complete lack of productivity. The potential for the repeating of its past history is certainly there.

THE EAST AFRICAN HIGHLANDS

South of Ethiopia are the East African highlands, which are included in Uganda, Kenya, Tanganyika, and part of Northern Rhodesia. In addition to this great highland area centering about the rift valleys of East Africa, there are outlying tropical lands in Angola and Southwest Africa. Civilization slowly spread toward these lands. Yet the climate is no barrier. These are tropical highlands, with the moderate temperatures and the varied vegetation and animal life that are found in all such areas.

Some ideas did work south. Agriculture, domestication of animals, iron working, pottery making, politically structured societies with kings, nobles, and commoners—to name a few important ones—all spread south into this area and beyond. These formed the basis of a Neolithic way of life: agricultural village settlements, with occasional development of full-fledged kingdoms complete with capital cities On this basis a moderate population density was established by the beginning of the European colonial era. Under benevolent European control, with tribal warfare and cannibalism diminished and the disease of both men and animals increasingly brought under control, population has grown. In some areas, the population can only be described as dense; around Lake Victoria in the East African Highland, for example, sizable areas have populations of more than 500 people per square mile.

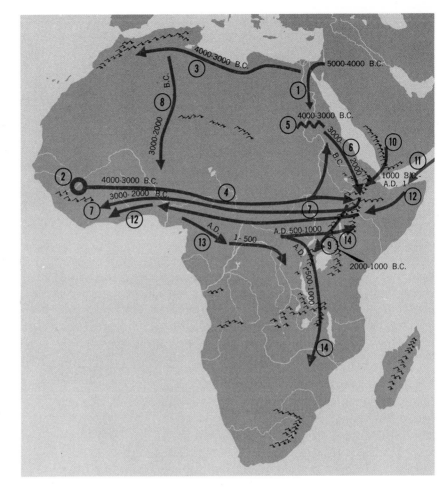

Map 8-3 Cultural Currents in Africa

The striking features of this map are the dominance of the east-west cultural flow in Africa north of the equatorial rain forest, and the focusing of influences from west, north, and east on Ethiopia. The relatively weak flow to the south followed the East African highland. Most of the movements that we can detect depended on the acquisition of new cultural means to better utilize the land. The West African crops were dry country plants. The forest regions of Africa were not opened up for agricultural dominance until the arrival of Malaysian and American crops carried across the Indian Ocean by traders. The first of these crops arrived before the time of Christ. It was utilization of these crops that triggered the Bantu expansion in Africa.

5000–4000 B.C.
  1. Plant and animal introductions to Egypt
4000–3000 B.C.
  2. West African center of agricultural origins
  3. Spread of Near Eastern agriculture across North Africa
  4. Spread of West African agriculture across the Sudan to Nubia and Ethiopia
  5. Contact of two agricultures in Nubia
3000–2000 B.C.
  6. Spread of cattle keeping without milking from Nubia into Ethiopia and thence
  7. Westward across the Sudan
  8. Berber trade brings southwest Asian crops to the Sahara and adjacent Africa

2000–1000 B.C.
  9. Cushites expand southward from Ethiopia following the East African highlands
1000 B.C.–A.D. 1
  10. Semites invade East Africa and begin penetration of Ethiopia
  11. Indonesians dominate trade across the Indian Ocean and bring southeast Asian plants
  12. Which spread to the Guinea coast
A.D. 1–500
  13. The Bantu utilize the Malaysian plants to expand into the Congo
A.D. 500–1000
  14. The Bantu expand on into highlands and south to Zimbabwe

The most interesting question to ask is this: If the highlands of Abyssinia could repeatedly give rise to kingdoms, why did the equally good, or even better, highlands of the East African lake region so rarely give rise to anything even remotely resembling civilization? The physical environment is excellent. The proximity to Ethiopia provided potential access to ideas. Again we face the question of the success of the Negro as a possible carrier of civilization. It would seem easy to choose the racial answer, but this is in fact too simple.

It should be noticed that all of black Africa was bypassed for a long time in the period of western European expansion. However, we have seen that such choices are often made neither on the basis of the physical geography, nor the race of mankind in question. Often the decision is made in terms of location, and equally important, the stage of development of the people in the area. This is like Spanish California: it, too, was too distant in proportion to what it had to offer, good land, good climate, but undeveloped people. This may be said to describe Africa.

The flow of ideas in Africa was considerable. By 5000 B.C. agriculture with cattle keeping had spread from Mesopotamia to the Nile. An African agriculture had also begun along the Niger River, and it included drought-resistant plants that spread eastward, north of the wet forest lands. Sometime between 3000 and 4000 B.C., these agricultures met in the area to the north of Ethiopia, and between 3000 and 2000 B.C. cattle keeping minus milking was added to Ethiopian agriculture. Cattle keeping then spread west again across Africa.

Before 1000 B.C. an Ethiopian people, the Caucasoid Cushites, expanded southward. Their choice is of particular interest. Since this was a highland agricultural people, their expansion was through the East African highlands: it was these people who founded Zimbabwe and extracted gold for export to India. After A.D. 500 milking spread into Africa and the Cushites were one of the peoples receiving this idea and then passing it on to the south. The Cushites were then largely displaced from the highlands by the expanding Bantu tribes about A.D. 1000. The area where the Cushite influence was strongest and where racially mixed remnants of these people still exist is in northern Tanganyika, where the whole landscape is different from the rest of Negro Africa. The land is in permanent agricultural production and is fully occupied; there is no brush land lying fallow, such as accompanied a shifting type of agriculture and as is common throughout most of Africa. Instead, there is a developed, cultivated, well-kept landscape.

THE EXPANSION OF THE BANTU

The Bantu expansion is of particular interest. It is based in part on their obtaining crops suitable for growing in the wet forest country. These plants reached them from Malaysia, whence they had been carried by traders crossing the Indian Ocean. Trade with northeastern Africa is very ancient, going well back into Egyptian times. By 1500 B.C. trade with Ethiopia had carried cotton from there to the Indus Valley region by sea. Transport by sea is indicated by the absence of cotton in the intervening land areas. Before A.D. 1, Asiatic plants adapted to growing in the warm, humid forest conditions were brought into East Africa. We know from linguistic evidence that Indonesians were extremely active in this trade, for the language on Madagascar, where many of these people settled, is Indonesian.

When these plants were spread into Africa, a new opportunity existed. The Niger type of plants and the Mesopotamian plants were better adapted to dry country than to rain forests; agricultural expansions in Africa had therefore avoided the rain forest. Notice that it was not that agriculture was impossible in the tropical forest, but that it was not profitable with the type of plants in use. It was the introduction of plants well-suited to forest agriculture that changed the situation. We do not know just why it was the previously obscure Bantu people that seized upon this opportunity. The problem is somewhat like trying to explain why it was the English that began the industrial revolution. It could have been any one of a number of peoples, and the final decision may have been dependent on some extraordinary individual. Or, for the Bantu, they may have been edge-of-the-rain-forest farmers, barely getting by trying to grow wheat and milo maize. Bananas, yams, and taro would and did open up a new world of opportunity.

Once the Bantu expansion was underway it generated enormous momentum. The Bantu people swept through the wet forest, into the highlands, and southward. They were still expanding southward at the expense of the relatively small Bushman Hottentot peoples when they were met by the Europeans of the early nineteenth century who were expanding northward, also at the expense of the Bushmen and Hottentot peoples.

This again illustrates the dominant role of cultural equipment. As long as one set of ideas prevailed and one type of agricultural equipment was available, one pattern of flow of ideas prevailed in Africa. With the introduction of a new set of plants, a new pattern became possible and was soon exploited. It is too easy to overemphasize the promptness of these spreads (notice in Map 7–3 the long lags). It is normal for most of these spreads to take a millennia or so. Some of the traits were useful in areas in which they were in fact very slow to spread. Cattle keeping is a good example. Cattle also exemplify the nonobviousness of uses that seem obvious to us: milking for example, which was quite late in appearing in Africa south of the Nile. However, the Africans found a way to "milk" a cow that is anything but obvious to us: some tribes bleed their cows and drink the blood.

The mountainous northeast corner of Africa as a cultural center becomes understandable, then, when the currents of cultural connection are considered in relation to the peoples, crops, and trade routes of the day. The spread of ideas down the mountainous side of Africa illustrates that highlands can be highways as well as barriers, depending on men and their ideas.

The African question is now at a boil. Mankind's expansion over the earth and steadily developing transportation facilities combined with the steady growth of demand for raw materials—added to the growing awareness of all the peoples of the earth of the potentiality for all mankind to have a high standard of education and productivity and consequently a high standard of living—is now penetrating this area. Despite the present turmoil which may set African development back decades, or even centuries, the African highlands with their fine equatorial climates and resources of soil, waterpower, and minerals are obviously potential centers of cultural growth and development. However, physical geography is passive. Action, development or nondevelopment, is a socio-political problem and there the prospects are poor.

SOUTHEAST ASIAN TROPICAL MOUNTAINS

The Southeast Asian tropical mountain lands present somewhat a similar picture. They too are distant from the early centers of civilization. As civilization spread eastward, it reached India and then China. As these great centers of culture developed, their influences came to overlap in the Southeast Asian area. Influences from India reached across the Bay of Bengal not only to adjacent Burma, but to Siam, Malaya, Sumatra, Java, Borneo, and up to the Philippines. Beginning about the time of Christ, this civilizing force established kingdoms of large size in these areas. Such great ruins as Angkor Wat (see page 167) testify to this influence from India, as do also the dances of Bali and much else in this whole area. Chinese influences reached down the coast and to the offshore islands. Chinese traders were voyaging to India before the time of Christ and probably for a very long time before Christ. (See Maps 2–1 and 2–3.)

In this crossroads of cultural contacts, there could have arisen a mighty center of civilization. If mountains in the tropics, because of their beneficial cool climates and great variety of soils, plants, animals, and minerals are advantageous, we might expect to find a highland civilization here, but this did not develop. The reasons are not hard to find. The

A Hill Station in India. The British established settlements such as this so as to escape from the heat during the hottest parts of the year by taking advantage of the 3° decrease in temperature per 1000 feet of elevation. *Embassy of India.*

agricultural outlook of these people was strongly oriented toward lowland gardening with the rice plant as the most important of their food plants and with tropical lowland root, fruit, and spice plants also important. This focused attention on the plains, not on the highlands. As a result, the Southeast Asian highlands are relatively empty.

This is not to say that highlands are always barriers. We have in the past 2000 years had an example of the fact that highlands may be highways. The peninsula of Southeast Asia, including Burma, Thailand, and Indochina, was originally Mon-Khmer in speech and strongly Indian in culture. Their speech is now mostly Sino-Tibetan, though they are racially and culturally little changed. A review of the history of this region shows that repeatedly through the past 2000 years, relatively simple mountain-forest farmer-folk have worked their way southward along the mountain chains and thus outflanked the lowlanders. Repeatedly they have been able to take over governmental

controls, and in this way they have imposed their language.

One suspects that the mechanics of this may well have been somewhat like the Aztec take-over in Mexico. The mountaineers were probably used as mercenary troops and by their strategic position were able to stage a military coup. Our main interest here, however, is the fact that the mountains served as their highway, not as barriers to men's movements. Even this deserves to be stated more fully and carefully. The mountains that for centuries had been barriers to the lowland-oriented Mon-Khmer people, who absorbed culture from the lowland-oriented people of India, were corridors for the movement of the highland-oriented Sino-Tibetan people. It was the cultural orientation, not the physical structure, that was decisive.

Eastward as one penetrates Oceania, levels of civilization decline (see Map 3–10). The center of India's influence was on the nearest islands, Java and Sumatra. The farther islands, Borneo, Celebes,

Timor, and others, were less developed. This probably repeats an ancient pattern of the spreading of ideas eastward from the continent, with successive waves in part limited by man's ability to cope with the physical geography and by the degree of the penetration of the preceding ideas necessary for the establishment of the next set. Here, as in Africa, a point is reached where the necessary ideas had either not reached, or had not had time to engender developments sufficient for the next steps to be taken. This line is met at New Guinea, where the Oceanic Negro people held this vast island (ten times the size of Puerto Rico) and a series of adjacent islands. This part of Oceania is known as Melanesia.

NEW GUINEA

The highlands of New Guinea are extensive. They are estimated to cover 12 percent of the land area and to contain 40 percent of the people. The people live in the valleys of the highlands, often at elevations above 5000 feet, which means that they live in a mesothermal climate, with high daily ranges of temperature due to their high altitude, and with the possibility of frost at the upper end of their habitat. Rainfall is high, averaging from 80 to 100 inches per year and more. Much of the mountain land below 8000 feet is grassland. This is thought to be the result of clearing and burning of the landscape by the natives, for detailed reporting of the life of the natives makes clear that they destroy large amounts of forest and eventually convert large areas into grassland. This is also widely reported from the interior highlands of Borneo and elsewhere in Southeast Asia. There are very aggressive grasses in this area, which seemingly accounts for the great speed at which this type of landscape is created. Frequent man-set fires in these grasslands perpetuate them. As in all mountainous regions the soils vary greatly from slope to slope and from rock formation to rock formation.

Although the population of new Guinea is often called Negroid, it seems more closely related to the Australoid group than the Negroids of Africa. Man has been present in adjacent Indonesia from the opening of the Middle Pleistocene, perhaps 600,000 or so years ago. There is a long evolutionary series on Java, but just when man managed to pass the deep-water straits that divide the New Guinea-Australia area from the Indonesian area, we do not know. Considering the smallness of the water barriers and man's ability to cross small water gaps, an early crossing is probable.

Cultural contacts are apparent from the plants used and the arts practiced by the New Guinea highland people. They have not only Asiatic plants and animals such as the pig, but most surprisingly, some of the highland people have as their principal crop the American sweet potato. They also have and use the American tobacco. We have no real knowledge of when these American plants reached here, but even the remote highlands of New Guinea felt the flow of ideas from both Asia and America. On the basis of these ideas and materials, the people of remote interior highland New Guinea had advanced to a primitive Neolithic village-dwelling way of life.

They had lived in small triblets, usually continuously at war with their near neighbors. It is of interest that a shifting agriculture supported populations in local concentrations of 100 to 300 per square mile, but with large empty areas in between these pockets. In these areas of concentration, sufficient food was produced from a relatively small amount of land to leave a great deal of leisure. Much of this was spent in head hunting or simple warfare. The warfare was an activity in which a thousand warriors on a side might prance and feint all day long with only a few casualties on each side, although men occasionally were killed outright in battle, and more died of infected wounds. It was a satisfyingly dangerous sport.

Fighting, weapon making, and many skills such as the making of women's skirts and house building were in the hands of the men. They also aided the women in the heavy work of preparing fields. Once the fields were cleared and thoroughly prepared, they were turned over to the women, whose duty it was to plant and cultivate and harvest. Families lived in small compounds with the one or more wives of a man each having her own sleeping hut. Cooking was done in a large communal building but even there each woman had her own fireplace. The men lived and slept in the men's house.

Most of the preliminary steps toward building the basis of a civilization had been taken. Agriculture had been introduced, population density had built up, leisure existed because there was an adequate food supply—but the surplus energy was not spent productively. Social structure was very simple: might made right. If a man could not protect his women and pigs and fields, he deserved to be robbed and his women assaulted. Status was based largely on prowess in warfare against outsiders and on brute force applied inside the tribe. Wants were few, and they were supplied largely from the local scene.

To change this, social advances were needed. The energy dispersed in warfare needed to be channeled into useful production, and the simplest way in which to accomplish this would have been an increased trade, which would have required the production of a surplus of some material for trade. Trade also requires stability and some degree of security for travel. However, the highland interior of New Guinea was so remote that only within the past decade have we discovered valleys with thousands of settled farming people, who in the mid-twentieth century had never even heard of a white man. This was not due entirely to mountains. The people of the coast were little more advanced when first seen by Europeans.

It is not difficult to think of uses for these highlands. Their agricultural possibilities are large; they would be natural places to produce coffee, tea, and similar commercial crops, and they could be utilized for cattle production. Rainfall of 100 inches and more in the highlands, well distributed through the year, assures the presence of large amounts of potential hydroelectric power. The area has been little explored for minerals, though important gold fields have been found. Its potential must be said to be largely unknown, but it is likely that it is quite great.

Highland New Guinea has a better physical-geographical base than the Andes, which nurtured a civilization at greater elevation and under conditions of considerable aridity, or the Tibetan highland, which also reached the level of civilization at very high elevations. New Guinea's failure both in its highlands and in its lowlands is due to its geographical location. Distance from the centers of ideas worked against an early start toward civilization, and its cultural lag further delayed growth. Nevertheless, the area was well into the agricultural village-dwelling stage of development, and ripe for the town-dwelling stage, when the Europeans erupted over the world. The specialized needs of an expanding Europe—high-value materials, such as spice in Indonesia, where proximity to idea centers had led to an earlier start, or open land where a more isolated people melted quickly from the area, as in Australia—were not present in New Guinea. New Guinea, whether in its moderate temperatured uplands or its steaming lowlands, has lingered on in its stone age.

SUMMARY

The tropical mountain environments of the Old World may be summarized as follows. The only mountainous areas that had growths to the level of civilization were Ethiopia and Indonesia, and in Indonesia civilization centered in the lowlands rather than the highlands. In both cases these lands owed their stimulus to being reached by impulses from the great Near Eastern center of civilization. The other tropical mountain areas were sufficiently far beyond the reach of these influences that they became cultural laggards. Thereafter, civilization passed them by in preference for other lands, even if they were much more distant lands.

NEW WORLD TROPICAL MOUNTAIN LANDS

In America the story is quite different from the Old World, for the tropical mountains lie in the center of the civilized area. The Toltec-Aztec civilization developed on the plateau of Mexico, and the great ancient series of civilizations of Peru and Bolivia were centered on the high plain, the Altiplano, of the Andes. Between these two peaks of American Indian civilization there was a conspicuous tendency for high cultures to be strung out along the mountain chains that linked the two centers. It must not be overlooked, of course, that this was not the only location for civilization in pre-Columbian America. The Mayas lived in a tropical lowland and part of the Peruvian civilization lay in the desert oases along the coast. Nevertheless, there is a conspicuous correlation between high culture and the tropical mountains.

What is cause and what is effect here? Did the mountains provide a better opportunity? Or did culture simply begin in such a position that the tropical mountains were in the favored location? We have seen that in the Old World the answer was largely one of access to the ideas streaming out from the center of civilization in the Near East.

Was there something particularly different in the New World? For instance, were there diseases in the lowlands of the New World that tended to place a greater advantage on the highlands? This cannot be true, for many, if not most, of the scourges of the tropical lowlands of America seem to have been introduced in the post-Columbian period. This is certainly true of malaria, yellow fever, and the bubonic plague, to name only three. The tropical lowlands of America actually seem to have had greater freedom from adverse disease conditions than did those of the Old World. If this is a cause that favors the development of the tropical highlands, then there was less reason for man to concentrate in the highlands of America than there was in the Old World. One suspects that the location of the beginning of civilization in America must have been the key factor.

There is a great deal of controversy over how, when, and where civilization started in America. It becomes increasingly clear, however, that its beginning was in tropical America. Evidence steadily accumulates that Asiatic people came to this part of America very early, and that they brought a flood of advanced knowledge. It is clear that the means to do this existed in such things as great sailing rafts, such as Thor Heyerdahl's Kon Tiki. These rafts were pre-Columbian in America and used centerboards and fore-and-aft-rigged sails. They were able to sail against the wind and small ones could make up to five or six miles an hour. As Heyerdahl demonstrated by sailing a log raft out into Polynesia and Eric de Bischopps demonstrated by sailing a bamboo raft from Polynesia to Peru and a log raft back to Polynesia, even unskilled operators of such equipment could cross vast oceanic stretches. Archeologically the centerboards that were used on such craft have been found in graves in Peru at least as early as A.D. 1000, and just how much earlier they were in use has yet to be determined. The evidence suggests that the homeland of these craft is Southeast Asia and their antiquity is probably quite great.

A recent study of the origin of the calendrical systems of Middle America suggests that the basic ideas for this highly developed astronomical system were brought to America about 700 B.C. This fits with data from such diverse fields as art, mythology, mathematics, and botany, all of which indicate that Asiatic men came to America and much of which points toward India as a major source. This is of great interest in that art, mathematics, and intricate calendrical systems are not the sort of things carried by simple fisherfolk, but rather by priests, kings, and learned men. Deliberate voyages were probably made across the expanse of the Pacific

Andes Highlands, State of Mérida, Venezuela. (*Above*) At elevations above 8000 to 10,000 feet the forest is replaced by grass and brush. In pre-Columbian South America only the potato was grown at such heights, but after 1500, wheat was successfully introduced. (*Below*) Cultivation with primitive, cow-drawn plows was originally introduced by the Spanish, and represented an enormous technological advance in fifteenth-century America. Retention of this method in the twentieth century shows the cultural lag in such areas. Similar plows are still used also in lowlands. Compare rice cultivation, page 126. *Embassy of Venezuela.*

beginning at least as early as the second millennium B.C. and continuing with interruptions to historic times.

These people reached a land that already was embarked on the road to civilization. Agricultural beginnings in America have been dated back to 6000 B.C. in Mexico and to 2500 B.C. on the coast of Peru. There is little reason to think that these are the earliest agricultural sites; they are simply the earliest yet found. They suggest that the incoming Asiatic voyagers found village-agricultural beginnings already in existence. We seem to have no hint as to why these incoming people preferred the mountains. It is a fact that one cannot land on the west coast of America without being confronted by mountains. It has further been suggested that a primary reason for their coming to America was the search for metals, and certainly the metal sources in America are in those western mountains, especially the gold, silver, and copper that the early metal-using people would have sought. At any rate, the highlands of tropical America became centers of growth and development and Indian civilization came to flourish in them.

THE SPANISH IN THE HIGHLANDS OF THE NEW WORLD

The Spanish assessment of the New World started with this same outlook—wealth seeking—and developed settled populations desired as subject peoples. Between 1500 and 1520 the Spanish hacked out a foothold in the Caribbean and probed the edge of the continent. In 1520 they began their penetration of the two continents of North and South America. In the next 20 years, they blocked out the areas that they wanted to develop. They sent ships on expeditions into the Pacific and scouted the coasts north and south; then sent land expeditions through the eastern United States to some point in the Great Plains, such as western Kansas; and they sent another up the west coast of Mexico, through the Southwest and out into the plains. Southward they crossed the Andes, found the Amazon, and sent a ship down its length, out to sea, and northward to the Caribbean shore of South America. They found that the two great centers of population and wealth were in Mexico and Peru. Between them lay lands with moderate cultural development and wealth and population. To the north and south of this central area there was increasingly less population, less cultural development, and no gold or silver.

There were few Spaniards; they could not physically take and hold all of two continents with the handful of men available. They chose to seize those areas where there were mines that could be made to produce more of the wealth they found there. Thus the Spaniards, too, went to the mountains—perhaps somewhat in parallel to the Asiatics who had preceded them.

In the mountains of Peru the Spaniards for the first time met the effects of truly great altitudes. It must be remembered that in this time there were no means for measuring the heights of mountains. Unquestionably the snow-covered Andes were high, but the Spaniards had seen snow-covered mountains in Spain. However, they found that they had strange problems to face in these South American mountains that no one seems to have experienced in the European mountains. The first accounts were greeted as unlikely stories. The Spaniards said that as they climbed these mountains they found areas where the air made them seasick. Their choice of a parallel sickness was not bad, for the illness that they described was characterized by nausea and vomiting, just as in seasickness. However, it was well known that the sea's movement was in some way related to sea sickness, and not even the Spanish storytellers claimed that the mountains moved. As a matter of fact, they gave a very good account for their time of the phenomena. In the words of one Father Acosta, in abridged form:

I have wanted to say all this in order to describe a strange effect which the air or the wind which blows has in certain lands of the Indies, namely that men get seasick, yea, even more than at sea. There is in Peru a very high mountain range. I had heard of the effect of the air of this mountain and I started out prepared as best I could according to the information which is given out there by those they call old hands or guides. As I went up "the stairs" as they call the highest part of that range of mountains, I was suddenly seized with such a mortal anguish that I was of a mind to throw myself off the horse onto the ground. I was seized with such retchings and vomitings that I thought I should give up my soul, for after the food and phlegm came bile and more bile, this one yellow and the other green, until I came to spit up blood. If it had gone on, I believe I would most assuredly have died, but it only lasted a matter of three or four hours until we got down a good long way and came to more healthy air-temper.

It is not only that passage of the Pariacaca Range which has this effect but the whole great mountain which runs for more than five-hundred leagues in length. Wherever one goes through it one feels this strange distress, though more in some places than in others. It is felt more by those who go up from the seacoast than those who descend from the heights of the plains. Animals feel this also.

I hold the opinion that this region is one of the highest places on earth. In my view the snowy passes of Spain and the Pyrenees and the Alps of Italy are as common houses compared to tall towers. I am persuaded that the element of air there is so thin and delicate that it does not provide for human respiration, which needs it to be thicker and more tempered. I also believe this to be the reason for the stomach's being so greatly upset and the whole man put out of balance.*

This is both a good description of the effects of mountain sickness and a penetrating analysis of the causes of this malady by a man who had none of the advantages of modern chemistry, geography or physiology at his disposal. Nevertheless he recognized that it was something in the nature of the atmosphere at great heights that was the cause of this distress. What we would say in modern terms is little different. With the decreasing pressure that accompanies increasing altitude the density of the surrounding air decreases. At 17,500 feet one half of the atmosphere is below you, and one must breathe much more air to obtain an adequate

amount of oxygen. There may, in addition, be complex physiological reactions to the decreased pressure. These effects are noticed by individuals at differing elevations. Many people experience nosebleeds, headaches, and nausea as low as 10,000 feet. Thereafter the percentage of people affected rises sharply. Very few people born and raised at low elevations can go as high as 13,000 feet without experiencing mountain sickness. Those raised there, however, are not troubled by the elevation. In Peru men live permanently at elevations as high as 17,000 feet, but this is probably about the limit for any man.

This raises numerous questions. How did the first men penetrate to such great heights? Why did they do so? How long does it take for lowland men to become adapted to these elevations?

Some of these questions are not answerable with any great certainty. All life forms tend to spread wherever they can. Baboons in Africa live from sea level to 10,000 feet elevation. Men everywhere have used adjacent mountains as part of their hunting and gathering range. Because of their great diversity of plant and animal products, they are attractive areas. Further, in times of drought, they have unfailing water supplies. Some of the plainsmen would in time remain in the foothills. Soon some of the foothill dwellers would be permanent residents in the mid-heights. By this process, men would work their way up to the greatest heights that offered any possibility of food. Thus several generations would pass and the men involved would gradually get used to the conditions of higher elevations. Man can become fitted to very high elevations; in the Andes men live up to heights of 17,000 feet, but this is exceptional. The bulk of Peru's population lives on the 12,000-foot plateau, and most of the people live nearer 10,000 feet above sea level.

Physiological Problems at High Altitudes

These are not altitudes that men enter easily. The Spanish experience again supplies most interesting data. It should be remembered that at least some of the Spanish came from the Spanish pla-

---

* C. Monge, *Acclimatization in the Andes* (Baltimore: Johns Hopkins University Press, 1948), pp. 1–4.

teau, which averages 3000 feet in elevation. Nevertheless, when the Spanish went up into high elevations they met great physiological problems. Reproduction virtually ceased; nor was this limited to men: bulls, horses, dogs, and particularly cats were affected. In one case of 12 sheep taken to 12,000 feet, only 6 reproduced. Some of the infertile ones were then sent down to 7500 feet, and some of them then bore young. It was only after some time that children were born and much later that children began to survive. Then, as the Spanish priests noted, it was usually those that were part Indian. As Carlos Monge—who has studied the effects of altitude in those high regions—says, there is today no purely white race in these altitudes. The people present are a mixture of white and Indian, with the faculty of resistance to great altitude carried over from the Indian parentage.

This does not mean that none of the Spanish were able to reproduce in these high elevations. The effect was variable. The effect of the anoxia (lack of oxygen) was in some cases complete and lasting sterility. In other cases, however, the effect was a temporary one, and after some time, the individual's physiology was able to adjust to the condition and fertility returned. Selection was abrupt for some, for those who could not reproduce, saw their genetic line extinguished.

Monge presents interesting data on the fertility rate among the present Peruvian population. The population is now in two areas: about 66 percent is in the highlands above 8000 feet; and 28 percent is in the lowlands below 800 feet. This is partially due to the physical geography: the lowlands can be irrigated; the foothills are extremely arid, not readily irrigated, and hence have relatively few people— only 6 percent of the population; and the highlands have more moisture and on the Altiplano have areas that can be irrigated. The number of children per thousand women between 15 and 45 years are for the coastal lowlands, 144; for the foothills, 174; and for the highlands, 164. At first glance these figures suggest a large effect by elevation with optimum conditions in moderate altitudes: out of

the heat of the lowlands but below the cold of the highlands.

There could be numerous reasons for this. It could be related to the relatively small population density. Most infectious diseases spread in proportion to the number of contacts between infected people. The less dense the population, the less the frequency of contacts, the slower the spread, and the lower the disease rate. It is especially the infectious dysenteries and such things as measles and small pox that kill the children in primitive societies. Conditions for their spread are at an optimum in crowded cities and towns. These are most common on the coast and in the highlands of Peru.

In the highlands the relationship between women of child-bearing age and infants under one year suggests very good reproduction rates between 7000 and 12,000 feet, but with a considerable drop off above 12,000 feet. The high rate of reproduction of the highland people is just what the Spanish reported. But why then should there be a decrease above 12,000 feet? Is this an elevation effect? Those living at such very high altitudes may be the poorest of the Indian people, and the result may be nutritional. Of course, it may also be strictly physical environment: at some point the increasingly lower oxygen content of the atmosphere must go beyond the possibility of man's adjustment. In the transition zone, there would be expectable physiological disturbances and these would expectably appear in such physiologically critical areas as reproduction.

Recent physiological studies tell us something of the mechanism of this sterility. At very high elevations women are unable to maintain sufficiently great oxygen concentrations in their blood to supply foetal growth. Women with certain heart defects have the same difficulty at low altitudes. Races adapted to high elevations maintain higher oxygen levels through increases in red blood cells, lung capacity, and circulation.

When the rewards were high enough, the Spanish lived in the heights. At Potosí one of the greatest silver mines of the world was found: in the first two centuries of Spanish operation there, two billion dollars worth of silver was produced. This vast wealth attracted 20,000 Spanish and a working force of 100,000 Indians. The elevation was 13,600 feet, too high for plainsmen. The Spanish paid the price; for 53 years, no Spanish child born there lived. For a long time the Spanish sent their wives to lower altitudes to bear their children but even then the children often died when brought up to the high altitudes.

The on-the-spot reporting of the Spanish priests is again worth quoting. Here is Father Cobo's sixteenth-century account, shortened, but in his own words:

Those Indians who are born in high and extremely cold regions may be raised and survive better than those born in temperate and hot regions. The Indians are healthiest and multiply the most prolifically in the cold air-tempers, which is quite the reverse of what happens to children of the Spaniards, most of whom when born in such regions, do not survive. It is most noticeable that those who have half, a quarter, or any admixture of Indian blood are all raised with the same loving care as the pure Spanish children and yet, the more Indian blood they have, the better they survive and grow.*

These difficulties were so great both for the Spanish and for their domestic animals that they soon moved their capital down from the highlands where the bulk of the people and the mines were, to Lima, where they were physiologically more at ease. Interestingly enough, 100 years later the Spanish commentators found this a bit difficult to understand. By that time domestic animals had undergone selection and adjustments to such high altitudes and the valley of Jauja where the first capital had been placed was declared a fertile, productive, and healthful area for man and beast whether of European or American origin. Nevertheless, the cultural factor of resistance to change has maintained the capital at Lima, despite the fact that the coast is the minor population center of the country. This

phenomenon, of course, is not unknown in other places: Annapolis, for instance, is the capital of Maryand by a similar historical accident, and the capital is maintained there despite considerable inconvenience.

The Inca's Highland Empire

The Incas, beginning about A.D. 1000, developed a great empire based on the Altiplano. From these great heights they reached down into the arid coast lands and subjugated the lowland riverine oases toward the Pacific, but they left the steaming-lowland jungle folk to the east alone. Two problems arise here. How did the highlanders manage to conquer the lowlands? Why did they avoid the humid lowlands and seize the arid lowlands? As usual, the question that we are asking here is: To what extent was this choice physically determined and to what extent was it culturally determined?

The Inca conquests eventually took in all of the irrigation-based city-state oases of the coast. The Incas never penetrated to a like degree into the hot, wet lowlands along the foothills of the Andes. Since these were two utterly different climates, was the reason chiefly climatic? If the people of the Andes are physiologically adjusted to cold, then they would have particular difficulty in tropical heat. This difficulty would be considerably greater in the hot, wet climates than it would be in the hot, dry climates. This was discussed in the opening sections of the book. It will be recalled that in hot, wet climates the cooling by evaporation of perspiration is greatly slowed down.

It is quite probable that the people of the Altiplano are adjusted to cold and quite possibly they have a slightly different metabolic rate than most of mankind. We have recently found that the Tierra del Fuegians and the Australian aborigines have such physiological adjustments, and much the same thing is reported for these people. One of the Spanish priests noted that the people always felt warm, that their hands were warm even in very cold weather, and he commented that they could lay down on the ground and sleep comfortably even in

* *Ibid,* pp. 31–32.

Machu Pichu, Ruins of the Ancient Inca Fortress City in the Andes of Peru. The highland people of the Inca empire were physiologically adjusted to life in these high mountains. *Pan American–Grace Airways.*

a snow storm that covered them with six inches of snow.

However, there are alternative explanations that suggest that a single-factor explanation is, as usual, probably wrong. In the desert areas the population was concentrated in the riverine oases: it was vulnerable to attack. It was also highly organized and productive, hence susceptible to conquest and worth taking over. The forest dwellers of the Amazon, on the other hand, were scattered, mobile, shifting agriculturists with little political structure. They were hard to hit, hard to hold, and had little that the Incas wanted. The combination of difficult physiological-climatological problems and sociopolitical problems seems to be the answer for the Incas expanding in one area much more than in another.

The Incas knew all about the effects of changing altitude; they knew that highlanders sent to the lowlands were prone to sickness. We know now that such illnesses resulted from exposure to new dis-

eases, the lack of acclimatization to high heat, and perhaps pressure and oxygen changes. Combined, they made the highlanders highly susceptible to pneumonia, chronic bronchitis, lung abscesses, and tuberculosis of the lungs.

The Incas guarded against the effects of changes from one climatic zone to another with great care. When they attacked the lowlands, they prepared two armies. One was held in reserve so that if the campaign either in the hot wet lowlands or the hot dry lowlands exceeded two months, the first army could be replaced and returned to the highlands before physical deterioration set in. When people were conquered, the Incas often dispersed the conquered people and replaced them with loyal subjects. Care was taken to send highland people to highland locations, and lowland people to lowland locations. To the Incas, the people were a major resource and pains were taken to preserve them. They were perfectly aware of the fact that if they transplanted highland people to the hot lowlands or lowland people to the highlands, that they would sicken and die. Indeed, this became a form of death sentence. A man could be condemned to exile in a climate so different from his homeland that he could be expected to die.

Spanish Mismanagement of Highlands and Lowlands

The Spanish king issued decrees that the Inca policy be followed; unfortunately, he was far away and the Spanish on the spot were greedy for gold. In spite of the king's orders, therefore, lowland Indians were taken to the highest areas for labor in the mines and highland Indians who had to pay their taxes in gold or silver had to go to the lowlands to work for wages. In 1556, the viceroy reported that of 300 men who went down to the coast for work, not 20 would ever reappear in his homeland. He issued orders that this was to be stopped. Negroes were requested for labor in the hot lowland mines; and it was observed that Negroes sent to the highland mines simply died. In the midst of all this turmoil, the Spanish told the viceroy that they were certainly not going to work the mines themselves, and that if he wanted production to continue, the Indians would have to be used. They recommended that the Indians so used be kept at elevations to which they were accustomed: lowland Indians for lowland mines and highland Indians for highland mines. There was lengthy legislation that all tended in the same direction: the Indians must not be moved radically from one climate to another. Even the tax laws were changed so that the Indians who lived in areas where gold and silver were not produced were allowed to pay in wool or cotton.

Despite royal decrees, the bitter protests of the Spanish priests, and the efforts of some of the officials, however, the Indians were moved about radically and abused terribly. The result was a catastrophic loss of life. This can be seen in the comparatively empty desert oases that contain the ruins of great cities and in the equally impressive ruins in the highlands. The Spanish had here entered an area of civilization, great mining wealth, and immense contrasts in climate. The contrasts were so great and concentrated in so small a lateral space that men adapted to one climate could be moved into another so drastically different that the results would be physiologically catastrophic: this is one of the most extreme environmental contrasts and limitations that the varied environments of the world provide. Even then cultural wisdom could have prevented such a wastage, for the Inca civilization had dealt with the same problem and handled it with little difficulty.

In these lands today, the same problems exist. Mining is carried on at immense altitudes. For instance, the copper mines at Cerro de Pasco are even higher than the silver mines of Potosí. Labor still moves up and down the mountains seeking employment. Monge, the major student of the effects of high altitude on man in the Andes, complained bitterly as late as 1948 that little attention was even then paid to the great cost in human life in moving men from the highlands to the lowlands. Of all the areas of the world, these very high altitudes are the clearest cases of human physiological adjustment to the extreme physical conditions met.

BOLIVIA TODAY: THE POTENTIAL

Although Bolivia and Peru began with great empire, great wealth in precious metals, and with a relatively dense population of politically stable people organized into a model socialist state, they have gone down the scale of cultural and political status. Under the mismanagement of the Spanish profiteers, the population was reduced to a fraction of its original strength. After the Spanish empire collapsed, the old Inca empire was broken up: parts of it went to Peru, Bolivia, and Chile. From a rich, stable empire, this part of the world declined into a poor, unstable society wracked by revolutions, limited education, and low productivity, and in cases such as Bolivia, the situation seemingly drifts from bad to worse. Can it be that the highlanders are not suitable for development in our modern economy?

Rafts on Lake Titicaca, Bolivia. These reed-bundle rafts are widely dispersed over the world and often used by primitive people. Their survival here seems to be related to the scarcity of timber on the high, cold Altiplano of Bolivia. *Pan American-Grace Airways.*

We already know that the men now there can live, work, and reproduce with no difficulty. Bolivia has major metal resources: tin, lead, and zinc. Tin is the major one of these, but for a long time it was monopolized by one man and the profits did the people little good. Now the government has taken over the mines, and productivity of the worker has dropped. This is parallel to the British experience where government take-over of the coal mines led not to increased but to decreased production. Bolivian tin is relatively costly to mine and is therefore in a disadvantageous position in the world market. Bolivia's problem is to find other outlets for its people's potential productivity. This requires energetic development of education, finding individuals with the genius to develop products, organize production, and capture markets—but this amounts to changing the whole Latin American culture pattern. Free-enterprise entrepreneurship is totally foreign to their whole way of life. But this amounts to saying that it is the way of life, not

the highland interior position of the country that is hindering development.

Bolivia may well be compared with Switzerland:

	Area (square miles)	*Population*	*Exports* (millions of dollars)	*Imports* (millions of dollars)
Bolivia	412,000	4,000,000	113	169
Switzerland	16,000	5,000,000	804	881

Could Bolivia do what Switzerland has done? Switzerland is notable for its political stability, which aids in making it an international banking center. Surely this lies within the power of the Bolivians to accomplish. If Bolivia had a stable government and if it had banking houses of proven repute, then international capital, and especially Latin American capital, could well flow to it. There is nothing in the physical geography that prevents this.

Switzerland's major agricultural effort is in dairying. Bolivia has a vastly greater land area and much of it is potential cattle-producing land. If New Zealand from its position in the midst of the world's oceans can enter the international market with dairy products, wool, and fabrics and compete with Switzerland in these same items, then surely Bolivia could enter this area also. We think almost automatically of the Swiss success in the making of watches. Small nations often specialize in some highly skilled product of this sort. The Dutch, for instance, are the most important diamond cutters of the world, and there are probably countless opportunities of this sort in the world, many of which could, through the application of human energy, be developed in the physical geography of Bolivia. One of Switzerland's important industries is tourism. Switzerland is scenic and hygienic, and Swiss service is among the world's finest. Bolivia is more scenic, for its mountains are higher; its snow is equally good for skiing; and it has, in addition, tropical lowlands, exotic primitive people, incredibly magnificent archeological ruins, picturesque lakes such as Titicaca and Poopó, and immense valleys that plunge down the eastern slope of the Andes becoming more tropical by the mile. But Bolivia is mostly unhygienic and the services that tourists cherish are in most rudimentary stages of development. But all of these are human failures in the face of potential resources that another people might well make a source of wealth. The block is not in the physical geography or in the physical men—it is, as usual, in the cultural setting.

THE ANTIOQUEÑOS: A HIGHLAND SUCCESS STORY

In Colombia there is an interesting development that illustrates that a rebirth of the highlands as a center of energy and cultural growth is possible. Here in the highland valleys of the northern part of Colombia, in the province of Antioquia on the slopes of the mountains flanking the Cauca River, are a group of people of Spanish descent who have been growing in numbers and expanding throughout the highlands. They are noted for their energy and thrift, and characterize themselves as "the Yankees of South America." They are shrewd and aggressive individualists who are prouder of being Antioqueños than of being Colombians. Things were not always so.

The beautiful slopes of the ranges flanking the Cauca River had had a dense Indian population, but this largely disappeared under the impact of the European arms, diseases, and disruptions. Development of the land during the colonial period was based on gold mining, but the mines were poor, largely placer mines, and they were worked by individual laborers to a great extent. There were few Indians and few Negroes, so the Spaniards had to work, and a tradition of hard work was thus established. This is quite contrary to much of Latin America, where it is the tradition that men of Spanish descent do no manual labor. As was common in the Spanish colonial lands, there were few European women; the result here was a mixed race: a composite of Negro, Indian, and white.

The mines were poor, and the people by concentrating on them condemned themselves to poverty. Until the end of the colonial period they remained backward, illiterate peoples of the mountainous interior of Colombia. So far it would sound as if the interior location in high mountains with all the remoteness of Colombia from the world centers of intellectual ferments and economic inovation and growth in the north Atlantic areas was doing its expected work.

The royal inspector who was in the province from 1784 to 1787 initiated a series of changes that were to overcome the obstacles of mere physical environment. Juan Antonio Mon y Velarde instituted far-reaching social, economic, and judicial reforms. He encouraged the foundation of agricultural settlements in the cool, malaria-free uplands; he offered bounties for the introduction of new crops; and vagrancy laws were drawn up to send idlers to the new agricultural settlements. Here we meet the role of the unusual individual and see that within a cul-

Scenes from Antioquia, Northern Colombia. (*Right*) Antioqueños. (*Below*) Antioqueño Cattle. *James J. Parsons.*

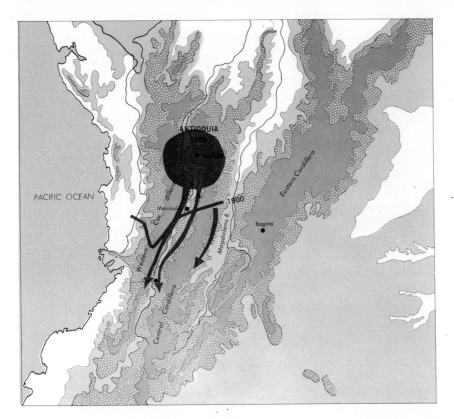

Map 8-4 Antioqueño Settlement in the Andes

The original Antioquia was the territory in the mountains on either side of the Cauca River, centering on the city of Medellín. After 1790 expansion was down the western flank of the Central Cordillera to Manizales, which was reached by 1850. Vigorous expansion after 1850 followed the high mountain flanks down the Western Cordillera and both flanks of the Central Cordillera, but staying out of the Cauca and Magdalena river valleys. The line marked 1900 indicates the extent of the expansion by that date. The linear expansion along the mountain flanks and the avoidance of the hot low valleys show the tendency of man to stay in the kind of environment to which his culture is adapted. A wet rice cultural expansion might have been just as linear, but restricted to the valley bottom.

ture there is still room for the exercise of the individual will.

By the opening of the nineteenth century, the highland population was growing and beginning to expand southward into the forest-covered mountain slopes to the south of Medellín. The main current of expansion was south and southwest (see Map 8–4), but it could equally well have been northward. The expansion was spurred on by a short-lived boom in rubber and by rumors of gold and dreams of vanilla and cinchona and cochineal plantations. Dreams are not unimportant. Because men dreamed, they pushed into the forests and cleared land and produced something. It turned out that for a time the fortunes to be made were in the more prosaic corn and hog industry so well known in Iowa. In Colombia, however, it was a shifting agriculture that produced corn and other crops for the hogs, fol-

lowed by a ten-year fallow in forest. The hogs went to market on their own legs, driven over trails, sometimes in herds of hundreds. Later coffee became the important crop.

At first, only gold and silver could stand the cost of export. Until late in the nineteenth century coffee had to be moved out over mountain trails by mule or ox train. The movement of some valuable goods encouraged the building of roads, and better roads encouraged more export and, of course, an increased return flow of goods and materials. This feed-back system has functioned so well that the coffee production in the hands of the Antioqueños has risen to the level that 70 percent of Colombia's production comes from their area. This is produced on small holdings in the hands of private owners, who also produce much of their food stuffs on their own lands.

Another important element in the Antioqueño economy is cattle. They have their own special breed: a white animal with black ears. Speculation as to the origin of these peculiar animals includes the possibility that they are the descendants of a breed of cattle that the Romans introduced into Spain. These are thrifty animals able to eat tropical grasses and resist tropical diseases. The Colombians have recently been introducing grasses and managing pastures in order to improve their cattle production both for meat and for dairy, for these products are among the critical shortages in many tropical regions. In the lower lands large landholders have managed pastures: these are relatively large holdings of 40 acres or more, with a number of such plots fenced so that the cattle may be rotated from one pasture to the other, thus giving the grass a chance to recover between grazings.

In the search for better grasses suited to equatorial conditions, an accidental introduction was made of *Melinis multiflora*, African molasses grass. This grass provides nutritious grazing, a protective mantle for the land, is tolerant of poor and eroded land, and spreads itself rapidly. It has taken over large areas of the country, healing the abandoned lands and turning them into useful pastures. It is at home in the *tierra caliente* and reaches well up into the *tierra fría*. Since its accidental introduction in 1906, it has nearly taken over the temperate lands of Colombia. Far from the physical environment dominating man, here man is busily reordering the physical environment to meet his needs.

Antioqueño expansion is continuing. The economic base is broadening, and the population is growing and continuing to spread into new territory. The population growth has been phenomenal; there has been a doubling every 28 years since 1828. They have grown from about 50,000 people in 1880 to nearly 100,000 people in 1900 to over 3,000,000 people in 1950. This represents a shift in their percentage of the Colombian population from 10 percent in 1835 to over 25 percent in 1938. This population growth has been accomplished with increasing economic strength rather than declining status,

for the increase of productive people has led to the growth of cities, the building of roads, and to general economic development.

All is not perfect by any means. The standard of living in comparison with the United States is low, and health standards are abysmally bad. And the population growth is in spite of heavy handicaps. Especially in the lands below the *tierra fría,* the incidence of hookworm, dysentery, malaria, typhoid, syphilis, and gonorrhea is high. Hookworm is the worst. Infection runs close to 90 percent. However, this is clearly the result of lack of the habit of wearing shoes and the failure to use latrines. Typhoid simply reflects the absence of modern water-supply measures, while malaria results from a combination of the absence of screening and the lack of mosquito control and antimalarial drugs. The description of malaria in Colombia applies equally well to the upper Mississippi valley in America in the period when colonists first pushed into that area and lived in housing about comparable to Colombian housing.

A further health problem for the Antioqueños has increased with the growth of cities. Prostitution has proliferated in the cities, and the results are very high rates of venereal disease.

These problems have varied climatic controls. Malaria is much more serious in the *tierra caliente* than in the *tierra templada,* and is almost nonexistent in the *tierra fría.* Hookworm is limited by temperature, but is even more limited if human patterns of hygiene are changed. The same is true of typhoid; and venereal disease is rightly called a social disease. It is not sensitive to physical climate, but to moral climate.

The Antioqueños, then, supply a case history of a people at first seemingly handicapped by a mountainous interior location and then stimulated by a socio-economic program into a populational and territorial expansion along the adjacent mountain slopes. Their explosive population and economic growth has put them ahead of the racially and culturally similar countrymen who had the identical territory available for development. To the non-Antioqueños it was a remote, empty, mountainous,

Detail from the Temple of Quetzalcoatl, Teotihuacán, Mexico. The name Quetzalcoatl combines the words for the Quetzal bird and for snake. It is often translated as Plumed Serpent, and represents one of the great culture-bearing god-like beings who are so vividly enshrined in Mexican Indian mythology. *Mexican National Tourist Council.*

Ruins near Oaxaca, Mexico. The great geometric forms such as are shown here were the bases for temples. In many details they reproduce Old World forms. *Mexican National Tourist Council.*

Panoramic View of Mexico City. This modern metropolis has been built on the site of the Aztec capital, Tenochtitlán. *Mexican National Tourist Council.*

geographically handicapped area. To the Antioqueños it was a glorious opportunity.

THE MEXICAN HIGHLAND

The other center of civilization on the highlands of America in pre-Columbian times was in Mexico. Here the Spanish found the brilliant Aztec empire flourishing when they entered America. The civilization had roots deep in the past. Cities with ceremonial centers were in existence on the plateau of Mexico at least as early as 1000 B.C. Cities always imply developed agriculture, political structures, trade, and transportation. Ceremonial structures of great size tell still more about the degree of political development, religious beliefs, and surpluses of labor that can be channeled into works of art and architecture. By all of these measures the Aztec developments were comparable to Egyptian and Mesopotamian developments.

The center of the Mexican highland culture was the great city of Tenochtitlán, present-day Mexico City. The elevation here is 7347 feet. This height is not great enough to create the physiological stress that the heights of Peru and Bolivia create, but it is high enough to make the climate moderate. Typically, the sun is warm but the shade is cool. The Spanish found Mexico City standing in the marshes at the edge of a lake. It had causeways leading into the city and aqueducts brought a supply of good water. The city had a circumference of about ten miles and a population of about 300,000 people. It had immense pyramids with temples on their tops, huge palaces, and such things as zoos, great markets to which goods from over a wide area were brought, and so forth. It was a large, bustling center of empire.

In some ways the Aztec empire resembled the Inca empire: both were located on plateaus surrounded by high mountains; and both were preceded by earlier empires. The Incas were preceded by the Tiahuanaco, to name but one important one; the Aztecs had built upon the Toltec empire. In both areas there was a long history of cultural growth and development with civilization extending back at least into the first millennia B.C. Both of these empires had expanded by conquering the neighboring people, but the Incas had solidified their hold more firmly than the Aztecs had. The Aztec empire was composed of numerous city-states, and there was almost constant strife between the various groups, which served the useful purpose of supplying thousands of captives that could be used for sacrifices demanded by their religious beliefs. It has been seriously argued that the expenditure of life in this way was great enough to hold the population down to the levels their way of life could support. This was certainly a grim way to control population growth.

As in South America, the Mexican highland culture had reached down into the adjacent warm and humid lowlands and conquered Mayan people there. This provides sharp contrast with the Inca history, where the expansion was toward the arid lands, and not into the hot, wet lowlands. With most of the people living at an elevation of a mile to a mile and a half above sea level, the Mexicans must, to some extent, have been "highland" people with some, even if minor, adjustment to the conditions of cool, dry air. (Annual range of temperature at Mexico City is from 20° F. to 85° F. and the rainfall is 26 inches.) If hot, wet climates are difficult barriers to such people, why did they not expand to the north where there were more similar climates?

The reasons seem to have been that to the north of central Mexico there were only wild tribes, while in the adjacent lowlands there were great city-states. Thus the cultural situation was reversed: in Peru the city-states were in the arid lands and the tribal peoples were in the wet lands, and the expansion was toward the city-states. In Mexico, the city-states were in the hot, wet lowlands and tribal people were in the arid lands, and the expansion still was toward the areas of dense, settled, civilized population.

This tendency continued when the Spanish entered Middle America. They rapidly surveyed the scene. There were numerous geographic areas, each with differing climates and accessibility to Spain and varying plant and animal potential. The land most like Spain in soil and climate, and hence the land that the Spanish could most easily have developed in the ways that they knew best, was in California and Chile; yet neither became a center of Spanish development. The lands nearest to Spain, the lands most easily reached by sea, were the Caribbean islands, yet the Spanish did little with these beautiful and fertile lands. They were left largely empty to fall into the hands of the French and British freebooters. Instead, the Spanish seized two of the three great centers of population and cultural development and made them the centers of the development of their New World empire. Both of these were highland empires, the Aztec and the Inca. They largely ignored, except to destroy, the lowland Mayan empire.

At first, there seems to be a perfect correlation here between avoidance of the hot, wet lowlands and preference for the high, dry plateaus. This correlation loses almost all of its force when it is noted that it is also a perfect correlation with the distribution of major sources of precious metals. The limestone lowland of the Yucatan peninsula lacks metals, and the Spanish choice was for areas where there were settled peoples who had precious metals, and where there were known mines. Remember that in California, where there were no settled peoples and no known mines, the Spanish did nothing with the land, despite its desirable climate and fine soils. They thereby missed the fabulous gold of California and the immense silver wealth of Nevada.

SUMMARY

An over-all view of the highlands of the tropical regions of the world, then, shows a familiar pattern.

Those areas that were in or near the centers of growth of civilization shared in that growth. The presence of ideas made it possible to develop mountain lands and high plateaus to the level of civilizations and empires. Today there is no great world power located in the highlands of the tropical regions, but there is no apparent reason in physical geography that this should be so. The tropical plateaus and highlands, such as those of Abyssinia,

East Africa, and Middle America, offer large enough bases with equable climates, abundance of strategic minerals, potential water power, and great variety of soil, vegetation, and animal life. Today the development of transportation makes their terrain and position less of a negative factor than it may have been in the past. Even in the past, however, it was not sufficient to prevent the development of civilization in such regions when men willed to do so.

MID-LATITUDE MOUNTAIN LANDS

For convenience the mountains between the tropics and 60 degrees north and south will be considered the mid-latitude mountain lands. The American mountain masses of the western United States and Canada, the Andes of Chile in South America, and in Eurasia the immense belt of mountains reaching from Spain to China, all are mid-latitude mountains. In Africa it includes highlands at each end of the continent. The mountains in southeast Australia, Tasmania, New Zealand, and Japan are discussed elsewhere. They will be referred to here only in the summary.

In the tropics the mountains gain temperature advantages by their elevation. In mid-latitudes the results of elevation are complex. On the west sides of continents in latitudes near 30 degrees, there is aridity; there mountains have the advantage of greater moisture. Farther north with steadily falling seasonal and annual average temperatures, mountain lands begin to suffer from too much cold. All the other features of mountains already discussed—the great variability of slope and exposure to sun and rain, accompanied by many different kinds of plants and animals within short distances—remain true of the mid-latitude mountains.

NEAR EASTERN DEVELOPMENTS

In the Old World, civilization began in the shadow, poetically speaking, of the mountain lands. Indeed, there is a possibility that the first important

steps toward civilization were taken on the mountainous plateaus of Asia Minor. It is in this area that wheat and barley, our earliest domestic grains, originated. This is also the home of the stone fruits, cherry, peach, almond, and of such animals as the domestic sheep and goat—and quite probably the center of origin of domestication of animals. Whether civilization began in the highlands, the foothills, or the plains, is something that we may never know. Unquestionably, however, the highland masses included in what are now Turkey, Iran, and Afghanistan early shared in the growing civilization of the Near East.

Anatolia

The area of modern Turkey, somewhat larger than Texas, is to be thought of as like the western part of the United States. The coastal climate is like that of California, but there is a rapid ascent to a plateau that is much like the Great Basin country. There is much arid land, but there are also many ranges that stand high enough to catch moisture and to send living streams down to the surface of the plateau which averages 3000 feet elevation, creating a rich irrigation potential. Some of the ranges were glaciated in the past and are snow capped in winter today. During the glacial past this area was studded with lakes, just as in the American Great Basin.

As early as 2000 B.C., this area was the seat of the Hittites. Basing themselves on this highland peninsula, they were for centuries a dominant power in the Near East. In later times Anatolia has been the seat of a mighty Turkish empire. It is one of the curiosities of history that we live in a time so shortly after the collapse of the Turkish empire, and yet tend to forget that from this highland a gigantic pincers movement was directed against Europe that nearly changed the course of history. The physical base that served for the development of civilization and empire is still there. The region is rich in its variety of climates, in potential water power and irrigable areas, and in such agricultural bases as good forests. It is not its highland geography, but its present state of political and economic stagnation that handicaps this land.

Iran and Afghanistan

Much the same can be said of Iran and Afghanistan. They have been the scene of great civilizations; they could again be developed, productive countries. The turn of history, the direction of cultural growth, the changes of dynasties, but most of all, the total cultural pattern of the people has not been in tune with the economic revolution that began in northwestern Europe, and which has still not reached them in any effective way. These areas once were near the center of Eurasian growth and development, but have been out of the main stream of developments for the past 2000 years. This lag is not due to their position, for these highland countries lie in the crossroads of Eurasia and Africa. The location of political-economic growth, however, has ignored this crossroads situation due to the culturally induced explosion on the "isolated" northwestern end of the European peninsula.

The spread of ideas, as we saw earlier, was from the eastern end of the Mediterranean westward. It went from the mountainous Near East to mountainous Crete and from there to mountainous Greece and thence to mountainous Italy. Civilization was later in time and lesser in development as distance to the west increased. Spain was late, and the cultural influence of the Near East was markedly diminished. The beautiful Atlas Mountain region, the exact climatic and physiographic equivalent of the southern California region, only belatedly entered the realm of the civilized world. That mountains of themselves are no barrier to development is well illustrated by Italy, or Spain at various times.

SPAIN: A MEDITERRANEAN MOUNTAIN LAND

Spain is a varied land. The edges are Mediterranean in climate and the southern valleys are warm, but most of Spain is a plateau about 3000 feet in elevation, with ranges of mountains towering above the plain. In latitude, altitude, and climate it is comparable to Turkey. If Portugal is included, the land areas are comparable, but the population of the Iberian Peninsula is twice that of Turkey. Spain's plateau is semiarid and alternates between freezing cold in winter and blazing hot in summer. Madrid can have 107° F. in July and −7° F. in January. The mountains are forest-covered and in winter, snow-covered. Streams from these mountains carry large volumes of water in the time of snow melt in the spring, but fall to low volumes in the summer period. Further, most of these rivers are deeply entrenched in the plateau so that their water is not easily distributed for irrigation. However, streams descending from well-watered mountains to semiarid plains are potential water-power and irrigation resources, as the arid American West shows.

A land with its plateau averaging 3000 feet above sea level, liberally crossed by mountain ranges with peaks to heights of 11,000 feet, is mountainous highland country—a good mid-latitude mountain land. Has this been a good environment or a poor one? Was it the highlands and the mountains that determined this? If not, what were the causes?

Spain is today a land dominated by farming, and it is still a primitive agriculture. The principal crops are wheat and barley, and 75 percent of these crops are harvested and threshed by hand. The United States was on this level about 100 years ago. There is a wide range of other crops: Cork, olives, onions, grapes, and oranges are typical. Spain is one of the world's leading wine and cork producers.

A Megalithic Tomb of the Bronze Age at Ciudadella, Minorca, Balearic Islands. During this period influences from the eastern Mediterranean were strongly felt in Spain. *Embassy of Spain.*

Livestock is important, with sheep being by far the most important. Mining is the other important source of wealth. Spain is highly mineralized and despite the fact that mining has been carried on here for about 4000 years, it is still one of the major mineral producing areas of the world. Coal, iron, copper, lead, and mercury lead a lengthy list of available minerals. Spain is no have-not nation, yet she is today one of the world's poorer nations. How can this be? Is this the effect of the mountains and arid plateaus?

The Historical Background

Spain early shows signs of being inhabited by skilled people. In Upper Paleolithic times, 20,000 years ago, men were painting the walls of caves in Spain with the most advanced art that man had yet achieved. It compares favorably with some of the art produced today. Later, there is clearly African influence in the art of Spain. There is a constant repetition in Spanish history of her place as a bridge

connecting Europe to Africa. The slight break at Gibraltar has seldom stopped men from crossing in force in either direction. In the sixth century B.C., Celtic peoples from France poured down through the Pyrenees and dominated much of Spain. About 100 B.C., the Iberians, racially Mediterraneans, entered Spain from the north of Africa and became a dominant people. Later, Germanic tribes poured in. Like the Strait of Gibraltar, the Pyrenees seem to have been slight bulwarks, for armies moved north or south through them depending on the tides of cultural dominance and apparently irrespective of their nature as "barriers." However, the Pyrenees are as good a physical barrier of their kind as one is likely to find. They present a high continuous wall extending practically from sea to sea. As with all such natural barriers, the most important factor is the differential in human forces on the two sides.

The Phoenicians traded with Spain, and Carthage founded trading cities there. Modern Cartagena is the descendant of New Carthage. The Romans could

Roman Aqueduct, near Nerja, Malága. This aqueduct remains as evidence of Rome's former importance in the Iberian peninsula. *James J. Parsons.*

not allow Carthage to have the wealthy peninsula, and this was one of the major causes of the Punic Wars. The Romans destroyed eventually Carthage and developed Spain themselves. Under Rome, the Iberian Peninsula was united and Hispania became one of the most prosperous areas of Roman power. With the disintegration of Roman power upon the outbreak of the Germanic tribes in A.D. 409, Spanish unity was destroyed; it was not to be put together again for another thousand years.

Vandals and Goths made their way through Spain, and the Visigoths established a kingdom there for almost 200 years. Christianity came to Spain, but unity and prosperity remained mainly a memory. Then, in 711, the Muslims arrived from North Africa and took all but one corner of the peninsula; after an interval of mismanagement, a strong ruler, Abd-er-Rahman, came to power in A.D. 756. His descendants established their capital at Córdoba and made this a city second only to Constantinople, the greatest city in Europe at that time. Muslim Spain, at this time, was a leader far in advance of most of northwestern Europe. There were more universities teaching more medicine and mathematics, and stressing more literature and philosophy, than were to be found anywhere else in Europe. When the Muslims fell to fighting among themselves, the Spanish Christian kings who had been steadily, though slowly, pressing the Muslims southward, began in 1031 a major drive to push them out of Spain. After 1212, the Muslims were limited to Granada in the south, and here they established one of the greatest and most splendid of all of the Muslim realms. This lasted until 1492 when, united by the marriage of Ferdinand and Isabella, the rulers of Aragon and Castille, the Spanish finally drove the Muslims out of the country.

Then came empire. Columbus tried to find the East Indies by sailing west, and found the West "Indies" instead. The immense wealth of the Aztec and Inca empires, followed by the sustained production of the mines of the New World, then poured into Spain. As we have already seen, the mines of Potosí alone produced at the rate of a billion dollars a century for two centuries. If Spain had been great in the past, this should have been the time of its greatest height. Instead, the chaos of international politics and kings prevailed. The Spanish monarchy became a branch of the Hapsburg dynasty and thus involved Spain in the Holy Roman Empire. Spain, thereafter, at times included parts of Italy and the Netherlands. Sometimes her kings spoke no Spanish, and at all times they were involved in wars with the French, or the British, or were

Cuarto Real de Santo Domingo, the Alhambra, Granada. Built in 1248–1354, the Alhambra is one of the finest examples of Moorish architecture in Spain. *Embassy of Spain.*

squandering treasure trying to put down Protestantism in the Netherlands. The treasury was stripped to build an armada to attack England, and the immense fleet was lost to warfare and storm.

With the French Revolution, not only was there further disastrous involvement in international affairs, but the germs of nineteenth-century liberalism, rationalism, atheism, anarchism, and socialism were introduced, and, given typical extremist development by various Spanish groups, tore the precarious political structure apart. Weakened by internal dis-

sension, Spain lost her colonies one by one between 1800 and 1830. This is not to be wondered at. Rather, it seems remarkable that so small a country with its handful of people had had the energy and genius to hold so much of the earth so long.

Liberalism had fostered divisive forces, such as clericalism versus anticlericalism, monarchism versus republicanism, and separatism versus union. Spaniards, by their own account, are extremists and were wracked by such differences more than any other nation. For more than 100 years revolutions oc-

Medieval Fortress at Medellín. Fortresses on this plan existed throughout northwest Europe. This one symbolizes the reconquest of Spain for western civilization. *Embassy of Spain.*

Steel Mills at Avilés. Such mills mark the coming of the industrial revolution to Spain. *Embassy of Spain.*

curred at the rate of about one every three years. When civil war broke out in the 1930s Soviet Russia backed the communist-socialist-anarchist group, and the Italian and German fascists backed the other. Spain became an international battlefield, and the situation proved to be the prelude to World War II. The country was torn apart, the people set against one another. The Communist-backed group massacred priests, professors, landowners and industrialists, and the little people on the land became cannon fodder for both sides.

General Franco's action defeated the Communist-backed forces, but the country he saved was torn, impoverished, and bitterly divided. All the gold from the treasury had been seized by Communist Russia, and thousands of Spanish children had been kidnapped and taken to Russia for indoctrination. Faced by the impoverished residue of a state that had long been wracked by internal strife, Franco established a dictatorship. Although bitterly criticized, his action served to give Spain 25 years of stability, the most it has had in more than a century. During this time universal education has been attempted, and for the first time in modern history the literacy rate in Spain is now approaching that of the other developed western European nations. Despite the fact that Franco saved Spain for the Free World and by keeping the country out of World War II saved Gibraltar from falling into the hands of the fascists who had aided him in the Civil War, he was condemned as a dictator. Spain was quarantined by part of the Western world, denied membership in the United Nations—though the

Communist dictatorship was not denied membership—and until recently excluded from the aid that the United States has extended to the rest of the world so freely that aid was offered even to the Communist nations.

Spain's Physical Geography and Present Status

This may seem like a long recital of political history. It has a purpose. What geography could overcome such fantastic mismanagement, such continuous war and destruction of men and facilities and resources? If Spain, a mountainous highland country is today a poor land, are we to conclude that it is because it is a poor environment? Is it not more reasonable to recall that whenever it was given good rule, whether autocratic or not, whether Christian, Muslim, or pagan, that it has been a center of brilliant cities with great universities and a leader of the whole of Europe?

Further comparisons can make this even clearer. Spain has an area of near 200,000 square miles, and a population of about 30,000,000. (See Table 8–1.)

Spain is somewhat like California. Both have great variety of land forms and climate. Both have high year-round rainfalls in their northwestern corners, high rainfalls and winter snow covers on their mountains, a winter maximum of rainfall over most of their area, large areas of rainfall of about 10 to 20 inches. By most measures Spain is richer: more arable, less arid, and better mineral resources. California in 1500 lagged more than 10,000 years behind Europe and Spain was one of Europe's leaders. California began its growth in 1850 and

Table 8-1   Spain and Other Countries Compared

	Area	Arable (percent)	Meadow and Pasture (percent)	Forest and Woodland (percent)	Other (percent)	Population Density		
						(millions)	(per square mile)	(per arable acre)
Spain	200,000	37	46	10	7	30	150	450
Switzerland	16,000	12	41	25	22	5	312	2500
United States	3,000,000	23	36	23	18	180	60	240
Texas	267,000	20	62	12	6	8	35	175
California	158,000	11	23	41	25	16	66	920

Near Elvas, Portugal. Flat-topped oaks, shaped by cutting for firewood, stand in grain fields and pastures, illustrating multiple use of the land. By cutting the top of the tree, the acorn-bearing branches are kept low, shading of the ground crop is reduced, and the acorn yield is probably increased. *James J. Parsons.*

by 1950 was a leading state in the world's leading nation, and by the 1960s was first in population among the states of the United States. Spain meanwhile, had stood still, and hence declined in relative position. Spain is today about 50 years behind California.

Spain has three times as high a percentage of arable land as Switzerland, but only one half the density per square mile, or one fifth the density per square mile of arable land. Switzerland's wealth is not all agricultural, of course. It is built on dairying, banking, and manufacturing (one half the world's watch trade). As noted in this context before, banking requires a stable government and a reputation for integrity, and any nation could develop these qualities. Spain's agricultural base is both absolutely and relatively better than Switzerland's. Spain's potential for industrial development is much greater because of the presence of basic raw materials and a large working force with low wage demands, which could give Spain an impor-

tant advantage during a developmental period. The main point here is that Spain, now rated as a poor nation and often described as such because of its physical geography, proves to be quite the opposite—it is a relatively well-endowed area in terms of physical geography.

Comparison with the United States again places Spain in an advantageous position in terms of percentage of arable land. Comparison with Texas, not a mountainous land, but more nearly the size of Spain, and an area with much arid land, again shows Spain to be well off in useful land. Further, in all of these comparisons, the number of people in Spain is relatively high compared with American densities. While there is great concern today about the growth of population, it must not be overlooked that people are the productive force of nations. In Europe, today, the countries with rapidly increasing production are importing manpower. Even Italy, the chronic source of overpopulation in Europe, is beginning to feel a labor shortage. Spain then, is, again in an advantageous position. She has her own manpower potential, but it is still only in part a potential because labor is increasingly useful only as it is educated, trained, and organized for production.

To a considerable extent, Spain has made significant beginnings in these developments. Primary-school education in Spain is free and compulsory. There has been a period of freedom from wars and there is now an improved international climate in regard to Spain. With greater access to international capital and markets, it is possible that Spain can, if her internal affairs are kept in order, rapidly rise again to a position of leadership. Recent economic controls have greatly strengthened her gold reserves. Construction now under way will give Spain the world's greatest reservoir at Salto de Aldeadavilla. Certainly there is nothing in her physical geography that prevents development and there is much of great advantage for such a development.

SWITZERLAND

If one were to pick a piece of land that was seemingly overwhelmingly handicapped by a mountainous terrain, Switzerland would make an excellent choice. Within the 16,000 square miles of Switzerland there is little flat ground and a great deal of very high mountainous land; this is portrayed by these figures: arable, 12 percent; meadow and pasture, 41 percent; forest and woodland, 25 percent; other, 23 percent. In addition, the Swiss are divided linguistically, ethnically, and in religion. People of Italian, French, and Germanic ancestry and language and of Catholic and Protestant faith make up this nation. They have no outlet to the sea of their own, and they have few mineral resources.

The Swiss plateau, with an elevation of about 2500 feet, has the bulk of the population. The temperature is moderate, not hot in summer and not too cold in winter. Nevertheless, even at an elevation of 2500 feet, the decrease in temperature is about 10 degrees below what would be expected at sea level. Even the plateau of Switzerland, therefore, has

summer and winter temperatures that would be expected at sea level in areas much farther to the north. On the high mountains, with temperature decreasing at the rate of 3 degrees with each 1000 feet of increased altitude, the limit of grain cultivation is found at about 4000 feet. Above 9000 feet snow stays the year around. Between the upper limit of grain growing and the zone of perpetual snow, the land is used for forest and for pasture.

In all of the mountain lands of Europe there is a strongly developed system of vertical seasonal movements to take advantage of the summer grazing in the alpine meadows, and this is particularly well known for Switzerland. It should not be overlooked that it is also well developed in Spain, Italy, and generally throughout the mountains of Europe. However, such seasonal movements of cattle were rare or unknown elsewhere in the world before 1600. In Switzerland, there is not much space for lateral movement. In Spain, the movement of the herds to the mountains often involves long drives across the lowlands to reach the mountain masses. In Switzerland, the movement is normally only one of a few miles up the local mountain side. The Swiss often have a major farmstead at low elevation, where grain is grown and where fodder for the stock is stored for winter feeding. In spring as the snows begin to melt, the cattle are sent up the mountain to their summer pastures. Part of the family may go up with them to stay for the summer. At other times, there are very complex movements of people and herds up and down the mountain according to the season, the work load, and the particular crop to be harvested.

There are also settlements in Swizerland well up in the mountains near the edge of the limit of grain growing. Villagers persist here with a way of life that was probably established during the Neolithic age. They live in snug houses whose back ends are built into the hill slope, with the only door and a single window facing downhill. The window is for light, not ventilation. The house has hay stored in its upper part, and cattle are kept in the back part of the one very large, ground-floor room.

(*Above*) Medieval Switzerland is represented by the village of Gruyères. Such survivals are major tourist attractions. (*Opposite*) The flat-topped mountain, the woods, and the meadows in this scene near Flims are typical of Switzerland's attractive scenery. *Swiss National Tourist Office.*

Cooking and eating are carried on at the front of the room, and sleeping is in curtained bedsteads along the sides of the room. The stove is for cooking only; heat is provided by the animals. This might be described as the original hay burning, heating, and air-conditioning system. The heat of the animal bodies keeps the room at a comfortable temperature; their respiration keeps the humidity high.

While the thought of living quite so closely with cattle is offensive to our modern sensibilities, especially to our noses, it was the way of life of our northern European ancestors for a very long time, indeed, until a relatively short time ago.

It often seems as if there must be a racial tolerance to the smells of cows and horses. Most people find the smell of the stable tolerable, but this does not extend to all animals. While the stablelike smells in the Washington zoo house for zebras and giraffes and their kin is pungent but pleasant, the house that holds the lions and tigers is rarely endurable. We know that most of the northern Europeans lived very closely with their animals throughout the Neolithic period, and many of the peasant

people of Europe still do. It is not a mountaineer's trait; it is an old European trait that has been preserved in a few mountain villages in Switzerland. But even the preservation of old ways of doing things is by no means found only in mountains—old ways of doing things last today in such lowland spots as the Hebrides and other isolated areas.

The miracle of Switzerland is the building of a high level of productivity and hence a high standard of living on so small and mountainous a physical base. Many things have entered into this. Switzerland occupies a position astride some of the principal passes that lead from Italy into central Europe. For many centuries trade has funneled through this highland area. Traders carry ideas as well as goods. Ideas are the key things in growth and development of nations and areas. Switzerland, therefore, has had a good position, but this too can easily be overemphasized.

Why should the major flow of ideas go through the passes? Why not go by sea to the mouth of the Rhône River and thence up that easy valley to the heart of Europe? Or from the other side, why not follow the Danube to the head of the Rhine and thus again penetrate Europe without having the difficult task of crossing the Alpine passes? An explanation based on the mountain-pass theory is too simple. On close scrutiny we find that the principal pass, the Brenner, is not even in Swiss territory. Further, the use of passes through mountains when easier low routes exist immediately suggests that political considerations such as the blocking of other routes by unfriendly powers were important. A major cause for the use of the Alpine passes was, of course, the importance of northern Italy as a center of commercial and industrial activity in medieval times and later. However, this is not a geographical factor so much as it is a cultural-historical factor.

The Swiss Confederation came into being in 1291, but its present political unity dates to the nineteenth century. The agricultural-dairying way of life has long been well established, as have been such pursuits as skilled woodworking in the southern German and Swiss region. To these skills the Swiss have added watch-making, to become the world's leaders in this field. They are also important manufacturers of textiles and machinery, and they have a notable chemical industry. All of this has been developed in a nation virtually lacking in what to our modern industrial age has seemed "required" raw materials: coal, iron, petroleum. Instead, they have developed to the maximum the hydroelectric power that is potentially present in every mountain land within the humid climatic zones. As an example of Swiss enterprise, the Grand Dixence, a dam now under construction, will reach a height of 940 feet and will be the world's highest dam. Within the past 150 years, the Swiss have grown faster in industrial and commercial development than the majority of the European nations and now have one of the highest standards of living.

All this success has been in spite of their mountainous land with its "limitations." The energetic Swiss have made their mountains an asset by capitalizing on their scenic beauty and their opportunities for mountain climbing and skiing. What the Swiss have done is possible to most of the rest of the mountain lands of the world, but is particularly readily duplicated by the other mountainous areas of Europe, populated with similar people, located in the same highly developed part of the world, and possessing as many, and often more, basic resources. Yet some of the other mountainous areas of Europe are losing population—the Massif Central of France, for instance. The reason often advanced is that it is a mountainous region. The reason cannot be that simple.

ASIATIC AREAS

There are immense mountain lands in Asia. Japan is a mountainous land, and in some ways its development is to be compared with Switzerland: this has already been discussed (see Chapter 6). Japan has made its solution one which in large part turns its back on its mountains. It agriculture is largely based on rice (one half the arable land being devoted it), a flat-land crop. Even when the hill country is used, it is flattened at great cost by terracing. But like Switzerland, the Japanese solution has been to take the path of industrialization, as indeed every advanced nation today has done. It is not a matter of mountains or no mountains, but of organization and motivation for industrial production.

China, too, can be discussed as a mid-latitude mountain land. China, as now developed, is not mountainous, but the China with the largest potential is. Most of China is mountainous to hilly land. This is well expressed in the figures for the distribution of its type of land: arable, 10 percent; meadow and pasture, 20 percent; forest and woodland, 8 percent; other, 62 percent. Most of the land in the ambiguous classification of "other" is rough, mountainous land. South China is largely mountainous, as is western China. Despite the immense hydroelectrical potential in these regions, and the immense mineral resources known to exist there, these are the least populated parts of China. Again, it is not the mountains that prevent development, it is the total outlook of the agrarian-minded Chinese. If and when the Chinese seriously enter the era of the industrial revolution, these very areas, now the emptiest part of their land, will probably be the most important part of their territory.

Tibet

Tibet is the Old World equivalent of the Altiplano of Peru and Bolivia. It is even higher, for the average elevation is 16,000 feet. The mountains start from here and go up to Mt. Everest's world record, 29,000-foot height. This land is so high and the 15,000- to 17,000-foot plateau is so surrounded by mountain ranges that very little moisture can reach it. The height alone is sufficient to limit the precipitation to low amounts. Since the capacity of the air to hold moisture is so related to its temperature that the lower the temperature the lower the moisture capacity of the air, and since the air temperature decreases at the rate of 3 degrees per 1000 feet increase in elevation, it follows that the air on the Tibetan plateau must be about 50 degrees cooler than that at sea level in the same latitude. The consequences are cool air of low moisture-carrying capacity and a precipitation on the plateau of about 8 inches. In these altitudes, precipitation does not increase as one goes on up the mountains, but tends to decrease. Therefore, there is relatively little opportunity to use dependable water supplies coming down off the higher mountains for irrigation of the arid plateau. Unquestionably, the same effects of high elevation on the physiology of man are effective in Tibet as they are on the Altiplano of Peru. However, the local variety of mankind must be assumed to be well adjusted to life under these unusual biological conditions.

Tibet has an area of nearly 500,000 square miles, and an estimated population of perhaps one and a quarter million prior to the Communist Chinese attack, which took the form of a veritable war of extermination. It is quite clear that the population is small and the density of population among the earth's lowest. Are the causes physical? Is it the high elevation, the mountains, or the aridity? Of these factors we have already seen that the mountains as such cannot stop developments. High elevation is not sufficient to prevent acclimatized races of mankind from flourishing even at such elevations as these; there is a town in Tibet, Gartok, at 15,000 feet elevation. Of the factors of the physical environment, the most limiting one seems to be the climatic combination of low temperatures and low precipitation. Are these sufficient to prevent man from developing a denser population on these high arid plateaus?

The present way of life of most of the Tibetans is that of herder; horses, sheep, goats, cattle, camels, and yaks are the principal herd animals. The yak is an oxlike animal with a heavy coat of hair and is capable of living and working at very high altitudes. It gives a milk that is rich in butter fat. The agriculture of Tibet is mostly carried on in the lower valleys; barley, wheat, turnips, and cabbages are typical Old World plants grown there. The Tibetans also grow the Andean potato, a plant capable of being grown in the great altitudes of the plateatu. Actually, there is a whole complex of domestic plants peculiar to the Andean plateau that could be grown on the Tibetan plateau. The following questions then arise: Are the Tibetans limited in number by their preference for a pastoral way of life? Could their numbers be multiplied several times by shifting to a high-altitude type of agriculture? Could this larger population be profitably put to work mining some of the known, extensive, but largely untouched, mineral resources of this vast mountain area? Is it impossible to think of Tibet being developed as a Switzerland of the Orient? Certainly there are some limitations that Tibet has that Switzerland escapes. It is difficult to think of a tourist industry in a country where most of mankind would become violently ill from the effects of the altitude. Yet if tropical heat is oppressive, then Tibet offers an immense recreation area that is so located as to be readily available to

Lake Louise and Victoria Glacier, Banff National Park, Alberta, Canada. When developed tourist facilities exist, mountains are centers of attraction that become economic assets. The Swiss Alps and the Teton Range, Wyoming, are other examples of such realized assets. The Andes and the mountains of New Zealand are as yet undeveloped in this respect. *National Film Board, Ottawa.*

the greatest mass of mankind. It is not physical geography that decrees that the Asiatic masses cannot afford delightful trips to scenic Tibet.

Tibet is a Buddhist nation. The development of this religion in Tibet has been into Lamaism. The great monasteries dominate the country: prior to the tenth century, they were strongly united and made of Tibet a strong kingdom. Since then they have tended to be divided. It is estimated that at present the number of lamas may number as high as 500,000. Since most of them are celibates, this creates a strange population structure, and both polyandry and polygamy are practiced by the lay population. The main effect of withdrawing so much of the male population from the reproductive part of the population must, of course, be to limit the rate of population growth.

While at first glance the great altitude, aridity, and cold of Tibet would seem to be sufficient causes for the low population of the region and the lack of development of industry, further consideration raises some doubts. If the people are maintaining themselves despite the adverse physical geography and social practices, then there would seem to be little hindrance to man in the biological field. The presence of a good variety of domestic animals, some variety of domestic plants, and the certainty that there are still more useful high-altitude plants that could be introduced to make the land more productive of food stuffs suggests that there are considerable unexploited possibilities for increasing the population of the land. Just what the real potential of the land is, only time will tell. Pastoral nomadism, lamaism, and a position remote from the main stream of the industrial revolution have combined to keep Tibet from achieving anything like the Inca empire.

SUMMARY

The mid-latitude mountains, then, show much the same range of human achievement as the other climatic areas or the tropical mountains. Around the Mediterranean they are or have been at times centers of civilization, empire, and cultural growth. Mountainous lands in mid-latitudes may be nearly totally undeveloped as are the highlands of South Africa, which lay far beyond the range of penetration of ideas, or highly developed as in modern Switzerland. They may be largely ignored as in the Chinese highlands, despite the obvious (to Western eyes) advantages of the region, or alternately viewed as a center of wealth and learning and as a low point in achievement as in Spain. Such variability in human achievement in moderately similar environment cannot be a physical, environmentally determined result.

HIGH-LATITUDE MOUNTAIN LANDS

The high-latitude mountains pose one of the most formidable problems that man has faced. In Alaska and adjacent Canada there are high mountains, including the Brooks Range, running east and west to the north of the Yukon Valley; the Alaskan Range to the south; and the north–south trending ranges of the northern Rockies and coast ranges that join in this area. These are high mountains: Mount McKinley, 20,300 feet high, in the Alaskan Range is the highest peak in North America. While the Brooks Range is not now glaciated, this is not due to the lack of cold; it is the result of too little precipitation there to sustain a snow cover. The forest border is found along the southern foothills of these mountains. Their slopes are tundra; their tops are barren rock. Much the same can be said of the Alaskan Range. These are not areas where any kind of agriculture can be carried on, and there is very little animal life. There is no attraction in such areas with the exception of possible great mineral strikes, or the development of a tourist industry based on the permanent snow supplies in such areas as the Alaskan Range. With the shrinking of the world through the expansion of air transportation, it is becoming feasible to have ski resorts in Alaska to let those addicted to skiing develop it into a year-round sport. Many people now ride on trains for 12 to 24 hours to reach snow areas in the New England area; by air, Alaska is no farther. In the main, however, these arctic mountain areas are the world's emptiest. Even the deserts have more people than the arctic mountains. These are the extreme deserts of the northern lands.

In the Old World, the Scandinavian highland, the northern part of the Ural Mountains, and the northwestern part of Siberia are mountainous areas with latitudes north of 60 degrees. All of them are marked by the limitation of tree growth to low elevations and in warm exposures. All of these mountain masses were glaciated in the past and some of them retain minor glaciers today, and as in America, these are among the emptiest parts of our world. Man lives in the lowlands between these mountain masses, and he rarely finds any use for the highlands. They have little feed for his herds except on their lower slopes; their barren rocky upper slopes, having little or no vegetation, can support little or no animal life.

There is, then, nothing there of value for man with the possible exception of minerals. As in the New World, then, the arctic mountain lands are empty.

The physical environment of these arctic mountains is as physically determined a barrier to man as we have on earth, but even this must be carefully stated. At our present state of development, we see little of value in them; however, we can even now clearly foresee that any major find of mineral wealth in such areas would lead to the rapid development of transportation, settlement, and the exploitation of whatever this source of wealth might be. The parallel is the case of the development of the iron resources of the Quebec-Labrador area. Twenty years ago it would have been considered folly to predict that thousands of people would soon be settled in that seemingly forbidding region and that the probable trend would be toward still fuller development, with maintenance of fairly large populations in the region for an indefinite time.

As was suggested above, one of the uses that some of the arctic mountain regions may have is for recreation. Rapid transportation places these areas within easy reach of the increasingly leisure-possessed working force of the industrial world. This same world is being pressed by an increasing population, which is crowding our traditional vacation areas. Who can say that the arctic mountain areas may not have a future as the ultimate refuge for those who want to get away from the mass of mankind? The constant snow cover may attract the athletic, the stark beauty of the barren ranges may attract the esthetic. We have the technological ability to build and maintain cities in them if we wish. At the moment, we do not wish to do so. This is different from saying that the physical environment denies the possibility of our doing so.

CONCLUSION

Mountains, then, must be considered a special problem in cultural geography. They offer great variations in short distances, and for industrial man, they are exceptionally favorable for discovering minerals and developing water power (in humid areas). In the deserts, mountains are centers of advantage because of their water-catching. The steep slopes present difficulties for transportation, with water transportation the most hampered, overland transportation intermediately so, and air transport the least affected. Technological change clearly alters the potential of most mountain areas. Truly great elevations in mountains become virtually an absolute barrier to mankind, for most of mankind is barred from elevations above 11,000 feet, and only the races that have long lived in the highest mountains can reproduce above these levels. This becomes of significance only in low-latitude mountains, for from mid-latitudes poleward, the lowered temperatures associated with increasing elevation place such elevations above the timber line. Only the obtaining of minerals provides any reason for going so high. At any rate, only a tiny fraction of the earth is actually above 17,500 feet, the approximate limit for man's permanent biological adaptation to residence in mountains.

In general, man's accomplishments in mountains follow the familiar pattern of access to ideas. Those mountainous areas in or near great centers of political, social, and economic growth have shared in these advances. As the centers of cultural action have shifted, some mountain areas have alternately been advantageously and disadvantageously located, and their fortunes have varied accordingly. Once again, it is demonstrated that the decisive factor is cultural rather than physical, with the limitation that in these lands we have met, through lowered oxygen content and air pressure changes with elevation, an absolute limit for man's expansion unless he is to be fed bottled oxygen or placed in a pressurized housing. A less absolute limit is also set by the lowered temperatures even at moderate elevations in high latitudes. The decrease in vegetation and soil cover leads inevitably to a decrease in carrying capacity for animals, and soon there is little in the landscape except minerals. Only if there are concentrations of valuable minerals does such an environment hold any attraction for contemporary man. It seems excessively optimistic to think of very high elevations in the tropics or even moderate elevations in the high latitudes as ever becoming areas of great attraction for mankind.

9-The Northern Forest Lands

NORTH AMERICA

EUROPE

A S I A

AFRICA

EQUATOR

SOUTH AMERICA

AUSTRALIA

THE NORTHERN FOREST lands are found only in the northern hemisphere. There are no lands in the latitudes of 60 to 70 degrees in the southern hemisphere, while in the northern hemisphere there are the vast areas of North America and of Eurasia in these positions. Instead of four or five comparable areas around the world, we have for this climatic type only two.

THE PHYSICAL SETTING

In high latitudes, the seasonal changes are extreme. Summers the sun may shine for 24 hours or disappear only an hour or two. The mid-winter sun will rise above the horizon for only an hour or two. North of 67 degrees, it will not rise at all. With no solar energy coming in, and with radiation from the earth escaping into outer space, the temperature of the land falls. In these areas there are great masses of land, and the interior of these lands is far from the sea, the only great reservoir of heat that could temper the extremes of the climate. Lacking such oceanic influences, both winters and summers can be extreme in their temperatures. Winter cold is at its greatest not along the continental margins in the north, but in the deep continental interiors in high latitudes. An example of such a cold spot is found at Verkoyansk at 67 degrees north in Siberia. Here the January average temperature falls to −60° F. The absolute cold record is about −90° F. This is truly great cold, yet note that Verkoyansk is a town; people live under such conditions.

Surprisingly, the interiors of continents in such latitudes can also be hot. Fairbanks, Alaska, at 64 degrees north and in the interior of Alaska, in most years has a summer day that reaches 90° F. At Fort Yukon the extreme temperatures recorded range from 100° F. to −78° F. In these latitudes, there is considerable variation in temperature from the coast inland. On the coast winters are milder, and summers are cooler than in the interiors. It is noticeable that this type of climate reaches the west side of continents at about 60 degrees, but comes ten to twenty degrees farther south on the east coasts of continents. This is because the average flow the wind in these latitudes is from west to east, bringing oceanic-tempered weather to the west coasts and continental-interior extreme temperatures to the east coasts. Thus, although Seattle and Quebec have about the same latitudes, Seattle has a mild marine west-coast type of climate and Quebec has long, cold winters and short, hot summers. The range of temperature included in these lands is great. Along their southern boundaries the average for January is about 20° F., but along their cold boundaries it may be −20° F. to −60° F. Summer has much less variation: all these lands vary between 50° F. and 70° F. in July, comparatively mild temperatures. It is the winter cold that most markedly sets these areas apart from the rest of the world.

The natural vegetation is forest. This varies from good forests along their southern boundaries to an increasingly thin cover of smaller and smaller trees to the northern limit of tree growth. It is not the existence of extremely great cold, but the lack of enough summer warmth that limits tree growth. This limit is found to be approximately the line that separates lands with no month above 50° F. and those that have at least one month above that temperature. Trees will survive, though they can hardly be said to thrive, if at least one month goes beyond this temperature, but for really good growth, trees need much more warm weather than that. Coniferous trees predominate, though there are also considerable birch and aspen. The northern forest is called *taiga*.

Rainfall in the northern forest lands is moderate to low. In the continental interiors, the totals are

(*Left*) A Medieval Castle at Turku, Finland. (*Below*) The 1947 Olympics at Helsinki. (*Opposite*) City Scene, Tampere. Finland lies north of 60° in the arctic forest land. A climatic analogue would be Anchorage, Alaska. While Alaska is a land of recent settlement, thinly populated and only recently developed, Finland is a land of ancient settlement with fair-sized, well-developed cities. *Consulate General of Finland, N.Y.*

between 10 and 20 inches; on the continental margins, where the maritime air masses can penetrate, the rainfall may rise to 40 inches per year. Low temperature throughout most of the year allows little evaporation; while the ground, frozen during half the year or more in some areas, prevents the draining away of the water underground. The vegetation has little solar energy with which to work and is virtually dormant during the cold period, and hence it gives off relatively little water. The result is ground that is frequently soggy and seems like a land with much greater rainfall than actually falls.

The wetness of the landscape is increased by the presence of great numbers of lakes, a heritage of

the glacial period. The glaciers so recently disrupted the previous drainage system by gouging holes here and dumping sands and gravels there that the streams have had little opportunity to cut through the dams and fill the hollows. Postglacial time in these regions varies from about 12,000 years ago along their southern borders to a still current glacial state in a few places. Parts of Alaska and Labrador, for example, are still glaciated. These are not the coldest areas, but the areas of higher precipitation, for glaciers were not the result of cold so much as they were of high amounts of precipitation in the form of snow falling in areas with summers too short to melt off all of the winter snow. Whatever the causes of the glaciers, the mark

Arctic Forest in Finland. The Finns call this their "green gold." *Consulate General of Finland, N. Y.*

Moving Timber to Market by Stream, Finland. Typical birch-spruce stands in the arctic forest. *Finnish Tourist Association.*

that they left on our northern lands is impressive. This is most easily seen from the air or on a map. The boundary between the land occupied by the last glacier and that land not recently glaciated can be drawn with considerable accuracy simply by marking off the areas with innumerable natural lakes from that part of the landscape with few or none.

The recency of the glacial past is of great importance also in determining the characteristics of the soils of these regions. Materials that have not been exposed to weathering for great lengths of time have more soluable minerals left in them. Therefore they are potentially rich. In most of these northern forest regions this is of little importance, for these are not agricultural lands except along their southern boundaries. The recent disappearance of the glaciers is also indicated by the exposure of much rock, for where the land stood relatively high, the ice stripped off much of the soil mantle, and the time lapse has not been sufficient to produce from these exposed rocks another mantle of weathered materials. This condition has been a boon to prospecting in these areas.

In discussing these lands it has been possible to speak of the climate and forests and past glacial history without differentiating the Eurasian lands from the American ones. In most ways this is one great area. The plant and animal distribution reflects the fact that the lands are grouped around the north pole, and that the minor gap between Asia and America at the Bering Strait has frequently been nonexistent in the geological past. This has allowed plants and animals to move back and forth. Consequently, the lands around the north pole share similar species of trees and bushes, caribou and mice. That this exchange of plants and animals from Asia to America through this now arctic gateway has gone on for a long time is illustrated by the redwoods. Asiatic trees in their origin, the redwoods migrated millions of years ago through the Alaska region into America, and today they survive in only three areas: the coast of California, the Sierra Nevada of California, and in the inner part of China. There is a similar distribution for the Torrey pine: the southern coast of California and on the islands of Japan. Later in time elephants and buffalo migrated to America and horses out of America by this same route. It is through this ancient connection between the Old and the New Worlds that the first men probably made their way into the Americas.

The physical structure of the Old World lands and those of the New have similarities also: both have great central plains that drain to the arctic sea; both have mountainous areas on their east and west sides; in both cases it is the Pacific edge that has the greater mountain mass; and both have great rivers. In the American arctic, the Yukon and in Asia, the Ob, Yenesei, and Lena are listed among the twenty largest rivers in the world. In these vast areas with their enormous exposures of rock are found some of the world's great mineral reserves. Both areas face on the arctic in the north, are bounded by the Atlantic and Pacific on their sides, and along their southern boundaries meet forested mid-latitude lands, grasslands, and arid lands.

Given these physical similarities, what has been their human histories?

MAN IN THE NORTHERN FOREST LANDS

The human histories of the northern forest lands have to be shorter, or at least more interrupted, than the history of occupance in most of the world, for these lands have repeatedly been glaciated. The American lands were almost entirely ice covered, for only small areas of Alaska escaped glaciation. In Asia the ice cover was less extensive. The largest ice mass lay over Scandinavia and spread outward. In Siberia glaciation was largely limited to the mountain masses and their adjacent foothills.

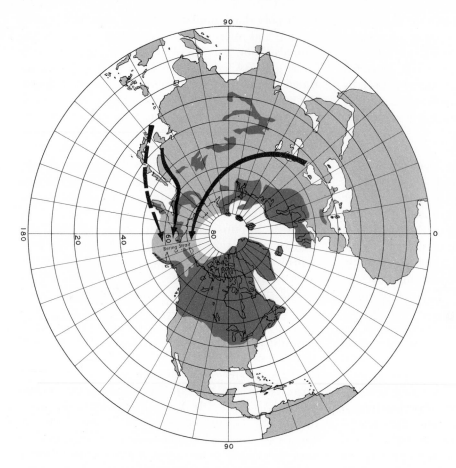

Map 9-1 North Polar View of the World

Formerly glaciated areas are shown in dark shading. At Bering Strait the land is shown as it would be at a time of glacial lowering. The arrows suggest possible routes by which men may have reached North America. Probably all three of these routes were used at different times. Plants and animals as well as men frequently traveled back and forth through this northern gateway in late geologic time.

By the time of the second glacial, Sinanthropus, the Chinese man, was already living on the edge of the northern forest lands; this was about 400,000 years ago. It is quite probable that by then man was occupying land along the southern edge of this climatic zone all the way to Europe, though our record in western Europe is clearest for man during interglacial periods, for man apparently withdrew from Europe during glacial periods. Man finally stayed in Europe during the last glacial period, the Würm, that began about 70,000 years ago.

We know that in this immense expanse of time between 400,000 and 70,000 years ago man was developing physically to some extent, but that, even more importantly, he was developing culturally. He was making more and better tools from a greater variety of materials, making more adequate housing and clothing and learning to control fire. Tailored skin clothing, the spear thrower, the oil lamp, and a wide assortment of stone tools evolved. As in the case of the industrial revolution—where centuries of hidden developments paved the way for the burst of the nineteenth-century industrial development—tens of millennia were going into the development of traits that were to make possible the use of the northern lands. This development finally gave man the equipment to live in cold climates and to hunt the great game animals that lived on the forest-tundra border; men then followed their game wherever it lead them.

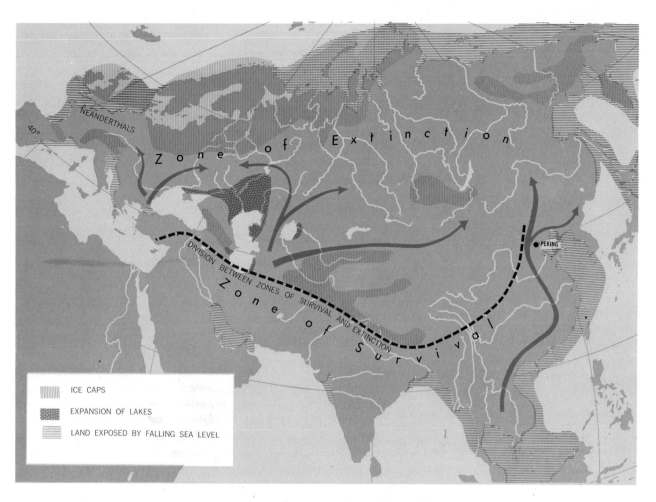

Map 9-2   Early Man in the Old World Arctic

The principal glaciated areas of the north are indicated, as well as the larger areas of continental shelf exposed by the lowering of sea level. The arrows suggest major lines of the spread of men into the cold-winter zones of the arctic forest. People with advanced hunting skills spread into Siberia during the last glacial epoch. There is an interesting correlation between the appearance of such "great hunters" adapted to arctic life and the disappearance of big game, especially the elephants (mammoth and mastodon). Elephants survived into the Christian era in most areas south of the line drawn here, but were exterminated quite early north of it. Wild elephants did survive in northwest Africa into Roman times; in the Fertile Crescent into Old Testament times; in India, Burma, Siam to the present; and in northern China to 1000 B.C. There surely has been continuous occupation by man of these areas of extreme winter cold for at least 20,000 to 30,000 years. It probably was representatives of these arctic hunters who entered America during the last glaciation, displacing many of the simpler cultured earlier people and exterminating much big game—such as the native American horses, camels (except in Andean South America), elephants, giant beaver, giant buffalo, and the like. The arrow leading to Peking indicates the spread of men of Southeast Asian cultural pattern northward. They seem not to have been specialized hunters and not to have exterminated big game.

UPPER PALEOLITHIC HUNTERS

One corridor led from southeastern Europe south of the Urals toward Lake Balkash and on into the Selenga River drainage, and thence to Lake Baikal. During the last glaciation, probably as early as 30,000 years ago, men were living on the river terraces in this area: skilled hunters, who killed mammoths, deer, horse, and reindeer. They built semisubterranean houses, the roofs of which were formed of interlocking reindeer horns, and whose side walls were shored up with mammoth bones. There are traces of this way of life roughly along the 50th parallel all the way from the Atlantic to the Pacific.

We do not know the origin of this new hunting skill. Because a great deal more archeological work has been done in western Europe than elsewhere, we know more about that region, and since we know more, we tend to assume that this is the place of origin. It is much more likely that the origin of this way of life developed at some intermediate area, perhaps in the area of the Black, Caspian, and Aral seas, and spread both northwest and northeast. That there was a common source is shown by the similarity of tools, ways of life, and even art forms. In western Europe and inner Asia, men were not only hunting similar great animals in similar ways, they were also representing them similarly in ivory carvings and in making similar ceremonial staffs. While one may argue that life in a cold climate requires clothes and housing, that clothes must be made to fit the limbs, and that snug houses have to be built underground, no such argument can account for the similarity of art forms and ceremonial forms. As a matter of fact, not even the form of houses and clothing is satisfactorily explained in this way, for the people living in the cold northern forest lands of Canada did not build similar underground houses or equally well-tailored clothing as those found in the Asiatic area.

The introduction of specialized hunting skills was to change much of the northern parts of the world.

The hunters were, in a sense, too successful, for they exterminated the largest animals. The mammoths were used up by the close of the ice age. As the ice withdrew, the hunters moved farther north. The preferred prey there was the reindeer, while in the more forested lands to the south, horse and deer were important. The significance of the development of the hunting way of life with its abundance of meat and hides and the associated skills of clothing and snug housing is that these skills opened up to man the occupation of the cold continental-interior lands on a scale not previously possible.

It is probably significant that at this time similar ways of life appear in the Americas. At present, our most important information is coming from the unglaciated areas to the south and the west of the glaciated area. Skilled hunters, doing much the same things that the Eurasian skilled hunters were doing, appear widely spread over North and South America before the time of the last ice retreat. These people are known in America as the Folsom and Clovis people. They made distinctive, large spear points. They hunted mastodon and mammoth, horse, camel, and ground sloth, as well as smaller game. As with the men of Eurasia, they were so successful that they exterminated most of these animals. We know that the Folsom spear points date to about 10,000 years ago, and the Clovis points are older. Sandia points are still older, for they have been found beneath a stalagmite layer in a cave, while the Folsom points were above the stalagmite layer. Some large interval of time associated with a climatic change is recorded by this placement.

It is in the zones of the world held by these specialized hunters that the greatest extinction of large game animals occurred. It was in northern Eurasia that the elephants, rhinoceros, and other large game animals disappeared. They survived in southern Asia and Africa, where specialization was in the direction of agriculture rather than hunting. In America the impact of the hunting cultures was especially great. Perhaps it was because the incoming hunting people spread more suddenly through lands that had been previously held by people specialized on gathering with hunting a minor activity. Whatever the cause, it is clear that after the hunting people appeared, many of the big game animals of the Americas disappeared. This is probably to be viewed as another of the human modifications of the landscape.

REINDEER PASTORAL NOMADISM IN EURASIA

In Asia, a complex series of changes took place that did not occur in America. The idea of domesticating animals instead of hunting them originated somewhere in southwestern Asia, and as we have seen, whole series of animals were brought under human control. The idea of domestication spread to the northern forest people. Since their land was too cold and too poor in the fodder plants suited to horses and cows, they applied the idea to the available animal, the reindeer; and an entirely new way of life using the northern forests was created. The reindeer can live on the arctic and subarctic vegetation and withstand the great cold of the deep continental interiors without being sheltered in barns, and without requiring any storage of hay or other foodstuffs to carry it through the winter. Its requirements are for suitable range.

A primary food for the reindeer is the so-called reindeer moss. This is a low growth, and a given area, can sustain a herd for only a short time. The herds then must be moved frequently, and the reindeer people can have no permanent home. They must be free to move over broad areas in company with their herds. This way of life can never lead to dense settlement of the land, but it does offer a more secure way than does hunting in the same environment. Instead of being dependent on the presence or absence of the reindeer, with possible starvation occurring in the years that the wild herds bypass a territory in search of new pastures, the domestic herd assures a constant food supply kept at hand and under control. The animals can also

be milked, or ridden, or used to pull sleighs. They yield hides and furs, sinews, antler, and bone—useful raw materials for clothing, tents, thread, and tools.

The people of northern Eurasia have a fully developed way of life that is dependent on the reindeer. They have finely developed tents that enable them to move about freely and that are snug even in the immense cold of inner Asia. The form of the tent varies greatly from area to area. In central Siberia it is made of felt and mounted over a portable wooden frame. There is an inner lining to the tent that increases the insulating quality and absorbs the moisture released by the humans. When the lining is saturated it is unfastened and taken outdoors where the temperature may be −10° or −20° F. The moisture quickly freezes and the lining is then beaten with sticks and the ice crystals fly out. This is "dry cleaning" or, more accurately, cold drying. That these people use felt tents points the direction of the origin of the trait, for felt is made by the pastoral nomads of the inner Asian grasslands.

The use of the reindeer varies. In some areas they are ridden, but in most areas they are not. Most people use them for pulling sleds. The sleds vary greatly in shape: from boat-shaped affairs to toboggans to sleds with runners. The reindeer may or may not be milked and may or may not be ridden; this variation suggest that reindeer domestication was not a single invention that then spread as a developed cultural unit. Rather, the variability looks more like the result of a number of people from the grasslands to the south of the northern forest lands entering these cold lands and finding that their horses, cows, goats, and sheep could not stand the great cold; they then substituted the native reindeer. Alternately, it may have been that the old residents of the northern forest, through long and intimate contact with the peoples along their southern border, adapted the idea of domestication to the reindeer. Those in the west would be in contact with people such as the Turks, who milked their domesticated animals. Those in the east would learn from such people as the Chinese, who did not milk them. The great horse nomads were in the east of Eurasia, and riding would be expected there more than in the west.

We do not yet know the time and sequence of events in man's occupation of Eurasia in any detail. After the specialized hunters who were there in the Upper Pleistocene, we know little until practically modern times. The ancient hunters of the elephants probably remained as forest hunters. When the idea of domestication spread through the grasslands of Central Asia, and through the woodlands of western Europe, the hunters must have been displaced from the grasslands. It is tempting to account for the sudden expansion of some of the Mongoloid people by suggesting that they were the first to apply the idea of domestication in the inner Asian lands. Domestication of sheep began about 10,000 years ago and domestic cattle appear by 7000 years ago. Nomadism in inner Asia may have begun about 3000 B.C. No one at the moment knows when reindeer nomadism began; considering the slowness of man's learning, it would not be unexpected if it had taken another 2000 years or so for a beginning to be made.

Once the idea was born that the wild deerlike animals that ranged the treeless tundra in the summer and the wooded taiga in the winter could be treated like cows and horses, the northern forest man had a significantly surer source of subsistence. Reindeer herding is so recent that the animals are barely tame, and it is often a question of whether man is driving or following the herd. The animals are kept close and in part are attracted to the men by the salt that they supply. The herds are moved (or followed) from summer to winter ranges. Animals are killed for meat, and for hides.

The thickly haired hides are the source of warm clothing. The clothing is tailored to fit and double suits are worn to increase the protection against the cold. Tailored clothing is a widespread trait throughout Inner Asia. It is distinctly non-European and not at all typical of any of the tropical or sub-tropical people, all of whom use robes and similar flowing garments. The trousers and coat type of dress made possible the occupation of the high arctic but their development seems to have been in the high mid-latitudes.

THE ABSENCE OF REINDEER HERDING IN NORTH AMERICA

In the American forest lands there is a virtually identical physical environment, occupied by a closely related people, and having in the landscape a wild animal, the caribou, that is very closely related to the reindeer. In America, however, this animal was never domesticated. Why? The opportunity, the need, even the access to the idea that it could be done were certainly all present.

Most of the land was held by two linguistic groups. Western Canada was held by the Athabascan-speaking peoples. Eastern Canada and the adjacent United States was held by Algonkin-speaking people. These people hunted in the forests, fished in the innumerable lakes and streams, and gathered berries in the short summer. They lived in tents and wore skin clothing, but their clothing was not nearly as warm as that of the Eskimos, who live in areas subject to less extreme cold than the interior lands occupied by these forest Indians. Here, again, we meet the lack of compelling force in the environment. The Indians knew of the Eskimos, often fought with them, and had every opportunity to know about their superior clothing. The Indians certainly needed such clothing for greater comfort and efficiency, even if not for absolute survival. Like the Tierra del Fuegians, they simply did not choose to change.

It is sometimes stated that there are large numbers of caribou in our north. There are. But the area is immense, and the numbers are not great in proportion to the area. The large herds that are shown in pictures and described in stories appear only at certain times and places. They are the result of concentration of migrating animals coming from huge summer grazing areas and moving toward winter grazing grounds. Such herds frequently move through a given pass through mountains or between lakes. The Indian people were accustomed to slaughter a large part of their winter needs at such points at the time of the fall migration. All was fine if the herd appeared on schedule. However, the herd occasionally migrated by another route to a less overgrazed area. Famine then struck the Indian group that had staked its survival on the appearance of the herd at its usual passage.

Why did no genius arise to say: Let us domesticate them! Why did no word of what their neighbors in Siberia had done leak through to these people? It has been the theme of this book that geniuses with new ideas are the rarest thing on earth, and that even when a new idea is created and put to work, it may be an extremely long time spreading even to adjacent people in obvious need of the idea. We may well surmise that the idea of domestication reached at least some of these people, for many traits have a distribution right across the Bering Strait. The bow and arrow entered America via Alaska, and a long series of increasingly complex forms of bows suggest that there was a long-continued flow of ideas. The magic flight myth, a myth as recognizable as the George Washington and the cherry tree story, was common to northern Asia and northern North America. Ideas about how to make sleds, bark canoes, and snow shoes all crossed. Surely with all of these transfers of knowledge, someone must have mentioned the possibility of domesticating the reindeer-caribou.

The perfect example of how much opportunity there was for the transfer of ideas is found in the report of one of the Jesuit missionaries sent to Canada in the early colonial days and later transferred to Siberia. In Canada he worked among the northern forest people and converted many of them to Christianity. Years later, working among similar people in Siberia, he met a woman whom he had converted in eastern Canada. This woman had been captured in warfare, made a slave, and traded from tribe to tribe until she had reached Siberia. It is unlikely that this is the only instance of its kind,

or that movement was only in one direction. Ideas clearly crossed from the Old World to the New, intermittently and over a long period of time. The idea of domestication of the American equivalent of the reindeer simply was not taken up.

The Eskimos had villages on both sides of the Bering Strait. Those on the Asiatic side were in contact with Asiatic reindeer herders, but the Eskimos never took up this way of life. The United States government decided that what the Eskimos needed was a better source of income, and it seemed logical to get them to raise reindeer. Interestingly, it was decided to get reindeer from Siberia. Why not start with the easily tamed caribou? Instead, men were sent to Siberia to purchase a herd and to drive it to Alaska, crossing the ice at the Bering Strait. The herd was managed for a time by the Eskimos in the Point Barrow region, with the supervision of government employees. Shortly, however, the herd was turned over to the Eskimos. The herd prospered, and soon there were half a million reindeer in Eskimo hands. Such large numbers of animals can not be kept near a permanent village, but must be moved about over wide areas in order to have adequate grazing. For a time all went well, and the Eskimos had an abundance of meat and hides. They even had more animals than they could actually use, but there was no market for the surplus.

The tending of the herds was in conflict with the Eskimo way of life. The Eskimos are specialists in sea hunting. They are not fishermen, for their major prey are the sea mammals, and these are hunted, not fished. Not only have these animals been their major source of food, but their whole way of life—including their value system—is built around these animals. Of greatest prestige value is the killing of whales. Further, the Barrow Eskimos live in a large village. Social life is extensive and greatly appreciated. Reindeer herding interfered with all of this. Whaling time comes in the spring, and the men then form crews and take boats to the openings that are forming in the sea ice. There they wait for whales to come along; they stay there for weeks, and the entire whaling season lasts for a month or two. So great is the prestige attached to whaling that the men often waste the best of the sealing season waiting in vain for a whale. Eskimos were reluctant to forego the excitement and pleasure of either whaling or village life to spend lonely weeks following herds of reindeer around.

The result of the cultural pressures was that the Eskimos took less and less care of their herds as they increased in size and had to be cared for at greater and greater distances from their villages. Presently the herd began to dwindle through loss to wolves, through loss from wandering away and joining with the caribou, and just plain loss through neglect. Today, there are no domestic caribou in the hands of the Point Barrow Eskimos. There was abundant need; there was a perfect physical setting, and there was abundant know-how supplied. A start was made, and success seemed assured—and then the whole enterprise failed because herding and a nomadic way of life did not fit into the Eskimo's scheme of things. It is not easy to launch new ideas.

We have here the clues as to why herding did not take root among the Eskimos in the past. Since the Eskimos held both sides of the Bering Strait, this reduced to a low level the possibility of the forest Indians learning of reindeer herding. Since the Eskimos were on most unfriendly terms with the forest Indians this still further reduced the learning possibility.

It was the forest Indians that might well have taken up the herding way of life; they were more accustomed to moving about following game and the seasonal abundance of fish and berries. Curiously, there seems to have been almost no attempt in modern times to get this northern forest people of America interested in reindeer herding, although they were already more dependent on the caribou than the Eskimos were. Through the action of such forces as these, the practice of herding caribou in America failed to develop. Not only did the idea not spread directly, but it was not hit upon independently. Nowhere in North America were herd animals handled as domesticates. Only in South America, where the llama was domesticated and where we have reason to believe that there was massive Old World influence, was anything of this sort tried.

The reindeer was not the only useful animal on the scene. The musk ox was formerly widespread. This animal is a small, oxlike and sheeplike creature that can stand the greatest cold without shelter and will feed itself in the tundra or arctic forest. It is now limited to a few spots in the remote arctic. This is not because this is where it lives best, but because this is the only area where the absence of man lets it live. Recent attempts at raising these animals in captivity in New England show that they are easily tamed. They yield excellent meat and very fine wool. They require no expensive barns, no cutting and storing of winter feed, and they are a dual purpose animal whose products would probably be more acceptable in the world market for meat and textiles than reindeer-caribou products. However, these animals were not domesticated in the past, nor are they being used today as a means of bringing the vast northern forest-tundra areas into our modern economy.

MODERN USE OF NORTHERN FOREST LANDS

USE BY NATIVE PEOPLES

In the Old World, the reindeer-herding way of life persisted into the present from the Lapps in the north of Finland clear across the north of Siberia to the vicinity of the Bering Strait. It has come to dominate the whole area, even including the treeless border of the Arctic Ocean, which in

Reindeer Herd in Northern Sweden. *Swedish National Travel Office.*

Lapps, Reindeer Herders of Northernmost Europe. The Lapps range from Norway across Sweden and northern Finland. In their dependence on reindeer herding they share an arctic forest way of life found all the way to eastern Siberia. In details of dress, sleds, and reindeer use, however, there is wide variation from the Atlantic to the Pacific. Here a group is picnicking. *Swedish National Travel Office.*

A Cree Bringing His Furs to a Hudson's Bay Company Post at Moose Factory Island, James Bay, at the Southern End of Hudson's Bay. Indians still harvest furs in the arctic forest of America. These vast, nearly unoccupied forest lands continue to yield furs, but man has thought of no new use for them. *National Film Board, Ottawa.*

America is held by the sea-ice hunters. This way of life has been left little disturbed by the modern world. Except for such extractive activities as mining lumbering (on the southern margins), and obtaining furs, we have little use for these northern lands.

In the New World, the picture has been of similarly little change. This is still Indian North America. The earliest modern manner of utilizing it was by drawing the Indians into the fur trade. This was a reasonable approach, for the Indians were skilled trappers, dispersed over the country, and valuable fur-bearing animals were there. These Indians were producing nothing else of any value to modern Western society, and they wanted the goods that that economy was producing. The fur trade that grew up under the French, and later the British, neatly linked the wants of both.

It has sometimes been assumed that the northern forests are swarming with fur-bearing animals. After all, they have for centuries supplied large quantities of valuable pelts to the world. But this is another caribou-in-migration type of question. The area from which the pelts are assembled is vast. Each Indian trapper operates a trap line that covers many square miles of territory. The yield per acre is small. Why should it be otherwise?

The ability of a land to support animals, in last analysis, is related to the amount of plant food that the land provides. The amount of plant life is dependent on the length of the growing season, the distribution and amount of water, and the amount of solar energy available to the plants. In nearly all of these factors the northern forest lands fall into the low-productivity category. Water is present; but for most of the year it is locked up as ice. The part of the year that is above freezing is short, and even then undependable, for frost may occur early or late on the southern border of these regions, or in any month of the year along their northern borders. Solar energy varies from none north of 67 degrees in winter, to weak sun distributed over a long period of the day. Summer sun at 60 degrees north has a noon elevation equivalent to a winter noon sun in mid-latitudes. It only manages to warm the land because of the extra hours that it shines. Thus the total amount of insolation that the plants can utilize is limited to the brief period of long, low sun in the middle of the brief warm period. The result is a low amount of vegetative growth.

This condition shows up in many ways. It takes three to ten times as long to produce a saw log in the northern forests as it does in our southern forests. The dream of vast herds of caribou grazing on the tundra during the summer and wintering in the shelter of the northern forest in the winter gets a particularly rude shock. The winter browse is the reindeer moss, which grows 6 to 19 inches high under the trees. However, experience shows that once it is grazed down it may take 10, 20, or 30 years to regrow to the level that it will again support a herd—which means that there must be approximately 20 times as much land in reserve as is grazed in any one winter. This land relationship reduces the efficiency of the grazing industry enormously. Under good management in the American South, an acre of pasture can carry one cow per year. In the northern forest, it would likely require several acres to supply grazing for one caribou for one winter, and 20 years of recovery time would have to be allowed. Similarly for the fur industry: a muskrat marsh in the Chesapeake Bay area probably yields tenfold the pelts per acre that a comparable area in the northern forest does; and there are probably more deer per acre in Pennsylvania than there are Caribou per square mile in the northern forest.

The production of furs in the northern forest, then, is not the result of the area's being overcrowded with fur-bearing animals, but our having few other uses for these lands. This leaves the northern forest lands of both the Old World and the New among the least changed parts of the world.

USE BY INDUSTRIAL SOCIETY

For our modern industrial society, with its supporting mechanized agriculture, these lands supply needed pulp wood and exotic furs, but we have few uses for them that requires our placing any great number of people in them. We can put people there, if we choose to do so. This is well shown by the mining developments.

Mining

A spectacular example of the way in which man can move into and develop "impossible" areas is furnished today by the iron rush into Canada. It has long been known that there were extensive iron-ore deposits in the Labrador-Quebec area. This has remained in the category of: "Interesting, but so what?" Few areas are as isolated, undeveloped, and unpopulated—and have been described as having so rugged a climate. The great peninsula lying between Hudson Bay and the Saint Lawrence has remained a virtual wasteland since the days of the European discovery. Almost the entire population of Quebec is concentrated along the Saint Lawrence, and most of it along the Quebec to Ottawa sector. However, the view of this area has now begun to change.

Climatically this area is comparable to the Amur River region of the Russian maritime provinces, where population densities are 2 to 25 per square mile and the sizable town of Komsomolsk is located north of 50 degrees. The Labrador-Quebec area is between 50 and 60 degrees north. The isotherm for 0° F. (the temperature line connecting points having 0° F.) in January runs through the center of the region, and most of the area is poleward of the 50° F. July isotherm. The isotherm for 0° F. in January also runs close to Winnipeg and Fairbanks, but Fairbanks is somewhat warmer and

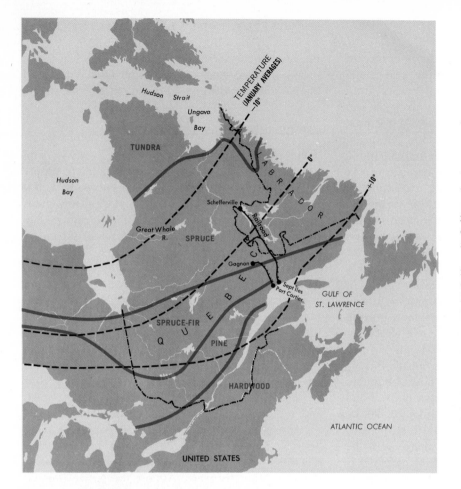

The map shows labels: TEMPERATURE (JANUARY AVERAGES) −10°, Hudson Strait, Ungava Bay, TUNDRA, Hudson Bay, LABRADOR, 0°, Schefferville, Great Whale R., SPRUCE, Railroad, +10°, Gagnon, QUEBEC, Sept Iles, Port Cartier, GULF OF ST. LAWRENCE, SPRUCE-FIR, PINE, HARDWOOD, ATLANTIC OCEAN, UNITED STATES

Map 9-3 Vegetation and Temperature in Labrador

The vast empty wilderness of the Ungava peninsula is now being developed for its enormous iron resources. Development is in the provinces of Labrador and Quebec. The distribution of vegetation in the area as well as the January average temperatures indicate the increasingly arctic conditions to the north. Canadian settlement has been in the hardwood zone with little occupation of the pine forest. The attraction of mineral wealth has now led to the extension of settlement into the spruce forest to well above the line for 0° in January. While this seems cold, many settled parts of the earth are colder in winter. The Labrador area, however, is unusually cool in summer for its latitude.

Winnipeg is much warmer in summer. Only the northern part of this area is tundra; most of it is forest covered. Along the Saint Lawrence, the forest is made up of white, Norway, and jack pine. North of this is a mixed spruce and fir forest. Still farther north, spruce forest extends almost to Ungava Bay (see Map 9–3). The northern limits of the pine forest and of a growing season of 90 days or more are approximately the same. These varied measures of climatic severity do not suggest that this is useless land, yet the French settlement in this area was limited to the tongue of hardwoods that reached up the Saint Lawrence. It is one of the oddities of the history of the spread of Western civilization that this land has been judged to be of such low utility: our view is now changing.

The sources of iron ore in the United States have been dwindling. There is an over supply in the world market, but no nation wants to be dependent on overseas movement of so critical a material as iron ore if it is possible to avoid it. Exploration has shown that the amount of Labrador-Quebec ores is enormous and that the quality is very high. The main body of ore occupies a 50-mile-wide trough that extends north–south for 750 miles and reaches into Labrador. Once the decision was reached to develop these ores, the necessary steps were taken to raise funds and proceed with the required work.

Ninety percent of the funds have come from United States sources; eight United States steel companies have pooled their capital to undertake what many people considered to be an impossible job. More than 300 million dollars were spent in developing the first mines, and a 360-mile railroad was built from Sept Îles to Schefferville. Until this project was begun, there was no such town as Schefferville: it was built to order, to hold 5000 people, complete with stores, churches, hospitals, bowling alleys, and movies.

It had to be a whole town, complete with such amenities as schools, churches, stores, and theatres, for the kind of workers that are desired are the permanent, settled, married, family men. In isolated circumstances such as this, only this type of man can be expected to settle down and become part of a stable working force. But children must have schools, and wives need some social life; and the inclusion of churches completes the needs of any normal social group. The parallel is close to that of the Panama Canal. The difference is that the development in Labrador was designed to avoid the mistake of ever having a population of restless, quarrelsome, ever-changing single men for a working force.

In addition to this social problem, there were severe physical problems. What do you do about a water supply in a land where the average temperature for January is 0° F.? Either a deep source of water must be found, or surface water must be dammed up in reservoirs of such depth that they will be several times as deep as the thickest ice to be found. This is not as formidable as it sounds: 6 feet of ice is about the maximum expectation in severe continental climates. A reservoir with 60 feet of deep water is not difficult to construct in any hilly terrain. In winter it is more of a problem to supply the water to buildings. Pipes must be deeply buried or heated, but in mid-winter the waste must eventually be dumped on some surface to freeze, for the great cold of the area stops all surface drainage. Freezing then stores up the enormous volume of wastes from the settlement until the summer sun melts the whole mass away.

There are also problems in house building. Where the ground freezes very deeply every winter and thaws every spring, buildings are heaved around by the expansion and contraction. Much of the north-ern forest area and most of the tundra area of the earth is perpetually frozen. This condition is called perma frost. Building on perma frost is particularly difficult; the building becomes a center of heat, and it then begins to melt its way into the frozen ground. This melting goes on unevenly and presently the building has taken on a permanent tilt. But as for all such problems, there are possible solutions: the simplest is to insulate the ground from the effect of the heating building.

But there are innumerable problems. Automobiles are difficult to operate at very low temperatures, for oil becomes a solid below certain temperatures, and metals become brittle. Ideally a car should not only have antifreeze, but the motor should be kept warm even when the car is standing idle. Yet this is readily accomplished: electrical heating elements can be placed in the engine blocks and plugged into the electrical circuit at home or into a similar plug attached to each parking meter in town, with the cost of the electricity paid for as part of the parking fee. The point here is that although there are indeed many problems, there are also solutions. The particular solution used depends on the cost involved: the decision must be made in terms of whether the gain in occupying a given area is sufficient to justify the costs. So far, it has been mining that has led to extensive modern settlement of the northern forest. Gold first, as in Alaska, but now a whole series of metals each of greater bulk and lower unit value than the preceding one have been developed as the costs of operating in this unusual environment have been reduced.

Environmental Costs

Such costs are everywhere, not just in extreme environments. For instance, although cars in the far north may have to be heated during winter, we are finding that cars in most of our large urban centers are going to have to have costly fume controls attached to them. In the Los Angeles basin where the smog situation has reached intolerable limits, the first attempt to control automobile exhaust fumes is now being introduced. It is clear that most

Wheat Growing in Arctic Forest Land at the Dominion Experimental Station in Canada. This area, located 100 miles north of the Peace River district, at 58° N. produces prize-winning grain. The past fifty years has been a period of increasing warmth in high latitudes, aiding in the growing of grain at such extreme latitudes. No one knows how long this climatic amelioration will continue. *NFB photo, Canadian Information Service.*

A Canadian Oil Well in the Midst of Wheat Lands, Edmonton. Discovery of extensive oil fields in the Canadian midwest has been an economic boon. *National Film Board, Ottawa.*

of our large urban centers are going to have to take similar measures. Because of the unusual structure of the lower atmosphere at Los Angeles, more costly measures are going to have to be taken there than elsewhere. It is the opinion of several million people that the costs are worthwhile in order to obtain the benefits of living in that area.

Similar analyses would show that each region bears its share of costs. Tropical regions bear the costs of heat, humidity, and associated accelerated rates of deterioration of most organic materials, and a higher cost of control of animal life, particularly those life forms that either attack man directly or indirectly. Mid-latitudes carry not a lesser burden but a double burden. Much of the eastern United States struggles with a super tropical summer with all of its costs and burdens, and then has to shoulder the problems of living in a subarctic winter. Every fall the standard Easterner, when the last of the leaves has been raked up and dug out of the gutters on the roof, the storm windows put up, and the antifreeze put in the car, must make the annual mental struggle of whether to bother about snow tires or just to depend on chains. This follows, of course, on a period when he wrestled with exhaust fans, discussed buying an air conditioner, could not work comfortably at night because the light attracted bugs that somehow or another managed to get through any screening that man has yet devised that would not also cut off air circulation.

There are environmental costs everywhere. We tend to overlook those that we are familiar with and have come to take for granted. We tend to exaggerate those that are unfamiliar to us. While the costs of living in one area as compared with another are unequal, there seems to have been no concerted attempt to measure them realistically. It would not be easy to do so. Many of the costs are hidden, or indirect, or only partially environmental.

Future Development in Canada

In the Labrador-Quebec wilderness, the development period has spanned a decade. Today steam shovels dig the ore from the open pit mines in 8-ton bites, and ore trains run 24 hours a day, 8 months of the year. The entire operation is mechanized for the speedy handling of immense tonnages. Ore cars are dumped two at a time in 67 seconds. It takes less than three hours to load a 20,000-ton ore ship. Annual production from the Schefferville area has reached 13,000,000 tons.

Another development is already underway at Gagnon, 200 miles to the south, where 200 million dollars have been invested. The ore at Gagnon is concentrated to get the higher grade produce demanded for modern smelters: 20 million tons of ore are now mined annually and reduced to 8 million tons of highly concentrated iron ore at Gagnon. It is then shipped by rail 193 miles to Port Cartier on the Saint Lawrence River. Here a 50-foot deep harbor is being blasted out of the rocky shore line.

Changes in the techniques of steel-making, together with a growing demand for steel and lessening demand for iron make these expensive developments economically feasible. The concentrates are less bulky, and hence less costly to haul, and when fed into the furnaces they increase the yield of steel by 20 percent.

These two immense investments that are changing the human geography of a piece of land twice as large as Texas, are apparently only a beginning. At Wabush Lake, between Schefferville and Gagnon, another giant project is underway; it repeats the previous ones: mines, concentrators, town site, railroad, and inevitably new ports and new ore carriers. A long chain of supporting industries throughout Canada and the United States from equipment makers to stock brokers will be energized in the financing, building, maintaining, and profiting from this multi–hundred-million-dollar venture. Labor is pouring into the area, for the wages are high. The developments that are now all concentrated in the southern end of the iron trough will furnish the springboard for northward penetration of the area as these immense deposits are worked out. Geological exploration indicates that there are rich deposits along Ungava Bay and along Great Whale River on Hudson Bay. The deposits along Ungava Bay

Aerial View of Iron Mines at Ungava, Canada. These mines in the far north illustrate modern man's ability to extract from the earth the materials useful to his economy. *Iron Ore Co. of Canada.*

can be reached by short rail lines from ports along the Hudson Strait, but production will be hampered by a short shipping season due to ice conditions in the North Atlantic. The effect of the penetration of a former wilderness by three separate rail lines and the establishment of a permanent population that has been doubling and redoubling is difficult to forecast. Some of the effects, however, are already apparent.

Sept Îles was an unimportant little town located on the shores of the Saint Lawrence 500 miles east of Montreal. In 1950 it had 1500 inhabitants; in 1960 it had 15,000—making it the fastest growing city in the province of Quebec. All values go up with such a population growth: real estate values have risen from 150,000 to over 56,000,000 dollars in this ten-year period. This region is now one of the major iron producing and shipping areas of the world. Production in 1965 is estimated to be about 30 million tons of iron ore and ore concentrates. Most of this will be shipped in giant ore carriers. It can move

by sea to any world port, or can go up the St. Lawrence Seaway to reach the immense inland market around the Great Lakes.

The rail lines could make possible the efficient tapping of the immense areas of forest for lumber and pulp. Since this area is almost entirely in the Canadian shield, a highly metamorphosed mass of ancient crystalline rock, further mineral concentrations are to be expected. The presence of a developed mining industry and a transportation net could make useful known deposits that up till now have been too costly to work. The presence of a large industrial population should make it feasible in the southern part of this area to produce some farm produce, especially such crops as potatoes, for local consumption; a dairy industry to supply the local needs should also be profitable. The iron ore deposits may then serve as a means of opening up an area that has long been potentially useful but the development of which has lagged because it could not bear the cost of such developmental installations as railroads. The extensiveness of the ore deposits seems to assure at least 100 years of mining activity in the area, and that much long continued occupation and development of the area is likely to lead to broader development. It seems unlikely that northern Quebec will ever revert to its former condition of virtual uninhabited wilderness.

TRANSPORTATION PROBLEMS

In the northern forest lands, there are few roads or railroads. The cost of transportation is therefore high. But where is cause and effect in this? Is the northern forest a difficult area in which to build and maintain roads? Or, is the absence of a good road network the result of the absence of population? Roads can be built: the Alcan Highway was pushed through to Alaska in amazingly short time. Despite a relatively low use, it is maintained through a vast and relatively empty territory which, because of the road, is gaining population. Much of the road follows well drained divides, and the maintenance cost is relatively low; the major costs are met at river crossings where ice jams and floods make anything except a major bridge a temporary affair. The bridges can be built to stand, but the cost is high in proportion to the use now being made of the road. But use of the road will be held down as long as there are such weak links in the system.

In building the railroad to Fort Churchill on the Hudson Bay, some years ago—in an attempt to provide a shorter route to the sea for central Canadian wheat—the problem of crossing swampy ground in summer was neatly solved. It was noted that there was no difficulty in winter, for the swampy ground was frozen like rock. The engineers therefore put a blanket of gravel over the muck sufficient to insulate it during the brief summer; this gave a ribbon of perma frost for the railroad to run on that was good throughout the year.

It has often been noted that the rivers in the northern forest regions run the wrong way: most of the large rivers run to the frozen sea. Taken

with the innumerable lakes and ponds that interrupt the landscape, the waterways seem more of a nuisance to land travel than a help. This is a tropical or mid-latitude outlook on the landscape, for the time to travel in the northern forest is in the winter, not in the summer.

The water areas in winter are frozen to great depths. They can then bear immense loads. The surrounding terrain is also covered with snow, and snow has the happy quality that it smoothes out the terrain somewhat and provides a cover offering slight resistance to friction—anyone who has been sledding knows these qualities of ice and snow. This then makes the northern forest easy terrain through which to transport goods. In actual practice, tractor trains are made up to move goods through these territories; large caterpillar tractors pull long lines of cargo sleds. The frozen rivers, lakes, and streams function as highways; portages are easily made by taking to the snow. What seems to be a tropical or even to most mid-latitude people as a hopeless situation, proves to be advantageous.

It is questionable whether a dense net of railroads will ever be built in the northern forest lands. If we can move heavy goods by tractor trailer in the winter, why go to the immense cost of building and maintaining railroads? Why build highways either? We have moved from a time dominated by the railroad to one dominated by the automobile and truck, and seem quite surely to be headed for one where air travel will be dominant. Nowhere is this futuristic view given a more realistic flavor than in the northern forest areas.

At Fairbanks, the outskirts of the city are ringed with airports, which are thickly parked with small airplanes. Highways are limited, but travel is almost unlimited. In summer these light planes are put on pontoons, and they use the ever present pond and stream as their landing fields. In winter they don skis and can land wherever there is an open stretch of snow, thus opening up not only all lakes and streams as potential landing areas, but any clearing. Since air travel is much faster and light planes can be bought for the price of an automobile and can operate on a mile for mile basis at lower rates, why bother with the huge costs of highway building and maintenance? Since air travel in the northern forest regions can take advantage of their much greater density of lakes to serve as natural landing fields in summer and winter, these regions actually have an advantage over other climatic areas.

POTENTIAL USES

The northern forest lands can be used: their potential usefulness has steadily been increasing as we have mastered the problems of transportation, housing, water supply and heating. For a long time our utilization of them remained nearly at the level of man's first penetration. For early men they were a source of game; for European man they were long a source of furs. Later we have used them as a source of timber and minerals. The possibility of making far greater use of them exists, for we could use their enormous extent for reindeer-caribou meat-and-hide production, or for musk ox production, for instance. We could also use their entire extent for summer resort areas: along with the increasing crowding of other parts of the world and growing ease of air travel, this northern lake land is becoming simultaneously more attractive and approachable.

It cannot be expected that these lands can produce either plant or vegetable materials at similar rates to those of lands of lower latitudes. Such production is dependent on solar energy. These are lands of most unequal seasonal distribution of solar energy, with an annual total that is far lower than the mid-latitude and tropical areas. Nonetheless, there is considerably more potential in these lands than is now being utilized. Will we then begin to use them?

There are two conflicting tendencies. The world population is growing rapidly. This would seem to suggest that we should be putting more and more people into such lands as these. In practice, however, we find that potentially more useful lands (nearer to centers of civilization, with better developed transportation networks and so forth) are faced with decreasing population. In 18 farm states in mid-America, 61 percent of the counties lost population between 1950 and 1960. The population explosion that we hear so much about would seem to be better described as an implosion than an explosion. Mankind is concentrating in a few, largely urban areas. The empty parts of the world are becoming emptier, not fuller. In general, the northern forest lands seem more likely to continue to empty out than to fill up. This will not be due to the land nearly so much as it will reflect the decisions of man concerning the kind of life that he chooses to lead.

OLD WORLD–NEW WORLD: PAST AND PRESENT

The two northern forest areas of the world, that in the hands of the Soviet Union and that in American, mostly Canadian, hands, have strikingly similar physical make-ups. They have similar climates, land forms, vegetation, and animal life, and both areas have mineralized zones. Men entered both areas at least as early as 20,000 years ago as specialized hunters of the great mammals of the arctic such as the mammoth. In both areas, their hunting efficiency was great enough to exterminate the biggest of the big game, and the men then came into an ecologic balance with the more numerous, more rapid breeding, smaller game, such as the reindeer, caribou, moose, deer, and rabbits. Relatively recently, the uses of these lands diverged. The introduction of the idea of domestication of animals and their utilization for transportation, milking, and nomadism in the Old World gave rise, by the transfer of these ideas to the hunting people of the northern forest, to a new way of life in the northern forest that was also extensible into the tundra. As we have seen, the lesser time, the limited contact, and the orientation of the peoples at the Bering Strait blocked the spread of these ideas to the New World.

In the Old World, the exploitation of the northern forest lands for timber began early, but was limited by transportation problems. The extraction of products of high value in proportion to their weight, such as furs, very early led the Europeans especially the Russians, to spread through the northern forest areas. It was this fur trade, as we have seen, that led the Russians clear across Siberia and into the Pacific, and down the Pacific coast to pose a threat to Spain's colonial claims. The French and later the British development of fur trade throughout Canada was a later duplication of this type of utilization of these lands. Currently both the Russians and the Americans are simultaneously pushing agricultural developments northward into these areas, extracting forest products in increasing quantity from them, and exploiting the mineral resources. The similarities are partially geographic, partially economic (the comparative advantage of these lands at our present stage of development leaves them in the extractive stage), and partially cultural. Striking dissimilarities arise now because of the differing socio-economic philosophies of the Soviet Union and of the West.

It is easy to overstress the similarities. There are differences. The development in America is largely done by individual corporations in a free market economy. Development is heavily mechanized to reduce the need for labor. Labor in the northern forest lands is scarce, must largely be imported, and supported at great cost. In addition, above average pay must be given to attract the labor force and hold it. The development in the Soviet system follows a different pattern. Machinery is in short supply, but labor is cheap. Upheavals in the heart of Russia have supplied a continuous flow of political-exile labor, and when there is no upheaval, labor can simply be recruited or drafted. The only cost associated with this labor is housing, feeding, clothing, and, if necessary, guarding it. Little attempt is made to supply more than a minimal standard of living. Under the Soviet philosophy, a human being only exists to serve the state, and is therefore expendable. The development of their Siberian areas, therefore, goes ahead at a cost in human welfare and loss of life that is not acceptable in Western society. The only people in the Soviet north that have the amenities that are available for all at Schefferville are the Soviet officials and the officers of the massive police force that controls the area.

10-The Polar Lands

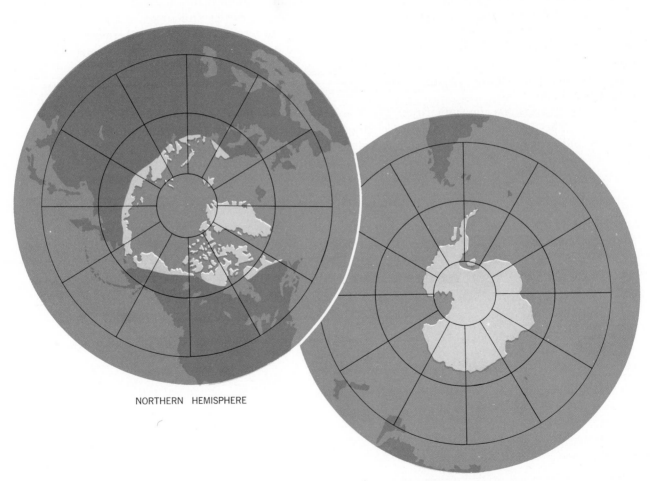

NORTHERN HEMISPHERE

SOUTHERN HEMISPHERE

THERE ARE TWO POLAR areas. One, Antarctica, is an ice capped continent and until the present has had no human occupation. The other is an ice-covered ocean with human occupation on its shores and the edges of its ice flows. Man learned to live on the edge of the treeless zones near perpetual ice when the ice masses covered most of northwestern Europe and all of northern North America. When the last great ice retreat began, about 20,000 years ago, men had finally amassed enough environmental control through housing and clothing that they could follow their familiar environments northward to the shore of the arctic sea.

THE PHYSICAL SETTING

The treeless arctic areas, north of the isotherm for 50° F. for the warmest month, resemble the grasslands. They are covered with vegetation, but it is a uniformly low-growing, plant cover. There are mosses, lichens, sedges, grasses, and herbaceous plants. In the brief summer there are bright flowers and much green. The plants are adapted to withstand great cold, a short growing season, and a perpetually frozen subsoil. In the tundra areas of the world, the ground never thaws for more than a few inches. Beneath that, the ground is always frozen, and often to very great depths: such deeply frozen ground is called permafrost. The soils are often classified as muck soils, though on well-drained ridges there are more normal soils. With the ground frozen, water can drain away only with great difficulty. The result is that when the summer thaw comes, much of the land is a great wet spongy surface.

This wetness persists in spite of the fact that the total rainfall is low. Tundra areas generally receive less than 10 inches of rainfall per year, and this comes mostly in spring and fall. Winter is particularly dry, and total depth of snow cover is small. If this is contrary to your picture of the arctic, you must correct your view. The major centers of the glaciers were not in the high arctic, but lay in lower latitudes: over Scandinavia, northern Quebec, and the Rockies along the Canadian border. There was so little snowfall in Alaska that the Yukon Valley was never glaciated, nor was much of the arctic coastal plain of Siberia and North America.

The climatology of this situation is quite simple. In winter, these areas are intensely cold; the capacity of air masses to hold moisture is related to their temperature in such a way that the lower the temperature, the less the moisture capacity. Consequently, the very cold winter air masses contain very little moisture. Unless oceanic air masses can be brought into these areas, there can be little winter precipitation, which would of course come in the form of snow. The arctic ocean does not supply much moisture to the arctic regions since it is frozen over most of the time. In both the arctic and the antarctic, the major movement of the wind is from the cold, dry interiors outward.

The result is that the snows of the high arctic come in the spring and the fall when the air is "not too cold to snow." The snow of winter blizzards is largely made up of snow whipped up off the surface of the ground. However, there are not many gales in the arctic in winter, for the arctic in winter is the center of the polar high, and in the center of a high pressure system, there is little wind. Strong winds are related to large changes of air pressure over short distances. In the arctic in winter the land is cold, and the ice-covered sea is cold: there are no great contrasts. Therefore, the wind is moderate in strength and largely from the northeast. Much the same is true of the antarctic: the violent winds are on the continental margins where the land-sea contrasts are great.

(*Above*) Nordura River Valley, Iceland. (*Left*) Herring Boats. (*Opposite*) The Modern City of Reykjavík. A nearly treeless volcanic land with much of its land buried by an ice cap, Iceland supports a literate energetic people who make much of their living from the sea. *Embassy of Iceland.*

THE ESKIMOS

The dominant winds are the polar easterlies. Their reality is brought out vividly by the fact that the Eskimos at Point Barrow, the northernmost point of the United States, use them to find their way. Out on the tundra, everything looks alike. The snow is gray; the sky is gray; and there is no clearly defined skyline: gray melts into gray. The sun is not visible, and there are no land marks: no trees, no hills, nothing to break the sameness of the land wherever you look.

"How can you find your way around without a compass?" you may ask an Eskimo.

"Easy," he says. "See those ripples in the snow? Up here in winter the wind always blows from the northeast, and those ripples always form at right angles to the wind. So they point northwest and southeast."

The snow in the arctic is not deep. There is usually less than two feet, but it covers everything. At Point Barrow, Alaska, heavy equipment is moved across the land on broad-runnered sleds pulled by tractors. Engineering crews go out in houses mounted on such sleds and so can sleep in warm comfort wherever the day's work ends. The Eskimos move about freely with their light dog-drawn sleds. Where contractors, exploring for oil in the area, dump trash, the Eskimos come, load their sleds, and haul off ponderous loads for such light equipment as a sled drawn by half a dozen dogs. The sliding power of the snow is a real virtue.

Eskimo Pottery Lamp from the Yukon Tundra, Alaska. The bowl is filled with oil and dry moss used as a wick. Such lamps as these first appeared about 20,000 years ago in the archeology of southern France. *Smithsonian Institution.*

ORIGIN OF SOME ESKIMO CULTURAL TRAITS

The problem of using the tundra is little different from that of using the northern forest lands. Only the absence of timber for building and for fuel is greatly different, but this is no small difference. How could men live in the arctic without fuel and shelter?

It has often been said that the Eskimos are the perfect example of man's response to a difficult environment. Lacking wood, they invented the snow house. Lacking fuel, they invented the oil lamp. Needing warm clothing, they invented the finest tailored skin clothing, and the bone needle with which to sew the skins. They did this in the arctic, we are given to understand, in response to the needs of life in the arctic. There is only one thing wrong with this argument: no one, not even a Tierra del Fuegian, could live long enough in the arctic to make this series of inventions. The inventions had to be made elsewhere and then utilized to make living possible in the arctic. The situation is exactly like the American agricultural expansion into the grasslands.

Some Eskimo traits can be traced with considerable certainty to quite different climates from those where the Eskimos now use them. The oil lamp is an example. In the arctic, there is little or no wood; the Eskimo heats the interior of his house by burning oil in an open dish, with a wick of moss. In principle, this is exactly like the kerosene lamps that were in common use in Western society prior to the development of gas lights and electricity, and which are still widely used in nonelectrified rural areas. It is also identical in principle to the oil lamps that were in use in Greece, Egypt, and Rome. We can trace these lamps far back in time. They were in use in western Europe 20,000 years ago by the Upper Paleolithic people. Hence the Eskimo probably did not invent this useful item, but got it from some other people. Just who did invent it is not known. It may well have come out of the southwest Asian center of inventiveness and spread west into Europe and east into Siberia.

Eskimo clothing most probably was not invented in the arctic, but in lands where it was much less required for survival than desired for comfort. We also find that bone needles appear in the Upper Paleolithic cultures in Europe. So far as our present evidence goes, it would appear that tailored skin clothing was developed somewhere 20 degrees or more to the south of the arctic lands of the Eskimo.

The Eskimo weapons are highly specialized items. Bone and horn are very widely used to make harpoon points. These points are slotted, barbed, and toggled and have inset stone blades in their tips and on their sides in a way that duplicates the work of the reindeer hunters of the Upper Paleolithic period of Europe. The spear thrower, an important weapon for the Eskimo when hunting sea mammals in his kayak, is also an ancient weapon, appearing at least as early as the Upper Paleolithic. The Eskimo underground house is also at least of this same age, and it was in use over wide areas far to the south of the arctic. In short, all of the technical inventions that the Eskimos have that are essential to life in the high arctic were in use 20,000 years or more earlier in more southern latitudes. The accumulation of these inventions in other areas made possible man's invasion of the treeless arctic.

An Eskimo in His Kayak, White Bay, Canada. The harpoon and harpoon line are laid out on the deck. Eskimo-type harpoons appear as early as the Upper Paleolithic age in western Europe, where skin boats also survived into modern times in Ireland. *National Film Board, Ottawa.*

It has often been noticed that many of the Eskimo cultural traits are like those of the Upper Paleolithic people of Europe. How this is to be interpreted has varied through time. The stone lamp, tailored skin clothing, harpoons, spear throwers, semisubterranean houses, engraving on bone and ivory, and carving figures in the round are only a partial list of the traits that the Eskimos share with the Upper Paleolithic people of Europe of 20,000 years ago. Further, these and other facets of culture such as magic flight myths and bear ceremonialism have a nearly continuous distribution from western Europe into North America. Recent Russian archeological discoveries and analyses indicate that the Upper Paleolithic people near Lake Baikal are Europoid men who followed the ice border to the east and suggest that these similarities are actually due to the spread of men and ideas. They certainly support a view that ways of life are enormously persistent, that inventions are uncommon, and that the spread of ideas is dominant over independent invention.

Eskimo culture in the form that we know it today is often said to be only about 2000 years old. That Eskimo speech is relatively uniform from one end of the arctic to the other suggests that their spread across the American north is not very ancient. On the other hand, this tells us nothing about how ancient their culture may be in Siberia. Further, archeological work in Alaska and Canada adds continuously to the list of pre-Eskimo cultures that occupied that area. Man surely has lived there for 10,000 years, and Eskimolike equipment is required for life there.

ESKIMO SOLUTIONS TO ARCTIC HOUSING

The Underground House

The Eskimos are often thought of as living in snow houses. However, only about 25 percent of

Eskimo Igloo under Construction, Northwest Territories, Canada. This large triple-domed igloo is for the ceremonial drum dance. *National Film Board, Ottawa.*

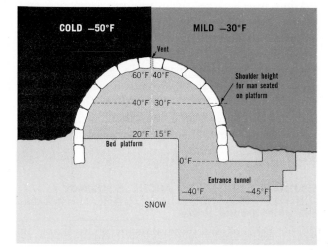

Figure 10-1 Cross Section of an Eskimo Snow House. The method of constructing an Eskimo house from blocks of snow is suggested in the drawing. The house is normally banked up with snow about the base, and a tunnel is dug for an entrance. It is important to have the platform inside at least 18 inches higher than the level of the entrance tunnel. The heat produced by the occupants will then make the interior moderately warm. If an oil lamp is used, the house can become comfortably warm.

It is an oddity of such a structure that the colder it is outside, the warmer it can be inside. If the temperature outside is extremely cold, the air inside can get quite warm before melting of the roof begins. In this diagram, at −50° F. outside, a temperature of about 60° is indicated just under the roof and a temperature of 40° at shoulder height for a man sitting on the bed platform. Somewhat colder inside temperatures are suggested for outside temperatures in the −30° to −40° range. With outside temperatures warmer than 20° below zero, the snow house is not useful and tents must be used instead.

them have ever seen one, for only the Central Eskimos build them, and they are the least numerous of the Eskimo groups. The largest population of Eskimos is in Alaska. There the ancient house was the underground house, almost exactly like those built in Siberia 20,000 years ago. The house is dug down into the ground. A roof is formed of timbers, or bone, or antler, or a combination of all of these materials. In the past in Siberia, mammoth bone was commonly used, and in Alaska whale bone was similarly used. The roof was covered with sticks, grass, and finally sod, making a thick, well-insulated covering. Entrance was either through a hatch in the roof, or through a tunnellike entrance to the side.

Inside the house a relatively large number of people occupied a small space. Their body heat alone was sufficient to raise the temperature, and further heat was added by cooking over oil lamps. Even when not cooking, the oil lamp was kept going to provide light. Temperature in these houses was normally in the 80s and the humidity was very high. Under these conditions there was no need for clothing. In addition, if clothing were worn indoors it would become saturated with moisture; then when worn outdoors, its insulating qualities would fail and the wearer would freeze. It was not only comfortable, but intensely practical to shed the clothing in the entry and live indoors in a state of complete undress. The Upper Paleolithic artists, who lived in similar houses from Siberia to Europe, portrayed people as unclothed, suggesting a similar way of life at that time.

The Snow House

The snow house is a remarkable invention. It involves the principle of the arch, rotated to form a dome. The Eskimo was not aware of this as an abstract principle. An arch of stone must be supported until the key stone is put in place. The arch will then bear many times its own weight. In the snow house, the Eskimo is able to build his arch without supporting scaffolding because snow has adhesive qualities. The right kind of snow is required: it must be of adequate thickness and must

have been packed by the wind to the proper consistency. Wind-packed snow can be cut into large blocks and lifted and stood on edge. Building a snow house consists of finding this kind of snow, cutting large blocks, setting them on edge in a circular plan, and spiralling the blocks upwards and inwards as the walls are raised. It is a neat trick requiring some skill, but no more than can be acquired with a minimum of directed practice.

The snow house has enormous advantages. Once completed, it is strong: wind cannot blow it away or make it shake and flap in the annoying manner that a tent does. It is completely windproof and practically soundproof. Once fully stabilized, in part by the occupants' breath being absorbed into the snow and freezing the blocks more tightly together, it is strong enough so that a polar bear can stand on top of it. It makes carrying a tent unnecessary, and it makes it possible to build a snug shelter where there is no wood, and where the ground is too frozen to allow one to dig an underground house. A house can be set up in about an hour's time; it can then be abandoned without a qualm after a day or a week if the conditions of the hunt suggest that it would be better to move on.

It is usually thought that the interior of a snow house must be cold. This is not true, for they can be kept very warm. The floor is dug out, leaving a bench along the sides. Furs are placed on this bench to provide insulation so that sitting there will not melt the snow beneath. The body heat of several people in a snow house will raise the inside temperature to 20° to 30° F. when the outside temperature is —20° to —30° F. If an oil lamp is lit for cooking or for light, the temperature will then go still higher.

Whether or not the snow roof will melt is determined by the temperature inside the igloo, the thickness of the roof, and the temperature outside the igloo. If the heat flow through the roof keeps in balance so that the inner wall of the roof stays at 32° F. or less, all is well. If the heat is not flowing through the roof fast enough, the inside of the roof will begin to melt and drops of water will form.

To an Eskimo, this is notice that action must be taken. He can throw on his parka, duck outside, and scrape some snow off the roof. There will then be a more rapid heat loss through the thinner insulating barrier and the inside temperature will balance. Or he can poke a piece of stove pipe up through the roof, providing a ventilator through which some of the interior heat can escape. This, too, can be regulated; if too much heat escapes and it begins to be cold, one can stuff a glove in the ventilator to cut the heat loss down.

The interior of a snow house is light in daylight, and even moonlight will give sufficient light for dressing and cooking. In bright sunshine, men have been known to go snow blind inside a snow house. If artificial light is needed, a candle, because of the reflecting ice crystals in the snow dome, gives ample, soft, diffuse light.

Entrance to an igloo is by a sunken tunnel. This requires locating the house in an area having about three feet of snow cover. The tunnel leads into the sunken floor to take advantage of the properties of air: warm air rises and is trapped near the ceiling; the cold air lies in the tunnel and in the welllike central area. It is essential that the sleeping bench be at least 18 inches above the level of the tunnel entrance. The air temperature in the floor of the tunnel may be −40° F.; the bench level where people sit, 20° F.; and the apex of the ceiling, 60° F. When the igloo temperature rises, some clothing must be shed lest it become damp. The clothing is then hung in the tunnel where it will be kept dry by the cold, and will be handy when the Eskimo is ready to go out.

The temperature contrasts in a tent and a snow house are striking. With no heat and with an outside temperature of −50° F., the interior of the tent will reach −10° to −20° F. Under the same conditions in an igloo, the temperature near the roof will remain above freezing and at the sleeping platform level will not drop even close to 0° F.

Life in an igloo can be exciting at times. The dome shape catches the sounds coming through the snow crust and focuses them on the interior. When the sled dogs are bedded down in the snow outside and the family is snug inside, there is little for the Eskimo to fear, except the polar bear. If a bear should come into camp and attack the sled dogs, the Eskimo must get out quickly. Dogs are precious because the Eskimo depends on them for his ability to move rapidly through his snow-covered land. Fortunately, the approach of a polar bear is signaled by the crunching noise of his feet in the snow, which is picked up by the snow house and amplified to warn the Eskimo.

Americans who have used the snow house in their explorations in the arctic have evolved a system for such emergencies. One man each night has the duty in case of such attack to spring out of his sleeping bag, grab his gun, and rush out of the igloo to shoot at the bear before he can destroy any of the dogs. The rest of the crew stops to put on clothes before they rush out. A nearly naked man can stand a few minutes of −20° or −30° F. By that time his companions are on the scene and he can duck back into shelter and warmth.

In one recorded experience, men on a mountain-climbing expedition built a snow house. On entering it they noted that the temperature was −27° F. After 20 minutes their body heat had raised the temperature 60 degrees to 33° F. When they lit a single burner gasoline stove, the temperature became very warm, and 20 minutes after turning the stove off, the temperature of their igloo was 65° F.

The snow house is a tremendously useful invention that every people in extremely high mountains or extremely cold snowy conditions "need," but it has remained the possession of the Central Eskimos. It did not spread into Siberia, nor was it reinvented there, or in Scandinavia, or the Alps, or the Himalayas. Even more surprising, it has very reluctantly been adopted by polar explorers, especially in Antartica where it would be at maximum usefulness. Instead, if one reads the accounts of the early expeditions there, men struggled with heavy tents, in which they found little relief from the cold and in which they often could not sleep because the wind made the canvas crack and bang like cannonading.

Eskimo Clothing. Available material is used to make clothing that is suitable for the various changes in climate. (*From left to right*) A spring outfit of seal skin is waterproof and light in weight. A woman's squirrel-skin outfit is warm and flexible, but fragile. The winter suit of caribou skin is the warmest, and it is also light and strong. Eider-duck skins make a light and warm summer outfit, but one that is too delicate to stand up under heavy use. *Smithsonian Institution.*

ESKIMO CLOTHING

A man fully clothed in Eskimo fashion worries as much about overheating while working as he does about freezing. Eskimo clothing utilizes the insulation value of fur, that is, the trapping of air in the fur to form an insulating layer. The effect of this insulation is spoiled by dampness; hence the clothing must be kept dry, both in the house and in use. It is imperative that the Eskimo not overexert himself so as to perspire actively. When heavy work is necessary, the Eskimos may be seen loosening their parkas at the throat and at the waist in order to let body heat escape, or even shedding one layer of clothing. Clothing is worn in two layers: one set, fur side in; another set, fur side out. Boots, gloves, and scarves are worn. The clothing is loose fitting for active work, but is tight at the top to prevent the loss of body heat, which means a tight belt and a tight throat. The hood is important for cutting down loss of heat from the head and neck areas. One of the few Upper Paleolithic statues with clothing indicated

Eskimo Clothing. The long, loose-fitting but tailored garment is well designed to allow free movement for activity while retaining a maximum of body warmth. *American Geographical Society.*

that we have shows a woman wearing a parkalike hood. It has been said that the Eskimo does not live in a personal arctic climate, but in a tropical climate: in his house he lives in high heat and humidity; in his double-fur suit, boots, and gloves he carries this warm climate with him into the arctic world, and is normally snug and warm even under conditions of extreme external cold.

This anecdote is told of the comfort that the Eskimo experiences at home in his own clothes and environment. An arctic explorer brought an Eskimo couple to visit New York. He outfitted them in standard western clothing and showed them the town. When it was time for the Eskimos to return,

he saw them off on the ship that was to take them to northernmost Greenland. The Eskimo woman burst into tears at the departure. The explorer was touched at such a display of emotion and asked why the tears, thinking of course that she would reply that she was going to miss him. Not so. She explained that she felt sorry for him, being left behind to live in uncomfortable clothes in this awfully cold place.

It is not true, of course, that the Eskimo is never cold. Some of his work requires long periods of sitting still and the cold can then be a problem. The Eskimo's sleeves are so loose fitting that under these circumstances he can withdraw his arms and fold them over his chest. This reduces his surface of radiation still further and aids him in keeping warm. Further, both the Eskimo's face and hands are noticeably warmer than those of other people. In the Eskimo skull the openings for the blood vessels that supply the face region are large, indicating that an increased-blood-flow type of physical adaptation has occurred. A similar adaptation making possible increased blood flow into the hands so that they remain warm and capable of doing dexterous work under extremely cold conditions is further indication that the Eskimo is physiologically adapted to his extremely cold environment. Whatever the ultimate source of the classic Eskimo culture, its bearers have surely been living in cold environments for a very long time.

SEA-MAMMAL HUNTING

The Eskimos obtain their food largely from sea mammals. In the middle of the winter, seals are caught when they come up to breathe through holes in the ice that they maintain as the sea ice thickens. The Eskimos sit for long hours at these holes when they find them. In the summer, seals are speared on the ice. Walrus are harpooned; this is big game, for a walrus weighs a ton or more and can deal destructive blows with his tusks. Yet this sport pales when compared to the Eskimo's hunting of the whale.

Umiak and Crew, 1869. This type of large skin boat is capable of extended voyages, as the Irish demonstrated with their very similar craft called curaghs. Eskimos used such a boat for whale hunting as well as general transportation. *American Geographical Society.*

Whale hunting in the north is done in the spring when the whales begin moving northward along the cracks that are opening in the ice. Eskimo crews station themselves along these "leads." Each crew has a large open boat made of skin stretched over a light wooden frame. The boat is mounted on blocks at the edge of the open water and the crew settles down to wait. When a whale comes along the edge of the ice, the harpooner gets in the bow of the boat and the crew lines the sides, set to hurl the boat, harpooner and all, at the whale. The harpooner plunges the harpoon into the great beast; the whale dives and the harpoon line is let run out. With it go floats of inflated seal skins. The whale, wounded and hampered by the pull of the floats, sooner or later must surface. The original boat and any other boats in the vicinity are waiting for him when he comes up in order to drive more harpoons home. This process goes on until the exhausted whale lies weakened on the surface. The boats then come alongside the whale and drive lances into vital areas. It is a hazardous and thrilling business with an enormous yield of meat as the goal. Whales run

a ton to the foot and 20- and 30-foot whales are the usual catch.

The whale is now awash in the sea. "Land" is a shelf of ice standing three to five feet out of the sea. How can they lift this tonnage onto that shelf? When it is on the shelf, the distance to the village may be one or more miles away over broken and often shifting sea ice. Our estimate of primitive man's ability gains enormously from watching the Eskimos handle this problem.

First, a ramp is chiseled out of the sea ice. The Eskimo knows no formal physics, but here he is employing the principle of the inclined plane. The whale's head is towed to this ramp, and slits are cut in the side of the head. Long ropes are then led through the slits, up onto the ice, around blocks of ice, and back again. Poles are then put through the lengths of rope, and by twisting, a powerful purchase is created that drags the massive head up onto the ice a ways. Cutting tools are then brought into play and as much of the flesh as can be reached is cut away. The lines are then rerigged and the carcass is hauled out another short distance.

Eskimo Radio Operator at Cambridge Bay, Northwest Territories, Canada. The Eskimo quickly learns skills and earns standard wages for jobs like this. Thus drawn into modern life, he often leaves his old arctic-hunting way of life. *National Film Board, Ottawa.*

The scene is one of wild, colorful activity. The meat is hauled back onto the ice in chunks. The whole village descends on the scene with all the carrying equipment obtainable. Sleds, dogs, women, and children all come and all work. The ice is soon a great mass of pink to red from the blood of the blocks of meat that are being dragged back from the butchery. Joy is intense, for this mass of meat is insurance against hunger for a long time to come. It will be eaten greedily on the spot and in the village. Much of it will be buried in the frozen ground to be preserved for later need. The whole carcass will be shared with the whole village. The original crew will get certain privileged pieces, but the rule is that all share in the kill. By this means, as long as there is meat coming into the village, all are kept alive. The fortunate hunter simply cannot keep his family fat while others starve. When he runs into bad luck, he can in turn claim meat from those that have had the good fortune to get a seal or a bear or a caribou. This is a normal outlook on food among primitive peoples, and offers the kind of security our insurance policies accomplish today.

The Eskimos illustrate the fact that men can live in almost any part of the earth. They have a highly specialized and ingenious culture that makes of the treeless arctic sea edge a useful environment. Far from being unhappy with their lot, the Eskimos are always described as among the happiest of people on the earth. They are not depressed by the long night of winter. Quite the contrary; they are much more comfortable in the winter than in the summer. Summer is a time of slush and wet; travel overland is difficult; and the myriads of mosquitoes are a terrific nuisance. Tents are poor substitutes for the snug snow houses of the Central Eskimos and the thaw often makes the underground houses of the western Eskimos damp. The return of the good cold dry winter with its crisp snow brings ease of travel by dog sled swiftly gliding across the land. Darkness is not so bad: the moonlight shining on the snow makes things almost as light as day, and the aurora borealis adds further light.

THE IMPACT OF INDUSTRIAL SOCIETY

At Point Barrow the Navy exploration for oil brought the Eskimos high wages and contact with the benefits of civilization. The Eskimo men were employed in the shops of the arctic contractors. They proved to be quick to learn to handle modern machinery and became not just proficient but expert. Since they were paid the same as all the rest of the labor, they found themselves with an abundance of money. This was spent in interesting ways. They built frame houses, which look very much like Midwestern frame cottages, and they heated these with stoves using coal mined many miles away and hauled to the village. Warm houses demanded refrigeration, and refrigerators came into use in the arctic. Skin boats had outboard motors attached to them. Rifles and shotguns came into general use, and fancy dress parkas were made of cotton cloth.

When the search for oil ceased, the high income was cut off. The large number of Eskimos who had gathered at Point Barrow for this work then had a number of choices. They could go to Fairbanks or farther south and get employment, for they were now skilled tractor drivers, machinists, and carpenters. They could not stay where they were and use these skills. They could revert to their old hunting way of life. Or they could just sit there, using up the money that they had and hoping that something would happen. Actually all three courses were taken.

Some of the Eskimos went to Fairbanks for employment. For most of them, the way of life was too strange and they have tended to return to the arctic. Some have stayed at Point Barrow and tried to get by on whaling and sealing. They have to operate the coal mine in order to heat their frame houses, for oil lamps will not heat the airy space of a frame house. Some have gone back to moving along the edge of the arctic ice seeking seals. The over-all effect, however, has been to move some of the Eskimos out of the arctic ice edge way of life. Probably the seeds of discontent planted will lead to a steady decline in the number of Eskimos that continue to live in the high arctic.

The impact of industrial society on similarly situated peoples will probably have much the same result. New ways of life will be introduced, and new wants will arise that can only be met by continuing to live within the industrial society, or at least to produce something that the industrial society wants. The over-all result is likely to be the abandonment of the simpler economies that have survived in isolated regions such as the arctic and the withdrawal of the people who have lived in these areas to centers where employment is more readily available. This will be a continuation of the general withdrawal of mankind from areas that for tens of millennia have been considered useful lands and the increasing concentration of mankind in areas now considered attractive.

ANTARCTICA: UNINHABITED OR UNINHABITABLE?

The antarctic has had no human population until the present period of exploration. There are now so-called permanent bases on the edge of the ice cap, and in this period of exploration we have learned a number of things about this vast area. There are some ice-free spots, and they have been in existence for quite some time, for they contain the carcasses of seals that have been dated by carbon-14 as about 2000 years old. But these are mere specks of bare rock in an immensity of ice and snow.

Ice is now melting off of Antarctica. Should it all melt off the sea level would rise at least 100 feet and probably 250 feet, and the habitable plains of the world would be inundated. Florida, Denmark, Holland, and similar areas would be lost to mankind. Gaining Antarctica would probably be viewed as small recompense by people not accustomed to polar life.

Antarctica can be approached only with difficulty. It is surrounded by the world's stormiest seas. In most of the area a floating shelf of ice extends out to sea from the land, although this is hardly discernible since the land is buried under one to two miles of ice. Only on the Palmer Peninsula does the south polar land approach another land. Here the South Shetland Islands, off the end of the Palmer Peninsula, lie in nearly the same latitudes as their namesakes to the north of Scotland. They are separated from the islands of Tierra del Fuego by the Drake Passage. This is a 350-mile-wide waterway, swept by frequent wild storms, and often containing floating ice. This was an absolute barrier to man.

Is this correctly stated? Would it not be more correct to say: This was an absolute barrier to the kind of men that occupied the southern tip of South America in prehistoric times? Certainly we can and do cross this water gap today. The Norse crossed greater distances in more northern waters that also were storm swept and ice filled and settled in Iceland and Greenland. The failure of man to colonize the unglaciated tip of the Palmer Peninsula is much more realistically described as being due to the absence of the required means of navigation in the hands of the men in the adjacent land.

But could men, any men, live on a continent that, with insignificant exceptions, is covered a mile or so thick with ice? The answer is that he surely could. Had the Eskimos reached Antarctica, they would have found it a good land for their way of life. After all, they were not dependent on the land

for any of their requirements. They could build a highly satisfactory house out of snow, make thoroughly satisfactory weapons and utensils out of bone, and fine clothing out of hides and furs. In Antarctica they would have found a sea filled with seals and whales. The seal population on the islands off the Palmer Peninsula is estimated to have been in the millions, before our fur hunting virtually exterminated them. There are still great numbers of seals in the area. These include such huge forms as the leopard seal. The penguins also would be a valuable food source. The abundance of whales in the antarctic ocean makes this the major whale fishery of the world today, and as we have seen, the Eskimos knew how to catch these animals. The oil from whale and seal would supply the needed fuel and light that the Eskimos knew how to use in oil lamps.

It is one of the accidents of history that the parts of the world closest to Antarctica were not held by people with boating skills to reach it. However, even if the Tasmanians or the Tierra del Fuegians with their rafts and their bark canoes managed to reach the frozen continent, they lacked the clothing, housing, and economic skills to have survived. As with the Eskimo, it is too late to be stimulated to invent clothing, housing, oil lamps, and all the rest of the needs of survival in the high latitudes when you arrive there. It is necessary to arrive in such difficult conditions with the equipment already in existence.

The earliest boat people to approach these frozen southern lands were probably the Polynesians. The people of New Zealand preserved in their accounts of great voyages mention of sailings so far south that they saw ice fields in the sea. But these were a tropical maritime people, and ice floating in the sea was sufficient reason for them to turn back. They had the boats but none of the other cultural equipment or the psychological orientation to take up life in such a land, even if they had reached it. Antarctica is empty, then, not because no men could have lived there, but because no men with adequate equipment for living there ever came within striking distance of it. The solution to life in high latitudes was reached in the continental mid-latitudes, probably in proximity to the glacial ice masses. These ways of life never penetrated into the parts of the southern hemisphere that might have put men so equipped within striking distance of another continent that could have been used to support another Eskimo cultural world. Antarctica is not uninhabitable; it is simply uninhabited.

SUMMARY

However, it is not likely that mankind is now going to flow into the arctic or the antarctic in any appreciable numbers. The tendency for mankind to pile up in great urban centers is the rule of the day. We are much more likely to continue this concentration of people than to revert to the ancient pattern of a much more uniform distribution of mankind over the entire earth, even including the arctic, and only excluding the antarctic.

The arctic stands as another example of the fact that man's penetration into difficult areas usually requires the accumulation of "know-how" in a more favorable area. Once the ideas are assembled, the new area can be taken over. The arctic also illustrates the failure to adopt a potentially useful trait, such as reindeer herding, if it fails to fit the established way of life. It is also an illustration of the way in which such a failure prevents a more distant people, who might well have taken up the trait, from receiving the idea. We are back to the conditions postulated for the uniform earth in the opening chapter.

The arctic is neither so forbidding nor so attractive as its greatest opponents or its greatest proponents have painted it. It can be used. It cannot be made to yield vegetable and animal life in proportion to those parts of the world that receive greater sunlight and moisture. It is sunlight that is the energy source that underlies the entire plant-production–animal-feeding food chain. The arctic receives a minimum of solar energy; therefore it can produce a minimal amount of the biological base for animal existence. The point, however, is that we are not using even that minimum, and that this is a human decision, not an environmental one.

11-The Role of Physical Environment and Culture

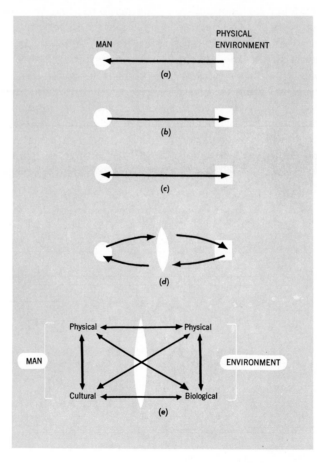

THE PROBLEM with which we began is the nature of the relation of man to his environment. The question, we noted, has been answered at various times in various ways. The ancient and perennial answer has been that the physical environment makes man do what he does. Sometimes it is softened to, "influences him in what he does." Although at times in the previous chapters we seem very nearly to have said, "The physical environment has very little to do with what man does," rather obviously the environment exists and must be dealt with. Fundamentally, the answer that our examination of man on the earth has given is that man's culture is the *primary* determining factor. The environment is *secondary* in its role in almost all cases. The role of the environment is determined primarily by the culture of the man. The same physical environment plays an entirely different role for the farmer, the manufacturer, the hunter, the pastoralist. Therefore, it cannot be the environment that is the determining factor. This has been illustrated many times in the preceding chapters.

THE RELATIONSHIP OF PHYSICAL ENVIRONMENT AND CULTURE

Much of the problem can be put into simple diagrams, as in Figure 11–1. At *a,* the arrow suggests that the physical environment acts directly on man and that this is the only action going on.

(*Opposite*) Figure 11-1 Man-Land Relationships. The nature of the relationship of man to his environment has been variously described: (*a*) The physical environment acts directly on man. (*b*) Man acts directly on the physical environment. (*c*) Each acts directly on the other. (*d*) Reciprocal action is indirect because it is conditioned by culture. (*e*) In reality the situation is complicated because of the great number of factors and the variety of their relationships.

This is clearly false. At *b,* the diagram shows the opposite: man acts on his environment and there is no contrary action. This, too, is false. At *c,* the double-pointed arrow suggests action and reaction: the environment acts on man and man on the environment. This is better, but it still is misleading, for the environment rarely acts directly on man, and the way in which man reacts on the environment is not described when it is simply attributed to man in general. Men with different cultures react differently to similar environments. Partly this is due to their cultural interpositions, clothing, housing, heating, and so forth, and partly it is due simply to their outlook. Similarly, for the direct action of men on the environment: it is, again, culturally formed. Farmers may cut and burn that part of the forest which they need for agriculture, but pastoralists are likely to burn the whole forest down.

The diagram at *d* indicates the relationship by the placement of a lenselike figure between man and the environment. This lense can be thought of as the filter through which the physical environmental influences must pass before they can act on man, and through which man will view the environment and thus have his action on the environment determined. The diagrams could be complicated indefinitely; the final diagram (*e*) only begins to indicate the complexity of the nature of the problem. There is physiological, psychological, economical, political, spiritual, and sociological man. The physical environment is composed of weather and climate, fresh- and salt-water bodies, flora and fauna, both macro and micro geology, soils, and land forms. Each of these items could be subdivided. There is potential action and reaction between every element of the cultural and the physical environments.

Theoretically, there should be an enormous number of combinations of man and land. In one sense there are: no two humanly occupied parts of earth

469

are exactly alike. Nevertheless, there are broad similarities. The order that emerges from a study of the potential chaos is primarily a cultural one. There are cultural worlds and their similarities are greater than the innumerable potential combinations would lead one to expect. This is a further illustration of the importance of the cultural forces in human geography.

To understand man's use of the land, his effect on the land, and the land's effect on human cultures, we must then focus on the cultural processes. The most important of these for our problem are invention and diffusion. These two processes act through time and space and cause cultural change, and it is cultural change that leads to the differing human landscapes of the earth. Not every cultural change appears in the landscape, and not every change in the landscape is due to man. The leaves on trees in mid-latitudes change color and fall without any reference to man's activity; but the amount and kind of tree left in the landscape may be largely determined by man. Changes in jazz styles probably do not affect the landscape, but changes in art styles may, as witness the modernistic buildings that add their sometimes odd accents to the landscape.

Invention and the Spread of Ideas

The spread of ideas begins with invention. Although invention is the work ultimately of an individual, it is culturally formed. Calculus requires not only a great mind, but a setting for that mind such that it both has the opportunity to work in higher mathematics and has access to a vast array of preceding work that makes possible the next step forward. It is not the physical environment that sets this stage, but the social environment. When the great cultural centers were in the hot, dry lands of the Near East, the great mathematical advances occurred there. Later they were in the Mediterranean climates, and now they are in the cold and stormy climates of higher mid-latitudes.

Shifting to more natural systems such as animal domestication or plant domestication does not change the situation. There were potentially domesticable plants and animals in all the environments that man occupied, not excepting the arctic. As we have seen, however, there were very few centers of origin of agriculture, if there was indeed more than one, and probably only one for the generic idea of domestic animals. The question of whether or not there was more than one origin of the basic idea of agriculture, with spread of the *idea* in some cases into areas where native plants were domesticated, is one that is still open for consideration. In any case, in no area were all the potential animals and plants domesticated. In most cases the plants and animals used were clearly spread from a few centers and often into areas where they were adapted to the local situation with great difficulty. Locally available plants and animals were not domesticated. All of this indicates the scarcity of truly creative and inventive minds coinciding with culturally permissive situations.

Once the creative mind has produced an idea that increases man's control over his environment, there is a potential, and usually a real, population growth. This means that there will now be an increased chance for the occurrences of great minds. The assumption here is that great minds occur as a proportion of a population, that they are simply the very high end of the normal distribution curve of ability. If their rate of occurrence is 1 per 100,000, then small populations must have very few of them, and to the extent that advancement is dependent on the production of superior minds, these small populations must lag. The creation of ideas by increasing the number of potential creators must, then, all other things being equal, provide more opportunities for further ideas that should in turn further increase the population; hence more creative people and still more ideas. If this progression were true, then the growth of knowledge and of population over the long run of human history should follow a curve of acceleration. This is a commonplace in diagramming the growth of knowledge (see Figure 11–2 below). This also is the probable shape of the human population growth curve. The very long Lower Paleolithic period was one when exceedingly little happened over immense lengths of time. It was also a time of extremely low human population. For example, a population figure for the British Isles during a Lower Paleolithic period as low as 1000 people has been suggested. If genius occurs at a 1 per 100,000 rate, there would be 1 per 100 generations, and he would have no like mind with which to communicate.

As inventions were made and population began to grow, there were more men in contact with other men. More ideas were exchanged and there was more stimulation of the brighter men. As was especially developed in the discussion of Ethiopia (Chapter 8), men with advanced knowledge communicate more fully with men of like advancement. The feed-back system tends to reinforce the advantage of the region with the head start. Finally, in some areas, the stage was reached where every man need no longer be a jack-of-all-trades; some men could specialize in certain pursuits and not only be more skillful at doing them but could create new ways of doing these things still better. Ultimately, growth of knowedge led to such increases of productivity that some men could be spared for such seemingly unproductive pursuits as astronomy, mathematics, map-making, and the like. These pursuits laid the foundation for even greater growths of knowledge.

Men produce ideas. Ideas make it possible for there to be more men to produce more ideas. This feed-back system may be unbelievably slow to start, but once it gains momentum its acceleration is logarithmic; and the long view shows just such a growth. We are currently experiencing a normal situation, a population explosion accompanying our exploding growth of knowledge.

However, the growth of knowledge made a geographically localized start, and this has had very great consequences, for the spread of knowledge (diffusion) requires contact and, all other things being equal, proximity promotes contact. There are other variables, not the least of which is cul-

tural receptivity. The Yumas were an example of nonreceptiveness. Time is also a factor, and it is probable that given more time the Yumas would have become more receptive, for the ability to take up ideas is related to cultural level. Diffusion then proceeds in time and space: it is culturally conditioned in both these dimensions, and meets some geographic conditioning in its space dimension.

Time and cultural change are diagrammatically shown in Figure 11–2. The duration of the differing cultural periods is strikingly uneven. Depending on what dates are accepted, the beginning of tool-making by man was somewhere between one and two million years ago. In the enormously long early period that is known as the Lower Paleolithic, hundreds of thousands of years have passed with almost no change visible in the archeological remains. The chart suggests something like three major increments of knowledge in perhaps 900,000 years. This would include such items as learning to flake stone in two fundamentally different patterns, to make simple chopping tools, and to use fire. In the Middle Paleolithic, at least an equal number of inventions seem to have been made in 150,000 years. New tools appear, and man becomes a skillful hunter of big game, and able to live in very cold climates. This suggests fairly efficient clothing. In the Upper Paleolithic, perhaps twice as much advancement was accomplished in about 20,000 years. Then about 10,000 years ago, agriculture appears, so far as our present knowledge goes, in the Near East. Thereafter the growth of knowledge and population becomes explosive.

Notice the change of scale that is necessary if this graph is to be kept within limits: hundreds of thousands, then tens of thousands, then thousands. The duration of these periods is shown on an unchanging scale in the upper part of Figure 11–2. Notice that on that scale it is not feasible to show any time division since the appearance of metals about 5000 years ago. It is worth mentioning again that the curve of growth of knowledge is of the same shape as the curve of growth of population.

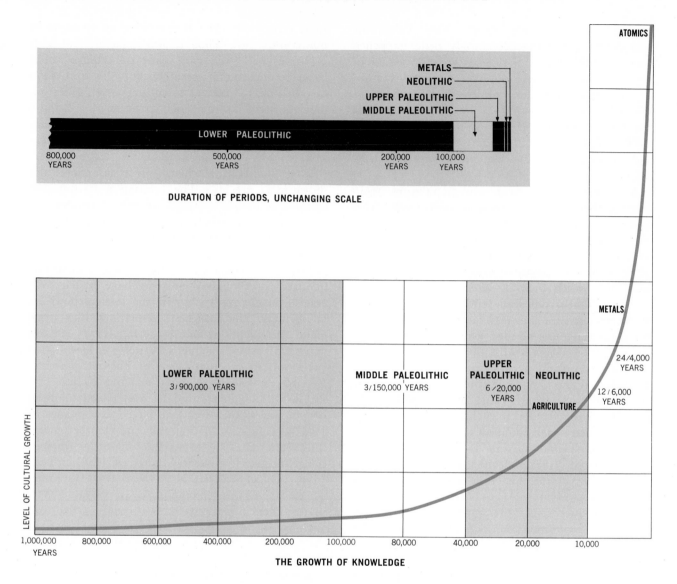

Figure 11-2 Cultural Growth Acceleration. (*Below*) Rates of cultural growth are suggested for the major cultural periods. The curve is logarithmic. Major or revolutionary increments of knowledge are shown as fractions: 3/900,000 years; 3/150,000 years. The enormously slow growth of knowledge during the time of extremely small populations and the immensely accelerated growth of knowledge during periods of increasing population are such that on this level of generalization the curve of population and the curve of knowledge are identical. In time, it is clear that population growth tends to increase knowledge and to grow further due to the increased well-being created by the new knowledge. Such a feedback system will create a curve like this. (*Above*) For purposes of comparison, the duration of periods is shown on an unchanging scale.

In the over-all picture it is clear that it is growth of knowledge that makes possible the growth of population, and that population follows with some lag behind the potential that exists at any moment. At the present time of incredibly rapid pyramiding of knowledge, it seems clear that the actual population is lagging very far behind the potential.

The spread of ideas from a center can be dealt with either in diagrams or mathematically and then checked against history. A diagrammatic presentation is used here (Figure 11–3). A uniform world is assumed with mankind in various Upper Paleolithic stages of existence. The beginning of agriculture is assumed to occur at X. The circles A, B, C, and D then mark out equal distances from the center, X. The assumption is made that ideas will flow radially (right side of figure) and laterally (left side of figure). In the radial flow, the ideas will reach the closest people A during the first time interval (in practice some thousands of years). After some time they too will enter the agricultural revolution. Their numbers will grow, and their cultural growth will begin to accelerate. In the next time interval, the ideas that have reached A will be passed on to the next closest people B.

Other things will also be happening. Cultural growth will be proceeding at a logarithmic rate at X, and there will be an increasing flow of ideas toward A. This is indicated by the wider arrow from X to A that is labeled 2. A, having made a start, will be increasingly receptive to ideas and will also begin to have a weak influence on X, thereby giving X a still greater advantage in cultural accumulation. The beginning of a flow of ideas toward X in stage 2 is indicated by the arrow from A to X that is labeled 2. The successive flows of ideas to A are shown by arrows with thickness indicating greater flow. Thus the flow from X to A is assumed to increase greatly through time due to the increasing advancement of X as the major producer of cultural growth, and because of the parallel growth of A, constantly increasing its receptivity to ideas.

The return flow of ideas from A to X will

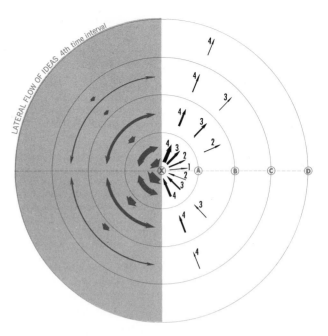

Figure 11-3 The Flow of Ideas from a Center of Origin. The flow of ideas from a center of origin of a massive breakthrough such as the invention of agriculture might be so diagrammed. The assumptions are a uniform earth and uniform man. If a people X achieves this breakthrough, its population and learning will begin to grow at an accelerated rate. The flow of ideas to the people at A is shown in four time intervals. The outflow from A is assumed to increase in time, and this growth is suggested by progressively thicker arrows. The reach of ideas is considered to be progressively farther through the time intervals and to be progressively diminished by distance. A cultural effect is also implied. At stage 4, a people located at D would be unprepared to accept the full flood of ideas that a people at A, having experienced three preparatory stages, could accept. The lower right quadrant diagrams the return flow of ideas. These must start later and be less under the conditions hypothesized here. The left half of the diagram adds the lateral-flow picture, here portrayed as it might be at stage 4. Outflow and inflow, as well as lateral or peripheral flow, are shown by proportionally thick arrows.

increase steadily with cultural growth at *A*. (This model is approached in reality by the British–United States historical situation.) For the more distant areas, the same assumptions are made. The great advantage of the area of origination is clear: given a cultural breakthrough at any point on the surface of a uniform earth, a radial pattern of spread with retention of dominance by the center and with declining cultural level accompanying increasing distance is to be expected.

On the left-hand side of the figure, arrows are entered to suggest the nature and extent of lateral flow of ideas that would become important as the field of cultural advancement widened. They are shown here as they might be in the fourth time interval. The inner areas, being more advanced, are both more productive and more receptive to ideas. Consequently, the greatest lateral flow of ideas is nearer the center. Hence both radial and lateral flow tend to reinforce the initial lead of the cultural areas, as shown by the weighted arrows.

Cultural Growth

The cultural growth can be shown in logarithmic curves in terms of the same four time stages (Figure 11–4). Here the people *A* are assumed to start with a level of 1 at stage 1, by which time the people *X* have doubled their cultural wealth and reached level 2. One time interval (stage 2) would see a doubling of cultural content for *A* and sufficient influence from them on the adjacent people *B* to give these a cultural level of 1. Meanwhile *X* has again doubled its cultural wealth and is at level 4.

A will have started *B* on its road of development. All areas beyond the reach of the new ideas will have remained at or near their original cultural levels. Their numbers are too small to allow for much self-starting.

In the next time interval (by stage 3) *A* will have advanced to level 4, and *B* can be assumed to have reached the cultural level of 2 and to have influenced the adjacent people *C* to give them a cultural level of 1. By this time *X* has again doubled its cultural wealth to level 8 on self-generation of ideas, and it

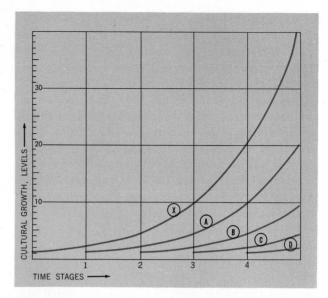

Figure 11-4   The Rate of Growth of Population and Ideas. This diagram shows the same phenomena as Figure 11-3. *X*, having made a start, begins accelerating growth. Even assuming perfect transmission of ideas, people at succeedingly greater distances will begin their cultural growth at a later date. All other things being equal, the other cultures will never catch up with *X*, *B* will never catch up with *A*, and so forth. Historically, the influence of an individual (Perón in Argentina) or a politico-economic system (Communism in Russia) can and normally does eventually slow the leader's (*X*'s) pace and allows a late starter to exceed in development. It is usually a nearby people who overtake when the leader falters, not a distant group. The sequence in history has been Near East, Greece, Rome; not Near East, Australia, Tierra del Fuego.

would not be unreasonable to credit this people with a pick up of 1 level from the surrounding peoples who have made a start in cultural growth beyond the Paleolithic levels.

The continuation of this process gives the initial group an ever-widening lead. Groups at even modest distances from the center will rapidly be left so far behind that the situation we described for the California Indians or the Australian natives comes into play. When the cultural gap becomes too wide, cultural transmission is inhibited and the tendency is either for one people to replace the other, or for the advanced people to tend to bypass the cultural tarriers. In a diagrammatic way this is what should have happened on the earth. As we have seen in many case histories, this is in fact somewhat the way things did occur. Of course, abstract treatments such as this leave out the human factors. Collapse of an empire or freezing of a bureaucratic caste system or an Alexander the Great can break up the beautiful symmetry of the curves.

If we move now from a uniform earth to the actual earth, we can check this diagram by comparing the known spread of agriculture with the theoretical diagram. This is shown on Map 11–1. Concentric circles are drawn around the area in the northern end of Mesopotamia that at the moment seems to be the best candidate for the place of origin of agriculture in the Old World. The first circle is at a distance of 500 miles, the second at 1000, the third at 2000, the fourth at 3000. The spread of agriculture by 5000 B.C. was largely to contiguous, similar regions, with the exception of its early appearance in the dissimilar region of the Nile Valley. By 4000 B.C. the spread elongated along a few natural routes: down the Mediterranean to northwest Africa, up the Nile, eastward toward India. The Mesopotamia plain was also occupied by agriculturists in this time interval. The next thousand years saw the shores of the Mediterranean widely settled by agriculturists and agriculture began to spread up the major river valleys into Europe, moved into the edge of the desert in northwestern Africa, and leaped to China and to India. By the year 2000 B.C., agriculture had been pushed north nearly to its northern climatic limits and had spanned the continent of Eurasia. The areas of notable lag are Africa south of the Sahara and Oceania beyond the nearer parts of Malaysia. The general conformity to a spreading out from a single center is moderately good.

The distortions from a radial spread are largely the effect of the physical geography. The major distortion parallels the very strong east-west axis of the physical features of Eurasia and North Africa. The limit of agriculture to the north was determined by cold, to the south by aridity. The major mountain chains run east-west. The Mediterranean Sea-

Persian Gulf axis is also an east-west one. The importance of the sea axis was probably accentuated by the cultural effect of sea travel. Thus the Mediterranean seems very early to have been an axis for the long-distance movement of ideas. There is a strong suggestion of a very early movement of agricultural ideas coastwise from the Persian Gulf toward India, and from that area toward the mouth of the Red Sea. In slightly later time, the India to Red Sea via southern Arabia route was to become so important that it is known as the Sabaean Lane. The distributions here suggest that it may have been assuming importance as early as 2000 B.C. The vast desert area of the Sahara seems to have been an important barrier to the spread of agriculture. It was penetrated by the Nile corridor and later was flanked by the sea routes, but the total effect was a great diminution of the contact.

The Role of Agriculture

The physical environment clearly played a role in shaping the early spread of agriculture. Notice, however, that use or nonuse of sea routes is culturally determined. It is also true that the northern limit is culturally determined; it is the decision to practice agriculture that is primary. The climatic limit is to a cultural way of life, and is actually associated with particular plants whose use is culturally determined. The environment is there and is not to be ignored, but the exact nature of its determining role is determined by the culture being limited.

Any analysis such as this is at the mercy of new information. The beginning of agriculture in the Near East, formerly estimated at 5000 years ago, is now dated at about 10,000 years ago. The dates for the arrival of agriculture in the distant parts of the world are imperfectly known. There is question as to whether there were separate agricultural origins in the Far East, and even the possibility that the origin of agriculture was in the Southeast Asian area. The analysis presented here tends to weaken the thesis of a Southeast Asian origin for agriculture, since it was not Southeast Asia that experienced the

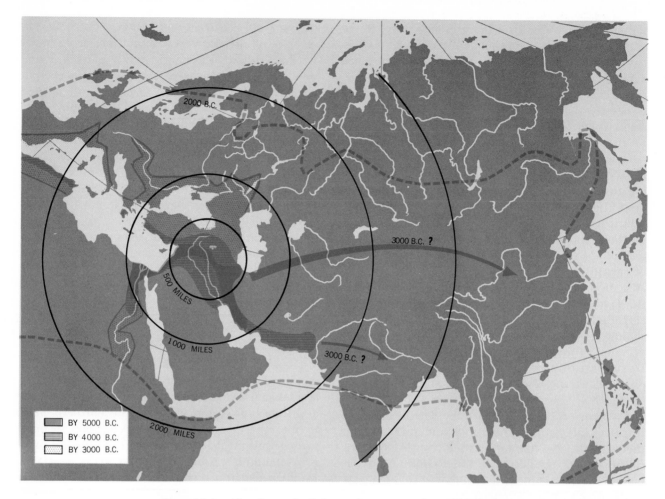

Map 11-1   The Spread of Agriculture over the Old World

Circles 500, 1000, 2000, and 3000 miles in radius are centered on what is presently believed to have been the area of the origin of agriculture in the Near East. The areas actually occupied are designated by shading, advancing from 5000 B.C. to 4000 B.C. to 3000 B.C. The limits of argiculture by 2000 B.C. are suggested by the dashed line. The interaction of cultural and physical geography are apparent in the east-west distortion of the distributions. This is in part purely physical; the lay of the land and the climatic zones run that way. In part it is also cultural; the possession of shipping made the Mediterranean, the Persian Gulf, the Indian Ocean, and the island world of Southeast Asia into highways of diffusion. Without boats, they would have been barriers.

earliest population and cultural growth, as might have been expected if it had priority in agricultural origins. On the other hand, since Southeast Asia and especially India are extremely poorly known archeologically, it would be premature to become dogmatic about it. Nonetheless, the total picture as we know it today suggests: agricultural beginnings in the Near East with a consequent initial start that gave that area cultural primacy for at least 5000 years.

It should be abundantly clear by now that the patterning of ways of life on this earth is the result of a few fundamental processes that function on this most ununiform earth. The results are more understandable in terms of these processes than through a view that shifts the primary shaping of the cultural world to the physical environment. As we have repeatedly seen, similar physical environments do not cause similar cultural environments. On the other hand, similar cultural backgrounds will repeatedly convert otherwise dissimilar physical environments into reasonable facsimiles of the homeland where the culture originated. The overriding forces in human geography, then, are cultural forces. Neither geographical determinism nor racial determinism is nearly as productive of insights into the growth and development of culture as is a cultural-historical study.

The Role of Location and Time

The role of location and time in relation to cultural growths and developments has been shown to be of critical importance. In this final chapter it may have been overstressed. It is worthwhile, therefore, to review how complex the flow of cultural growth may be and to note that this complexity is determined today more by culture than it is by physical geography. The Mediterranean area may serve as a good example. In terms of proximity to the center of origin of the industrial revolution,

it should early have begun a meteoric advance. Instead, as we have seen, it lagged greatly. The causes of the lag here were cultural forces of such magnitude that they could overcome proximity, contact, and physical geographic advantage. The Mediterranean cultures, devastated by wars and occupations and with stagnant social systems, simply were not receptive to the industrial revolution. They were in this no different from the Yumas, who were also nonreceptive to the ideas of the agricultural revolution. In the case of the Mediterranean countries, the passage of sufficient time has brought enough receptivity so that they are now entering onto an accelerated growth curve of productivity. Cases could be cited indefinitely, but in large part that is what this book has done.

HUMAN WILL AND CULTURAL VARIETY

The lesson that emerges is the simple one of human control over human actions. It is human will that is decisive, not the physical environment. The human will is channeled in its action by a fabric of social customs, attitudes, and laws that is tough, resistant to change and persistent through time; and yet it is a delicate thing that, like a fabric, can under some circumstances rip or, in others, become unraveled. Over-all, however, the most striking things about culture are its enormous power to shape man's actions and color his view of the actual world and its ability to persist through immense lengths of time with only slow change as new ideas are tried or not tried, fitted in or rejected. Though man may be said to adjust to his environment, it must always be remembered that he adjusts to it as he sees it, and that this is culturally determined. This human image of the world is the ultimate reason why various cultural worlds exist and why their resemblances cut across environmental differences and similarities.

BIBLIOGRAPHY

THE MAIN PURPOSE of this bibliography is to cite books and articles that will give the student a starting point for further reading. The author has not hesitated to cite works by men with viewpoints more deterministic than his own, feeling that the student should meet different points of view. Besides, much excellent geography has been written by men who presented their data well, though viewing the man-land relations deterministically. Griffith Taylor is a good example. Some of the author's own work is included so that students who wish to explore his personal contribution to certain areas may find their way to papers scattered widely through the social science journals.

The vast number of articles on geography and the fact that they do not appear in the ordinary library catalogue make it hard for the student to find his way into the richest realm of material. There are two principal bibliographic aids: *Aids to Geographical Research* and *Current Geographical Publications.*

Aids to Geographical Research by John K. Wright and Elizabeth T. Platt (American Geographical Society Research Series No. 22, Columbia University Press, N.Y., 1947) provides a complete guide to the literature on geography, topically and regionally. If in doubt about how to start investigating any topic or country, consult Wright and Platt.

Current Geographical Publications, published monthly by the American Geographical Society, lists current additions to the Society's library and includes much of the geographical literature of the world. Usefully indexed.

Focus is another publication of the American Geographical Society that is of great usefulness. It is a leaflet series designed to present current reports on various countries of the world and occasionally on special topics. Each is written by someone acquainted with the country, summarizes the physical and social setup of the area, and includes a brief bibliography. Since *Focus* provides so useful a beginning for further work, the list of all countries and topics presented, with year of publication, is given here. The list is complete through December, 1963.

AFRICA

Algeria, 1961. Angola, 1956. Congo (Brazzaville), 1962. Congo (Leopoldville), 1961. Egypt, 1951. Ethiopia, 1955. Gabon, 1961. Ghana, 1959; rev. ed. 1960. High Commission Territories of Southern Africa, 1963. Kenya, 1953. Liberia, 1961. Libya, 1955. Madagascar, 1958. Mauritania, 1961. Morocco, 1952. Mozambique, 1958. Nigeria, 1954. North Africa Arid Realm, 1954. Resources of the Tropics—I, 1952. Rhodesia and Nyasaland, 1956. Rwanda and Burundi, 1963. Sierra Leone, 1957. Somalia, 1956. South West Africa, 1960. Sudan, 1958. Tanganyika, 1962. Tunisia, 1957. Union of South Africa, 1953.

ANTARCTICA, 1956.

ARCTIC

Resources, 1952.

ASIA

Burma, 1960. Cambodia, 1962. Ceylon and the Colombo Plan, 1955. China's Agricultural Resources, 1960. China's Resources for Heavy Industry, 1958. Formosa, 1955. Hong Kong, 1953. India's Agricultural Problems, 1963. India's Industrial Growth, 1956. India's Languages and Religions, 1956. India's Population Problem, 1954. Indonesia, 1956. Iraq, 1954. Iran, 1951. Israel, 1951. Japan, 1952. Kashmir, 1962. Korea, 1950. Korea, 1961. Malaya, 1958. Nepal, 1956; rev. ed., 1961. Pakistan, 1952. Resources of the Tropics —III, 1954. Sabah (North Borneo), 1963. Thailand, 1962. Turkey, 1953. Viet Nam, 1951.

AUSTRALASIA

Australia, 1957. New Zealand, 1960.

CENTRAL AMERICA, 1958.

Guatemala, 1963.

EUROPE

Austria, 1954. Czechoslovakia, 1962. Denmark, 1961. European Economic Community, 1962; rev. ed., 1963. France, 1953. Germany, 1952. Great Britain, 1952. Greece, 1957. Hungary, Romania, Bulgaria, 1960. Iceland, 1959. Ireland, 1955. Italy, 1953. Netherlands,

479

1954. Poland,·1952. Portugal, 1958. Ruhr, 1950. Scandinavia, 1955. Spain, 1954. Sweden, 1960. Switzerland, 1955. Yugoslavia, 1951.

NORTH AMERICA (except United States, which is listed separately)

British Caribbean Federation, 1956. Canada, 1959; rev. ed., 1961. Cuba, 1958. Dominican Republic, 1960. Mexico, 1959. Puerto Rico, 1953. Puerto Rico, 1963. St. Lawrence Seaway, 1960. Virgin Islands, 1961.

PACIFIC ISLANDS

Micronesia, 1963. Philippine Islands 1961. Western New Guinea, 1962.

SOUTH AMERICA

Argentina, 1958. Bolivia, 1959. Brazil, 1958. Chile, 1957. Colombia, 1957. Ecuador, 1959. Guianas, 1957. Paraguay, 1956. Peru, 1961. Resources of the Tropics—II, 1953. Uruguay, 1957. Venezuela, 1952.

SOVIET UNION

Agricultural Resources, 1955; rev. ed., 1963. Resources for Heavy Industry, 1955; rev. ed., 1963. Oil, 1950.

UNITED STATES

Alaska, 1953. Alaska, 1962. Arid Realm, 1953. California, 1957; rev. ed. 1961. Changing South 1951. Coal, 1959. Energy, 1963. Hawaii, 1959; rev. ed., 1961. Los Angeles, 1962. New York City, 1952. Polio, 1951. Radio and TV, 1960. San Francisco, 1959. Water, 1951.

GENERAL

Human Starvation, 1954; rev. ed., 1961. Outlook for Aluminum, 1961. Outlook for Rubber, 1955. Outlook for Steel, 1951. Outlook for Uranium, 1960. Outlook for Wood, 1951. World's Underdeveloped Lands, 1959; rev. ed., 1961. Water—Our Most Important Mineral, 1957.

PHILOSOPHY OF GEOGRAPHY

Man-land Relationships Viewed Deterministically

Determinism is the opposite view to that taken in this book. Students should read its major proponents to see how divergent the various views are.

Huntington, Ellsworth, *Civilization and Climate*. New Haven, Conn.: Yale University Press, 1915. This earliest of Huntington's major works shows most clearly the extreme physical environmental determinist's methodology, but most of his books have the same viewpoint and methods. His last major work *Mainsprings of Civilization* (New York: John Wiley & Sons, Inc., 1945) added a biological determinism to his physical environmental determinism and never reached cultural consideration although passing acknowledgment was made that culture plays a role in determining human actions.

Semple, E. C., *The Geography of the Mediterranean*. New York: Holt, Rinehart and Winston, Inc., 1931. Semple knew her geography and history and wrote beautifully, but her work has the bias of her day, hence the role of the physical environment is stressed. Her *American History and Its Geographic Condition* (Boston: Houghton Mifflin Company, 1933) is also worth consulting.

Taylor, G. (ed.), *Geography in the Twentieth Century: A Study of Growth, Fields, Techniques, Aims and Trend*. London: Methuen & Co., Ltd., 1957. This useful volume presents many aspects of geography, including the history of the subject, European schools of thought, the determinist, possibilist, and other viewpoints, and many short articles on special topics, such as physical geography, polar lands, tropical lands, geopolitics, and race. The bibliographies accompanying the articles provide material for further study in these many areas of inquiry. G. Tatham's article "Environmentalism and Possiblilism" is especially recommended for its review of the development of thought in this vital part of geographic philosophy.

Man Seen as Dominating His Environment

The books and papers cited here supply examples of the nature and extent of man's action in shaping his physical environment.

"The Decline of North Africa: Climatic or Human?" *Annals of the Association of American Geographers,* vol. 41, 1951, pp. 116–132. Much of North Africa, a granary for Rome, looks desertic now. Has the climate changed or has man damaged the land?

Salaman, R. N., *The History and Social Influence of the Potato*. Cambridge, England: Cambridge University Press, 1949. The introduction of a new food plant can be more explosive in its effect than assumed climatic changes, as is seen in importation of the South American potato to Europe, especially Ireland.

Stewart, O., "Burning and Natural Vegetation in the United States. *The Geographical Review,* vol. 41, 1951. pp. 317–320. Man and fire can change vast areas.

Thomas, W. L., Jr. (ed.) *Man's Role in Changing the Face of the Earth*. Chicago: University of Chicago Press, 1956. This storehouse of knowledge illustrates man's dominance over the physical environment. Various papers that appear in this book are cited in the sections that follow.

Human Origins and Man in America

Coon, Carleton S., *The Origin of Races*. New York: Alfred A. Knopf, Inc., 1962. This encyclopedic treatment of the origin of man and the development of races can be used as a source book, and through its bibliography various areas of human development, e.g., physiologic adaptation to climate, can be further explored.

Carter, George F., "Man in America: A Criticism of Scientific Thought." *Scientific Monthly*, vol. 73, no. 5 (November, 1951), pp. 297–307.

———, "Origins of American Indian Agriculture," *American Anthropologist*, vol. 48, no. 1 (January–March, 1946), pp. 1–21.

———, *Plant Geography and Culture History in the American Southwest*. Viking Fund Publications in Anthropology No. 5. New York: Viking Fund, Inc., 1945.

———, *Pleistocene Man at San Diego, California*. Baltimore, Johns Hopkins University Press, 1957.

———, "The Role of Plants in Geography," *The Geographical Review*, vol. 36, no. 1, 1946, pp. 121–131.

ARID LANDS

Bailey, W., "Climate and Settlement of the Arid Region," in *Climate and Man: Yearbook of Agriculture, 1941*. Washington, D.C.: U.S. Department of Agriculture.

Bowman, Isaiah, *Desert Trails of the Atacama*. Special Publication No. 5. New York: American Geographical Society, 1924.

Braidwood, R. J., B. Howe, and others, *Prehistoric Investigations in Iraqui Kurdistan*. The Oriental Institute of Chicago, Studies in Ancient Oriental Civilization No. 31. Chicago: University of Chicago Press, 1960.

Castetter, E. F., and W. H. Bell, *Yuman Indian Agriculture*. Albuquerque, N.M.: University of New Mexico Press, 1951.

Coon, Carleton S., *Caravan: The Story of the Middle East*. New York: Holt, Rinehart and Winston, Inc., 1951.

Dickson, H. R. P., *The Arab of the Desert*. London: George Allen and Unwin, Ltd., 1951.

Frankfort, H., *The Birth of Civilization in the Near East*. Bloomington, Ind.: Indiana University Press, 1951.

Gautier, E. F., *Sahara, the Great Desert*. New York: Columbia University Press, 1935.

Huzayyin, S., "Changes in Climate, Vegetation, and Human Adjustment in the Sahara-Arabian Belt," in W. L. Thomas, Jr. (ed.), *Man's Role in Changing the Face of the Earth*. Chicago: University of Chicago Press, 1956.

Jaeger, E. C., *The North American Deserts*. Stanford, Calif.: Stanford University Press, 1956.

Ludwig, E., *The Nile*. New York: Garden City Publishing Co., 1939.

———, *The Problems of the Arid Zone*, Research Series 12. Paris: UNESCO, 1962.

Vedder, H., *Southwest Africa in Early Times*. London: Oxford University Press, 1938.

Wellington, J. H., *Southern Africa, A Geographical Study*. London: Cambridge University Press, 1955.

White, G. (ed.), *The Future of the Arid Lands*. Washington, D.C.: American Association for the Advancement of Science, 1956.

Carter, George F., "American Civilization Puzzle," *Johns Hopkins Magazine*, vol. 8, no. 5 (February, 1957), pp. 9–24. Also in C. Brooks and R. P. Warren, *Modern Rhetoric* (New York: Harcourt, Brace & World, Inc., 1958).

———, "Maize to Africa," *Anthropological Journal of Canada*, vol. 1, no. 2, 1963, pp. 3–8.

———, "Movement of People and Ideas across the Pacific," in Jacques Barrau (ed.), *Plants and the Migrations of Pacific Peoples*. Honolulu: Bishop Museum Press, 1963.

———, "Plants across the Pacific," *American Antiquity* (Memoirs), vol. 18, no. 3, part 2 (January, 1953), pp. 62–71.

———, "Plant Evidence for Early Contacts with America," *Southwestern Journal of Anthropology*, vol. 6, no. 2 (Summer, 1950), pp. 161–182.

THE WET TROPICS

Bartlett, H. H., "Fire, Primitive Agriculture and Grazing in the Tropics," in W. L. Thomas, Jr. (ed.), *Man's Role in Changing the Face of the Earth*. Chicago: University of Chicago Press, 1956. A broad-gauge study with an extensive bibliography.

Camacho, J. A., *Brazil: An Interim Assessment*. London and New York: Royal Institute of International Affairs, 1952.

Deschamps, H., *Madagascar*. Paris: Berger-Levant, 1951.

Ginsburg, N., and C. F. Roberts, *Malaya*. Seattle: University of Washington Press, 1958.

Gourou, Pierre, *The Tropical World*. London: Longmans, Green & Co., Ltd., 1954.

Hirsch, J., "Comfort and Disease in Relation to Climate" in *Climate and Man: Yearbook of Agriculture, 1941*. Washington, D.C.: U.S. Department of Agriculture.

James, P. E., "Trends in Brazilian Agricultural Development," *The Geographical Review*, vol. 43, 1953, pp. 301–328.

Kimble, G. H. T., *Tropical Africa* (2 vols.). New York: The Twentieth Century Fund, 1960. Encyclopedic coverage.

Lee, D. H. K., *Climate and Economic Development in the Tropics*. New York: Harper & Brothers, 1957.

———, *Physiological Objectives in Hot Weather Housing*. Washington, D.C.: Housing and Home Finance Agency, 1953.

Lowenthal, D., "Population Contrasts in the Guianas," *The Geographical Review*, vol. 1, 1960, pp. 41–58. A study of British, French, and Dutch settlement side by side in tropical lowlands with differing resulting landscapes.

Morley, S. G., *The Ancient Maya*. Stanford, Calif.: Stanford University Press, 1956.

Murdock, G. P., *Africa's People and Their Cultural History*. New York: McGraw-Hill Book Company, Inc., 1959. The best recent compendium of factual material on African cultures.

Pendleton, R. L., *Thailand: Aspects of Landscape and Life*. New York: Duell, Sloan & Pearce, Inc., 1962.

Robequain, C., *Malaya, Indonesia, Borneo and the Philippines*. New York: Longmans, Green & Co., Inc., 1958.

Spencer, J. E., *Land and People in the Philippines: Geographic Problems in Rural Economy*. Berkeley, Calif.: University of California Press, 1952.

Stone, R. G., "Health in Tropical Climates" in *Climate and Man: Yearbook of Agriculture, 1941*. Washington, D.C.: U.S. Department of Agriculture.

Thompson, J. E., *The Rise and Fall of Maya Civilization*. Norman, Okla.: University of Oklahoma Press, 1956.

Thorp, James, "Climate and Settlement in Puerto Rico and the Hawaiian Islands," in *Climate and Man: Yearbook of Agriculture, 1941*. Washington, D.C.: U.S. Department of Agriculture. The emphasis is on poverty--stricken Puerto Rico, and the conclusion is that the two alike regions owe their economic differences to cultural factors, not physical geographical ones

Twenty years later, Thorp's analysis is being proved correct by Puerto Rico's rapid economic development.

Waibel, L., "European Colonization in Southern Brazil," *The Geographical Review*, vol. 40, 1950, pp. 529–47. A German geographer's report on land, people, and politics in settlement problems.

Winslow, C. E. A., and L. P. Herrington, *Temperature and Human Life*. Princeton, N.J.: Princeton University Press, 1949.

THE MEDITERRANEAN CLIMATE

Allbaugh, L. B., *Crete: A Case Study of an Underdeveloped Country*. Princeton, N.J.: Princeton University Press, 1953.

Caughey, J. W., *California*. Englewood Cliffs, N.J.: Prentice-Hall, Inc., 1953.

East, W. G., *Mediterranean Problems*. London: Thomas Nelson & Sons, Ltd., 1943.

Gentilcore, R. L., "Missions and Mission Lands of Alta California," *Annals of the Association of American Geographers*, vol. 51, 1961, pp. 46–72.

Hanson, E. P., *Chile: Land of Progress*. New York: Reynal & Hitchcock, Inc., 1941.

Leighly, John, "Settlement and Cultivation in the Summer-Dry Climates," in *Climate and Man: Yearbook of Agriculture, 1941*. Washington. D.C.: U.S. Department of Agriculture.

McBride, G. M., *Chile: Land and Society*, Research Series 19. New York: American Geographical Society, 1936. A warmly appreciative and understanding but none the less expert and revealing study of a twentieth-century survival in America of Old Spain. Still valuable for any student of Latin American problems.

McWilliams, Casey, *Southern California Country: An Island on the Land*. New York: Duell, Sloan & Pearce, Inc., 1946.

Myers, J. L., *Mediterranean Culture*. London: Cambridge University Press, 1944.

Newbigin, M. I., *The Mediterranean Lands: An Introductory Study in Human and Historical Geography*. New York: Alfred A. Knopf, Inc., 1924.

———, *Readings on the Geography of the Mediterranean*. New York: American Geographical Society, 1943.

Taylor, T. G., *Australia: A Study of Warm Environments and Their Effect on British Settlement*. London: Methuen & Co., Ltd., 1945.

Wellington, J. H., *Southern Africa: A Geographical Study* (vol. 1, Physical Geography). London: Cambridge University Press, 1955.

EAST COAST MID-LATITUDE FOREST LANDS

Brown, Ralph, "The Land and the Sea: Their Larger Traits," *Annals of the Association of American Geographers,* vol. 41, 1951, pp. 199–216. This short discussion of the colonial eastern seaboard and its role in colonial America can serve as an introduction to Ralph Brown's important work on colonial American geography. Interested students will want to follow this with more reading of Brown's works.

———, *Mirror for Americans; Likeness of the Eastern Seaboard, 1810.* New York: American Geographical Society, 1943.

Creel, H. G., *The Birth of China.* New York: Frederick Ungar Publishing Co., 1954.

Harris, Chauncy D., "Agricultural Production in the U.S.: The Past Fifty Years and the Next," *The Geographical Review,* vol. 47, 1957, pp. 173–193.

Higbee, E. C., "The Three Earths of New England," *The Geographical Review,* vol. 42, 1952, pp. 425–438.

Pendle, G., *Argentina.* London and New York: Oxford University Press, 1961.

———, *Uruguay.* London and New York: Oxford University Press, 1963.

Prunty, Merle, Jr., "Land Occupance in the Southeast: Landmarks and Forecast," *The Geographical Review,* vol. 42, 1952, pp. 439–461.

———, "The Renaissance of the Southern Plantation," *The Geographical Review,* vol. 45, 1955, pp. 459–491.

Raine, P., *Paraguay.* New York: Scarecrow Press, Inc., 1956.

The River Plate Region: An Economic Survey of Argentina, Paraguay, and Uruguay. New York: The Commission on Commerce and the Marine of the American Bankers Association, 1924.

Rostlund, Erhard, "The Geographic Range of the Historic Bison in the Southeast," *Annals of the Association of American Geographers,* vol. 50, 1960, pp. 395–407.

Sauer, C. O., "The Settlement of the Humid East," in *Climate and Man: Yearbook of Agriculture, 1941.* Washington, D.C.: U.S. Department of Agriculture.

Shen, T. H., *Agricultural Resources of China.* Ithaca, N.Y.: Cornell University Press, 1951.

Taylor, G., *Australia* (includes chapters on New Zealand and neighboring islands). Skokie, Ill.: Rand McNally & Co., 1931.

WEST COAST MID-LATITUDE FOREST LANDS

Butland, G. J., *Chile: An Outline of Its Geography, Economics and Politics.* London: Royal Institute of International Affairs, 1956. Small but good.

Clark, J. G. D., *Prehistoric Europe: The Economic Basis.* New York: Philosophical Library, Inc., 1952.

Curry, Leslie, "The Climatic Resources of Intensive Grassland Farming: The Waikato, New Zealand," *The Geographical Review,* vol. 52, 1962, pp. 174–194.

Evans, E. E., *France: A Geographical Introduction.* London: Christophers, Ltd., 1937.

Eyre, John D., "Mountain Use in Japan," *The Geographical Review,* vol. 52, 1962., pp. 236–252.

Freeman, T. W., *Ireland: Its Physical, Historical and Economic Geography.* New York: E. P. Dutton & Co., Inc., 1950.

Hance, W. A., "Crofting Settlements and Housing in the Outer Hebrides," *Annals of the Association of American Geographers,* vol. 41, no. 1, 1941, pp. 75–87. A description of the survival of ancient ways of life in these communities so close to the center of growth and development in northwest Europe.

Landheer, B. (ed.), *The Netherlands.* San Francisco: United Nations Series, 1943.

Stamp, L. D., *The Land of Britain, Its Use and Misuse.* London: Longmans, Green & Co., Ltd., 1948.

Taylor, G., *Australia* (includes chapters on New Zealand and neighboring islands). Skokie, Ill.: Rand McNally & Co., 1931.

Trewartha, G. T., *Japan: A Physical, Cultural and Regional Geography.* Madison, Wisc.: University of Wisconsin, 1945.

Van Veen, J., *Dredge, Drain, Reclaim: The Art of a Nation.* The Hague: N. V. Nijhoff, 1955.

THE GRASSLANDS

Bartlett, H. H., "Fire, Primitive Agriculture, and Grazing in the Tropics," in W. L. Thomas, Jr. (ed.), *Man's Role in Changing the Face of the Earth.* Chicago: University of Chicago Press, 1956.

Gourou, Pierre, *The Tropical World.* London: Longmans, Green & Co., Ltd., 1954. Contains discussion of tropical grasslands.

Jefferson, Mark, *Peopling the Argentine Pampas.* New York: American Geographical Society, 1930.

Malin, J. C., "Man, the State of Nature and Climax: As Illustrated by Some Problems of the North American Grasslands." *Scientific Monthly,* vol. 74, 1952, pp. 1–8. Malin, a historian, exceeds most natural scientists in his grasp of the overall physical setting and combines a keen social insight to make his studies outstanding. See his various grassland papers.

Roseveare, G., "The Grasslands of Latin America." *Bulletin of the Imperial Bureau of Pastures and Field Crops No. 36.* Aberystwyth, Wales, 1948.

Shantz, H. L., and C. F. Marbut, *The Vegetation and Soils of Africa,* Research Series No. 13. New York: American Geographical Society, 1923.

Sprague, H. B. (ed.), *Grasslands: A Symposium at the New York Meeting of the American Association for the Advancement of Science, 1956.* Washington, D.C.: American Association for the Advancement of Science, 1959.

Stapdon, R. G., *A Tour in Australia and New Zealand: Grasslands and Other Studies.* London: Oxford University Press, 1928.

Thornthwaite, C. W., "Climate and Settlement in the Great Plains," in *Climate and Man: Yearbook of Agriculture, 1941.* Washington, D.C.: U.S. Department of Agriculture.

Trewartha, G. T., "Climate and Settlement of the Sub-humid Lands," in *Climate and Man: Yearbook of Agriculture, 1941.* Washington, D.C.: U.S. Department of Agriculture.

Vowles, H. P., *Ukraine and Its People.* Edinburgh: W. & R. Chambers, Ltd., 1939. The Ukraine represents the European end of the great inner Asian grassland.

Webb, Walter Prescott, "Geographical-Historical Concepts in American History," *Annals of the Association of American Geographers,* vol. 50, 1960, pp. 85–97. This is Webb's explanation of how he reached his insights on Americans and their grassland.

———, *The Great Plains.* Boston: Ginn & Company, 1931. This is a most readable book which illustrates both the role of human outlook and the role of adaptation of inventions made elsewhere to the occupation of a particular environment.

Wedel, W. R., "Environment and Native Subsistence Economies in the Central Great Plains," *Smithsonian Miscellaneous Collection,* vol. 101, 1951, pp. 1–29. The prehistoric picture of human settlement in the American grasslands.

Carter, George F., "Ecology-Geography-Ethnobotany," *Scientific Monthly,* vol. 70, no. 2 (February, 1950), pp. 73–80.

MOUNTAIN LANDS

Blomer, R. (ed.), *Ecuador: Andean Mosaic.* Stockholm: Gebers, 1952.

Dundas, C., *Kilimanjaro and Its People.* London: H. F. & G. Witherby, Ltd., 1924.

Fisher, W. B., and H. Bowen-Jones, *Spain, A Geographical Background.* London: Christophers, Ltd., 1958.

Ford, T. T., *Man and Land in Peru.* Gainesville, Fla.: University of Florida Press, 1955.

Harrer, H., *Seven Years in Tibet.* New York: E. P. Dutton & Co., 1954.

Matthiesen, P., *Under the Mountain Wall, A Chronicle of Two Seasons in the Stone Age.* New York: The Viking Press, Inc., 1962. A description of life among primitive people in the mountains of New Guinea.

Monge, C., *Acclimatization in the Andes.* Baltimore: Johns Hopkins University Press, 1948.

Ogrizek, D., and J. G. Rüfenacht (eds.), *Switzerland.* New York: McGraw-Hill Book Company, Inc., 1949.

Osborne, H., *Bolivia: A Land Divided.* London: Royal Institute of International Affairs, 1954.

Parsons, James J., "Antigueño Colonization in Western Colombia," *Ibero Americana: 32.* Berkeley, Calif.: University of California Press, 1949. This monograph was the major source for discussion of the Antigueños. Interested students will find it a rich source.

Peattie, R., *Mountain Geography.* Cambridge, Mass.: Harvard University Press, 1936.

Simoons, F. J., *Northwest Ethiopia: Economy and People.* Madison, Wisc.: University of Wisconsin Press, 1960.

Thompson, C. H., and H. W. Woodruff, *Economic Development in Rhodesia and Nyasaland.* London: Dobson Books, Ltd., 1954.

Toniolo, A. R., "Studies of Depopulation in the Mountains of Italy," *The Geographical Review,* vol. 27, 1937, pp. 473–477.

THE NORTHERN FOREST LANDS

Bal'zak, S. S., and others, *Economic Geography of the U.S.S.R.* . Translated from the Russian. C. D. Harris, editor of the American edition. New York: The Macmillan Company, 1949.

Barevsky, B., *Siberia: Its Resources and Possibilities.* Washington, D.C.: Government Printing Office, 1926.

Gjessing, G., *Changing Lapps, A Study in Culture Relations in Northernmost Norway.* London: University of London, 1954.

Hare, F. K., "Climate and Zonal Divisions of the Boreal Forest Formation in Eastern Canada." *The Geographical Review,* vol. 40, 1950, pp. 615–636. Focused on the Labrador-Ungava region in which a great mining development is now proceeding, but valuable for description of northern forest conditions.

Humphreys, Graham, "Schefferville, Quebec: A New Pioneering Town," *The Geographical Review,* vol. 48, 1958, pp. 151–166. The first of the towns built for the exploitation of Eastern Canadian iron ore.

Kimble, G. H. T., and Dorothy Good, *Geography of the Northlands.* American Geographical Society Special Publication No. 32. New York: John Wiley & Sons, Inc,. 1955.

Mead, W. R., *An Economic Geography of the Scandinavian States and Finland.* London: University of London Press, 1958.

Putnam, D. F., and D. P. Kerr, *A Regional Geography of Canada.* Don Mills, Ont.: J. M. Dent & Sons (Canada), Ltd., 1961.

Shabad, T., *Geography of the U.S.S.R., A Regional Survey.* New York: Columbia University Press, 1961.

Stefansson, Vilhjalmur, "The Colonization of Northern Lands," in *Climate and Man: Yearbook of Agriculture, 1941.* Washington. D.C.: U.S. Department of Agriculture.

Stone, K. H., "Populating Alaska: The United States Phase," *The Geographical Review,* vol. 42, 1942, pp. 384–404.

Taylor, G., *Canada, A Study of Cool Continental Environments and Their Effects on British and French Settlement.* London: Methuen & Co., Ltd., 1947.

THE POLAR LANDS

Ahlmann, H. W., *Land of Ice and Fire.* London: Paul, Kegan, Trench, Trubner & Co., Ltd., 1938.

Freuchen, Peter, *Book of the Eskimos.* Cleveland: The World Publishing Company, 1961.

Gould, L. M., "Antarctic Prospect," *The Geographical Review,* vol. 47, 1957, pp. 1–28.

Lee, C., *Snow, Ice, and Penguins.* New York: Dodd, Mead & Company, Inc., 1950.

Simpson, F. A. (ed.), *The Antarctic Today: A Mid-Century Survey.* Wellington, New Zealand: A. H. & A. W. Reed, 1952.

Sonnenfeld, J., "An Arctic Reindeer Industry: Growth and Decline," *The Geographical Review,* vol. 49, 1959, pp. 76–94.

Stefansson, V., *The Friendly Arctic.* New York: the Macmillan Company, 1943.

Thorarinsson, S., "*The Thousand Years Struggle Against Ice and Fire,*" Miscellaneous Papers No. 14. Reykjavík: Museum of National History, 1956.

INDEX

A

Abacus, 92

Ability, normal distribution of, 25

Acapulco, Mexico, 174

Aconcagua River, Chile, 221

Acorns, as food in California, 206

Acosta, Fr., mountain sickness, 398

Adelaide, 232, 234

Aden, British outpost in Saba, 386

Africa: cultural achievements, 390; disease burden, 158; milking, 156; modern development, 159; Negro accomplishment, 157–159; nondomestication of local animals, 158; origin of man, 10–11; plant domestication, 158; proximity to stimulation, 157; railroads, 159; south of Sahara, 26; summary of progress, 156

North Africa: camel, 64; compared with California, 181, 204; cultural rise and fall, 374; economic base, 203; history, 201; land use, 201; Mediterranean climate, 181, 200–201; modern potential, 204; population, 201; Roman influence, 60

South Africa (dry land): absence of agriculture, 57; Bushman origins, 105–106; compared with Great Basin, 80; future, 108; Hottentots, 108; isolation, 80; location, 42; potential, 108

South Africa (Mediterranean land): Bantu-European conflicts, 227; Boer land use, 229; cattle keeping, 226; compared with California, 226; crops, 229; economic growth, 231; European occupation, 226; mineral discoveries, 229; mixture, 227; native development, 231–232; physical description, 224; race, 226, 230, 232

tropical, 153ff.; climate, 153; Congo basin climate, 153; cultural stimuli, 156; hydroelectric potential, 154; Malaysian food plants, 156; mineral fuels, 154; physical geography, 153–154; Semites displace Indonesians, 156; sleeping sickness, 158; soils, 154

Agriculture: absence of, in Indian California, 205; relation to population, 36, 146; shifting type, 146; spread of, 55, 57, 183, 475

origin of, 55; Africa, 158; America, 397; Australia, 33; California, 214; Egypt, 55, 65, 69; Fertile Crescent, 55; Jericho, 36; Southwest versus Southeast Asia, 475, 477

Ainu, 20, 334

Air lines, focus on Near East, 59

Alaska: Alcan Highway, 449; compared with Norway, 311; temperature ranges, 429; tourist potential, 426

Alaskan Range, 425

Alcan Highway, 449

Algeria, 200, 201

Algonkin, inhabitants of eastern Canada, 438

Alphabet, origin of, 30

Alpine passes, in Switzerland, 422

American grasslands. See United States, Grasslands

American Indian: origins of civilization, 92–100, 395; origin of race, 20–22; time of entry into America, 20. See also various tribes

American Southwest. See United States, Southwest

Amur River region, compared with Labrador-Quebec region, 443

Anatolia, 411

Andes, compared with Sierra Nevadas, 220

Angkor Wat, Indian influence in Southeast Asia, 391

Animal domestication. See Domestication of animals

Antarctica, 466–467; dated seal carcasses, 466; potential for Eskimos, 466

Antecedents, 29; for industrial revolution, 295–296

Antioqueños, 404–407; cattle, 407; coffee, 406; colonial situation, 404; expansion, 406; health problems, 406; population growth, 407

Apache: origins, 88; on plateau, 78; raiders, 77, 88; versus Spanish, 354.

Apartheid, 230

Aquaba, Gulf of, 60, 374

Araucanians, 222

Argentina: adjunct to Peruvian mines, 101; colonial relations with Spain, 271; economic growth, 273; Indians, 271; northwest compared with Great Basin, 101–102; pampas, 364–366; railroad development, 273; settlement compared with U.S., 273

Arid lands, 39–113; age of plants, 47; distribution in South America, 41; domestic animals, 50; effect of grazing, 50; location, 40; mountains as moisture barriers, 41–42; Old World–New World comparisons, 113; survey of cultural levels, 52; temperature ranges, 43; vegetation influenced by man, 202. See also individual countries

Arizona: American view of, 78; center of development, 78; early settlement, 78; hypothetical boundaries, 78; plateau region, 78, 85; southern Arizona, 77–78; Spanish assessment of, 78

Arroyos, causes of, 50

Asian influences: in America, 27; in Ecuador, 99–100; in Peru, 93. See also Trans-Pacific contacts

Atacama Desert, 45

Athabascans: raiders in Southwest, 64, 88; western Canadian origin, 88, 438

Atlas Mountains, 200. See also Africa, North

Australopithecines, 11

Australopithecus, 11, 12

Australia: delayed settlement, 282

dry lands: aboriginal culture, 109–110; British development, 111–112; location, 42

grasslands, 367–368

Mediterranean lands: aboriginal occupation, 232; agriculture, 234; British settlement, 233; description, 232–234; European discovery, 233; lack of comparative advantage, 234; population, 234; settlement in South Australia, 234–235